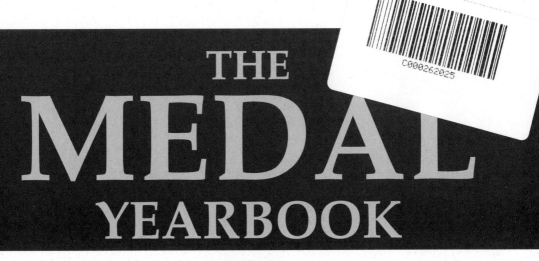

THE MEDAL YEARBOOK

2018

Edited by

John W. Mussell, FRGS
and
the Editorial Team of MEDAL NEWS

ISBN: 978 1 908828 38 5
Hardback edition ISBN: 978 1 908828 39 2

Published by

TOKEN PUBLISHING LIMITED

40 Southernhay East, Exeter, Devon EX1 1PE, UK
Telephone: 01404 46972
e-mail: info@tokenpublishing.com   Website: www.tokenpublishing.com

USA and Canadian distributor:
Tanya Ursual, PO Box 788, Kemptville, Ontario, Canada, KOG 1JO

Front cover illustration: The South Africa Medal 1877–79 and Cape of Good Hope General Service Medal pair awarded to Captain J. Bodkin, Cape Mounted Rifles

Printed in Great Britain by Latimer Trend & Company, Plymouth

CONTENTS

Index to advertisers

FOREWORD

WELCOME to the 2018 edition of the MEDAL YEARBOOK, the 24th such tome that Token Publishing has produced and the second in the smaller format sans modern Commonwealth medals. The decision to take out the current Australia, Canada, New Zealand and South Africa medals wasn't an easy one to make but, as was explained last year, it was necessary, mainly to reduce the ever-growing size of the publication. Our "beloved" Royal Mail is relentlessly pushing prices up and up (no one else could get away with such a dreadful business model of penalising those who stay loyal to them but the Royal Mail's position in the UK means they still can), and the clamour to reintroduce the MEDAL NEWS cumulative index was such that in order to keep postage costs (and print costs too—the recent drop in the pound against the dollar and Euro has meant an increase in paper costs, although how much of that is profiteering remains to be seen!) at a reasonable level something had to give—and it had to be the Commonwealth countries. We are still keen to produce a separate volume covering the countries that we have had to leave out (along with others) and if you feel you can help with that please do let us know. We would also like to know exactly what you would like to see included, for example, do you want it to become an exhaustive guide to all Commonwealth countries and their medals, published maybe once every five or six years or would you prefer to see it as an annual or bi-annual publication just covering the major countries? Again do please let us know.

The omission of the Commonwealth countries doesn't mean that we have cut back on other aspects of the book though and, once again, this year sees a raft of new information (and new medals) included. It never ceases to amaze us how we are still learning about this fascinating hobby, and how much this book has changed over the past two decades, and we are inordinately grateful to all of you who have, once again, been kind enough to send in additions, corrections, new pictures etc. We have always said we want this book, the handbook for the medal hobby, to be the absolute best it can be and always welcome all your thoughts and comments, please don't stop them coming in.

It isn't just this book that has changed in the past two decades of course, the whole medal world has changed—it has gone from being a small offshoot of coin collecting to a popular hobby in its own right (not to mention a thriving multi-million pound industry). The internet has added an extra dimension with the amount of research that is available with just the click of a mouse, enabling us all to know far more about "our men" than ever was possible before, allowing us to see our collections as far more than just accumulations of metal and silk. Prices too have changed and a quick glance back to a MEDAL YEARBOOK from the mid-1990s will show you just how much of an increase there has been. The biggest surge in prices came about ten years ago when new research opportunities and records on-line mean that even the humble World War I pairs started going up and up, they more than doubled in price in just a couple of years. Whilst that increase was great for those who had bought for investment, it certainly wasn't good for the hobby, as youngsters in particular found themselves priced out and new collectors were discouraged simply because of the sheer amount of money they felt they would have to part with in order to attain a decent collection. Thankfully that relentless upward trend has abated and in the past couple of years things have levelled off—prices are still high of course but they aren't going up at an unsustainable rate anymore. As long as they were, there was always the danger of a bubble, one that could burst at any time, potentially damaging the hobby quite badly. Thankfully that crisis has been averted! In some cases, particularly with the more "everyday" items, prices have softened a little but don't be fooled—quality is selling and selling well. A quick glance at any auction will illustrate just how much people are still prepared to pay for decent groups, with some of the money fetched being really quite eye-watering—at least for we mere mortals!

Of course, the hobby isn't about money and what is worth how much. It's about history, it's about the man behind the medal, the story behind the campaign or the act of heroism for which the award was made. But few of us can ignore the fact that in order to obtain the medal and learn about the story, one has to fork out what is, on occasions, some serious cash and we like to know

(a) that the "serious cash" isn't too much, and (b) that we could, if we wanted, get some of that cash back. And that's where this YEARBOOK comes in. It cannot, of course, give every price for every permutation of medals to every rank, it is a guide only and the prices herein do not allow for rank/casualty status/regiment/other medal entitlement or any other such factors—such a task would be impossible. Any price a reader encounters in the YEARBOOK must be considered to be for a "basic" medal unless otherwise stated—external factors will always have an effect on that basic price. A World War I trio to a gunner in the Royal Artillery who survived the war and disappeared back to a relatively obscure life on Civvie Street will not, for example, fetch the same as a World War I trio to a Captain from the Ulster Division killed on the First Day of the Somme, even though the medals themselves may look the same. The same is true across history —South African General Service 1877–79 or "Zulu" medals, for example, may all look the same and prices of all of them have certainly been going up in recent years, but one to a Colonial unit with an *1877* clasp may be worth £2,000+, when one to a man in the same unit with an *1879* clasp might be worth far less. But a medal with the same clasp to a man in the 24th Foot who took part in the Defence of Rorke's Drift would be worth tens of thousands. To try to encompass such variety is beyond the scope of this or any other publication but we have done our best to give an "overview" which will allow the collector to have a basic knowledge with which to move forward. Even such a "basic" knowledge requires research though and whilst we regularly check dealers' lists, auction results, etc., we could not compile the MEDAL YEARBOOK without the help of some of the most respected specialists in their field and would like to particularly thank the many specialist auction houses who allow us to analyse their archives and the dealers who provide us with their current lists from which we gauge our prices. We are especially indebted to Chris Dixon of C. J. & A. J. Dixon Ltd, David Kirk of Morton & Eden and John Millensted of Bonhams. We would also like to record our thanks to the many readers who have provided new information which helps keep the book up to date, particularly Colin Hole, Gareth Keller, Michael O'Brien, Charles Riley, Malcolm Rouse, Allan Stanistreet, John Wilson and many members of the on-line British Medal Forum.

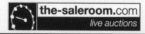

MARKET

Highlights

We review here the auctions covered in "Market Scene", the regular feature that appears each month in MEDAL NEWS, during the year July 2016–June 2017. Although there are more lots sold in London than elsewhere, simply because of the number of auction houses such as DNW, Spink, Bonhams, Morton & Eden, we also report Bosleys (Marlow), Lockdales (Ipswich), Warwick & Warwick (Warwick), Dominic Winter (South Cerney) and Wallis & Wallis (Lewes), who provide a good measure of the provincial auction scene. Readers will find more details about the lots listed below by referring to those editions of MEDAL NEWS in which the sales were originally reported. Here JOHN SLY spotlights some of the choicest items . . .

VICTORIA CROSSES AND GEORGE CROSSES

This year we had two Victoria Crosses, both sold at **DNW, July 22** and **March 1** respectively. The first was awarded to (Major-General) George Nicholas Channer, Indian Army: VC, CB, IGS Medal 1854 clasps *Umbeyla, Perak 1875-6, Jowaki 1877-8, Hazara 1888*, Second Afghan War Medal clasp *Peiwar Kotal*. Channer won his Cross on December 20, 1875, during the Perak campaign, and his group made £240,000. The second VC was awarded to (Acting Captain) George Sanders, 1/7th West Yorkshire Regiment, for his gallantry on July 1, 1916; in 1918 he was awarded a Military Cross. The full group consisted of the VC, MC, 1914-15 Star Trio, Coronation Medal 1937, and it sold for £268,800.

A posthumous George Cross was awarded to John Alexander Fraser, Civilian Defence Secretary and Assistant Attorney-General, Hong Kong; Fraser was captured when Hong Kong fell, and was eventually beheaded by the Japanese on October 20, 1943. The lot sold for £228,000. Another GC lot (exchange EGM) to (Acting Assistant Commissioner) George John Adamson,

Indian Police, comprised GC, King's Police Medal*, Indian Police Medal for Distinguished Conduct, 1914–15 Star Trio (Leicester Regiment), 1935 Jubilee, 1937 Coronation, 1953 Coronation, Efficiency Medal* clasp *India* (GV). In May 1936 Adamson (1896–1976) and his pilot, Cecil Kelly, ensured that a barge was saved from exploding in a dangerous situation. The lot achieved £21,600. Again at **DNW, May 10**, the George Cross group of Chief Officer George Preston Stronach was sold: GC, 1939–45/Atlantic/Africa Stars, War Medal, Coronation 1953, Jubilee 1977, Lloyd's War Medal for Bravery at Sea. Stronach took command of his burning ship, SS *Ocean Voyager*, when the Captain was killed; he repeatedly went back into the ship, which was full of aviation fuel and ammunition, searching for survivors. It sold for £216,000.

World War I VC group to George Sanders, 1/7th West Yorkshire Regiment, sold for £268,800 at DNW.

ORDERS AND DECORATIONS
2016

At **DNW, July 22**, the Knight Bachelor's Badge, OBE, Defence & War Medals, Yugoslavia, Order of the Crown was awarded to John Cecil Masterman, Chairman of MI5's XX Committee during World War II. It sold for £12,000. The DCM (GV), MM**, 1914–15 Star Trio, together with a gold Northumberland and Albert Edward Dock Employees Tribute Medal to (Chief Petty Officer) William Brown, Hood Battalion, RND made £43,200. The DCM (GVI), GSM 1918 clasp *Palestine*, 1939–45 Star, Defence & War Medals, Long Service Medal to WO II Walter Webb, 2/Queen's Regiment, reached £13,200. The DCM (GVI), MM (GVI), GSM 1918 clasp *Palestine*, 1939–45/Africa Stars, Defence & War Medals to (Sergeant) William John Knight, East Kent Regiment, sold for £14,400.

DNW, September 27-28, offered the group to Lieutenant-Colonel George Muttlebury, 2/69th Foot, comprising CB, Waterloo Medal, Netherlands, Military Order of Wilhelm. Muttlebury succeeded Colonel Charles Morice (killed at Waterloo) as CO of the battalion. The lot hit £24,000. The group to QM & Lieut-Col Edward Augustus Parker, RWF, consisted of OBE, MC (GV), DCM (EVII), IGS 1854 clasp *Hazara 1891*, QSA clasps *Cape Colony, Tugela Heights, Relief Of Ladysmith, Transvaal, Orange Free State*, KSA two clasps, 1914 Star & Bar Trio (MiD), Coronation 1911, and two foreign awards. Parker had a long career in the Royal Welch, and then on the Staff. The lot made £15,600. The DSO, 1914–15 Star Trio (MiD) to Lieutenant-Commander Mark Singleton, RN, was awarded for "bringing to surrender a body of about 11 officers and 250 Turkish troops". The successful bidder paid £10,800. The DCM (V), Crimea Medal four clasps, Turkish Crimea Medal was awarded to James Whitechurch, 8th Hussars, who was not a confirmed "charger". However, it still made £15,600. The CGM (GVI), 1939–45 Star, War Medal to Acting Leading Seaman Ronald Thirlwell, HMS *Mosquito*, was contested to £55,200. The GM (GVI), 1939–45/Africa Stars, Defence & War Medals, Efficiency Medal (Territorial) with two clasps, was awarded to Lance-Sergeant John Henry Hinton, RE, who, with his officer, disposed of a 250 pound bomb in Coventry, October 14, 1940. This achieved £6,600.

Baldwin's, September 28, offered the Small Army Gold Medal for Orthes to (Major-General) Charles Edward Conyers CB, 1/82nd Foot; this made £17,400.

At **Warwick & Warwick, October 19**, the MC (EII), OSM clasp *Afghanistan*, Diamond Jubilee Medal awarded to Marine Lewis Lockwood, RM, was sold for £10,620. A large amount of personal data was included with the lot, including photographs, a narrative of his service career, and "the bullet that wounded him".

Woolley & Wallis, October 19, offered the medals to (Group Captain) Harry Alexander Purvis, RAF: DFC, AFC*. Purvis was awarded the DFC for mine destruction; the AFCs were gazetted respectively July 11, 1940, and June 2, 1943. The lot sold for £6,100. Captain Harry Crewe Godley, Northamptonshire Regiment, was awarded the DSO (V), QSA Medal clasp *Belmont*. Godley with two companies held Enslin Railway Station for nine hours against overwhelming numbers. The lot achieved £4,392.

At **Bosleys, November 2**, the medals of Flight Lieutenant Charles Humphrey Matthewman, RAF, came up: DSO (1945), DFC* (1944 and 1945 respectively), 1939–45/ACE Stars, Defence & War Medals. The recipient was a specialist low level navigator. This achieved £3,840.

Lockdales, November 19, sold the DFC* (with copy bar), 1939–45/ACE Stars, War Medal. The DFC was gazetted in August 1942, the Bar in June 1945, effective from May 23, 1943, the day before he died; this lot reached £4,690. William Melville, the original secret service "M", was appointed MVO, and awarded RVM, MBE, 1902 Coronation Police Medal, and four foreign awards; together with considerable detail about his life and career, this achieved £5,159.

Bonham's, November 23, offered the DFC* (both 1945), 1939–45/ACE Stars, Defence & War Medals, GSM 1918 clasp *Malaya* to (Flight-Lieutenant) Stanley Turner, RAF; together with log books, photographs, and newspaper cuttings, this achieved £5,040. (WO II) Peter Forbes Fleming, Cameron Highlanders, earned the DCM (GV), MM (GV), QSA five clasps, 1914 Star & Bar Trio. Although the silver medals were "heavily polished", photographs were included. The lot made £3,000.

At Warwick & Warwick's October sale the gallantry group to Marine Lewis Lockwood sold for £10,620.

The Albert medal group of four to Corporal Alfred Edward Simms RFC/ RAF, which realised £10,200 at Spink's November sale.

At **Spink, November 24**, the medals awarded to (Corporal) Alfred Edward Simms, RFC/RAF, were sold: Albert Medal 2nd Class for saving life on land, 1914–15 Star Trio. The citation referred to January 3, 1916, when "a fire broke out inside a large bomb store…which contained nearly 2,000 high explosive bombs... Major Newall… poured water into the shed through a hole made by the flames…". This achieved £10,200. Frank Naden was awarded the DSO**, MC*, East & West Africa Medal (re-named Corporal, RMLI), Ashanti Star 1896 (Sergeant, RMLI) QSA Medal clasps *Cape Colony, Orange Free State, Johannesburg* (Sergeant, Volunteer Company, Cheshire Regt), 1914 Star & Bar (Colour-Sergeant, 6/Cheshire Regt), BWM & VM (MiD) (Lieut-Col), ED (Territorial riband bar), and three foreign awards. With a biographical review of his exploits and a portrait, the lot was bid up to £18,600. The MC [EII], Iraq Medal 2003, GSM 1962 clasp *Northern Ireland*, NATO Medal clasp ISAF, OSM 2000 clasp *Afghanistan*, Jubilee Medal 2012 (copy), ACSM, was awarded to Corporal Mark Ward, Mercian Regiment; he was awarded the MC in Afghanistan 2011, for at least two gallant actions. This hit £16,800. (Major) Peter Richard Warner White, Buffs, who served in Aden in 1958–59, and in Borneo in 1960, was awarded the MM (EII), GSM 1918 clasp *Arabian Peninsula*, GSM 1962 clasp *Borneo*, Pingat Jasa Malaysia Medal. The MM (gazetted November 1958) was for "his determination and courage during the assault up the precipitous escarpment of the Jebel Jehaf plateau…". The lot made £11,400. (Chief Inspector) Terrence Michael Slocombe, West Yorkshire Metropolitan Force, was awarded QGM, BEM with oakleaves, Police LSM. Slocombe won his QGM for his bravery at the Valley Parade fire disaster (May 11, 1985) and his BEM for the armed siege at Townville, Castleford (April 13–14, 1970). This lot sold for £12,000.

DNW, December 8, offered the group of (Group Captain) Horace Percy Lale, RFC and RAF, which was described as "unique": DSO (GV), DFC*, BWM & VM (MiD), IGS 1908 clasps *Afghanistan NWF 1919, Mahsud 1919-20, Waziristan 1919-21*, GSM 1918 clasp *Southern Desert, Iraq*, Coronation 1937. Lale claimed 23 victories during World War I, and developed precision bombing tactics on the North West Frontier. The lot sold for £24,000. CSM Thomas Patrick Carney, East Yorkshire Regiment was awarded MC (GV), DCM* (V), QSA Medal clasps *Cape Colony, Wittebergen, Transvaal, South Africa 1901, South Africa 1902*, 1914–15 Star Trio, Defence Medal, MSM (GVI), LS & GC (GV). It was recorded that this group is unique to the British Army. The successful bidder paid £18,000. "Remarkable and unique" was the Albert Medal in Gold for Saving Life at Sea to Captain William John Nutman, SS *Aidar*: Albert Medal First Class, Royal Humane Society small silver medal (successful), Lloyd's Medal for Saving Life at Sea, and four other awards. Nutman saved a fireman from drowning in extremely difficult circumstances. This sold for £16,800. The Albert Medal in Gold, for Saving Life on Land, with BWM & VM, was awarded to Corporal Herbert Frederick Ewington, AOC, who saved an injured fitter at Aldersgate Street Station in 1913. This made £13,200. The Albert Medal in Bronze for Land, Polar Medal (GV) clasps *Antarctic 1914-16, Antarctic 1917* was awarded to the late Victor George Hayward and others, who were cited for "gallant conduct in saving and endeavouring to save life while serving as members of the Ross Sea party of the Shackleton Trans-Antarctic expedition of 1914-17". This lot achieved £52,800. A DCM was awarded to William Chamberlain, RE, together with his Abyssinia Medal and LS&GC (V); at Magdala, Chamberlain cleared an enemy loophole by rifle fire. It sold for £19,200. (CSM) Thomas Day, RE, was awarded:

DCM (V), Ashantee Medal 1873 clasp Coomassie, South Africa Medal 1877 clasp *1879*, LS&GC (V). Day's DCM was awarded for bringing in the mortally wounded Sergeant Cowdy, 94th Foot, at Lydenburg. The lot made £19,200. A very rare CGM was awarded to Able Seaman Clifford Beese, HMS *Kiawo*, for his conspicuous courage when attempting the rescue of the steamers *Wanhsien* and *Wanting* in 1926. The lot achieved £31,200. Sergeant Cecil Thomas Rees, RM, won the MM (EII), NGS Medal 1915 clasp *Malaya*, GSM 1962 clasp *Borneo*, LS&GC, for the Jebel Akhdar campaign. Rees led C Coy SPS, Northern Frontier Regiment at Dhala Talib in December 1958; the bidding reached £40,800.

At **Warwick & Warwick, December 14**, (Major) Louis Wood's group comprised DSO (GV), QSA clasps *Cape Colony, Orange Free State, Johannesburg* (Bombardier, 74th Bty RFA), King's South Africa Medal two clasps, 1914 Star & Bar Trio (MiD); it made £2,183.

2017

At **DNW, March 1-2**, a "unique" group comprised DSO, Albert Medal 2nd Class for Sea, Jubilee 1897, South Africa Medal 1877 clasp *1879*, QSA clasps *Cape Colony, Orange Free State*, RHS Small Bronze Medal (unsuccessful). Edward Denman Thornburgh Cropper tried in vain in 1878 to save a crewman of the ship *Idaho*. The lot was bid up to £13,200. Robert Godfrey Wolseley Bewicke-Copley, Lord Cromwell from 1923, received the Knight of Grace of St John of Jerusalem, DSO (GVI) (1944), MC (GV), 1914–15 Star Trio (MiD), 1939-45 Star, Defence & War Medals, Coronation 1953, Italy, Al Valore Militare. From Italy in 1917, he was recalled in 1939, and commanded a company in 2/KRRC. On 26 May 1940 he was badly wounded defending Calais, and later taken prisoner. The successful bidder paid £8,400. A very scarce Conspicuous Service Cross, the last of the eight ever awarded, was awarded to Midshipman Arthur Geld Onslow; this CSC was for Somaliland 1904. He was commanding HMS *Onslaught* at Jutland when he was mortally wounded, dying June 1, 1916. This very rare medal reached £6,600. A DSC, 1914–15 Star Trio [MiD] named for Lieutenant William Henry Askew Bee, RNR, commanding HMT *Lord Heneage* on April 21–22, assisted in the capture of the German Auxiliary Cruiser *Aud*. The lot sold for £7,200. The MC**, BWM & VM, Defence Medal awarded to (Major) Tom Buckley, RMLI, was a medal short (1914–15 Star as Private). After

£31,200 was paid at DNW for the World War II gallantry group to Sergeant John Povall, RM.

Loos he was commissioned and rapidly promoted, although his three MCs were gazetted in the rank of Temporary Lieutenant; the lot achieved £7,800. The "rare" Royal Red Cross (2nd Class), MM, 1914–15 Star Trio, QARANC Cape Badge, France, Medal of Honour, was awarded to (Assistant Matron) Helena Kate Repton, BRC & St JJ. The MM was for her "bravery and conspicuous devotion" while serving at Queen Alexandra's Hospital, Dunkirk, when it was shelled. This realised £6,600. An Albert Medal in gold was awarded to (Major) Eglintoune Frederick Ross, Dorset Regiment, who discovered the fire in the arsenal at Ferozepore in 1906, and helped to control it. The lot was bid up to £18,000. (Captain) Thomas Henry Healey, Cameron Highlanders, was awarded his three DCMs for Giniss, Sarras, and Toski respectively. His group comprised DCM (V), Egypt Medal clasps *Tel-El-Kebir, The Nile 1884–85, Toski 1889, Gemaizah 1888*, Queen's Sudan Medal, Khedive's Star, Khedive's Sudan five clasps. It rose to £24,000. William Charles Ilsley, 16th Lancers, was awarded DCM (V), Egypt Medal clasps *The Nile 1884-85, Abu Klea*, Khedive's Star 1884–6. At Abu Klea Ilsley stood over Captain The 4th Viscount St Vincent, who had been wounded in the thigh, and killed nine Arabs with his bayonet. It went for £16,800. The DCM (GV), MM** (GV), 1914–15 Star Trio, St John Service Medal was awarded to Lance-Corporal William R. Peniston, who won all four of his gallantry medals on the Somme battlefields. The lot achieved £16,800. The group to (Sergeant) John Povall, 11th Battalion, RM, comprised CGM (GVI), 1939–45/Africa Stars, War Medal, Long Service Medal (GVI) (replacement), MSM (GVI). Povall was involved in a "daring" raid on Tobruk in September 1942. This lot made £31,200.

Bosleys, March 1, sold an "outstanding bomber command triple operation tour DFC, DFM pair of medals" to Pilot Officer Bernard Cunningham Bull (Flight-Sergeant on DFM). Bull took part in

72 operational flights in World War II, totalling 396 hours. The lot made £6,120. The DSC (1941), 1939-45/Atlantic/Africa Stars, Defence & War Medals to Surgeon Lieutenant Alexander Gibson Reid, RNVR, was awarded for his gallantry during the sinking of HMS *Mashona* during the search for *Bismarck* in May 1941. It achieved £1,920.

At **Lockdales, March 18**, the Air Force Medal, 1939-45/ACE Stars, Defence & War Medals, to (Flying Officer) Ernest Arthur Pullinger, RAF, achieved £2,510.

Bonhams, March 22, sold the lot to Admiral Sir Wilmot Hawksworth Fawkes: GCB, KCVO, Jubilee 1897, Coronation 1902. Fawkes had a very distinguished career, and this lot made £5,520. (Major) Hugh Ross Macintyre, RAMC, was awarded DSO (GV), MC* (GV), 1914–15 Star Trio. All three of Macintyre's awards had excellent citations relating to his care of the wounded. The lot made £4,800.

At **Woolley & Wallis, March 28**, the DSM named for ERA Ivan Charles Glover RN, HMS Penelope, was sold. Glover was killed when the ship was torpedoed. The successful bidder paid £3,034. The DCM (EVII), QSA, KSA, LSGC (GV), 1914-15 Star Trio to (Captain) Charles Deschamps Randall, Notts & Derby Regiment, who was killed in Gallipoli, sold for £3,539. The group to (Squadron Leader) John Tudor Powell Whittaker, RFC/RAF, comprised MC (engraved), BWM & VM, IGSM 1908 clasp *Wazirizistan 1921-24*, and four foreign awards, with a "small collection of photographs and research". The lot was knocked down for £7,584.

Spink, April 12, sold the Albert Medal in bronze to Captain Edward Twidle, SS *Bayropea*, for saving the life of a sailor before his ship blew up, for £6,240. The MC (EII) (dated 2012), GSM 1962 clasp *Northern Ireland*, Iraq Medal 2003, NATO Medal Non-Article 5, OSM clasp *Afghanistan*, Jubilee 2002, Jubilee 2012, ACSM, ACSM 2011 to (Bugle Major) James Andrew Davies, RGJ. His MC was gazetted September 27, 2012, "in recognition of gallant and distinguished services in Afghanistan during the period 1 October 2011 to 31 March 2012". This peaked at £15,600. A DFC* (1941, bar dated 1945), 1939-45/ACE/Africa Stars, Defence & War Medals to Squadron-Leader Alfred Denys Webb, RAF, who was awarded his first DFC for his service during Operation Colossus in February 1941, was offered; Webb's career was set out in detail in the catalogue. The lot reached £5,760.

Warwick & Warwick, April 19, sold the DFM (GVI) awarded to (Sergeant) T. P. Burke, RAF, together with his ACE Star, Long Service Medal (EII). The medals were accompanied by various written material and ephemera, and achieved £3,527.

The DSO (GV), 1914–15 Star Trio (MiD), Coronation 1911, TD (GV) to (Major) Charles Clifford Furness RFA were sold at **Baldwin's Of St James's, May 9**. For the DSO he "gained and brought back information which was invaluable to the operations…" The lot reached £2,040. Also sold was the DSC** (all three awards dated 1944), 1939–45/Atlantic/Italy Stars, Defence & War Medals, NGS Medal 1915 clasps *Cyprus, Near East*, Coronation 1937, Coronation 1953 to Captain Reginald Fife Whinney, RN. The catalogue offered research on Whinney's career, and the lot included a copy of his book *The U-Boat Peril*. It reached £15,000.

CAMPAIGN AND OTHER MEDALS

2016

At **DNW, July 22**, the Gold Medal for Vittoria clasp *St Sebastian*, MGS Medal clasp *Corunna*, and two Portuguese awards, to (Major-General) Charles Stuart Campbell, CB, 26th Foot, were sold. Campbell was severely wounded at St Sebastian. It made £26,400. The Crimean War Medal (impressed) with four clasps to Henry Parker, 11th Hussars, taken prisoner at the Charge, sold for £9,600. The South Africa Medal 1877

In March Bonhams achieved £4,800 for the DSO/MC group to Major Hugh Macintyre, RAMC.

clasp *1877-78-79* to John Connolly, 1/24th Foot, killed at Isandhlwana, sold for £10,800. The Polar Medal 1904 in bronze clasp *Antarctic 1914-16* was named for Timothy McCarthy, RNR, one of the men chosen by Shackleton for his boat journey from Elephant Island to South Georgia in April 1916; the lot hit £78,000.

Lockdales, September 17, sold the GSM 1962 clasp *Northern Ireland*, UN Cyprus Medal, South Atlantic Medal (rosette), Long Service Medal to (Staff Sergeant) Keith Henry Jacklin, Parachute Regiment, for £2,814.

DNW, September 27-28, offered the Field Officer's Gold Medal for Fort Detroit to (Lieutenant-Colonel) Peter La Touche Chambers CB, 41st Foot, who was in joint command of the regiment at Fort Detroit. He was also at the taking of Prome, Burma. The lot achieved £50,400. The MGS Medal clasp *Fort Detroit* to William Arter, 41st Foot, who was taken prisoner at Moravian Town, made £9,000. Another MGS, to Drum Major Thomas Watts, 43rd Foot, had ten clasps from *Busaco* to *Toulouse*; Watts was wounded at Badajoz and St Sebastian. The lot reached £6,600. The Waterloo Medal to Brevet Major Brooke Pigo(t)t, 2/69th, who was severely wounded at Quatre Bras, reached £10,800. The MGS clasps *Albuhera, Ciudad Rodrigo, Badajoz, Salamanca*, Waterloo Medal, to (Colonel) John Enoch, 23rd Foot, was bid up to £12,000. Drummer James Smith spent nearly 19 years soldiering in India: Punniar Star 1843 (un-named), Sutlej Medal for Moodkee clasps *Ferozeshuhur, Aliwal, Sobraon*, Punjab Medal clasps *Goojerat, Chilianwala*, Indian Mutiny Medal clasp *Delhi*, Long Service Medal (V). This lot was bid up to £6,600.

(Lieutenant) Duncan Charles Home, Bengal Engineers, was awarded the VC for blowing the Kashmir Gate in 1857; the Cross having been lost, his Punjab Medal clasps *Mooltan, Goojerat*, Indian Mutiny Medal clasp Delhi, were sold at **Baldwin's, September 28**. The lot made £26,400.

Woolley & Wallis, October 19, offered the NGS Medal 1793 with clasps *1 June 1794, 23 June 1795* to Michael Kinsale, a Landsman on HMS *Valiant*, which made £4,392.

At **Bosleys, November 2**, the MGS Medal clasps *Corunna, Nive, Nivelle*, named for (Ensign & Adjutant) Benjamin Rooth, 76th Foot, sold for £2,640; he was one of the officers who buried Sir John Moore.

Lockdales, November 19, offered a South Africa War Medal 1877 clasp *1879* to Major Joseph Ruscombe Poole, RA, who served in the First Boer War, was mentioned in despatches, and was killed in action at Laing's Nek, January 28, 1881. This achieved £8,208.

At **Bonham's, November 23**, the NGS Medal clasp *Gut Of Gibraltar 12 July 1801* was named for Chaplain James Giffard, HMS *Chester*; who ended as Vicar of Cabourn, Lincolnshire. The lot hit £5,400. (Lieutenant-General) Paul Anderson was awarded the Small Army Gold Medal for Corunna, Sultan's Medal for Egypt 1801, MGS clasp *Egypt*; he served in many theatres, much of the time closely associated with Sir John Moore. The lot achieved £34,800 The South Africa Medal 1877 clasp *1877-8-9* to William Chadwick, 1/24th Foot, an Isandhlwana fatal casualty, came in at £7,200.

Spink, November 24, offered the pair to Captain Angus Robin Franklin Dalgliesh: GSM 1918 clasp *Canal Zone* (The Buffs), Polar Medal clasp *Antarctic 1956*, awarded "for good services as [a member] of the advance party of the Royal Society Antarctic Expedition for the International Geophysical Year". The lot achieved £7,800. Yet another Isandhlwana fatal casualty appeared in this sale: South Africa Medal 1877 clasp *1877-8-9* to James Llewellyn, 2/24th Foot, who was killed aged 22. The successful bidder paid £9,600.

Morton & Eden, December 1, offered the NGS Medal clasp *14 March 1795* to (Admiral of the Blue) Robert Honyman, who was wounded at Genoa; in "extremely fine and lustrous" condition the lot hit £12,000. The MGS clasps *Vittoria, Orthes, Toulouse*, and Waterloo pair were named for Lieutenant Ralph Mansfield, 15th Hussars, who was wounded at Waterloo. This lot made £6,960. (Major) Arthur William Fitzroy Somerset, Grenadier Guards, was awarded Maharajpoor Star 1843, Sutlej Medal for Moodkee clasp *Ferozeshuhur*. Somerset was a highly distinguished Military Secretary to the Governor-General of India, who was mortally wounded at the battle of Ferozeshuhur. The lot made £12,600. A naval sub-lot to (Chief Bosun's Mate) William Johns comprised: Baltic Medal, Crimea Medal clasp *Sebastopol*, China Medal 1857 clasps *Fatshan 1857, Canton 1857, Taku Forts 1860* (all three medals un-named), Canada General Service Medal 1866 clasp *Fenian Raid 1866* (HMS *Aurora*), Long Service Medal (V) wide suspension, Turkish Crimea (HMS *Cambridge*). A service record accompanied the medals, and the catalogue set out some of his service details. The lot was bid up to £5,760. A Naval Brigade group was named for (Commander) Charles Richard Newdigate Burne, HMS *Philomel*, and author of the book *With The Naval Brigade In Natal*. QSA Medal clasps *Cape Colony, Tugela Heights, Orange Free State, Relief Of Ladysmith, Transvaal, Laing's Nek*, Coronation

Timothy McCarthy's Polar medal realised £78,000 at DNW in July.

Medal 1902, Chile, Order of Merit. He joined the Naval Brigade and was given command of two Naval 12-pounder guns. The successful bidder paid £5,760. The Kangra Earthquake Royal Red Cross Medal was awarded to Miss Alice Mabel Purkis, who was honoured for aiding the wounded at the Ghurkha Rifles barracks at Dharmsala which collapsed during the earthquake of April 4, 1905. This lot achieved £3,120. The DSM (Special Service 22 Oct 1916), Bar (3 January 1917) (GV), NGS Medal 1915 clasp *Persian Gulf 1909-1914* (HMS *Fox*), 1914–15 Star Trio (MiD), Long Service Medal (GV) (HMS *Fox*) were named for Chief Petty Officer William John Adams, who served in the crew of *Q-8* (ex SS *Vala*), which was sunk in August 1917. It made £4,080.

At **DNW, December 8**, Knight Commander of the Royal Guelphic Order breast badge, Field Officer's Gold Medal for Vittoria, MGS Medal clasp *Egypt*, Imperial Ottoman Order of the Crescent to (General Sir) Henry King, CB, KCH, KC. King had a long and active military career; he lost a leg in Egypt, and distinguished himself at Vittoria. This lot made £33,600. (Captain) Seymour Douglas Vale, RIM, received: CIE, IGS Medal 1854 clasps *Burma 1887-89, Chin-Lushai 1889-90,* China 1900 clasp *Relief Of Pekin,* AGS Medal 1902 clasp *Somaliland 1902-04,* BWM, Delhi Durbar 1911, USA Military Order of the Dragon. Vale had a fascinating military career; the lot sold for £9,600. The NGS Medal clasps *Nile, Acre 30 May 1799,* was awarded to (Brevet Major) Arthur Hull, Royal Marines, who served in *Theseus* with Horatio Nelson in the unsuccessful attack on Santa Cruz de Tenerife, achieved £36,000. The South Africa 1877 Medal clasp *1877-8-9* was named for George Hadden, 1/24th Foot, who was killed at Isandhlwana; it made £7,800. The South Africa 1877 Medal clasp *1879* to Michael Minehan, 2/24th Foot, who was confirmed as having survived at Rorke's Drift, was in a class of its own, and sold for £84,000.

Warwick & Warwick, December 14, included the Waterloo Medal to Charles Saville, 1/95th Foot; it achieved £2,596.

2017

At **DNW, March 1–2**, an NGS clasps *Endymion Wh President, Syria,* was named for William Bean, Carpenter, whose career lasted from 1803 to 1848; the lot reached £15,600. The Army of India Medal clasps *Allighur, Laswarree, Capture of Deig,* named

MSGM with five clasps to John Green, 66th Foot, made £1,680 at Bosleys.

for Dennis Driscoll, 29th Light Dragoons, sold for £14,400. The South Africa 1877 Medal clasp *1879* to Driver Charles Robson, RE, who was Captain John Chard's batman at Rorke's Drift.was sold by order of the family, and was accompanied by original letters and personal documents. It achieved £132,000. (Lieutenant-Colonel) William Vincent Moul, Cheshire Regiment, was responsible for escorting Sir Roger Casement to London for trial. His group consisted of IGS Medal 1854 clasp *Burma 1887-9,* QSA clasps *Cape Colony. Orange Free State, Johannesburg,* KSA two clasps, Coronation 1911. The lot achieved £9,600.

Bosleys, March 1, sold the MGS Medal clasps *Talavera, Albuhera, Vittoria, Pyrenees, Toulouse* awarded to John Green, 66th Foot, made £1,680.

At **Lockdales, March 18**, £2,271 was paid for the E & W Africa Medal clasp *Benin 1897* (Boy 1st Class HMS *St George*) with QSA clasps *Belmont, Modder River, Paardeberg, Driefontein, Johannesburg, Diamond Hill, Belfast* (AB, HMS *Doris*) awarded to J. W. Norris, with "much collector research and copy service papers".

Spink, April 12, offered the NGS clasp *Banda Neira* to Quarter-Master's Mate Henry Notley; it sold for £8,400. The successful bidder paid £9,000 for a South Africa War Medal 1877 clasp *1877-8-9* to James Llewellyn, 1/24th Foot, a fatal casualty of Isandhlwana. The New Zealand Medal reverse 1863-64 and a South Africa Medal 1877 clasp *1879* to (Lieutenant) Charles Lindsay, who served in South Africa with the Naval Brigade, was bid up to £6,240.

Warwick & Warwick, 19 April, sold the Second Afghan War Medal clasps *Peiwar Kotal, Charasia, Kabul, Kandahar,* Kabul to Kandahar Star, Egypt Medal clasp *Tel-El-Kebir,* Long Service Medal (V), Khedive's Star 1882, to John McIssac, 72nd Highlanders/Seaforth Highlanders, whose service record was included. The lot hit £1,824.

At **Baldwin's Of St James's, May 9**, the medals of a Light Brigade Charger were sold: Crimean War Medal four clasps, France, Medaille Militaire, Turkish Crimea Medal to Thomas Harrison, 11th Hussars. The citation for the French medal was quoted as saying that at Balaklava "he behaved very gallantly in galloping to the rescue of several colleagues who were fighting against overwhelming odds". It made £7,200.

> **All of these items and more were reported throughout the year in MEDAL NEWS**

(All prices quoted in this article include the buyer's premium charged by the respective auction houses.)

Guide To
PRICES PAID
When buying at auction

Buying at auction can be confusing to those not used to it—it isn't like buying from a dealer's list nor, crucially, like buying from an Internet auction. With a dealer the price you see is the price you pay (unless you can do some haggling that is) and with eBay and the like you bid up to the price you want and the price the auction ends at is how much the item will cost. "Real" auctions are a little different and you have to remember that when the hammer falls the final price might not be what you think.

Auctioneers make their money through buyers' premiums (and sellers' premiums' but that's another matter), i.e. a "fee" on top of the hammer price that goes directly to them, not the vendor. On top of that premium is VAT—which currently stands at 20% in the UK. VAT is only really relevant to those in the EU—buyers from outside are exempt although they may be liable for their own import duties and other taxes so it's always worth checking.

These "extras", often referred to by seasoned auction goers as the "bits", can add a significant sum to your purchase. For example, if you bid on an item up to £100 and that's where the hammer falls, it isn't £100 you pay—you will have to find that £100 plus the premium (this varies from auction house to auction house) plus VAT on that premium (not on the £100, just the premium)—that can add up to £24 to the original hammer price—not something to be ignored! It can all get rather confusing and can come as a shock to those new to the game or only used to buying at on-line auctions (it's worth noting that even if you bid on-line at a "real" auction you are still liable for the "bits": there have been those who believe that on-line bidding exempts them from the fees as they treat it like eBay!). Some buyers ignore the "bits" and concentrate on the hammer price, worrying about the extras only when they've secured their purchase. But as premiums rise most of us have to factor them in at the start—so remember, if you have a strict budget you may well have to stop bidding quite a bit before that figure is reached in order to come in on target. Of course, when you just have to have something, what do budgets matter…?

Below is an indication of what you will have to pay on certain hammer prices depending on the Premium (we've given you 10%, 15% 20% and 22.5% options—the actual premium varies so check with the auctioneer before bidding). These figures assume VAT at 20%. Happy bidding!

10 %				15%		
Hammer	Plus premium	Plus premium and VAT	Hammer	Plus premium	Plus premium and VAT
£75	£82.5	£84	£75	£86.25	£88
£175	£192.50	£196	£175	201.25	£206.50
£500	£550	£560	£500	£575	£590
£1500	£1650	£1680	£1500	£1725	£1770
£2500	£2750	£2800	£2500	£2875	£2950

20%				22.5%		
Hammer	Plus premium	Plus premium and VAT	Hammer	Plus premium	Plus premium and VAT
£75	£90	£93	£75	£91.80	£95/16
£175	£210	£217	£175	£214.38	£2222.25
£500	£600	£620	£500	£612.50	£635
£1500	£1800	£1860	£1500	£1837.50	£1905
£2500	£3000	£3100	£2500	£3062.50	£3175

WEARING

Awards

The wearing of Orders, Decorations and Medals is a complex subject too complicated to cover in a publication such as this. However, there are a number of questions that collectors frequently ask, so we have attempted to deal with these as fully as possible.

Full-size Awards Mounted for Wear

Orders, decorations and medals are worn on the left breast in a line suspended from a single brooch mount or a rectangular frame (court mounted), the latter gives a firmer grip which occasions less damage than medals hanging more loosely from a brooch. The brooch/frame is covered by the medal ribbons. The most senior medal (see the following Order of Precedence) is furthest from the left shoulder. The obverse of the medals should show (this will usually be the sovereign's head, coat of arms, cypher, etc.).

If more than five medals are worn (three for the Navy), they should not be suspended side by side, but overlapped, the senior medal and ribbon is the one to be positioned so it can be seen completely. Medals should be lined up straight by the bottom rim/point, the length of ribbon should be one and a quarter inches (33mm) from the top of the mount to the first clasp or the suspension, which ever is appropriate (one and three quarters (45mm) for the Navy). Where the awards differ in size then a ribbon adjustment will be necessary to ensure a straight line.

Emblems for Mentions-in-Despatches or King's and Queen's Commendations for personnel and civilians should be worn on the relevant campaign medal, for example on the Victory Medal for the First World War and the War Medal 1939–45 for the Second World War. Where a recipient has no relevant campaign medal, the MID or commendation emblem is worn directly on the coat after any medal ribbons, or, if no ribbons then in the position of a single ribbon.,

There are a number of awards for which the sovereign has granted permission that they be worn on the right breast, including:

Royal Humane Society Medals
Stanhope Gold Medal
Royal National Lifeboat Institution Medals
Order of St John of Jerusalem Life Saving Medal.

Foreign Orders, Decorations and Medals

The British sovereign's subjects are not permitted to accept and wear the orders, decorations and medals of a foreign country of which the sovereign is not head of state. Application can be made for wear and permission is of two types: (a) restricted, that is instructions are given as to the exact occasions on which the award(s) may be worn; (b) unrestricted which allows the item(s) to be worn on all occasions according to the Order of Precedence, that is, generally speaking, arranged after British awards by date—first orders, then decorations, followed by medals (there are exceptions for the members of the armed services serving in an overseas force and receive that country's awards).

Awards are worn on a variety of State, evening or other occasions and the rules governing the wearing of orders according to dress are quite detailed. The subject is covered fully in Medals Will Be Worn by Lieutenant Colonel Ashley R. Tinson (Token Publishing Ltd., 1999) and in Spink's Guide to the Wearing of Orders, Decorations and Medals (Spink, 1990). The wearing of awards in civilian clothes is also fully detailed in Wearing Your Medals in Civilian Clothes by Lieutenant Colonel Ashley R. Tinson (Token Publishing Ltd., 2003).

THE ORDER

of wear

The order in which decorations and medals should be worn in the United Kingdom and the Commonwealth, is set out below, as announced by the Central Chancery of the Orders of Knighthood.

Victoria Cross
George Cross
Most Noble Order of the Garter
Most Ancient and Most Noble Order of the Thistle
Most Illustrious Order of St Patrick (obsolete since the death of the Duke of Windsor, the last holder)
Knights Grand Cross, The Most Honourable Order of the Bath
Order of Merit
Knight Grand Commander, The Most Exalted Order of the Star of India
Knights Grand Cross, The Most Distinguished Order of St. Michael and St. George
Knight Grand Commander, The Most Eminent Order of the Indian Empire
The Order of the Crown of India
Knights Grand Cross, The Royal Victorian Order
Knights Grand Cross, The Most Excellent Order of the British Empire
Order of the Companions of Honour
Knight Commander, The Most Honourable Order of the Bath
Knight Commander, The Most Exalted Order of the Star of India
Knight Commander, The Most Distinguished Order of St. Michael and St. George
Knight Commander, The Most Eminent Order of the Indian Empire
Knight Commander, The Royal Victorian Order
Knight Commander, The Most Excellent Order of the British Empire
Baronet's Badge
Knight Bachelor's Badge
Companion, The Most Honourable Order of the Bath
Companion, The Most Exalted Order of the Star of India
Companion, The Most Distinguished Order of St. Michael and St. George
Companion, The Most Eminent Order of the Indian Empire
Commander, The Royal Victorian Order
Commander, The Most Excellent Order of the British Empire
Distinguished Service Order
Lieutenant, The Royal Victorian Order
Officer, The Most Excellent Order of the British Empire
Imperial Service Order
Member, The Royal Victorian Order
Member, The Most Excellent Order of the British Empire

Indian Order of Merit—Military
DECORATIONS
Conspicuous Gallantry Cross
Royal Red Cross, Class 1
Distinguished Service Cross
Military Cross
Distinguished Flying Cross
Air Force Cross
Royal Red Cross, Class II
Order of British India
Kaisar-I-Hind Medal
Order of St John

GALLANTRY AND DISTINGUISHED CONDUCT MEDALS
Union of South Africa Queen's Medal for Bravery in gold
Distinguished Conduct Medal
Conspicuous Gallantry Medal
Conspicuous Gallantry Medal (Flying)
George Medal
Queen's Police Medal for Gallantry
Queen's Fire Service Medal for Gallantry
Royal West African Frontier Force Distinguished Conduct Medal
King's African Rifles Distinguished Conduct Medal
Indian Distinguished Service Medal
Union of South Africa Queen's Medal for Bravery in silver
Distinguished Service Medal
Military Medal
Distinguished Flying Medal
Air Force Medal
Constabulary Medal (Ireland)
Medal for Saving Life at Sea
Indian Order of Merit (Civil)
Indian Police Medal for Gallantry
Ceylon Police Medal for Gallantry
Sierra Leone Police Medal for Gallantry
Sierra Leone Fire Brigades Medal for Gallantry
Overseas Territories Police Medal for Gallantry
Queen's Gallantry Medal
Royal Victorian Medal (gold, silver and bronze)
British Empire Medal
Canada Medal
Queen's Police Medal for Distinguished Service
Queen's Fire Service Medal for Distinguished Service
Queen's Ambulance Service Medal
Queen's Volunteer Reserves Medal
Queen's Medal for Chiefs

CAMPAIGN MEDALS

Campaign Medals and Stars, including authorised UN, EU, EC and NATO medals in order of date of participation in the campaign for which awarded, as well as GSMs and OSMs.

Polar Medals—in order of date of award

MEDALS FOR VALUABLE SERVICE

Imperial Service Medal
Indian Police Medal for Meritorious Service
Ceylon Police Medal for Merit
Sierra Leone Police Medal for Meritorious Service
Sierra Leone Fire Brigades Medal for Meritorious Service
Oversea Territories Police Medal for Meritorious Service
Badge of Honour

JUBILEE, CORONATION, DURBAR MEDALS

Queen Victoria's Jubilee Medal 1887 (gold, silver and bronze)
Queen Victoria's Police Jubilee Medal 1887
Queen Victoria's Jubilee Medal 1897 (gold, silver and bronze)
Queen Victoria's Police Jubilee Medal 1897
Queen Victoria's Commemoration Medal 1900 (Ireland)
King Edward VII's Coronation 1902
King Edward VII's Police Coronation 1902
King Edward VII's Durbar 1903 (gold, silver and bronze)
King Edward VII's Police Medal 1903 (Scotland)
King's Visit Commemoration Medal 1903 (Ireland)
King George V's Coronation Medal 1911
King George V's Police Coronation Medal 1911
King George V's Visit Police Commemoration Medal 1911 (Ireland)
King George V's Durbar Medal 1911 (gold, silver and bronze)
King George V's Silver Jubilee Medal 1935
King George VI's Coronation Medal 1937
Queen Elizabeth II's Coronation Medal 1953
Queen Elizabeth II's Silver Jubilee Medal 1977
Queen Elizabeth II's Golden Jubilee Medal 2002
Queen Elizabeth II's Diamond Jubilee Medal 2012
King George V's Long and Faithful Service Medal
King George VI's Long and Faithful Service Medal
Queen Elizabeth II's Long and Faithful Service Medal

EFFICIENCY AND LONG SERVICE DECORATIONS AND MEDALS

Medal for Meritorious Service
Accumulated Campaign Service Medals
Accumulated Campaign Service Medal 2011
Medal for Long Service and Good Conduct, Army
Naval Long Service and Good Conduct Medal
Medal for Meritorious Service (Royal Navy 1918–28)
Indian Long Service and Good Conduct Medal (for Europeans of Indian Army)
Indian Meritorious Service Medal (for Europeans of Indian Army)
Royal Marines Meritorious Service Medal (1849–1947)
Royal Air Force Meritorious Service Medal 1918–28
Royal Air Force Long Service and Good Conduct Medal
Ulster Defence Regiment Long Service and Good Conduct Medal
Indian Long Service and Good Conduct Medal (Indian Army)

Royal West African Frontier Force Long Service and Good Conduct Medal
Royal Sierra Leone Military Forces Long Service and Good Conduct Medal
King's African Rifles Long Service and Good Conduct Medal
Indian Meritorious Service Medal (for Indian Army)
Police Long Service and Good Conduct Medal
Fire Brigade Long Service and Good Conduct Medal
African Police Medal for Meritorious Service
Royal Canadian Mounted Police Long Service Medal
Ceylon Police Long Service Medal
Ceylon Fire Services Long Service Medal
Sierra Leone Police Long Service Medal
Overseas Territories Police Long Service Medal
Sierra Leone Fire Brigade Long Service Medal
Mauritius Police Long Service and Good Conduct Medal
Mauritius Fire Service Long Service and Good Conduct Medal
Mauritius Prisons Service Long Service and Good Conduct Medal
Overseas Territories Fire Brigades Long Service Medal
Overseas Territories Prison Service Medal
Hong Kong Disciplined Services Long Service Medal
Army Emergency Reserve Decoration
Volunteer Officers' Decoration
Volunteer Long Service Medal
Volunteer Officers' Decoration (for India and the Colonies)
Volunteer Long Service Medal (for India and the Colonies)
Overseas Territories Auxiliary Forces Officers' Decoration
Overseas Territories Auxiliary Forces Long Service Medal
Medal for Good Shooting (Naval)
Militia Long Service Medal
Imperial Yeomanry Long Service Medal
Territorial Decoration
Ceylon Armed Service Long Service Medal
Efficiency Decoration
Territorial Efficiency Medal
Efficiency Medal
Special Reserve Long Service and Good Conduct Medal
Decoration for Officers of the Royal Naval Reserve
Decoration for Officers of the Royal Naval Volunteer Reserve
Royal Naval Reserve Long Service and Good Conduct Medal
Royal Naval Volunteer Reserve Long Service and Good Conduct Medal
Royal Naval Auxiliary Sick Berth Reserve Long Service and Good Conduct Medal
Royal Fleet Reserve Long Service and Good Conduct Medal
Royal Naval Wireless Auxiliary Reserve Long Service and Good Conduct Medal
Royal Naval Auxiliary Service Medal
Air Efficiency Award
Volunteer Reserves Service Medal
Ulster Defence Regiment Medal
Queen's Medal (for Champion Shots of the Royal Navy and Royal Marines)
Queen's Medal (for Champion Shots of the New Zealand Naval Forces)
Queen's Medal (for Champion Shots in the Military Forces)

Queen's Medal (for Champion Shots of the Air Force)
Cadet Forces Medal
HM Coast Guard Long Service Medal
Special Constabulary Long Service Medal
Canadian Forces Decoration
Royal Observer Corps Medal
Civil Defence Long Service Medal
Ambulance Service LS & GCM
Royal Fleet Auxiliary Service Medal
Prison Service (Operational Duties) Long Service
  Medal
Jersey Honorary Police Long Service and Good
  Conduct Medal
Merchant Navy Medal for Meritorious Service
Rhodesia Medal
Ebola Medal for Service in West Africa
Royal Ulster Constabulary Service Medal
Northern Ireland Prison Service Medal
Union of South Africa Commemoration Medal
Indian Independence Medal
Pakistan Medal
Ceylon Armed Services Inauguration Medal
Ceylon Police Independence Medal (1948)

Sierra Leone Independence Medal
Jamaica Independence Medal
Uganda Independence Medal
Malawi Independence Medal
Guyana Independence Medal
Fiji Independence Medal
Papua New Guinea Independence Medal
Solomon Islands Independence Medal
Service Medal of the Order of St. John
Badge of the Order of the League of Mercy
Voluntary Medical Service Medal
Women's Voluntary Service Medal
South African Medal for War Services
Overseas Territories Special Constabulary Medal
Honorary Membership of Commonwealth Orders
  (instituted by the Sovereign, in order of date of award)
Other Commonwealth Members, Orders, Decorations
  and Medals (instituted since 1949 otherwise
  than by the Sovereign, and awards by States of
  Malaysia and Brunei in order of date of award)
Foreign Orders in order of date of award
Foreign Decorations in order of date of award
Foreign Medals in order of date of award

THE ORDER IN WHICH CAMPAIGN STARS AND MEDALS AWARDED FOR SERVICE DURING WORLD WAR I AND II AND KOREA WAR ARE WORN

1914 Star with dated "Mons" clasp "
  15th AUGUST–22nd NOVEMBER 1914"
1914 Star
1914/15 Star
British War Medal
Mercantile Marine War Medal
Victory Medal
Territorial Force War Medal
1939/45 Star
Atlantic Star
Arctic Star
Air Crew Europe Star
Africa Star

Pacific Star
Burma Star
Italy Star
France and Germany Star
Defence Medal
Canadian/Newfoundland Volunteer Service Medal
1939/45 War Medal
1939/45 Africa Service Medal of the Union of South Africa
India Service Medal
New Zealand War Service Medal
Southern Rhodesia Service Medal
Australian Service Medal
Korea Medal
United Nations Service Medal with bar KOREA

POST-NOMINAL LETTERS (as published in the London Gazette)
Recipients of some awards are entitled to use post-nominal letters including the following:

AE	Air Efficiency Award (officers)	CMG	Companion, The Most Distinguished Order of St Michael and St George
AFC	Air Force Cross		
AFM	Air Force Medal	CPM	Overseas Territories Police Medal
AM	Albert Medal	CSI	Companion, The Most Exalted Order of the Star of India
ARRC	Royal Red Cross, Second Class		
BEM	British Empire Medal	CVO	Commander, The Royal Victorian Order
BGM	Burma Gallantry Medal	DBE	Dame Commander, The Most Excellent Order of the British Empire
Bt or Bart	Baronet		
CBE	Commander, The Most Excellent Order of the British Empire	DCB	Dame Commander, The Most Honourable Order of the Bath
CB	Companion, The Most Honourable Order of the Bath	DCMG	Dame Commander, The Most Distinguished Order of St Michael and St George
CD	Canadian (Forces) Decoration		
CGC	Conspicuous Gallantry Cross	DCM	Distinguished Conduct Medal (King's African Rifles)
CGM	Conspicuous Gallantry Medal		
CH	Order of the Companion of Honour	DCM	Distinguished Conduct Medal (West Africa Frontier Force)
CIE	Companion, The Most Eminent Order of the Indian Empire	DCM	Distinguished Conduct Medal
CI	The Order of the Crown of India (women only)	DCVO	Dame Commander, The Royal Victorian Order
CM/MduC	Canada Medal	DFC	Distinguished Flying Cross

DFM	Distinguished Flying Medal	KG	Knight, Most Noble Order of the Garter
DSC	Distinguished Service Cross	KP	Knight, Most Illustrious Order of St Patrick
DSM	Distinguished Service Medal		
DSO	Distinguished Service Order	KPFSM	King's Police and Fire Service Medal
ED	Efficiency Decoration	KPM	King's Police Medal
EGM	Empire Gallantry Medal	KT	Knight, Most Ancient and Most Noble Order of the Thistle
EM	Edward Medal		
ERD	Army Emergency Reserve Decoration	LVO	Lieutenant, The Royal Victorian Order
GBE	Knight Grand Cross, The Most Excellent Order of the British Empire	MBE	Member, The Most Excellent Order of the British Empire
GCB	Knight Grand Cross, The Most Honourable Order of the Bath	MC	Military Cross
		MM	Military Medal
GCIE	Knight Grand Commander. The Most Eminent Order of the Indian Empire	MSM	Meritorious Service Medal (Navy, awards up to 20.7.28)
GCMG	Knight Grand Cross—The Most Distinguished Order of St Michael and St George	MVO	Member, The Royal Victorian Order
		OBE	Officer, The Most Excellent Order of the British Empire
GCSI	Knight Grand Commander, The Most Exalted Order of the Star of India	OBI	Order of British India
		OB	Order of Burma (distinguished service)
GCVO	Knight Grand Cross, The Royal Victorian Order	OB	Order of Burma (gallantry)
		QASM	Queens Ambulance Service Medal
GC	George Cross	OM	Order of Merit
GM	George Medal	QAM	Queen's Ambulance Medal
IDSM	Indian Distinguished Service Medal	QFSM	Queen's Fire Service Medal
IOM	Indian Order of Merit (civil)	QGM	Queen's Gallantry Medal
IOM	Indian Order of Merit (military)	QPM	Queen's Police Medal
ISO	Imperial Service Order	QVRM	Queen's Volunteer Reserves Medal
KBE	Knight Commander, The Most Excellent Order of the British Empire	RD	Royal Naval Reserve Decoration
		RRC	Royal Red Cross First Class
KCB	Knight Commander, The Most Honourable Order of the Bath	RVM	Royal Victorian Medal
		SGM	Sea Gallantry Medals
KCIE	Knight Commander, The Most Eminent Order of the Indian Empire	TD	Territorial Decoration
		UD	Ulster Defence Regiment Medal (officers)
KCMG	Knight Commander, The Most Distinguished Order of St Michael and St George	VC	Victoria Cross
		VD	Volunteer Officers' Decoration
		VR	Volunteer Reserve
KCSI	Knight Commander, The Most Exalted Order of the Star of India	VRD	Royal Naval Volunteer Reserve Decoration
KCVO	Knight Commander, The Royal Victorian Order		

NB By Royal Warrant dated June 14, 2012, medals titled "Colonial . . ." are to be renamed "Overseas Territories . . ."

THE ORDERS AND MEDALS RESEARCH SOCIETY

- Only national UK-based society dedicated to orders and medals.
- Global membership.
- National and regional conventions.
- 19 branches around the world.
- Information-packed quarterly Journal.
- Publishes research books by its members.
- Newly-redesigned website at www.omrs.org

Join online or contact the
Membership Secretary,
PO Box 248, Snettisham,
King's Lynn, PE31 7TA.
E-mail membershipsecretary@omrs.org

COLLECTING
Medal Ribbons

There is nothing new or old about collecting medal ribbons, in fact the founders of the present Orders and Medals Research Society originally set out as medal ribbon collectors. The ribbon has, ever since the early 18th century, been an important complement to the medal or badge of an order and its importance has grown over the years. Since those early orders of chivalry when it was deemed necessary to identify the various religious or secular orders one belonged to by the colour of its ribbon, the emphasis has been on the ribbon to identify the order or medal. This practice has continued down through the centuries, even to today when the avid enthusiast can recognise a warrior's medals simply by identifying his ribbons.

However, times are changing. The practice of wearing medals is on the decline, reserved only for ceremonial occasions, whilst the wearing of ribbon bars and the awarding of a single campaign or service medal with different ribbons to denote specific operations is on the increase. Our very own Operational Service Medal (OSM), the NATO medal and of course the plethora of United Nations medals are all classic examples of today's expansion of the medal ribbon. There is of course the growing cost of collecting medals and decorations compared to that of medal ribbons. There is also the down side to all of this—the opportunity to acquire medal ribbons has become a challenge to many, as sources such as tailors' shops, small ribbon manufacturers and numerous regimental or quartermasters stores have all gone into decline, if not altogether vanished.

Before one can collect ribbons properly one must first be able to identify them. It is therefore important to have a reasonable reference library—nothing elaborate or expansive is needed. It is probably wise to start collecting ribbons of the United Kingdom before branching out into those of other countries. There are several good books on the subject and most ribbons can be obtained quite easily.

The more one handles ribbons the quicker one starts to get a feel for the subject and gets to know which colours are used by certain countries or organisations; whether they always use silk or fine cottons; prefer moiré (watered) or corded ribbons; whether they use wide or narrow ribbons—all are skills one picks up along the way. However, today this can sometimes prove difficult as the quality of many modern manufactured ribbons is really quite poor compared to the silk watered ribbons of bygone days.

Once over the initial teething problems of deciding how to store ribbons and ultimately mount or display them, the desire to expand and even specialise creeps in. Do you collect ribbons from just one country, state or organisation such as the Red Cross or the United Nations? Campaign medals and their numerous emblems? Famous chests? Regimental battle streamers? Religious or chivalric orders past and present? British or foreign orders and their various rosettes? The choice can be endless. Whatever the path you choose, you will almost certainly have to do a little research to obtain the reason for the award and the colours adopted for the ribbon. In reality, a true ribbon collector will know just as much about the medal or decoration as they will about the ribbon. Depending on the amount of time you have, research can lead you to museums, reading rooms or even portrait galleries, as well as societies such as the Ribbon Branch of the Orders and Medals Research Society (see their advertisement opposite). But whatever path is chosen you will be in awe of the sacrifices made by mankind down the centuries.

MINIATURE
Medals & Decorations

Miniature medals are smaller representations of a recipient's original awards. Early miniatures were in the nature of personal jewellery, for wear when full-size awards would be out of place. As the awards were generally Orders, these miniatures tended to be "one-off" pieces made by jewellers.

The fashion of wearing awards in miniature probably originated in Europe at the end of the 18th century and was then adopted by British officers, possibly those who had encountered or served with other armies and had received foreign awards. The idea apparently became more widespread after Waterloo. There is portrait evidence at the National Army Museum of a British infantry officer wearing miniatures in a continental style in 1819.

It has also been suggested that miniatures were created for officers' ladies to wear. Though there is no equivalent portrait evidence to support this, it is entirely plausible and miniature awards converted to pendants and brooches are also known.

Following the institution of both new and retrospective awards, the 1840s saw rapid expansion in the range of makers and suppliers of miniatures. Some standardisation for 'mass production' was commercially sensible and though miniatures remained unofficial, the half-size of 18mm was widely adopted in Britain and medals were generally die-struck, usually in silver. Orders were in gold or silver-gilt, with detailed enamelling as appropriate. Though foreign awards are often smaller—perhaps down to 14mm or less—they are generally also available in British size for wear within a Briton's group.

The transition to wearing miniatures in formal social dress was a practical solution to the relative awkwardness of full-size medal groups at such occasions, especially at dinner. The trend also suited the gradual introduction of mess dress—as with miniatures, provided at an officer's personal expense and not an item of official uniform—to equate to civil "white tie".

Because there have been numerous makers over the years, none of them official, there are varying interpretations of the original designs. These varieties add extra interest for miniature medal enthusiasts who otherwise encompass a similar range of themes to those of other medal collectors. Generally, contemporary examples are always preferred, with the Victorian era being most popular. However, sometimes a more recent example must be accepted in lieu of a rare piece.

Where original medals are generally named, the opposite is true of miniatures. However, named examples are found and can lead to rewarding research; the flat reverse of a star or cross lends itself to naming, as does an equivalent full-size award.

Similarly, a group may have a plausible attribution leading to the story of the man (or woman) behind the medals. As with all acquisitions, seek provenance every time, especially where an attribution boosts the asking price (how many Trafalgar participants/ Rorke's Drift defenders/ Battle of Britain Aces, etc., were there really?).

Though miniature Orders may be beautifully crafted in gold, enamels and even precious stones, they are rarely hallmarked. This is probably as much to do with limited space as for any other reason. Occasionally a hallmarked medal or star may be found; as always, the devil is in the detail!

Collecting miniatures can provide as much enjoyment, education and camaraderie as any other aspect of this hobby, while increasing our wider understanding of the world of Orders, Decorations and Medals. It has the dual bonus of being less expensive and less greedy of domestic space than does pursuit of the larger originals. However, it may not take up any less so-called spare time!

The comments here are generally about British or Commonwealth awards and foreign awards found in groups to British recipients, as illustrated in this Yearbook. The prices quoted in this publication are for contemporary medals unless stated otherwise.

ORDERS
of Knighthood

The most colourful and romantic of all awards are those connected with the orders of chivalry. Many of them have their origins in the Middle Ages, when knights in armour formed the elite fighting force in every European country. From the idea of a select band of knights, pledged to the support of a king or an ideal (usually religious), sprang the orders of chivalry.

Many of the orders of chivalry existed in the Middle Ages but most of them died out as feudalism went into decline. In some cases they survived; in others they disappeared for centuries, only to be resurrected at a later date. Still others were devised and instituted in relatively modern times, and indeed, continue to evolve. For example, Canada instituted the Order of Canada in 1967 and both Australia and New Zealand introduced their own orders in 1975.

In their original form membership of the orders of chivalry were just as highly coveted as they are today, but the insignia was usually simple or even non-existent. The complicated system of insignia which now surrounds these orders is fairly modern, dating from the 16th century or later. Nowadays most orders also exist in several classes, with the insignia becoming increasingly elaborate with each higher class.

Britain's senior order is the Garter, and although it consists of one class only it provides a good example of the pomp and ceremony which often surrounds these awards. It was founded by King Edward III and is said to derive its name from the fact that the King was attending a dance one day, when a lady's garter slipped from her leg and fell to the floor. To save her the embarrassment of retrieving her garter—and thus letting everyone know it was hers—the King himself picked it up and tied it round his own leg. Lest anyone should doubt that it was his garter he said, in court French, "Let evil be to him who evil thinks". From this curious incident came the idea of a very exclusive order of knighthood, consisting of the sovereign and 26 knights.

The insignia of this order consists of a Garter, a mantle of blue velvet lined with taffeta with the star of the Order embroidered on the left breast, a hood of crimson velvet, a surcoat of crimson velvet lined with white taffeta, a hat of black velvet lined with white taffeta, with a plume of white ostrich and black heron feathers fastened by a band of diamonds, a collar of gold composed of buckled garters and lovers' knots with red roses, the George (an enamelled figure of St George slaying the dragon) suspended from the collar, the Lesser George or badge, worn from a broad blue sash passing over the left shoulder to the right hip, and the star, a silver eight-pointed decoration bearing the red cross of St George surrounded by the garter and motto.

The insignia is exceptionally elaborate, the other orders of chivalry varying considerably in their complexity according to the class of the order. The full insignia is only worn on special occasions. In the case of the Garter usually the Lesser George and the breast star are worn on their own.

On the death of a Knight of the Garter the insignia should be returned to the Central Chancery of Orders of Knighthood, and therefore few examples of the Garter ever come on to the market. Those that do are usually examples from the 17th and 18th centuries when regulations regarding the return of insignia were not so strict. In the case of the lesser orders, insignia is returnable on promotion to a higher class. All collar chains are returnable, although that of the Order of St Michael and St George could be retained prior to 1948.

British orders are manufactured by firms holding contracts from the Central Chancery of Orders of Knighthood, and the values quoted in this Yearbook are for the official issues. It should be noted, however, that holders of orders frequently have replicas of breast stars made for use on different uniforms and it is sometimes difficult to tell these replicas from the originals as in many cases the replicas were made by the court jewellers responsible for making the originals. In addition, many jewellers in such European capitals as Vienna, Berlin and Paris have a long tradition of manufacturing the insignia of orders for sale to collectors.

The badges and breast stars of orders of chivalry are very seldom named to the recipient and therefore often lack the personal interest of campaign medals and many gallantry awards. For this reason they do not command the same interest or respect of collectors. Nevertheless, in cases where the insignia of orders can be definitely proved to have belonged to some famous person, the interest and value are enhanced. In any case, these orders are invariably very attractive examples of the jeweller's art, and they often possess titles and stories as colourful and romantic as their appearance.

MEDAL NEWS

Published 10 times per annum, the magazine features articles, news, auction reports and the world renowned Medal Tracker service, invaluable when searching for lost medals and trying to reunite broken groups. This service, like the classified advertising, is free to subscribers. Also included in the magazine is the "What's On" section that lets collectors know about fairs, societies, auctions etc. Medal News' devotion to medals and battles comes in handy when tracing those missing family medals.

1. THE MOST NOBLE ORDER OF THE GARTER

KG Star
(a Victorian example)

Lesser George
(this early example has the
garter enamelled in blue)

Instituted: 1348.

Ribbon: 100mm plain dark blue. Not worn in undress uniform.

Garter: Dark blue velvet. Two versions may be encountered, with embroidered lettering and other details, or with gold lettering, buckle and tab. Worn on the left leg by gentlemen and on the left forearm by ladies.

Collar Chain: Gold composed of alternate buckled garters, each encircling a red enamelled rose, and lovers' knots in gold although sometimes enamelled white.

Collar badge: An enamelled figure of St George fighting the dragon.

Star: Originally always embroidered in metal thread, a style which continues in the mantle to this day. Prior to 1858 knights often purchased metal stars in addition and since that date metal stars have been officially issued. These consist of a silver eight-pointed radiate star bearing in its centre and red cross of St George on a white ground, surrounded by the garter and motto HONI SOIT QUI MAL Y PENSE (Evil be to he who evil thinks).

Sash Badge: The Lesser George, similar to the collar badge but encircled by an oval garter bearing the motto.

Comments: *Membership of the Order of the Garter is confined to the reigning sovereign, the Prince of Wales and 25 other Knights, and is the personal gift of the monarch. In addition to the 25 Knights there have, from time to time, been extra Knights, occasionally non-Christians such as the Sultans of Turkey or the Emperor of Japan. The Emperor Hirohito, incidentally had the dubious distinction of being the only person awarded the Garter twice: in 1922 and again in 1971, having forfeited the original award as a result of the Japanese entry into the Second World War in 1941. Sir Winston Churchill was invested with the insignia originally presented in 1702 to his illustrious ancestor, the Duke of Marlborough. All official insignia is returnable to the Central Chancery of Knighthood on the death of the holder. Ladies (other than royalty) are now eligible for the Order.*

VALUE:

Collar chain	Rare
Collar badge (the George)	From £50,000*
Star (in metal)	£5000–15,000
Star (embroidered)	£1000–2000
Mantle star	£1000–1500
Sash badge (Lesser George)	£15,000–50,000
Garter (embroidered)	£800–1000
Garter (gold lettering and buckle)	£4000–8000
Miniature	
Star (metal)	£460–575
Collar badge	£875–970
Sash badge	£400–460

Prices are for privately made examples many of which are jewelled and enamelled.

2. THE MOST ANCIENT AND MOST NOBLE ORDER OF THE THISTLE

KT Star

Instituted: 1687.

Ribbon: 100mm plain dark green. Not worn in undress uniform.

Collar Chain: Gold of alternate thistles and sprigs of rue enamelled in proper colours.

Collar Badge: The jewel is a gold and enamelled figure of St Andrew in a green gown and purple surcoat, bearing before him a white saltire cross, the whole surrounded by rays of gold.

Star: Silver, consisting of a St Andrew's cross, with other rays issuing between the points of the cross and, in the centre, on a gold background, a thistle enamelled in proper colours surrounded by a green circle bearing the Latin motto NEMO ME IMPUNE LACESSIT (No-one assails me with impunity).

Sash Badge: The medal of the Order is a gold figure of St Andrew bearing before him a saltire cross, surrounded by an oval collar bearing the motto, surmounted by a gold cord fitted with a ring for suspension. Examples are found in plain gold, or with enamelling and/or set with jewels.

Comments: *This order is said to have been founded in AD 787, alluding to barefoot enemy soldiers who cried out when they trod on thistles and thus alerted the Scots of an imminent attack. The order had long been defunct when it was revived by King James VII and II and re-established in December 1703 by Queen Anne. It now consists of the sovereign and 16 Knights, making it the most exclusive of the orders of chivalry. At death, the official insignia is returned to the Central Chancery. Ladies (other than royalty) are now eligible for the Order.*

VALUE:

Collar chain	Rare
Collar badge	Rare
Star (metal)	From £6000
Star (embroidered)	From £1000
Mantle star	£750–1500
Sash badge	From £10,000
Miniature	
Star (metal)	£500–550
Collar badge	£550–600
Sash badge	£400–450

Examples of Sash Badges

3. THE MOST ILLUSTRIOUS ORDER OF ST PATRICK

KP Star

Sash badge

Instituted: February 5, 1783.

Ribbon: 100mm sky-blue. Not worn in undress uniform.

Collar Chain: Gold, composed of five roses and six harps alternating, each tied together with a gold knot. The roses are enamelled alternately white petals within red and red within white.

Collar Badge: An imperial crown enamelled in proper colours from which is suspended by two rings a gold harp and from this a circular badge with a white enamelled centre embellished with the red saltire cross on which is surmounted a green three-petalled shamrock its leaves decorated with gold crowns, the whole surrounded by a gold collar bearing the Latin motto QUIS SEPARABIT (Who shall separate us?) with the date of foundation in roman numerals round the foot MDCCLXXXIII.

Star: A silver eight-pointed star, having in its centre, on a white field, the saltire cross of St Patrick in red enamel charged with a green trefoil bearing a gold crown on each leaf.

Sash Badge: The saltire cross in red enamel surmounted by a green shamrock with gold crowns as above, surrounded by an oval collar of pale blue with the Latin motto round the top and the date of foundation round the foot, the whole enclosed by a gold and white enamel surround charged with 32 shamrocks.

Comments: *Founded by King George III to reward the loyalty of Irish peers during the American War of Independence, it originally comprised the monarch and 15 Knights. In 1833 it was extended to include the Lord-Lieutenant of Ireland and 22 Knights, with certain extra and honorary knights. Appointments of non-royal Knights to the Order ceased with the partition of Ireland in 1922, although three of the sons of King George V were appointed after that date — the Prince of Wales (1927), the Duke of York (1936) and the Duke of Gloucester (1934). It became obsolete in 1974 with the death of the last holder. All items of official insignia were returned at death. Unlike the other two great orders, the sash for this Order is worn in the manner of the lesser orders, over the right shoulder.*

VALUE:

Collar chain	Rare
Collar badge	From £15,000
Star (metal)	£5000–7500
Star (embroidered)	£850–1000
Mantle star	£850–1200
Sash badge	From £5000
Miniature	
Star (metal)	£400–500
Collar/Sash badge	£650–750

4. THE MOST HONOURABLE ORDER OF THE BATH

GCB Star (Military)

Instituted: 1725.

Ribbon: 38mm deep red.

Collar Chain: Gold composed of nine crowns and eight devices, each consisting of a rose, a thistle and a shamrock issuing from a sceptre all enamelled in their proper colours. The crowns and devices are joined by gold, white-enamelled knots.

Collar Badge: A skeletal gold badge with an oval collar inscribed TRIA JUNCTA IN UNO (Three joined in one) in white enamelled letters, enclosing a thistle, rose and shamrock issuing from a sceptre, with a crown above the sceptre and two crowns below, at the sides.

Star: A silver flaming star surmounted by a circular gold band enamelled red bearing the motto round the top and having a laurel spray round the foot, enclosing three gold crowns enamelled in red.

Sash Badge: As the Collar Badge but smaller and without white enamelling.

Comments: *Established by King George I, this was a single-class Order comprising the monarch, a prince of the blood royal, a Great Master and 35 Knights of Companions (KB). It was re-organised at the conclusion of the Napoleonic Wars (see below). Ladies (other than royalty) are now eligible for the Order. Promotion to a different division permits the wearing of both types of insignia.*

VALUE:

Collar chain	Rare
Collar badge	£3000–4000
Star (metal)	From £5500
Star (embroidered)	£500–1000
Sash badge	£2000–3000

KNIGHT GRAND CROSS (GCB)

The Order was re-organised in 1815 in two divisions, Military and Civil. The Military Division had three classes: Knight Grand Cross (GCB), Knight Commander (KCB) and Companion (CB), while the Civil Division continued with the single class of Knight Grand Cross. In 1847 the Civil Division came into line with the Military, and divided into three classes.

Metal: Gold (1815–87), silver-gilt (1887–1901), silver gilt with gold centre (1902 on).

Collar Badge: The Military Badge is a gold Maltese cross of eight points, each point tipped with a small gold ball, and in each angle between the arms of the cross is a gold lion. In the centre of the cross is a device comprising a rose, thistle and shamrock issuing from a sceptre, and three imperial crowns . This device is surrounded by a red enamelled circle on which appears the Latin motto TRIA JUNCTA IN UNO (three joined in one) in gold lettering. The circle is surrounded by two branches of laurel, enamelled green, and below is a blue enamelled scroll with the German motto ICH DIEN (I serve) in gold.

The Civil Badge is of gold filigree work, and oval in shape. It consists of a bandlet bearing the motto, and in the centre is the usual device of the rose, thistle and shamrock issuing from a sceptre, together with the three crowns.

Star: A gold Maltese cross of the same pattern as the Military Badge, mounted on a silver flaming star (Military); or a silver eight-pointed star with a central device of three crowns on a silver ground, encircled by the motto on a red enamelled ribbon (Civil).

Sash Badges: Similar to the Collar Badges, they were originally made in gold but since 1887 silver-gilt has been substituted. They may now be worn at the neck when sashes are not worn.

VALUE:

	Military	Civil
Collar chain (gold)	Rare	Rare
Collar chain (silver gilt)	£8000–10,000	£8000–10,000
Collar badge (gold)	£3000–4500	£1250–1750
Star (metal)	£2500–3500	£1250–1750
Star (embroidered)	£350–500	£250–350
Mantle star	£750–1000	£650–850
Sash badge (gold)	£4000–6000	£2000–3000
Sash badge (gilt)	£1500–2000	£800–1200

4. THE MOST HONOURABLE ORDER OF THE BATH *continued*

KCB Star (Civil)

GCB Sash badge (Civil)

KCB Neck badge (Military)

KNIGHTS COMMANDERS (KCB) AND COMPANIONS (CB)

Holders of the KCB wear a neck badge suspended by a ribbon as well as a breast star. Prior to 1917 Companions wore a breast badge, the same way as a medal: but in that year it was converted into a neck badge.

Star: (KCB): (Military) a star with the gold Maltese cross omitted, and in the shape of a cross pattée, the three crowns and motto in the centre surrounded by a green enamelled laurel wreath. (Civil) similar but omitting the laurel wreath.

Breast Badge (CB): Similar to the Star but smaller.

Neck Badge (KCB): Similar to the Collar badges of the GCB but smaller, in Military and Civil versions as above.

Neck Badge (CB): Similar to the above, but smaller.

VALUE:

	Military	Miniature	Civil	Miniature
Knight Commander				
Star (metal)	£1250–1500		£750–850	
Star (embroidered)	£550–650		£450–550	
Neck badge (gold)	£3500–4500		£1200–1500	
Neck badge (gilt)	£1200–1500		£650–750	
Companion				
Breast badge (gold)	£2500–3000	£150–200	£750–850	£100–175
Breast badge (gilt)	£1000–1200	£60–100	£350–450	£55–85
Neck badge (gilt)	£800–950		£300–375	

5. THE ROYAL GUELPHIC ORDER

Instituted: 1815.
Ribbon: 44mm light blue watered silk.

KNIGHTS GRAND CROSS (GCH)

KCH Star (Military)

Collar Chain: Gold, with lions and crowns alternating, linked by scrolled royal cyphers.
Collar Badge: An eight-pointed Maltese cross with balls on each point and a lion passant gardant in each angle. (Obverse) in the centre, on a ground of red enamel, is a white horse of Hanover surrounded by a circle of light blue enamel with the motto in gold lettering NEC ASPERA TERRENT (Difficulties do not terrify). Surrounding this circle is a green enamelled laurel wreath. (Reverse) the monogram GR in gold letters on a red ground, surmounted by the British crown and surrounded by a gold circle with the date of the institution MDCCCXV. In the Military version two crossed swords are mounted above the cross and below a Hanoverian crown. In the Civil version the swords are omited, and the wreath is of oak-leaves instead of laurel.
Star: A radiate star with rays grouped into eight points, the centre being similar to the Collar Badge. Behind the laurel wreathed centre are two crossed swords (Military); in the Civil version the swords are omitted and the wreath is of oak leaves.
Sash Badge: Similar to the Collar Badge but smaller.

Comments: *Founded by HRH the Prince Regent (later King George IV), it took its name from the family surname of the British sovereigns from George I onwards and was awarded by the crown of Hanover to both British and Hanoverian subjects for distinguished services to Hanover. Under Salic Law, a woman could not succeed to the Hanoverian throne, so on the death of King William IV in 1837 Hanover passed to Prince Augustus, Duke of Cumberland, and thereafter the Guelphic Order became a purely Hanoverian award.*

VALUE:

	Military	Civil
Collar chain (gold)	From £25,000	From £20,000
Collar chain (silver gilt)	£10,000–12,000	£8000–10,000
Collar Chain (copper gilt)	£5000–6000	£3500–4500
Collar badge	£6000–8000	£2500–3500
Star	£5000–7000	£3000–4000
Sash badge	£8000–10,000	£6000–8000

KNIGHTS COMMANDERS (KCH) AND KNIGHTS (KH)

Knights Commanders wore a neck badge suspended by a ribbon, and a breast star, while Knights wore a breast badge only.
Star: As above, but smaller.
Neck Badge: Similar to the Collar Badge but smaller.
Breast Badge: Two versions, in gold and enamel or silver and enamel.

VALUE:

	Military	Miniature	Civil	Miniature
Star	£2500–3000		£1500–2000	
Neck badge	£3500–4000		£2000–2500	
Breast badge (gold)	£2500–3000	£450–550	£1200–1500	£500–600
Breast badge (silver)	£1000–1200			

KH Breast Badge (Military)

6. THE MOST DISTINGUISHED ORDER OF ST MICHAEL AND ST GEORGE

Instituted: 1818.
Ribbon: 101mm, 51mm, 38mm three equal bands of Saxon blue, scarlet and Saxon blue.

KNIGHTS GRAND CROSS (GCMG)

Knights Grand Cross wear a mantle of Saxon blue lined with scarlet silk tied with cords of blue and scarlet silk and gold, and having on the left side the star of the Order. The chapeau or hat is of blue satin, lined with scarlet and surmounted by black and white ostrich feathers. The collar, mantle and chapeau are only worn on special occasions or when commanded by the sovereign, but in ordinary full dress the badge is worn on the left hip from a broad ribbon passing over the right shoulder and the star on the left breast.

Collar Chain: Silver gilt formed alternately of lions of England, Maltese crosses enamelled in white, and the cyphers SM and SG with, in the centre, two winged lions of St Mark each holding a book and seven arrows.

Star: A silver star of seven groups of rays, with a gold ray between each group, surmounted overall by the cross of St George in red enamel. In the centre is a representation of St Michael encountering Satan within a blue circular riband bearing the motto AUSPICIUM MELIORIS AEVI (A token of a better age).

Sash Badge: A gold seven-pointed star with V-shaped extremities, enamelled white and edged with gold, surmounted by an imperial crown. In the centre on one side is a representation in enamel of St Michael encountering Satan and on the other St George on horseback fighting the dragon. This device is surrounded by a circle of blue enamel bearing the Latin motto in gold lettering. Silver-gilt was substituted for gold in 1887.

Comments: *Founded by HRH the Prince Regent and awarded originally to citizens of Malta and the Ionian Islands in the Adriatic Sea, both of which had been ceded to Britain during the Napoleonic Wars. The Ionian Islands were transferred to Greece in 1859. Towards the end of the 19th century, however, the Order was awarded to those who had performed distinguished service in the colonies and protectorates of the British Empire and in more recent times it has been widely used as an award to ambassadors and senior diplomats as well as colonial governors. Ladies are now eligible for this Order. In recent operations a number of awards have been made to military officers, presumably for "diplomatic" work.*

VALUE:

Collar chain	£4000–5000
Star	£2000–2750
Sash badge (gold)	£4500–5500
Sash badge (gilt)	£1500–2000

GCMG Star

6. THE MOST DISTINGUISHED ORDER OF ST MICHAEL AND ST GEORGE continued

KCMG Star

KNIGHTS COMMANDERS (KCMG) AND COMPANIONS (CMG)

Knights Commanders wear the badge suspended round the neck from a narrower ribbon of the same colours, and a breast star; Companions wear a neck badge. In undress uniform Knights Grand Cross and Knights Commanders wear the ribbon of Companions of the Order. Prior to 1917 Companions wore a breast badge, worn the same way as a medal, but this was then changed to a neck badge.

Star: A silver eight-pointed star charged with the red St George's cross and having the same central device as the GCMG Star. This was introduced in 1859.

Neck Badge: Similar to the sash badge of the GCMG but smaller. Those worn by Knight Commanders were of gold and enamel until 1887 but silver-gilt and enamel thereafter. The CMG neck badges are invariably of enamel and silver-gilt.

Breast Badge: Similar to the star of the KCMG but smaller and made of gold and enamel till 1887, and silver gilt and enamel from then till 1917.

VALUE:		Miniature
Knight Commander		
Star	£1200–1500	
Neck badge (gold)	£2000–3000	
Neck badge (gilt)	£1000–1500	
Companion		
Breast badge (gold)	£1500–1800	£100–150
Breast badge (gilt)	£800–1000	£85–125
Neck badge (gilt)	£550–600	

7. THE MOST EXALTED ORDER OF THE STAR OF INDIA

Instituted: 1861.
Ribbon: Broad light blue with white edges (GCSI); 50mm plain white (KCSI); 38mm plain white (CSI).

KNIGHTS GRAND COMMANDERS (GCSI)

KCSI Neck badge

The insignia consisted of a gold collar and badge, a mantle of light blue satin with a representation of the star on the left side and tied with a white silk cord with blue and silver tassels. The collar and mantle were only worn on special occasions and in ordinary full dress uniform a GCSI wore the star on the left breast and the badge on the left hip from a broad sash of light blue edged in white.

Collar Chain: Gold formed of lotus flowers, palm branches and united red and white roses. Later chains are silver-gilt.

Badge: An onyx cameo bearing the left-facing bust of Queen Victoria wearing an imperial crown, set in a gold ornamental oval containing the motto of the Order HEAVEN'S LIGHT OUR GUIDE in diamonds, on a pale blue ground surmounted by a five-pointed star in chased silver.

Star: A five-pointed star in diamonds resting on a circular riband of light blue enamel bearing the motto in diamonds, the whole set on a circular star of golden rays.

Comments: *Founded by Queen Victoria a few years after the British Crown took over the administration of India from the Honourable East India Company, it was intended primarily as an award to loyal Indian princes. The highest class was designated Knight Grand Commander, rather than Cross, because the majority of recipients were not Christians (either Hindus or Muslims). The Order at first consisted of the sovereign, a Grand Master (the Viceroy of India), 36 Knights Grand Commanders (18 British and 18 Indian), 85 Knights Commanders and 170 Companions. The GCSI was the most lavish of all British orders. It lapsed in 1947 when the sub-continent attained independence. Until then all insignia of this Order was returnable on the death of recipients. After 1947, however, recipients or their heirs were allowed in certain cases to purchase the star and badges of any of the three applicable classes, but not the collar chain of the Knight Grand Commander.*

VALUE:

Collar chain	—
Star and badge	From £40,000

KNIGHTS COMMANDERS (KCSI) AND COMPANIONS (CSI)

Knights Commanders wore a badge round the neck and a star on the left breast, while Companions originally had a breast badge which was transmuted into a neck badge from 1917 onwards.

Star: Similar to that of the GCSI but in silver.

Neck Badge: Similar to the collar badge of the GCSI but smaller and less ornate.

Breast Badge: Similar to the above but smaller and less ornate and fitted with a straight bar suspender. Subtle differences in the ornament at the foot of the blue border and the external ornament at the sides and foot of the oval.

Comments: *The second and third classes of the Order were awarded to Indian and British subjects of the armed forces and Indian Civil Service for distinguished service of not less than 30 years' duration.*

VALUE: *Miniature*

Star and Neck badge (KCSI)	£14,000–16,000	
Breast badge (CSI)	£6500–7500	£350–500 (gold), £200–250 (silver gilt)
Neck badge (CSI)	£6000–9000	

8. THE MOST EMINENT ORDER OF THE INDIAN EMPIRE

Instituted: 1878.
Ribbon: Deep indigo blue.

KNIGHTS GRAND COMMANDERS (GCIE)

KCIE Neck badge

The insignia consisted of a collar, badge and mantle of imperial purple or dark blue satin lined with white silk and fastened with a white silk cord with gold tassels, and having on the left side a representation of the Star of the Order. On ordinary full-dress occasions, however, Knights Grand Commanders wore the badge on the left hip from a broad sash, and a star on the left breast.

Collar Chain: Silver-gilt, composed of elephants, lotus flowers, peacocks in their pride and Indian roses with, in the centre, the imperial crown, the whole linked together by chains.

Badge: A gold five-petalled rose, enamelled crimson and with a green barb between each petal. In the centre is an effigy of Queen Victoria on a gold ground, surrounded by a purple riband originally inscribed VICTORIA IMPERATRIX but from 1901 onwards inscribed IMPERATRICIS AUSPICIIS (Under the auspices of the Empress). The letters I N D I A are inscribed on the petals in the first version, but omitted in the second.

Star: Composed of fine silver rays with smaller gold rays between them, the whole alternately plain and scaled. In the centre, within a purple circle bearing the motto and surmounted by the imperial crown in gold, is the effigy of Queen Victoria on a gold ground.

Comments: *Founded by Queen Victoria after assuming the title of Empress of India, it was originally confined to Companions only, together with the Sovereign and Grand Master. Members of the Council of the Governor-General were admitted* ex officio *as Companions. It was intended for award in respect of meritorious services in India but from the outset it was regarded as a junior alternative to the Star of India. In 1886 the Order was expanded to two classes by the addition of Knights Commanders up to a maximum of 50 in number. In 1887, however, it was again re-organised into three classes: up to 25 Knights Grand Commanders (GCIE), up to 50 Knights Commanders (KCIE) and an unlimited number of Companions (CIE). The Order has been in abeyance since 1947.*

VALUE:

Collar chain	From £20,000
Star and badge	£7000–9000

KNIGHTS COMMANDERS (KCIE) AND COMPANIONS (CIE)

The insignia of Knights Commanders consisted of a neck badge and a breast star, while that of Companions was originally a breast badge, converted to a neck badge in 1917.

Star: Similar to that of the GCIE but fashioned entirely in silver.

Neck badge: Similar to the collar or sash badge of the GCIE but in correspondingly smaller sizes and differing in minor details.

Breast badge: Similar to the sash badge of the GCIE but differing in minor details, notably the spacing ornament at the foot of the blue circle. Two versions exist, with or without INDIA on the petals of the lotus flower.

VALUE:		*Miniature*
Knights Commanders		
Star and Neck badge	£5000–7000	
Companions		
Breast badge (INDIA)	£2000–3000	£450–500 (gold)
Breast badge (smaller, without INDIA)	£1000–1250	£300–400 (gold)
Neck badge	£900–1000	£175–250 (gilt)

9. THE ROYAL FAMILY ORDER

QEII (reduced)

Edward VII

George V

George VI

Elizabeth II

Instituted: 1820.

Ribbon: 50mm sky blue moiré (1820); 38mm dark blue bordered by narrow stripes of yellow and broader stripes of crimson with narrow black edges (1902); 50mm pale blue moire (1911); 50mm pink moire (1937); 50mm pale yellow silk moire (1953). These ribbons are tied in a bow and worn on the left shoulder.

Descriptions: An upright oval heavily bordered by diamonds and surmounted by a crown, also embellished in diamonds. The oval contains a miniature portrait of the sovereign in enamels.

Comments: *Awarded to the Queen and female relatives of the reigning monarch. It was instituted by King George IV who conferred such orders on his sister, Princess Charlotte Augusta, wife of Frederick William, King of Wurttemberg, and his niece Princess Augusta Caroline, who married the Grand Duke of Mecklenburg-Strelitz. Queen Victoria instituted a separate Order (see next entry), but this Order was revived by King Edward VII in 1902 and continued by successive sovereigns ever since. The insignia of these Family Orders very seldom appear on the market and on account of their immense rarity they are unpriced here. Special badges are given to ladies-in-waiting.*

VALUE:

George IV	—
Edward VII	—
George V	—
George VI	—
Elizabeth II	—
Ladies-in-waiting badges	From £1000

10. THE ROYAL ORDER OF VICTORIA AND ALBERT

Instituted: 1862.

Ribbon: 38mm white moiré, in the form of a bow worn on the left shoulder.

Description: An upright oval onyx cameo bearing conjoined profiles of HRH Prince Albert, the Prince Consort and Queen Victoria. The badges of the First and Second Classes are set in diamonds and surmounted by an imperial crown similarly embellished, the badge of the Second Class being rather smaller. The badge of the Third Class is set in pearls, while that of the Fourth Class takes the form of a monogram "V & A" set with pearls and surmounted by an imperial crown.

Comments: *Personally awarded to female members of the Royal Family by Queen Victoria. This order became obsolete in 1981 with the death of Princess Alice, Countess of Athlone, the last surviving grandchild of Queen Victoria.*

VALUE:

First Class	From £35,000
Second Class	£25,000–30,000
Third Class	£15,000–18,000
Fourth Class	£8000–10,000

11. THE IMPERIAL ORDER OF THE CROWN OF INDIA

Instituted: January 1, 1878.

Ribbon: 38mm light blue watered silk with narrow white stripes towards the edges, formed in a bow worn on the left shoulder.

Description: A badge consisting of the royal and imperial monogram VRI in diamonds, turquoises and pearls, surrounded by an oval frame and surmounted by a jewelled imperial crown.

Comments: *Awarded by Queen Victoria to the princesses of the royal and imperial house, the wives or other female relatives of Indian princes and other Indian ladies, and of the wives or other female relatives of any of the persons who had held or were holding the offices of Viceroy and Governor-General of India, Governors of Madras or Bombay, or of Principal Secretary of State for India, as the sovereign might think fit to appoint. Her Majesty the Queen is the only surviving member of the Order.*

VALUE:
From £15,000   *Miniature*   £500–600

12. THE ROYAL VICTORIAN ORDER

Instituted: April 1896.
Ribbon: Dark blue with borders of narrow red, white and red stripes on either side, 44mm (KCVO and CVO), or 32mm (LVO, MVO and RVM). When insignia not worn the 32mm width is used by all classes on uniforms.

KNIGHTS GRAND CROSS AND DAMES GRAND CROSS (GCVO)

GCVO star

The insignia consists of a mantle of dark blue silk, edged with red satin, lined with white silk, and fastened by a cordon of dark blue silk and gold; a gold collar and a badge, worn only on special occasions. Knights wear the badge on the left hip from a broad ribbon worn over the right shoulder, with a star on the left breast, while Dames wear a somewhat narrower ribbon over the right shoulder with the badge, and a star similar to that of the Knights. Dames' insignia are smaller than those of the Knights.

Collar: Silver gilt composed of octagonal pieces and oblong perforated and ornamental frames alternately linked together with gold. The pieces are edged and ornamented with gold, and each contains on a blue-enamelled ground a gold rose jewelled with a carbuncle. The frames are gold and each contains a portion of inscription VICTORIA BRITT. FID. DEF. IND. IMP. in letters of white enamel. In the centre of the collar, within a perforated and ornamental frame of gold, is an octagonal piece enamelled blue, edged with red, and charged with a white saltire, superimposed by a gold medallion of Queen Victoria's effigy from which is suspended the badge.

Badge: A white-enamelled Maltese cross of eight points, in the centre of which is an oval of crimson enamel bearing the cypher VRI in gold letters. Encircling this is a blue enamel riband with the name VICTORIA in gold letters, and above this is the imperial crown enamelled in proper colours.

Star: Of chipped silver of eight points on which is mounted a white-enamelled Maltese cross with VRI in an oval at the centre.

Comments: *Awarded for extraordinary, important or personal services to the Sovereign or the Royal Family. Ladies became eligible for the Order in 1936. Most of the badges of the Royal Victorian Order are numbered on the reverse and are returnable on promotion. The early (QV) awards are unnumbered.*

VALUE:	Knights	Dames	Miniature
Collar			
gold	From £15,000	From £15,000	
silver gilt	From £6000	From £8000	
Star and Badge (GCVO)	£2500–3000	£2500–3000	£300–400

KNIGHTS COMMANDERS (KCVO), DAMES COMMANDERS (DCVO), COMMANDERS (CVO), LIEUTENANTS (LVO) AND MEMBERS (MVO)

The insignia of the Second, Third, Fourth and Fifth Classes follows the usual pattern. Knights wear a neck badge and a breast star, Dames a breast star and a badge on the left shoulder from a ribbon tied in a bow, Commanders the same neck badge (men) or shoulder badge (women), Lieutenants a somewhat smaller breast badge worn in line with other medals and decorations (men) or a shoulder badge (women) and Members breast or shoulder badges in frosted silver instead of white enamel. The two lowest classes of the Order were originally designated member Fourth Class or member Fifth Class (MVO), but in 1984 the Fourth Class was renamed Lieutenant (LVO) and the Fifth Class simply Member (MVO).

VALUE:	Gentlemen	Miniature	Ladies
Neck badge and breast star (KCVO)	£1800–2500	£200–250	£1400–1800
Neck badge (CVO)	£500–600	£40–60	£450–500
Breast or shoulder badge (LVO)	£400–500	£40–60	£370–400
Breast or shoulder badge (MVO)	£350–450	£35–50	£300–350

13. ROYAL VICTORIAN MEDAL

Instituted: April 1896.
Ribbon: As for the Royal Victorian Order (above); foreign Associates, however, wear a ribbon with a central white stripe added.
Metal: Silver-gilt, silver or bronze.
Size: 30mm.
Description: (Obverse) the effigy of the reigning sovereign; (reverse) the royal cypher on an ornamental shield within a laurel wreath with ROYAL VICTORIAN MEDAL below.
Comments: *Awarded to those below the rank of officers who perform personal services to the sovereign or to members of the Royal Family. Originally awarded in silver or bronze, a higher class, in silver-gilt, was instituted by King George V. Only two medals (both silver) were issued in the brief reign of King Edward VIII (1936) and only four bronze medals were issued in the reign of King George VI. Any person in possession of the bronze medal to whom a silver medal is awarded, can wear both, and the silver-gilt medal in addition if such be conferred upon him or her. Clasps are awarded for further services to each class of the medal, while the medals may be worn in addition to the insignia of the Order if the latter is subsequently conferred. To distinguish between British and foreign recipients, King George VI decreed in 1951 that the ribbon worn by the latter should have an additional stripe, these recipients to be designated Associates. In 1983 the order for wearing this medal was altered and it was no longer to be worn after campaign medals but took precedence over them. The medal is issued unnamed. A lapel badge or emblem for members of the Order to wear on everyday clothing was introduced in 2011.*

Ribbon for foreign Associates.

Emblem worn by members when in civilian dress.

VALUE:

	Silver-gilt	Miniature	Silver	Miniature	Bronze	Miniature
Victoria	—	£85–115	£250–350	£100–150	£200–250	£85–100
Edward VII	—	—	£250–350	£85–100	£175–225	£55–80
George V	£300–350	—	£225–275	£50–85	£250–300	£25–50
Edward VIII	—	—	Rare	—	—	—
George VI	£400–450	—	£225–275	£35–50	Rare	£20–30
Elizabeth II	£400–450	—	£225–275	£35–50	£400–450	£20–30

14. THE ROYAL VICTORIAN CHAIN

Instituted: 1902.
Ribbon: None.
Metal: Silver gilt
Description: A chain consisting of three Tudor roses, two thistles, two shamrocks and two lotus flowers (the heraldic flowers of England, Scotland, Ireland and India respectively), connected by a slender double trace of gold chain. At the bottom of the front loop is a centre piece consisting of the royal cypher in enamel surrounded by a wreath and surmounted by a crown. From this centrepiece hangs a replica of the badge of a Knight Grand Cross of the Royal Victorian Order. Ladies wear the insignia in the form of a shoulder badge suspended from a miniature chain with links leading to a rose, thistle, shamrock and lotus. An even more elaborate collar, with diamonds encrusting the crown and cypher, was adopted in 1921 and there is a ladies' version of this as well.
Comments: *Sometimes regarded as the highest grade of the Royal Victorian Order, it is actually a quite separate Order and was introduced by King Edward VII for conferment as a special mark of the sovereign's favour, and then only very rarely, upon Royalty, or other especially distinguished personages, both foreign and British.*

VALUE

	Gentlemen	Ladies
Chain (Omitted)	From £20,000	From £20,000
Chain with diamonds	Rare	Rare

15. ORDER OF MERIT

Order of Merit obverse

Order of Merit reverse

Instituted: 1902.
Ribbon: 50mm half blue, half crimson.
Metal: Gold.
Size: Height 50mm; max. width 35mm.
Description: A pattée convexed cross, enamelled red, edged blue. (Obverse) FOR MERIT in the centre surrounded by a white band and a laurel wreath enamelled in proper colours. (Reverse) the royal cypher in gold on a blue ground with a white surround and a laurel wreath as above. The cross is surmounted by a Tudor crown to which is attached a ring for suspension. Naval and military recipients have crossed swords in the angles of the cross.
Comments: *This highly prestigious Order consists of the sovereign and a maximum of 24 members in one class only. There is, however, no limit on the number of foreign honorary members, although only 11 have so far been admitted to the Order. It is intended to honour exceptionally meritorious service in the Crown Services or towards the advancement of the Arts, Learning, Literature and Science or other exceptional service. To date 185 awards have been made, including only nine ladies, from Florence Nightingale (1907) to Baroness Boothroyd (2005). The insignia of those appointed since 1991 have to be returned on the death of the recipient. The insignia of members appointed prior to that date is retained, but understandably few items have come on to the market.*

VALUE:

	Military	Civil
Edward VII	From £25,000	From £15,000
George V	From £25,000	From £15,000
George VI	Rare	From £15,000
Elizabeth II	Rare	From £10,000
Miniature	£250–300	

IMPORTANT NOTICE

The prices quoted in this publication are average figures for medals and decorations as individual items. Combinations with other decorations and campaign medals will produce a value usually well in excess of the aggregate of the individual items. Value will depend to a large extent on the personal factors and circumstances of the award, but where general factors are involved (e.g. the design of the medal, the period of issue or the campaign concerned, or in some cases the branch of the services) these are itemised separately. "—" indicates that either no examples have come onto the market or no examples have been issued. The figure in brackets (where available) is the approximate number awarded. In the lists which follow, it should be assumed that decorations were instituted by Royal Warrant, unless otherwise stated

16. THE MOST EXCELLENT ORDER OF THE BRITISH EMPIRE

Instituted: June 1917.

Ribbon: 38mm originally purple, with a narrow central scarlet stripe for the Military Division; rose-pink edged with pearl grey, with a narrow central stripe of pearl-grey for the Military Division (since 1936). A silver crossed oakleaf emblem for gallantry was instituted in 1957.

Comments: *Founded by King George V during the First World War for services to the Empire at home, in India and in the overseas dominions and colonies, other than those rendered by the Navy and Army, although it could be conferred upon officers of the armed forces for services of a non-combatant character. A Military Division was created in December 1918 and awards made to commissioned officers and warrant officers in respect of distinguished service in action. The insignia of the Civil and Military Divisions is identical, distinguished only by the respective ribbons. A promotion in a different division permits the wear of both types of insignia and in the case of gallantry awards a third type may be worn. A lapel emblem for wear on ordinary clothing was introduced in December 2006.*

GBE Star (2nd type)

Emblem worn by Members of the Order in everyday dress.

CBE Badge (2nd type)

KNIGHTS AND DAMES GRAND CROSS (GBE)

The insignia includes a mantle of rose-pink satin lined with pearl-grey silk, tied by a cord of pearl-grey silk, with two rose-pink and silver tassels attached. On the left side of the mantle is a representation of the star of the First Class of the Order. The mantle, collar and collar badge are only worn on special occasions. In dress uniform, however, the badge is worn over the left hip from a broad (96mm) riband passing over the right shoulder, while Dames wear the badge from a narrower (57mm) ribbon in a bow on the left shoulder; both with the breast star of the Order.

Collar: Silver-gilt with medallions of the royal arms and of the royal and imperial cypher of King George V alternately linked together with cables. In the centre is the imperial crown between two sea lions. The collar for Dames is somewhat narrower than that for Knights.

Star: An eight-pointed star of silver chips on which is superimposed the enamelled medallion as for the badge (Britannia or George V and Queen Mary). The star worn by Dames is smaller.

Badge: A cross patonce in silver-gilt, the arms enamelled pearl-grey. In the centre, within a circle enamelled crimson, the figure of Britannia, replaced since 1936 by the conjoined left-facing crowned busts of King George V and Queen Mary, surrounded by a circle inscribed FOR GOD AND THE EMPIRE.

VALUE:	1st type Britannia	2nd type King and Queen
Knights Grand Cross		
Collar	Rare	Rare
Badge and star	£3000–4000	£3000–4000
Dames Grand Cross		
Collar	From £6000	From £6000
Badge and star	£3000–4000	£3000–4000
Miniature stars	£300–350	£300–350

16. THE MOST EXCELLENT ORDER OF THE BRITISH EMPIRE continued

KBE Star

KNIGHTS COMMANDERS (KBE), DAMES COMMANDERS (DBE), COMMANDERS (CBE), OFFICERS (OBE) AND MEMBERS (MBE)

The insignia of these five Classes follows the same pattern as other Orders. Both Britannia and King and Queen medallion types have been issued.

Star: A star of four large points and four minor points in chipped silver, with the enamelled medallion superimposed. The star worn by Dames is smaller.

Neck Badge: Similar to the badge of the GBE but smaller and worn from a 44mm ribbon round the neck (men) or from a shoulder bow (ladies). Worn by KBE, DBE and CBE.

Breast Badge: As above, but in silver-gilt (OBE) or frosted silver (MBE), with shoulder versions for ladies, worn with a 38mm ribbon.

Gallantry Award: An emblem of silver crossed oak leaves was added to the ribbon of the CBE, OBE and MBE (1957–74).

*Oak leaf emblem for gallantry
(smaller when ribbon only worn).*

VALUE:	1st type Britannia	Miniature	2nd type King&Queen	Miniature
Badge and Star (KBE)	£1200–1500	£250–300	£1000–1200	£285–345
Badge and Star (DBE)	£1200–1500		£1000–1200	
Neck badge (CBE)	£350–400	£35–50	£350–400	£40–55
Shoulder badge (CBE)	£350–400		£350–400	
Breast badge (OBE)	£125–150	£15–25	£125–150	£20–40
Shoulder badge (OBE)	£125–150		£125–150	
Breast badge (MBE)	£125–150	£15–25	£125–150	£20–40
Shoulder badge (MBE)	£125–150		£125–150	

OBE badge (silver-gilt) and reverse of the MBE badge (frosted silver).

Ribbons: (top to bottom) OBE (Military) 1st type, OBE (Military) 2nd type, OBE (Civil) 1st type, OBE (Civil) 2nd type.

61

17. MEDAL OF THE ORDER OF THE BRITISH EMPIRE

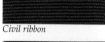

Civil ribbon

Instituted: June 1917.
Ribbon: 32mm plain purple (Civil), with a narrow scarlet central stripe (Military).
Medal: Silver.
Size: 30mm.
Description: (Obverse) a seated figure of Britannia facing right, her left arm extended and her right holding a trident, with the inscription FOR GOD AND THE EMPIRE round the upper part of the circumference; (reverse) the royal and imperial cypher GRI surmounted by a Tudor crown, the whole enclosed in a cable circle. Fitted with a plain ring for suspension.
Comments: *Instituted as a lower award connected with the Order, it consisted originally of a Civil Division, but a Military Division, distinguishable solely by the ribbon, was added in December 1918. This medal was issued unnamed but many were subsequently engraved or impressed on the rim privately. Fewer than 2000 medals were awarded before they were discontinued in 1922.*

VALUE:

		Miniature
Medal unnamed as issued	£375–450	£85–125
Attributable medal	£550–850	

Military ribbon

18. EMPIRE GALLANTRY MEDAL

Instituted: December 29, 1922.
Ribbon: Originally plain purple (Civil), with a thin scarlet central stripe (Military); from July 1937 rose-pink with pearl-grey edges (Civil) and a central pearl-grey stripe (Military). A silver laurel branch was added to the ribbon (1933), with a smaller version for wear on the ribbon alone.
Metal: Silver.
Size: 36mm.
Description: (Obverse) the seated figure of Britannia, her left hand resting on a shield and her right holding a trident, with a blazing sun upper right. The words FOR GOD AND THE EMPIRE inscribed round the upper part of the circumference, with FOR in the wave lower left above the exergue which bears the word GALLANTRY. (Reverse) 1st type has six lions passant gardant, with the Royal cypher in the centre surmounted by an imperial crown. The George VI issue has four lions, two either side and round the foot, in two concentric arcs, the words INSTITUTED BY KING GEORGE V. It is suspended from a straight bar ornamented with laurel leaves. Named in seriffed capitals engraved round the rim.
Comments: *This medal, officially known as the Medal of the Order of the British Empire for Gallantry, replaced the Medal of the Order of the British Empire and was awarded for specific acts of gallantry. It was abolished on the institution of the George Cross in September 1940, while it was announced in the London Gazette of April 22, 1941 that a recipient still living on September 24, 1940 but including posthumous awards after September 3, 1939 should return it to the Central Chancery of the Orders of Knighthood and become a holder of the George Cross instead. Not all EGMs, however, were exchanged or returned. Only 130 medals were issued, 64 being civil, 62 military and four honorary.*

1st type rev.

VALUE:

		Miniature
George V	£5000–7000	£170–230
George VI	£5000–7000	£170–230

Civil 1922

Military 1922

Civil 1937

Military 1937
(emblem smaller when ribbon only worn).

19. BRITISH EMPIRE MEDAL

Instituted: December 1922.
Ribbon: As MYB 18, but without the silver laurel branch.
Metal: Silver.
Size: 36mm.
Description: As MYB 18 above, but with the words MERITORIOUS SERVICE in the exergue. Suspended from a straight bar ornamented with oak leaves. A silver bar decorated with oak leaves was introduced in March 1941 for further acts, and is denoted by a silver rosette on the ribbon worn on its own. An emblem of crossed silver oak leaves was introduced in December 1957 to denote a gallantry award, a smaller version being worn on the ribbon alone. Named in engraved capitals round the rim.
Comments: *Formally entitled the Medal of the Order of the British Empire for Meritorious Service, it is generally known simply as the British Empire Medal. It is awarded for meritorious service by both civil and military personnel although for some years it was issued as a third grade bravery award, particularly for air raid deeds not considered to be of the level of the GC or GM. The medal may be worn even if the recipient is promoted to a higher grade of the Order. The gallantry awards, instituted in December 1957, ceased in 1974 on the introduction of the Queen's Gallantry Medal. No British awards were made for the BEM between 1995 and 2012 although Commonwealth awards were still being made, however, the medal was resurrected for Her Majesty the Queen's Diamond Jubilee Honours List for civilians only with over 250 awards announced. The Order of the British Empire emblem for gallantry instituted in December 2006 (qv) may also be worn by holders of the BEM.*

Civil 1922

Military 1922

Civil 1937

Military 1937

BEM Gallantry Emblem

VALUE:

	Military	Civil	Miniature
George V	£450–550	£300–400	£25–40
George VI GRI cypher	£350–450	£250–300	£20–35
George VI GVIR cypher	£350–450	£250–300	£20–35
Elizabeth II	£350–450	£250–300	£20–35
Elizabeth II with gallantry emblem	£850–1000	£750–850	—

20. THE ORDER OF THE COMPANIONS OF HONOUR

Instituted: June 1917.
Ribbon: 38mm carmine with borders of gold thread.
Metal: Silver gilt.
Size: Height 48mm; max. width 29mm.
Description: An oval badge consisting of a medallion with an oak tree, a shield bearing the royal arms hanging from one branch, and on the left a knight armed and in armour, mounted on a horse. The badge has a blue border with the motto IN ACTION FAITHFUL AND IN HONOUR CLEAR in gold letters. The oval is surmounted by an imperial crown. Gentlemen wear the badge round their necks, while ladies wear it from a bow at the left shoulder.
Comments: *Instituted at the same time as the Order of the British Empire, it carries no title or precedence although the post-nominal letters CH are used. The Order consists of the sovereign and one class of members. Not more than 50 men or women who have rendered conspicuous service of national importance were admitted, but in 1943 this was increased to 65. The Order is awarded in Britain and the Commonwealth on a quota basis: UK (45), Australia (7), New Zealand (2), other countries (11). It is awarded for outstanding achievements in the arts, literature, music, science, politics, industry and religion.*

VALUE

Gentlemen	£3000–3500
Ladies	£3000–3500

Miniature Uniface £200–250   Monogrammed reverse £300–400

21. THE BARONET'S BADGE

Baronet's badge—United Kingdom

(Nova Scotia)

(other Baronets)

Instituted: 1629.
Ribbon: 30mm orange watered silk (Nova Scotia); 44mm orange bordered with narrow blue edges (other Baronets).
Metal: Gold or silver-gilt.
Size: Height 55mm; max. width 41mm(Nova Scotia) or 44mm (later badges).
Description: An upright oval badge with a plain ring suspension. The badge of the Baronets of Nova Scotia was originally skeletal, with a shield bearing the lion rampant of Scotland, decorated with pearls and enamels, surmounted by a Scottish crown and surrounded by a blue border inscribed in gold FAX MENTIS HONESTAE GLORIA. The remaining badges (authorised in 1929) have a solid ground and a central shield with the red hand of Ulster surmounted by a crown and a border of gold and blue enamel decorated with roses (England), shamrocks (Ireland), roses and thistles combined (Great Britain) or roses, thistles and shamrocks combined (United Kingdom). Often engraved on the reverse with the recipient's title and date of creation.
Comments: *By Letter Patent of 1611 James I created Baronets whose knighthood became hereditary. In 1624, to raise money independently of Parliament, James I sold grants of land in Nova Scotia (New Scotland) to Scotsmen. In 1625 Charles I conferred on the holders of this land the title and dignity of Baronets of Nova Scotia with the title of Sir, and decreed that they should wear round their necks "an orange tawny ribbon whereon shall be pendent an escutcheon". After the Union with England (1707) English and Scottish baronetcies ceased to be created, being replaced by baronetcies of Great Britain. Irish baronetcies continued to be created until 1801 after which all new creations were of the United Kingdom.*

VALUE:

	Gold	Silver-gilt
Nova Scotia, 18th–early 19th centuries	£3000–4000	£850–1000
Nova Scotia, late 19th and 20th centuries	£1800–2000	£850–1000
England (rose surround)	£850–1250	£800–1000
Ireland (shamrock surround)	£850–1250	£800–1000
Great Britain (roses and thistles)	£850–1250	£800–1000
United Kingdom (roses, thistles and shamrocks)	£850–1250	£800–1000

22. THE KNIGHT BACHELOR'S BADGE

Instituted: April 21, 1926.

Ribbon: 38mm scarlet with broad yellow borders.

Metal: Silver-gilt and enamels. Some pre-war breast badges are in base metal.

Size: Height 76.50mm; max. width 56.50mm. Reduced in 1933 to 63.25mm and in 1973 to 54mm.

Description: An upright oval medallion enclosed by a scroll, bearing a cross-hilted sword, belted and sheathed, pommel upwards, between two spurs, rowels upwards, the whole set about with the sword-belt.

Comments: *The title Knight Bachelor (KB) was introduced by King Henry III to signify a battelier (one who fought in battle). The badge was authorised by King George V in response to a request from the Imperial Society of Knights Bachelors who wished to have a distinctive badge denoting their rank. The original badge was of the dimensions given above and affixed to the breast by means of a pin on the reverse. This badge was reduced in size in 1933 and again in 1973 when it was fitted with a ring for suspension by a ribbon round the neck. On 4 December 1998 Her Majesty the Queen signed an amending warrant permitting recipients of this honour to wear both a neck badge and breast badge.*

VALUE:

		Miniature
First type breast badge (1929–32)	£500–550	£55–75
Smaller type breast badge (1933–72)	£400–500	(Skeletal type
Neck badge (1973–)	£400–500	£40–55)

23. THE ORDER OF ST JOHN

Neck badge

Shoulder badge

Instituted: May 14, 1888 and at various dates in other countries.
Ribbon: Plain black watered silk. Sash ribbons for Bailiffs, 102mm; Dames Grand Cross, 57mm. Ribbons for Knights, 51mm; Ribbons for Dames were formerly in a 32mm bow and ribbons for Commanders, officers and Serving Brothers 38mm and 32mm for ladies, but under new regulations (October 2001) all ribbons below Grand Cross are now standardised at 38mm. In 1947, for all grades of the Order, when the ribbon only is worn, a small Maltese Cross in silver is carried on the ribbon to distinguish it against a dark background.
Metal: Gold, silver-gilt and silver, or base metal.
Sash badge: An eight-pointed gold Maltese cross in white enamel with two lions and two unicorns in the angles (*other countries have different animals in the angles*). Confined to Bailiffs and Dames Grand Cross.
Neck badge: Hitherto in the grades Knight/Dame, Commander and Officer badges worn by women were smaller than those worn by men, but in 2001 this distinction was abolished. The badges worn by Knights of Justice and Chaplains are in gold, while those worn by Knights of Grace and Commanders are in silver.
Star: The eight-pointed Maltese cross in white enamel without the lions and unicorns (Grand Cross and Justice) or with lions and unicorns (Grace and Sub-Prelate). A sub-Prelate is an Order Chaplain (so his badge is included above) who held high rank in the Church as distinct from the Order. The order ceased appointing Sub-Prelates in 1999, and as a result the Sub-Prelate's star (gilt with animals) is now obsolescent.
Shoulder badge: Worn by Dames of Justice in gold and Dames of Grace, Commanders, Serving Sisters and Officers (Sisters) in silver. It is now mounted on a ribbon with "tails" as in other British orders.
Breast badges: (Officers/Serving Brothers/Sisters) The Order badge with animals (UK lion and unicorn) in angles, originally in silver and enamel, in white metal or rhodium subsequently. Those worn by Serving Brothers have undergone six main phases:
1892–1939: a circular badge with white enamel cross and silver animals raised above the surface of the black enamel medal in a silver rim (two types of suspender) (type 1 & 2).
1939–1949: circular skeletal badge with ring suspension and the cross set in a silver rim, no black background (type 3).
1949–1974: the first badge resumed but with different ring suspender (type 4).
1974–1984: a badge of the same design but with the cross and animals flush with their background (type 5).
1984–1991: the cross and animals in white metal alone with no background or rim, slightly smaller than the Officer (Brother) cross and the whole convex on the obverse (type 6).
Since 1991: cross and animals thicker, with each arm raised and shaped on both sides of a central channel, the whole in rhodium (type 7).
Since 1999 a woman Officer or Serving Sister in uniform is invested with her breast badge on a straight ribbon.
Donats' badges: Gold, silver or bronze, consisting of the badge of the Order with the upper arm of the cross replaced by an ornamental piece of metal for suspension.
Comments: *The Most Venerable Order of the Hospital of St John of Jerusalem was incorporated by Royal Charter of Queen Victoria and granted the epithet Venerable in 1926 and Most in 1955; despite its title, it has no connection with the Knights Hospitallers of Jerusalem, who were subsequently based at Rhodes and Malta and now have their*

Officer/Serving Brothers/Sisters breast badge.

| 1st type (1892–early 1930s). | 2nd type (late 1930s). | 3rd type (Wartime issue up to 1947). | 4th type (1948– c. 1973). |

| 5th type (1974–84). | 6th type (1984–91). | 7th type (1991–). |

headquarters in Rome. In 1926 the Order was reorganised into five Classes like certain other Orders. A sixth class was added later. Both men and women are eligible for membership. Her Majesty the Queen is the Sovereign Head of the Order. Next in authority is the Grand Prior, followed by Bailiffs and Dames Grand Cross, Chaplains, Knights and Dames of Justice, Knights and Dames of Grace, Commanders, Officers, Serving Brothers and Sisters and Esquires. Associates were people who were not citizens of the United Kingdom, the British Commonwealth or the Republic of Ireland, or are non-Christians, who have rendered conspicuous service to the Order and may be attached to any grade of the Order. They wear the insignia of that grade, at one time distinguished only by a central narrow white stripe on the ribbon, but now all ribbons are identical. Donats are people who have made generous contributions to the funds of the Order. They are not enrolled as members of the Order but receive badges in gold, silver or bronze. The Statutes and Regulations were revised in 2004. The grade of Chaplain (gold badge) was abolished, but existing Chaplains could retain their insignia or be regarded as Commanders. Before 1999 a Chaplain could be appointed a Sub-Prelate if he held high office in the Church. A sub-Prelate wore the badge of a Chaplain and also a star with gilt lions and unicorns. Those few remaining have now been renamed Honorary Sub-Prelates, a term revived to designate the senior ecclesiastical officer of a Priory. This appointment carries no distinctive insignia.

VALUE:	Gold	Silver/Gilt	Bronze	Miniature
Bailiff badge and star	£2500–3000	£800–1000	—	
Dame Grand Cross	£2500–3000	£600–750	—	
Knight of Justice neck badge and star	£1000–1500	£500–650	£200–300	
Dame of Justice shoulder badge and star	£1000–1500	£500–650	£200–300	
Knight of Grace neck badge and star	—	£350–450	£175–275	
Dame of Grace shoulder badge and star	—	£350–450	£175–275	£25–40
Sub-Prelate neck badge		£200–250	£75–100	
Commander (Brother) neck badge	—	£200–250	£75–100	
Commander (Sister) shoulder badge	—	£50–75	£35–50	
Officer/ Serving Brother/Sister breast badge				
1st/2nd type	—	£65–85	—	£50–70
3rd type	—	£50–75	—	£50–70
4th type	—	£50–75	—	£30–40
5th type	—	£50–75	—	£30–40
6th type	—	£50–75	—	£20–30
7th type	—	£50–75	—	£20–30
Honorary Associates				
White enamelled cross 1869–87	—	£100–150	—	£20–30
Plain silver cross 1887–1926	—	£100–120	—	£20–30
Donat's badge	£250–300	£55–85	£45–55	£35–50

DECORATIONS

The award of decorations for distinguished military service is an ancient institution. In his Antiquities of the Jews, the historian Josephus relates that, in the second century BC, King Alexander was so pleased with Jonathan the High Priest that he sent him a gold button as a mark of favour for his skill in leading the Jews in battle. Subsequently Jonathan was presented with a second gold button for his gallant conduct in the field, making these incidents among the earliest recorded for which specific military awards were granted. The award of jewels, gold buttons and badges for valour was carried on in most European countries on a sporadic basis but the present system of decorations is essentially a modern one dating back no farther than the middle of the seventeenth century. Earlier medals were quasi-commemorative and include the famous Armada Medal of 1588. A few medals in silver or gold were awarded to officers for distinguished service during the English Civil War, although the first "official" rewards in Britain were probably those issued by Parliament to naval officers following their victories over the Dutch fleet in 1653.

Decorations may be divided into those awarded for individual acts of heroism and those conferred in recognition of distinguished military, political or social service. In general terms collectors prefer a decoration awarded for bravery in the field rather than a political honour given automatically to a civil servant, just because he happens to have been in a particular grade for a certain number of years. The debasement of civil awards, such as the OBE and MBE, is reflected in the relative lack of interest shown by collectors.

It is generally true to say that military decorations are more desirable, but it is important to note that one decoration may be more highly prized than another, while the same decoration may well be more valuable to collectors when issued in one period rather than in another. At one extreme is the greatly coveted Victoria Cross, few of which (including three bars) have been awarded since its inception. VCs won during the Crimean War (111 awarded) are usually less highly regarded than Crosses awarded during the First World War, where, although numerically greater (633) they were far more dearly won. Second World War Crosses are correspondingly more expensive as only 182 were awarded and even now comparatively few of them have ever come on to the market. Today, while pre-1914 Crosses would rate at least £100,000 and those from the First World War slightly more, Second World War Crosses start around £150,000 but have been known to fetch several times as much, depending on the precise circumstances and the branch of the services.

At the other extreme is the Military Medal, of which no fewer than 115,589 were awarded during the First World War alone. For this reason a MM from this period can still be picked up for under £600, whereas one from the Second World War would usually fetch about four times as much, and awards made during the minor campaigns of the 1930s or the Korean War often rate at least ten times as much.

The value of a decoration, where its provenance can be unquestionably established, depends largely on the decoration itself, whether awarded to an officer or an enlisted man, the individual circumstances of the award, the campaign or action concerned, the regiment, unit or ship involved, and the often very personal details of the act or acts of bravery. These factors are extraordinarily difficult to quantify, hence the frequent large discrepancies in the prices fetched by decorations at auction.

The addition of even relatively common decorations, such as the Military Cross or the Military Medal to the average First World War campaign medal group, invariably enhances its value very considerably while the addition of bars for subsequent awards likewise rates a good premium. Decorations awarded to officers tend to fetch more than those awarded to other ranks, mainly because they are proportionately rarer but also because it is usually easier to trace the career details of an officer.

Sometimes the rank of the recipient may have a bearing on the demand for a particular decoration: e.g. Military Crosses awarded to warrant officers are scarcer than those awarded to subalterns and captains. The branch of the armed services may also have some bearing. Thus a Military Medal awarded to a member of the RAF rates far higher than one awarded to a soldier, while a medal awarded to a seaman in one of the naval battalions which fought on the Western Front is also equally desirable.

Initially the Distinguished Service Order could be won by commissioned officers of any rank but after 1914, when the Military Cross was instituted, it was usually restricted to officers of field rank. DSOs awarded to lieutenants and captains in the Army in both World Wars are therefore comparatively rare and invariably expensive, usually as they were awarded for acts of heroism which in earlier campaigns might have merited the VC. As part of the 1993 review of awards, the Conspicuous Gallantry Coss (CGC) replaced the DCM and CGM to remove the distinction between officers and other ranks.

The opportunity for individual acts of bravery varied from service to service, and in different conflicts. Thus sailors in the Second World War generally had less scope than air crew. Consequently specifically naval awards, such as the Conspicuous Gallantry Medal and the Distinguished Service Cross, are much more scarce than the corresponding RAF awards for Conspicuous Gallantry and the Distinguished Flying Cross.

The addition of bars to gallantry decorations greatly enhances the scarcity and value of such medals. The VC, for example, has been won by only three men on two occasions; none of these VC and bar combinations has ever come on the market, but should one come up for sale, it is certain that the price would be spectacular. The average First World War MM is today worth around £500, but with a bar for second award its value immediately jumps to about three times as much, while MMs with two or more bars are very much more expensive.

It is important to note that in some cases (the DSO for example) decorations were issued unnamed; for this reason the citation or any other supporting documents relevant to the award should be kept with the decoration wherever possible to confirm its attribution.

Engraving of Gallantry Decorations

After the special investiture for the South Atlantic campaign held on February 8, 1983, the question as to why certain awards were engraved with the date only was raised within the Ministry of Defence. A joint service working party considered the matter and recommended that procedures for all decorations and medals for gallantry in the face of the enemy and for the Air Force Cross when awarded for a specific act of gallantry should be brought into line. A submission was accordingly made to the Queen by the Committee on the Grant of Honours, Decorations and Medals and in April 1984 Her Majesty approved the following:

(i)   That the Distinguished Service Cross, Military Cross, Distinguished Flying Cross and Air Force Cross when awarded for gallantry should be engraved with the personal details of the recipient with effect from January 1, 1984.
(ii)   That there should be no retrospection;
(iii)   That the badge of a Companion of the Distinguished Service Order should not be engraved (in common with the badges of other orders); and
(iv)   That the Royal Red Cross (RRC and ARRC) and the Air Force Cross when awarded for meritorious service should not be engraved.

Condition

The same terms are applied to describe the condition of medals and decorations as apply to coins, although the wear to which they are put is caused by other factors. In modern times, when the number of occasions on which medals are worn are relatively few and far between, the condition of most items will be found to be Very Fine (VF) to Extremely Fine (EF). Indeed, in many cases, the medals may never have been worn at all. A good proportion of Second World War medals and decorations are found in almost mint condition as they were not issued till long after the war, by which time their recipients had been demobilised. In some cases they even turn up still in the original cardboard box in which they were posted to the recipients or their next-of-kin.

Before the First World War, however, the wearing of medals was customary on all but the most informal occasions and when actually serving on active duty. Thus medals could be, and often were, subject to a great deal of wear. Medals worn by cavalrymen are often found in poor condition, with scratches and edge knocks occasioned by the constant jangling of one medal against another while on horseback. Often the medals in a group have an abrasive effect on each other. For this reason the Queen's Medal for Egypt (1882) for example, is comparatively rare in excellent condition, as it was usually worn in juxtaposition to the bronze Khedive's Star whose points were capable of doing considerable damage to its silver companion.

Apart from these factors it should also be remembered that part of the ritual of "spit and polish" involved cleaning one's medals and they were therefore submitted to vigorous cleaning with metal polish over long periods of service.

For these reasons medals are often sold by dealers "as worn"—a euphemism which conceals a lifetime of hardy service on the chest of some grizzled veteran. Because of the strong personal element involved in medal-collecting, however, genuine wear does not affect the value of a medal to the same degree that it would in other branches of numismatics. There is a school of thought which considers that such signs enhance the interest and value of a medal or group.

This line of thinking also explains the controversy over medal ribbons. Some military outfitters still carry extensive stocks of medal ribbons covering every campaign from Waterloo onwards, so that it is a very easy matter to obtain a fresh length of ribbon for any medal requiring it, and there is no doubt that the appearance of a piece is greatly improved by a clean, bright new ribbon. On the other hand, that ribbon was not the one actually worn by Corporal Bloggs on parade and, to the purist, it would spoil the total effect of the medal. Some collectors therefore retain the original ribbon, even though it may be faded and frayed. As ribbons are things which one cannot authenticate, however, there seems to be little material benefit to be gained from clinging rigidly to a tattered strip of silk when an identical piece can be obtained relatively cheaply. In reality, most collectors compromise by obtaining new ribbons while preserving the old lengths out of sentiment.

24. THE VICTORIA CROSS

Instituted: January 1856.

Ribbon: Crimson. Originally naval crosses used a blue ribbon, but since 1918 the crimson (Army) ribbon has been used for all awards. A miniature cross emblem is worn on the ribbon alone in undress uniform.

Metal: Bronze, originally from Russian guns captured in the Crimea. Modern research, however, reveals that guns captured in other conflicts, e.g. China, have also been used at various periods.

Size: Height 41mm; max. width 36mm.

Description: A cross pattée. (Obverse) a lion statant gardant on the royal crown, with the words FOR VALOUR on a semi-circular scroll. (Reverse) a circular panel on which is engraved the date of the act for which the decoration was awarded. The Cross is suspended by a ring from a seriffed "V" attached to a suspension bar decorated with laurel leaves. The reverse of the suspension bar is engraved with the name, rank and ship, regiment or squadron of the recipient.

Comments: *Introduced as the premier award for gallantry, available for all ranks, to cover all actions since the outbreak of the Crimean War in 1854, it was allegedly created on the suggestion of Prince Albert, the Prince Consort. Of the 1,358 awards since 1856, 836 have gone to the Army, 107 to the Navy, 31 to the RAF, ten to the Royal Marines and four to civilians. Second award bars have been awarded three times. The facility for posthumous awards, made retrospective to 1856, began in 1902 and was confirmed in 1907, while the early practice of forfeitures (eight between 1863 and 1908) was discontinued after the First World War. Two posthumous awards were made in the Falklands War, 1982. In 2005 Private Johnson Beharry was awarded the VC for valour in Iraq, and since then two posthumous awards have been made for Afghanistan: Corporal Bryan Budd in 2006 and Lance Corporal James Ashworth in 2012. The latest award is to L/Cpl Joshua Leakey of the Parachute Regiment (LG February 26, 2015) also for Afghanistan. In 2015 the Government increased the annuity paid to £10,000, tax free.*

VALUE:

	Royal Navy/Army	RFC/RAF	Miniature
1856–1914 (522)	From £120,000	—	£50–80
1914–18 (633)	From £150,000	From £175,000	£20–35
1920–45 (187)	From £175,000	From £200,000	£20–35
post-1945 (15)	From £150,000	—	£10–20

NB *These prices can only be construed as a general guide. Quite a few awards would exceed these price ranges, particularly Commonwealth examples or those appertaining to well known actions.*

Naval ribbon pre-1918. Naval, Army and RAF ribbon since 1918.

SELLING YOUR MEDALS?

Warwick and Warwick have an expanding requirement for medal collections, medal groups and related documentation and individual medals of value. Our customer base is increasing dramatically and we need an ever larger supply of quality material to keep pace with demand. The market has never been stronger and if you are considering the sale of your medals, now is the time to act.

FREE VALUATIONS

We will provide a free, professional and without obligation valuation of your collection. Either we will make you a fair, binding private treaty offer, or we will recommend inclusion of your property in our next specialist public auction.

FREE TRANSPORTATION

We can arrange insured transportation of your collection to our Warwick offices completely free of charge. If you decline our offer, we ask you to cover the return carriage costs only.

FREE VISITS

Visits by our valuers are possible anywhere in the country or abroad, usually within 48 hours, in order to value larger collections. Please telephone for details.

VALUATION DAYS

We are staging a series of valuation days across the entire country. Please visit our website or telephone for details.

EXCELLENT PRICES

Because of the strength of our customer base we are in a position to offer prices that we feel sure will exceed your expectations.

ACT NOW

Telephone or email Richard Beale today with details of your property.

Warwick & Warwick Ltd.
Auctioneers and Valuers
Chalon House, Scar Bank, Millers Road,
Warwick CV34 5DB

25. NEW ZEALAND CROSS

Instituted: 10 March 1869 (by an Order in Council, Wellington).
Ribbon: 38mm crimson. A silver miniature cross emblem is worn on the ribbon alone.
Metal: Silver with gold appliqué.
Size: Height 52mm; max. width 38mm.
Description: A silver cross pattée with a six-pointed gold star on each limb. In the centre are the words NEW ZEALAND within a gold laurel wreath. The cross is surmounted by a gold Tudor crown which is attached by a ring and a seriffed "V" to a silver bar ornamented with gold laurel leaves, through which the ribbon passes. The recipient's name and details are engraved on the reverse.
Comments: *The rarest of all gallantry awards, it was conferred for bravery during the second series of Maori Wars (1860-72). Only 23 Crosses were awarded, the last being authorised in 1910. This medal was called into being solely because local volunteer forces were not eligible for the VC. Today the Cross, with slight amendments to the design, is New Zealand's premier civilian award for bravery (see NZ2).*

VALUE: From £75,000
           Modern copy £650–750

           Miniature
               Contemporary   £750–1000
               Modern copy   £15–20

26. GEORGE CROSS

Instituted: 24 September 1940.
Ribbon: 38mm dark blue (originally 32mm). A silver miniature cross emblem is worn on the ribbon alone.
Metal: Silver.
Size: Height 48mm; max. width 45mm.
Description: A plain bordered cross with a circular medallion in the centre depicting the effigy of St George and the Dragon after Benedetto Pistrucci, surrounded by the words FOR GALLANTRY. In the angle of each limb is the Royal cypher GVI. The plain reverse bears in the centre the name of the recipient and date of the award. In the case of exchange awards, the date of the deed is given. The Cross hangs by a ring from a bar adorned with laurel leaves.
Comments: *The highest gallantry award for civilians, as well as for members of the armed forces in actions for which purely military honours would not normally be granted. It superseded the Empire Gallantry Medal whose holders were then required to return it and receive the GC in exchange. By Warrant of December 1971 surviving recipients of the Albert and Edward Medals were also invited to exchange their awards for the GC—a move which created a controversy which is still continuing, particularly among those who received the Albert Medal. Perhaps the most famous Cross was that conferred on the island of Malta in recognition of its gallantry during the Second World War. To date no second award bars have been awarded. Since its inception in 1940 the George Cross has been awarded 162 times, including four women (85 of these have been posthumous). In addition, 112 Empire Gallantry medallists, 68 Albert medallists and 69 Edward medallists who were eligible to exchange their awards for the GC have increased the total to 410. Most awards were made during World War II but it should be noted that since 1947 the GC has been awarded only 59 times (including one woman and the collective award to the Royal Ulster Constabulary, presented by Her Majesty the Queen at Hillsborough Castle on 12 April 2000). Arthur Bywater (who died in April 2005) was the only civilian to win both the GC and the GM but seven servicemen have won both. In 2015 the Government increased the annuity paid to £10,000, tax free.*

VALUE:
   Service awards 1940 to date   From £30,000
   Civilian awards 1940 to date   From £25,000
   Service exchange pre-1940   From £12,000
   Civilian exchange pre-1940   From £12,000
   Miniature   £15–20 *(in silver add £10)*

27. DISTINGUISHED SERVICE ORDER

Instituted: 1886.

Ribbon: 29mm crimson with dark blue edges.

Metal: Originally gold; silver-gilt (since 1889).

Size: Height 44mm; max. width 41.5mm.

Description: A cross with curved ends, overlaid with white enamel. (Obverse) a green enamel laurel wreath enclosing an imperial crown on a red enamel background; (reverse) the royal monogram within a similar wreath. The ribbon is hung from a top laureated bar and the cross is suspended from the ribbon by a swivel ring and another straight laureated bar. Additional awards are denoted by bars ornamented by a crown. Silver rosettes on the ribbon alone are worn in undress uniform. Since its inception, the DSO has been issued unnamed, but since 1938 the year of award has been engraved on the reverse of the lower suspension bar as well as the reverse of the bars for second or subsequent awards.

Second ward bar

Comments: *Intended to reward commissioned officers below field rank for distinguished service in time of war, and for which the VC would not be appropriate. Previously the CB had sometimes been awarded to junior officers, although intended mainly for those of field rank. It was also available to officers in both the other armed services. In September 1942 the regulations were amended to permit award of the DSO to officers of the Merchant Navy who performed acts of gallantry in the presence of the enemy. As a result of the 1993 Review of gallantry awards and resultant changes to the operational gallantry award system, the DSO is now awarded for "Leadership" — theoretically to all ranks (it is not awarded posthumously). The Conspicuous Gallantry Cross is now the equivalent reward for specific acts of gallantry.*

VALUE:	Unnamed single	Attributable group	*Miniature*
Victoria, gold (153)	£4500–6000	£6000–10,000	£100–120
Victoria, silver-gilt (1170)	£1500–2000	£3000–7500	£60–80
Edward VII (78)	£2000–2500	£5500–6500	£85–120 (gold)
George V (9900)	£1000–1500	£1500–2500	£45 (gilt), £100 (gold)
George VI 1st type 1938–48 (4880)	£1500–2000	£3000–5000	£45 (gilt)
George VI 2nd type 1948–52 (63)	£1800–2200	£4500–6000	£45 (gilt)
Elizabeth II	£3000–3500	£6000–8000	£35

28. IMPERIAL SERVICE ORDER

Instituted: August 1902.

Ribbon: 38mm three equal sections of crimson, blue and crimson.

Metal: Silver with gold overlay.

Size: Height 61mm; max. width 55mm.

Description: The badge consists of a circular gold plaque bearing the royal cypher and surrounded by the words FOR FAITHFUL SERVICE. This plaque is then superimposed on a seven-pointed silver star surmounted by a crown and ring for suspension. The badge of the ISO awarded to women is similar but has a laurel wreath instead of the star-shaped base.

Comments: *Instituted by King Edward VII as a means of rewarding long and faithful service in the Administrative and Clerical grades of the Civil Service at home and overseas. Women were admitted to the order in 1908. The order was awarded after at least 25 years service at home, 20 years and 6 months (India) and 16 years in the tropics, but in exceptional cases awards were made for "eminently meritorious service" irrespective of qualifiying period. No UK awards have been made since 1995 but some Commonwealth awards continue to this day. The George VI issue comes in two types: the early ones with GRI cypher and the later GVIR.*

VALUE:			*Miniature*
Edward VII	Gentleman (489)	£325–375	£25–30
	Lady (4)	£2000–2500	£200–300
George V	Gentleman (909)	£300–350	£20–25
	Lady (2)	£2200–2700	£200–300
George VI (608 Gentleman and 8 Lady)			
1st type	Gentleman	£325–375	£15–20
	Lady	£1200–1500	£200–300
2nd type	Gentleman	£350–400	£15–20
	Lady	£1500–1800	£200–300
Elizabeth II	Gentleman (2,153)*	£300–350	£10–15
	Lady (114)*	£1000–1200	£150–200

29. IMPERIAL SERVICE MEDAL

Instituted: August 1902.
Ribbon: Same as above.
Metal: Silver and bronze.
Size: 32mm
Description: Originally similar to the ISO but with a silver plaque and bronze star or wreath. In 1920 the ISM was transformed into a circular medal of silver with the sovereign's effigy on the obverse and a reverse depicting a naked man resting from his labours, with FOR FAITHFUL SERVICE in the exergue.
Comments: *Instituted at the same time as the ISO but intended for junior grades of the Civil Service.*

VALUE:

		Miniature
Edward VII, 1903–10 (c. 4,500) Star (Gentleman)	£100–150	£15–20
Wreath (Lady)	£500–600	£200–300
George V, 1911-20 (c. 6,000) Star (Gentleman)	£100–125	£12–15
Wreath (Lady)	£500–600	£200–300
George V Circular type		
Coinage profile, 1920–31 (c. 20,000)	£25–35	£10–15
Crowned bust, 1931–37 (c. 16,000)	£25–35	£10–15
George VI		
Crowned bust INDIAE:IMP, 1938–48 (c. 36,000)	£25–35	£10–15
Crowned bust FID:DEF, 1949–52 (c. 16,000)	£25–35	£10–15
Elizabeth II		
Tudor crown BRITT:OMN, 1953–54 (c. 9,000)	£25–35	£10–15
Tudor crown DEI:GRATIA, 1955– (c. 150,000)	£25–35	£10–15

30. INDIAN ORDER OF MERIT

Military

Civil

Instituted: 1837 (by the Honourable East India Company).
Ribbon: Dark blue with crimson edges (military) or crimson with dark blue edges (civil).
Metal: Silver and gold.
Size: Height 41mm; max. width 40mm.
Description: An eight-pointed star with a circular centre surrounded by a laurel wreath and containing crossed sabres and the relevant inscription. The star is suspended by a curvilinear suspension bar. The different classes were denoted by the composition of the star, noted below.
Comments: *The oldest gallantry award of the British Empire, it was founded in 1837 by the Honourable East India Company. Twenty years later it became an official British award when the administration of India passed to the Crown after the Sepoy Mutiny. Originally known simply as the Order of Merit, it was renamed in 1902 following the introduction of the prestigious British order of that name. There were three classes of the order, promotion from one class to the next being the reward for further acts of bravery. A civil division (also in three classes) was introduced in 1902. Ten years later the military division was reduced to two classes, when troops of the Indian Army became eligible for the VC. The civil division became a single class in 1939 and the military in 1945. Both divisions came to an end with the British Raj in 1947.*

VALUE:
Military Division
1837–1912 Reward of Valour

1st class in gold (42)	£6000–8500
2nd class in silver and gold (130)	£3500–4500
3rd class in silver (2740)	£1250–1750

1912–39 Reward of Valour

1st class in silver and gold (26)	£5000–6500
2nd class in silver (1215)	£500–750

continued

30. INDIAN ORDER OF MERIT continued

1939-44 Reward of Gallantry	
1st class in silver and gold (2)	Rare
2nd class in silver (332)	£850–1250
1945-47 Reward of Gallantry (44mm diameter)	£1850–2750
Civil Division	
1902-39 For Bravery (35mm diameter)	
1st class in gold (0)	—
2nd class in silver and gold (0)	—
3rd class in silver (39)	£1500–1850
1939-47 For Bravery (26mm diameter)	
Single class (10)	£3000–4000
Miniature	£150–250

NB *These prices represent unattributable pieces. Values can climb rapidly when in company with related campaign medals, particularly for the Victorian era.*

30A. CONSPICUOUS GALLANTRY CROSS

Instituted: October 1993.
Ribbon: White with blue edges and a red central stripe.
Metal: Silver.
Size: Max. width 36mm
Description: A cross pattée imposed on a wreath of laurel, with the royal crown in a circular panel in the centre. Suspended by a ring from a plain suspension bar.
Comments: *As part of the decision to remove distinctions of rank in awards for bravery, this decoration replaced the DSO for specific acts of gallantry as well as the Conspicuous Gallantry Medal and the Distinguished Conduct Medal. It was first awarded in 1995 to Corporal Wayne Mills of the Duke of Wellington's Regiment and in 1996 to Colour Sergeant Peter Humphreys of the Royal Welch Fusiliers, both for gallantry in action during service with the UN Peacekeeping Forces in Bosnia. Two awards were made in respect of gallantry by members of the SAS and SBS in Sierra Leone in May–June 2000. A further two awards were made to members of the SAS and two awards to members of the SBS in Afghanistan in October 2001–March 2002, while awards to Justin Thomas, RM, and Lance Corporal Michael Flynn, Blues and Royals, both for gallantry in Iraq, were gazetted in October 2003, and that to Sqdn Ldr I. J. McKechnie, Royal Air Force, was gazetted on 9 September 2005, making a total of 11 in the first decade. Since then other awards have been made taking the total number of awards to date to 60, including a collective award to the Royal Irish Regiment which appeared in the LG Supplement, December 18, 2006, and three posthumous awards.*

VALUE: From £65,000   *Miniature*   £20–25

31. ROYAL RED CROSS

First Class obverse

Second award bar

Instituted: 27 April 1883.

Ribbon: 25mm dark blue edged with crimson, in a bow.

Metal: Gold (later silver-gilt) and silver.

Size: Height 41mm; max. width 35mm.

Description: (Obverse) The *1st class* badge was originally a gold cross pattée, enamelled red with gold edges, but from 1889 silver-gilt was substituted for gold. At the centre was a crowned and veiled portrait, with the words FAITH, HOPE and CHARITY inscribed on three arms, and the date 1883 on the lower arm. Subsequently the effigy of the reigning monarch was substituted for the allegorical profile; (reverse) crowned royal cypher. *2nd Class:* in silver, design as the 1st class but the inscriptions on the arms appear on the reverse. Awards from 1938 have the year of issue engraved on the reverse of the lower arm.

Comments: *This decoration had the distinction of being confined to females until 1976. It is conferred on members of the nursing services regardless of rank. A second class award was introduced in November 1915. Bars for the first class were introduced in 1917. Holders of the second class are promoted to the first class on second awards. Holders of the first class decoration are known as Members (RRC) while recipients of the second class are Associates (ARRC). The second type GVI award is surprisingly scarce as only 50 first class and 100 second class were awarded.*

VALUE:

	First class (RRC)	Miniature	Second class (ARRC)	Miniature
Victoria, gold	£1000–1500	£90–100	—	
Victoria, silver-gilt	£500–600	£60–70	—	
Edward VII, silver-gilt	£800–1000	£100–120	—	
George V	£300–350	£25–35	£150–175	£12–25
George V, with bar	£450–550	£50–60	—	
George VI GRI	£300–350	£25–35	£220–250	£12–25
George VI GVIR	£350–450	£25–35	£250–300	£12–25
Elizabeth II	£300–350	£25–35	£200–250	£12–25

32. DISTINGUISHED SERVICE CROSS

Second award bar

Instituted: June 1901.

Ribbon: 36mm three equal parts of dark blue, white and dark blue.

Metal: Silver.

Size: Height 43mm; max. width 43mm.

Description: A plain cross with rounded ends. (Obverse) crowned royal cypher in the centre, suspended by a ring; (reverse) plain apart from the hallmark. From 1940 onwards the year of issue was engraved on the reverse of the lower limb.

Comments: *Known as the Conspicuous Service Cross when instituted, it was awarded to warrant and subordinate officers of the Royal Navy who were ineligible for the DSO. Only 8 EVII issued. In October 1914 it was renamed the Distinguished Service Cross and thrown open to all naval officers below the rank of lieutenant-commander. Bars for second awards were authorised in 1916 and in 1931 eligibility for the award was enlarged to include officers of the Merchant Navy. In 1940 Army and RAF officers serving aboard naval vessels also became eligible for the award. Since 1945 fewer than 100 DSCs have been awarded. As a result of the 1993 Review of gallantry awards and resultant changes to the operational gallantry award system, this award is now available to both officers and other ranks, the DSM having been discontinued. Since 1 January 1984 the award has been issued named.*

VALUE:

	Unnamed single	Attributable group	Miniature
Edward VII	—	From £20,000–45,000	£200–250
George V	£900–1000	£1750–3500	£25–35
George VI GRI	£900–1000	£1750–3500	£15–25
George VI GVIR	—	£2750–4000	£25–35
Elizabeth II	—	£7500–10,500	£15–25

33. MILITARY CROSS

Instituted: 31 December 1914.

Ribbon: 34mm three equal stripes of white, deep purple and white.

Metal: Silver.

Size: Height 46mm; max. width 44mm.

Description: An ornamental cross with straight arms terminating in broad finials decorated with imperial crowns. The royal cypher appears at the centre and the cross is suspended from a plain silver suspension bar.

Comments: *There was no gallantry award, lesser than the VC and DSO, for junior Army officers and warrant officers until shortly after the outbreak of the First World War when the MC was instituted. Originally awarded to captains, lieutenants and warrant officers of the Army (including RFC), it was subsequently extended to include equivalent ranks of the RAF when performing acts of bravery on the ground and there was even provision for the Royal Naval Division and the Royal Marines during the First World War. Awards were extended to majors by an amending warrant of 1931. Bars for second and subsequent awards have a crown at the centre. The MC is always issued unnamed, although since 1937 the reverse of the cross or bar is officially dated with the year of issue. As a result of the 1993 Review of gallantry awards and resultant changes to the operational gallantry award system, this award is now available to both officers and other ranks, the Military Medal having been discontinued. Since 1 January 1984 the award has been issued named.*

Second award bar

VALUE:	Unnamed single	Attributable group	*Miniature*
George V 1914-20 (37,000)	£600–750	£1000–1850	£25–30
one bar (3000)	£850–1200	£1500–2500	
two bars (170)	£1200–1750	£3500–4500	
three bars (4)	—	£8500–10,000	
George V 1921-36 (350)	—	£2000–3000	
one bar (31)	—	£3000–5000	
George VI GRI 1937-46 (11,000)	£700–750	£1500–2500	£25–30
one bar (500)	£1000–1500	£3500–4500	
George VI GVIR (158)	—	£3500–5500	£30–35
Elizabeth II	£850–1000	£8000–12,000	£25–30

34. DISTINGUISHED FLYING CROSS

Instituted: June 1918.

Ribbon: 30mm originally horizontal but since June 1919 diagonal alternate stripes of white and deep purple.

Metal: Silver.

Size: Height 60mm; max. width 54mm.

Description: (Obverse) a cross flory terminating with a rose, surmounted by another cross made of propeller blades charged in the centre with a roundel within a laurel wreath. The horizontal arms bear wings and the crowned RAF monogram at the centre; (reverse) the royal cypher above the date 1918. The cross is suspended from a bar decorated with a sprig of laurel.

Comments: *Established for officers and warrant officers of the RAF in respect of acts of valour while flying in active operations against the enemy. The DFC is issued unnamed, but Second World War crosses usually have the year of issue engraved on the reverse of the lower limb. After WWII it was expanded to include aviation officers of other services. As a result of the 1993 Review of gallantry awards and resultant changes to the operational gallantry award system, this award is now available to both officers and other ranks, the Distinguished Flying Medal having been discontinued. Since 1 January 1984 the award has been issued named.*

Second ward bar

Original ribbon.

Post-1919 ribbon.

VALUE:	Unnamed single	Attributable group	*Miniature*
George V 1918–20 (1100)	£2000–2500	£3500–5500	£25–35
one bar (70)	£2000–3000	£6000–7500	
two bars (3)	—	—	
George V 1920–36 (130)	—	—	
one bar (20)	—	—	
two bars (4)	—	—	
George VI GRI 1939–45 (20,000)	£2000–2500	£3000–4500	£25–35
one bar (1550)	£2500–3500	£4500–6500	
two bars (42)	—	—	
George VI GVIR 1948–52 (65)	—	—	£30–45
Elizabeth II	£1800–2000	£6500–8500	£25–35

(in silver add £5)

35. AIR FORCE CROSS

Instituted: June 1918.

Ribbon: 30mm originally horizontal but since June 1919 diagonal alternate stripes of white and crimson.

Metal: Silver.

Size: Height 60mm; max. width 54mm.

Description: (Obverse) the cross consists of a thunderbolt, the arms conjoined by wings, base bar terminating in a bomb, surmounted by another cross of aeroplane propellers, the finials inscribed with the royal cypher. A central roundel depicts Hermes mounted on a hawk bestowing a wreath; (reverse) the royal cypher and the date 1918.

Comments: *This decoration, awarded to officers and warrant officers of the RAF was instituted in June 1918 for gallantry on non-operational missions and for meritorious service on flying duties. After WWII it was expanded to include aviation officers of other services. Since the 1993 Review of gallantry awards it is now available to all ranks for non-operational gallantry in the air only (no longer for meritorious service also). Since 1 January 1984 the award has been issued named.*

Second award bar

Original ribbon.

Post-1919 ribbon.

VALUE:

	Unnamed single	Attributable group	Miniature
George V 1918-20 (678)	£1000–1250	£2250–2750	£25–35
one bar (12)	—	—	
two bars (3)	—	—	
George V 1920-36 (111)	£1500–2000	£2500–3500	
George VI GRI (2605)	£1250–2000	£2500–3500	£25–35
one bar (36)	£2000–2500	£3500–4000	
two bars (1)	—	—	
George VI GVIR (411)	£1000–1250	£1750–2500	£35–45
Elizabeth II	£1000–1250	£1850–3000	£25–35

(in silver add £5)

36. ORDER OF BRITISH INDIA

Instituted: 1837 by the Honourable East India Company.

Ribbon: Worn around the neck, the base colour of the ribbon was originally sky blue but this was altered to crimson in 1838, allegedly because the hair oil favoured by Indians of all classes would soon have soiled a light ribbon. From 1939 onwards the first class ribbon had two thin vertical lines of light blue at the centre, while the second class ribbon had a single vertical line. Originally these distinctive ribbons were only worn in undress uniform (without the insignia itself), but from 1945 they replaced the plain crimson ribbons when worn with the decoration.

Metal: Gold.

Size: Height 42mm; max. width 38mm.

Description: The first class badge consists of a gold star with a crown between the upper two points and a blue enamelled centre bearing a lion surrounded by the words ORDER OF BRITISH INDIA enclosed in a laurel wreath. The second class badge is smaller, with dark blue enamel in the centre and with no crown.

Comments: *Intended for long and faithful service by native officers of the Indian Army, it was thrown open in 1939 to officers of the armed forces, frontier guards, military police and officers of the Indian native states. There were two classes, promotion to the first being made from the second. Recipients of both classes were entitled to the letters OBI after their names, but holders of the first class had the rank of Sardar Bahadur, while those of the second were merely Bahadur. A few awards were made by Pakistan to British officers seconded to the Pakistani forces at the time of independence.*

Original ribbon.

1838 ribbon.

1st class, post-1939 ribbon.

2nd class, post-1939 ribbon.

VALUE:

		Miniature
1st class, light blue centre and dark blue surround	£1500–1750	£200–250
1st class, sky blue centre and surround (1939)	£1250–1500	£200–250
2nd class	£1000–1250	£200–250

NB The prices quoted are for unattributable awards.

37. ORDER OF BURMA

Instituted 1940.
Ribbon: 38mm dark green with light blue edges.
Metal: Gold.
Size: Height 52mm; max. width 38mm.
Description: The badge consists of a gold-rayed circle with a central roundel charged with a peacock in his pride azure, surmounted by an imperial crown.
Comments: *Instituted by King George VI, three years after Burma became independent of British India. Only 24 awards were made, to Governor's Commissioned Officers for long, faithful and honourable service in the army, frontier force and military police of Burma. By an amendment of 1945 the order could also be awarded for individual acts of heroism or particularly meritorious service. It was abolished in 1947.*

VALUE: £4000–5000   *Not known in miniature*

38. KAISAR-I-HIND MEDAL

Victoria obv.   *Victoria rev.*

Second award bar

Instituted: May 1900.
Ribbon: 37mm bluish green.
Metal: Gold, silver or bronze.
Size: Height 61mm; max. width 34mm.
Description: An oval badge surmounted by the imperial crown. (Obverse) the royal cypher set within a wreath; (reverse) FOR PUBLIC SERVICE IN INDIA round the edge and KAISAR-I-HIND (Emperor of India) on a scroll across the centre against a floral background.
Comments: *Queen Victoria founded this medal for award to those, regardless of colour, creed or sex, who had performed public service in India. Originally in two classes George V introduced a 3rd Class in bronze. The medals were originally large and hollow but were changed to smaller in diameter and solid during the reign of George V.*

VALUE:	1st class (gold)	Miniature	2nd class (silver)	Miniature	3rd class (bronze)	Miniature
Victoria	£1850–2250	£150–200	£450–500	£85–100	—	
Edward VII	£1850–2250	£150–200	£350–475	£85–100	—	
George V 1st	£1750–2000	£100–150	£350–475	£35–50	—	
George V 2nd	£1350–1750	£85–150	£300–450	£35–50	£150–175	£25–30
George VI	£1350–1750	£150–200	£350–475	£50–80	£150–175	£25–30

39. ALBERT MEDAL

Instituted: 7 March 1866.

Ribbons:

Gold (1st Class) Sea
16mm blue with two white stripes (1866)
35mm blue with four white stripes (1867–1949)

Bronze (2nd Class) Sea
16mm blue with two white stripes (1867–1904)
35mm blue with two white stripes (1904–71)

Gold (1st Class) Land
35mm red with four white stripes (1877–1949)

Bronze (2nd Class) Land
16mm red with two white stripes (1877–1904)
35mm red with two white stripes (1904–71)

Metal: Gold (early issues gold and bronze); bronze.

Size: Height 57mm; max. width 30mm.

Description: The badge consists of an oval enclosing the entwined initials V and A. The sea medals have, in addition, an anchor. The oval is enclosed by a bronze garter with the words FOR GALLANTRY IN SAVING LIFE, with AT SEA or ON LAND as appropriate, and enamelled in blue or crimson respectively. The whole is surmounted by a crown pierced by a ring for suspension. The first class medal was originally worked in gold and bronze and later in gold alone, the second class in bronze alone.

Comments: *Named in memory of the Prince Consort who died in 1861, this series of medals was instituted for gallantry in saving life at sea. An amendment of 1867 created two classes of medal and ten years later awards were extended to gallantry in saving life on land. In 1917 the title of the awards was altered, the first class becoming the Albert Medal in Gold and the second class merely the Albert Medal. It was last awarded in gold to a living recipient in April 1943, the last posthumous award being in May 1945. The last bronze medal awarded to a living recipient was in January 1949, and posthumous in August 1970. In 1949 the Medal in Gold was abolished and replaced by the George Cross and henceforward the Albert Medal (second class) was only awarded posthumously. In 1971 the award of the medal ceased and holders were invited to exchange their medals for the George Cross. Of the 69 eligible to exchange, 49 did so.*

2nd class land service medal.

2nd class land and sea service ribbons (until 1904).

1st class land service ribbon.

2nd class land service ribbon.
See also ribbon chart

VALUE:

	Civilian	Service	Miniature
Gold Sea (25)	From £12,000	From £15,000	£75–100*
Bronze Sea (211)	From £10,000	From £12,000	£50–75
Gold Land (45)	From £12,000	From £15,000	£75–100*
Bronze Land (290)	From £10,000	From £12,000	£50–75

*assumed gilt

40. UNION OF SOUTH AFRICA KING'S/ QUEEN'S MEDAL FOR BRAVERY (WOLTEMADE MEDAL)

Instituted: 1939 by the Government of the Union of South Africa.

Ribbon: Royal blue with narrow orange edges.

Metal: Gold or silver.

Size: 37mm.

Description: (Obverse) an effigy of the reigning sovereign; (reverse) a celebrated act of heroism by Wolraad Woltemade who rescued sailors from the wreck of the East Indiaman *De Jong Thomas* which ran aground in Table Bay on 17 June 1773. Seven times Woltemade rode into the raging surf to save fourteen seamen from drowning, but on the eighth attempt both rider and horse perished.

Comments: *This medal was awarded to citizens of the Union of South Africa and dependent territories who endangered their lives in saving the lives of others. It was awarded very sparingly, in gold or silver.*

VALUE:

		Miniature
George VI Gold (1)	—	£250–300
George VI Silver (34)	£2000–3000	£150–200
Elizabeth II Silver (1)	—	£150–200

41. DISTINGUISHED CONDUCT MEDAL

1st type obv.

Instituted: 1854.

Ribbon: 32mm crimson with a dark blue central stripe.

Metal: Silver.

Size: 36mm.

Description: (Obverse) originally a trophy of arms but, since 1902, the effigy of the reigning sovereign; (reverse) a four-line inscription across the field FOR DISTINGUISHED CONDUCT IN THE FIELD.

Comments: *The need for a gallantry medal for other ranks was first recognised during the Crimean War, although previously the Meritorious Service Medal (qv) had very occasionally been awarded for gallantry in the field. The medals have always been issued named, and carry the number, rank and name of the recipient on the rim, together with the date of the act of gallantry from 1881 until about 1901. Bars are given for subsequent awards and these too were dated from the first issued in 1881 until 1916 when the more usual laurelled bars were adopted. Since 1916 it has ranked as a superior decoration to the Military Medal. As a result of the 1993 Review of gallantry awards and resultant changes to the operational gallantry award system, the decoration has been replaced by the Conspicuous Gallantry Cross.*

Second award bar — type i

Second award bar — type ii

VALUE:

Crimea (800)	£2500–5000
Indian Mutiny (17)	£7000–10,000
India general service 1854–95	£4000–6000
Abyssinia 1867–68 (7)	£6000–8000
Ashantee 1873–64 (33)	£5000–6000
Zulu War 1877–79 (16)	£8000–12,000
Afghanistan 1878–80 (61)	£4000–6000
First Boer War 1880–81 (20)	£9000–12,000
Egypt & Sudan 1882–89 (134)	£5000–8000
India 1895–1901	£5000–6500
Sudan 1896–97	£4500–6500
Second Boer War 1899–1902 (2090)	£2000–3500
Boxer Rebellion 1900	£8000–10,000
Edward VII	Many rarities
George V 1st type (25,000)	£1000–3000
ditto, unnamed (as issued to foreign recipients)	£350–400
George V 2nd type 1930–7 (14)	£6000–8000
George VI, IND IMP 1937–47	£4000–6000
ditto, unnamed (as issued to foreign recipients)	£500–600
George VI, 2nd type 1948–52 (25)	£12,000–18,000
Elizabeth II, BR: OMN:	£10,000–18,000
Elizabeth II, DEI GRATIA	£15,000–20,000
Miniature (in silver add £5)	
Victoria	£75–85
Edward VII	£50–75
George V	Type I £35–45, II £70–100
George VI	Type I £15–20, II £25–40
Elizabeth II	£15–20

42. DISTINGUISHED CONDUCT MEDAL (DOMINION & COLONIAL)

Instituted: 31 May 1895.

Ribbon: 32mm crimson with a dark blue central stripe.

Metal: Silver.

Size: 36mm.

Description: As above, but the reverse bears the name of the issuing country or colony round the top.

Comments: *A separate DCM for warrant officers, NCOs and men of the colonial forces. Medals were struck for the Cape of Good Hope, Natal, New Zealand, New South Wales, Queensland, Tasmania, Natal and Canada, but only the last two actually issued them and the others are known only as specimens.*

VALUE:

Victoria Canada (1)	Rare
Victoria Natal (1)	Rare
Edward VII Natal (9)	Rare

43. DISTINGUISHED CONDUCT MEDAL (KAR & WAFF)

Instituted: early 1900s.

Ribbon: Dark blue with a central green stripe flanked by crimson stripes.

Metal: Silver.

Size: 36mm

Description: As no. 42, with either King's African Rifles or West Africa Frontier Force around the top of the reverse.

Comments: *Separate awards for gallantry were instituted in respect of the King's African Rifles (East Africa) and the West Africa Frontier Force (Nigeria, Sierra Leone, Gambia and the Gold Coast). These were issued until 1942 when they were superseded by the British DCM. An unnamed version of a George VI KAR DCM is known.*

VALUE:	Attributable groups
Edward VII KAR (2)	Rare
Edward VII WAFF (55)	£2500–3500
George V KAR (190)	£1500–2000
George V WAFF (165)	£1500–2000

44. CONSPICUOUS GALLANTRY MEDAL

Instituted: 1855.

Ribbon: 31mm white (RN) or sky blue (RAF) with dark blue edges. The Royal Navy ribbon was originally dark blue with white central stripe.

Metal: Silver.

Size: 36mm.

Description: (Obverse) the effigy of the reigning monarch; (reverse) the words FOR CONSPICUOUS GALLANTRY in three lines within a crowned laurel wreath.

Comments: *Conceived as the naval counterpart to the DCM, it was instituted for award to petty officers and seamen of the Royal Navy and to NCOs and other ranks of the Royal Marines. Originally awarded only for gallantry during the Crimean War, it was revived in 1874 to recognise heroism during the Ashantee War and has since been awarded, albeit sparingly, for other wars and campaigns. The Crimean issue utilised the dies of the Meritorious Service Medal which had the date 1848 below the truncation of the Queen's neck on the obverse. The raised relief inscription MERITORIOUS SERVICE on the reverse was erased and the words CONSPICUOUS GALLANTRY engraved in their place. When the decoration was revived in 1874 a new obverse was designed without a date while a new die, with the entire inscription in raised relief, was employed for the reverse. In 1943 the CGM was extended to NCOs and other ranks of the RAF. Both naval and RAF medals are identical, but the naval medal has a white ribbon with dark blue edges, whereas the RAF award has a pale blue ribbon with dark blue edges. It ranks as one of the rarest decorations: the only three medals issued in the present reign were awarded to Cpl. J. D. Coughlan, RAAF, for gallantry in Vietnam (1968), to Staff-Sergeant James Prescott, RE, during the South Atlantic War (1982) (posthumous) and to CPO Diver Philip Hammond, RN, during the Gulf War (1991). As a result of the 1993 Review and resultant changes to the operational gallantry award system, the decoration has been replaced by the Conspicuous Gallantry Cross.*

Second award bar.

RN first type ribbon

VALUE:		Attributable groups
Victoria 1st type (11)		£10,000–15,000
Victoria 2nd type (50)		£10,000–18,000
Edward VII (2)		—
George V (110)		£8000–12,000
George VI Navy/RM (80)		£10,000–20,000
George VI RAF (103)	Immediate	£10,000–20,000
	Non-immediate	£7000–8000
Elizabeth II (3)		—
Miniature		
Victoria		£50–80
Edward VII		£50–80
George V		£25–35
George VI		£15–20
Elizabeth II		£15–20

RN

RAF

45. GEORGE MEDAL

Second award bar.

Instituted: 1940.
Ribbon: 32mm crimson with five narrow blue stripes.
Metal: Silver.
Size: 36mm.
Description: (Obverse) the effigy of the reigning monarch; (reverse) St George and the Dragon, modelled by George Kruger Gray, after the bookplate by Stephen Gooden for the Royal Library, Windsor.
Comments: *Awarded for acts of bravery where the services were not so outstanding as to merit the George Cross. Though primarily a civilian award, it has also been given to service personnel for heroism not in the face of the enemy. Of the approximately 2,000 medals awarded, 1,030 have been to civilians. 27 second award bars have been issued.*

VALUE:

	Civilian	Service
George VI 1st type 1940–47	£3500–4000	£4000–4500
George VI 2nd type 1948–52	£3500–4500	£4000–5500
Elizabeth II 1st type 1953	£3500–4000	£4000–5500
Elizabeth II 2nd type	£3500–4000	£4000–5500

Miniature		
George VI, 1st type	£20–25	
2nd type	£25–30	
Elizabeth II, 1st type	£15–20	
2nd type	£20–25	
	Silver add £5	

46. KING'S POLICE MEDAL

Second award bar.

Instituted: 7 July 1909.
Ribbons: 36mm Originally deep blue with silver edges, but in 1916 a central silver stripe was added. Gallantry awards have thin crimson stripes superimposed on the silver stripes.
Metal: Silver.
Size: 36mm.
Description: (Obverse) the monarch's effigy; (reverse) a standing figure with sword and shield inscribed TO GUARD MY PEOPLE. The first issue had a laurel spray in the exergue, but in 1933 two separate reverses were introduced and the words FOR GALLANTRY or FOR DISTINGUISHED SERVICE were placed in the exergue.
Comments: *Instituted to reward "courage and devotion to duty" in the police and fire services of the UK and overseas dominions. Recognising the bravery of the firemen during the Blitz, the medal was retitled the King's Police and Fire Services Medal in 1940, but no change was made in the design of the medal itself. From 1950, the gallantry medals were only awarded posthumously and all medals were discontinued in 1954 when separate awards were established for the two services (see numbers MYB47 and 48).*

VALUE:

		Miniature
Edward VII (100)	£850–1000	£25–30
George V 1st type coinage head (1900)	£600–850	£20–25
George V 2nd type crowned head	£600–850	£40–50
George V for Gallantry (350)	£1000–1500	£15–20
George V for Distinguished Service	£500–600	£15–20
George VI 1st type for Gallantry (440)	£850–1250	£15–20
George VI 2nd type for Gallantry (50)	£1500–2000	£15–20
George VI 1st type for Distinguished Service	£500–550	£15–20
George VI 2nd type for Distinguished Service	£500–550	£15–20

KPM

KPM (Gallantry)

47. QUEEN'S POLICE MEDAL

Instituted: 19 May 1954.

Ribbon: Three silver stripes and two broad dark blue stripes. Gallantry awards have thin crimson stripes superimposed on the silver stripes.

Metal: Silver.

Size: 36mm.

Description: (Obverse) effigy of the reigning sovereign; (reverse) a standing figure (as on the KPM) but the laurel spray has been restored to the exergue and the words FOR GALLANTRY or FOR DISTINGUISHED POLICE SERVICE are inscribed round the circumference.

Comments: *The QPM for Gallantry has been effectively redundant since November 1977 when it was made possible to award the George Medal posthumously. Prior to this the QPM was the posthumous equivalent of the GM for police officers. Issued in New Zealand under Regulations dated November 18, 1959 by the Minister in Charge of Police.*

VALUE:		Miniature
Elizabeth II for Gallantry (23)	£1750–2500	£30–40
Elizabeth II for Distinguished Service	£550–750	£20–30

Gallantry

48. QUEEN'S FIRE SERVICE MEDAL

Instituted: 19 May 1954.

Ribbon: Red with three yellow stripes (distinguished service) or similar, with thin dark blue stripes bisecting the yellow stripes (gallantry).

Metal: Silver.

Size: 36mm

Description: (Obverse) effigy of the reigning monarch; (reverse) standing figure with sword and shield (as on KPM), laurel spray in the exergue, and inscription round the circumference FOR GALLANTRY or FOR DISTINGUISHED FIRE SERVICE.

Comments: *To date no award of this medal, which can be awarded posthumously, has been made for gallantry.*

VALUE:		Miniature
Elizabeth II for Gallantry	—	£30–40
Elizabeth II for Distinguished Service	£600–750	£20–30

Gallantry

48A. QUEEN'S VOLUNTEER RESERVES MEDAL

Instituted: 1999.
Ribbon: Dark green with three narrow gold stripes.
Metal: Silver.
Size: 36mm.
Description: (Obverse) effigy of Queen Elizabeth II; (reverse) five ribbons containing the words THE QUEEN'S VOLUNTEER RESERVES MEDAL. The medal is fitted with a large ring for suspension.
Comments: *Awarded to men and women of any rank in the volunteer reserves of all three services in recognition of outstanding service which formerly would have merited an award within the Order of the British Empire. Holders are entitled to the post-nominal letters QVRM.*

VALUE: £300–500   *Miniature* £10–15

48B. QUEEN'S AMBULANCE SERVICE MEDAL FOR DISTINGUISHED SERVICE

Instituted: July 2012.
Branch of Service: Members of the NHS Ambulance Service.
Ribbon: Dark green with central silver stripe and silver edges.
Metal: Silver.
Size: 36mm.
Description: (Obverse) the monarch's effigy; (reverse) the inscription FOR DISTINGUISHED AMBULANCE SERVICE around the ambulance service emblem.
Comments: *Issued to recognise exceptional duty and outstanding service of NHS ambulance personnel. The medals are named around the edge and recipients can use the post-nominals QAM.*

VALUE: —   *Miniature*   —

49. KING'S POLICE MEDAL (SOUTH AFRICA)

Instituted: 24 September 1937.
Ribbon: Silver with two broad dark blue stripes. Red stripes are added for gallantry awards.
Metal: Silver.
Size: 36mm.
Description: (Obverse) effigy of George VI and title including the words ET IMPERATOR (1937-49), George VI minus ET IMPERATOR (1950-52) and Queen Elizabeth II (1953-60). (Reverse) as UK (no. 47 above) but inscribed in English and Afrikaans. Inscribed FOR BRAVERY VIR DAPPERHEID or FOR DISTINGUISHED SERVICE VIR VOORTREFLIKE DIENS.
Comments: *Awarded to members of the South Africa Police for courage and devotion to duty. In 1938 it was extended to cover the constabulary of South West Africa.*

VALUE:
George VI 1st type 1937-49
    for Gallantry (10)   —
    for Distinguished Service (13)   —
George VI 2nd type 1950-52
    for Distinguished Service (13)   —
Elizabeth II 1953-60
    for Gallantry (20)   —
Elizabeth II 1953-69
    for Distinguished Service (3)   —
Not seen in Miniature

50. EDWARD MEDAL (MINES)

Instituted: July 1907.
Ribbon: Dark blue edged with yellow.
Metal: Silver or bronze.
Size: 33mm.
Description: (Obverse) the monarch's effigy; (reverse) a miner rescuing a stricken comrade, with the caption FOR COURAGE across the top (designed by W. Reynolds-Stephens).
Comments: *Awarded for life-saving in mines and quarries, in two grades: first class (silver) and second class (bronze). Interestingly, the cost of these medals was borne not by the State but from a fund created by a group of philanthropic individuals led by A. Hewlett, a leading mine-owner. Medals were engraved with the names of the recipient from the outset, but since the 1930s the date and sometimes the place of the action have also been inscribed. Since 1949 the medal was only granted posthumously and in 1971 living recipients were invited to exchange their medals for the GC, under Royal Warrant of 1971. Two silver and eight bronze medallists elected not to do so. This is one of the rarest gallantry awards, only 77 silver and 318 bronze medals having been granted since its inception. Only two second award bars have been awarded—both for mine rescues.*

VALUE:	Silver	Bronze
Edward VII	£2500–3500	£2000–2500
George V 1st type	£2000–2500	£1000–1500
George V 2nd type	£2500–3500	£1200–1800
George VI 1st type	£2500–3500	£1800–2500
George VI 2nd type	—	£2000–3000
Elizabeth II	Not issued	From £2000
Miniature		
Edward VII	£80–90	£70–80
George V	£70–80	£60–70
George VI	£70–80	£60–70

51. EDWARD MEDAL (INDUSTRY)

1st type rev.

2nd type rev.

Instituted: December 1909.
Ribbon: As above.
Metal: Silver or bronze.
Size: 33mm.
Description: (Obverse) effigy of the reigning monarch; (reverse) originally a worker helping an injured workmate with a factory in the background and the words FOR COURAGE inscribed diagonally across the top. A second reverse, depicting a standing female figure with a laurel branch and a factory skyline in the background, was introduced in 1912.
Comments: *Awarded for acts of bravery in factory accidents and disasters. Like the Mines medal it was also available in two classes, but no first class medals were awarded since 1948. Since 1949 the medal was only granted posthumously and in 1971 living recipients were invited to exchange their medals for the GC, under Royal Warrant of 1971. Two Silver and three Bronze recipients declined to exchange. A total of 25 silver and 163 bronze awards have been issued. Two awards were made to women, the rarest gallantry award to a lady.*

VALUE:	Silver	Bronze
Edward VII	£1800–2500	£1250–1750
George V 1st Obv, 1st Rev	—	£1500–1800
George V 1st Obv, 2nd Rev	£1500–2000	£1000–1250
George V 2nd Obv, 2nd Rev	—	£1250–1500
George VI 1st type	Unique	£1000–1250
George VI 2nd type	Not issued	£1500–2000
Elizabeth II 1st type	Not issued	£1500–2000
Elizabeth II 2nd type	Not issued	£1500–2000
Miniature		
George V	£150–200	£100–150
George VI	£70–80	
George VI Modern example	£15–20	

52. INDIAN DISTINGUISHED SERVICE MEDAL

Instituted: 25 June 1907.
Ribbon: Crimson with broad dark blue edges.
Metal: Silver.
Size: 36mm.
Description: (Obverse) the sovereign's effigy. (Reverse) the words FOR DISTINGUISHED SERVICE in a laurel wreath.
Comments: *Awarded for distinguished service in the field by Indian commissioned and non-commissioned officers and men of the Indian Army, the reserve forces, border militia and levies, military police and troops employed by the Indian Government. An amendment of 1917 extended the award to Indian non-combatants engaged on field service, bars for subsequent awards being authorised at the same time. It was formally extended to the Royal Indian Marine in 1929 and members of the Indian Air Force in 1940. Finally it was extended in 1944 to include non-European personnel of the Hong Kong and Singapore Royal Artillery although it became obsolete in 1947.*

Second award bar.

VALUE:

		Miniature
Edward VII (140)	£1000–1500	£80–90
George V KAISAR-I-HIND (3800)	£800–1200	£50–60
George V 2nd type (140)	£1250–1650	£50–60
George VI (1190)	£1000–1500	£40–50

53. BURMA GALLANTRY MEDAL

Instituted: 10 May 1940.
Ribbon: Jungle green with a broad crimson stripe in the centre.
Metal: Silver.
Size: 36mm.
Description: (Obverse) the effigy of King George VI; (reverse) the words BURMA at the top and FOR GALLANTRY in a laurel wreath.
Comments: *As Burma ceased to be part of the Indian Empire in April 1937 a separate gallantry award was required for its armed services. The Burma Gallantry Medal was awarded by the Governor to officers and men of the Burma Army, frontier forces, military police, Burma RNVR and Burma AAF, although by an amendment of 1945 subsequent awards were restricted to NCOs and men. The medal became obsolete in 1947 when Burma became an independent republic and left the Commonwealth. Just over 200 medals and three bars were awarded, mainly for heroism in operations behind the Japanese lines.*

VALUE:
£4000–5000

Miniature
£20–25 for late example, contemporary example unknown

Second award bar.

54. DISTINGUISHED SERVICE MEDAL

Instituted: 14 October 1914.

Ribbon: Dark blue with two white stripes towards the centre.

Metal: Silver.

Size: 36mm.

Description: (Obverse) the sovereign's effigy; (reverse) a crowned wreath inscribed FOR DISTINGUISHED SERVICE.

Comments: *Awarded to petty officers and ratings of the Royal Navy, NCOs and other ranks of the Royal Marines and all other persons holding corresponding ranks or positions in the naval forces, for acts of bravery in face of the enemy not sufficiently meritorious to make them eligible for the CGM. It was later extended to cover the Merchant Navy and Army, the WRNS and RAF personnel serving aboard ships in the Second World War. Of particular interest and desirability are medals awarded for outstanding actions, e.g. Jutland, Q-Ships, the Murmansk convoys, the Yangtze incident and the Falklands War. First World War bars for subsequent awards are dated on the reverse, but Second World War bars are undated. As a result of the 1993 Review of gallantry awards and resultant changes to the operational gallantry award system, this award has been replaced by the DSC which is now available both to officers and other ranks.*

Second award bar.

VALUE:		Miniature
George V uncrowned head 1914-30 (4100)	£1000–2000	£20–25
George VI IND IMP 1938-49 (7100)	£1000–2000	£15–20
George VI 2nd type 1949-53	£3500–4500	£30–40
Elizabeth II BR OMN 1953-7	£5000–8000	£10–15
Elizabeth II 2nd type	£5500–8500	£10–15

(in silver add £5)

55. MILITARY MEDAL

Instituted: 25 March 1916.

Ribbon: Broad dark blue edges flanking a central section of three narrow white and two narrow crimson stripes.

Metal: Silver.

Size: 36mm.

Description: (Obverse) the sovereign's effigy—six types; (reverse) the crowned royal cypher above the inscription FOR BRAVERY IN THE FIELD, enclosed in a wreath.

Comments: *Awarded to NCOs and men of the Army (including RFC and RND) for individual or associated acts of bravery not of sufficient heroism as to merit the DCM. In June 1916 it was extended to women, two of the earliest awards being to civilian ladies for their conduct during the Easter Rising in Dublin that year. Some 115,600 medals were awarded during the First World War alone, together with 5796 first bars, 180 second bars and 1 third bar. Over 15,000 medals were conferred during the Second World War, with 177 first bars and 1 second bar. About 300 medals and 4 first bars were awarded for bravery in minor campaigns between the two world wars, whilst some 932 medals and 8 first bars have been conferred since 1947. As a result of the 1993 Review of gallantry awards and resultant changes to the operational gallantry award system, this award has been replaced by the MC which is now available both to officers and other ranks.*

Second award bar.

VALUE:

		Miniature
George V uncrowned head 1916–30		£15–20
Corps/RA—single	£250–400	
in group	£400–550*	
Regiment—single	£400–550	
in group	£550–1000*	
named to a woman	£5000–6000	
unnamed as awarded to foreign recipients	£275–300	
George V crowned head 1930–38	£3500–5000	£70–100
George VI IND IMP 1938–48		
Corps	£1000–1800	£15–20
Regiment	£1500–2500	
unnamed as awarded to foreign recipients	£400–500	
George VI 2nd type 1948–53	£2500–5000	£25–40
Elizabeth II BR: OMN 1953–8	£3500–6000	£15–20
Elizabeth II 2nd type	£5000–8000	£15–20

(in silver add £5)

*Groups to RFC, RAF and RND will be considerably higher and obviously, medals with second (or more) award bars are also worth much more.

56. DISTINGUISHED FLYING MEDAL

Second award bar

Pre-1919

Post-1919

Instituted: 1918.

Ribbon: Originally purple and white horizontal stripes but since July 1919 thirteen narrow diagonal stripes alternating white and purple.

Metal: Silver.

Size: 42mm tall; 34mm wide.

Description: An oval medal, (obverse) the sovereign's effigy; (reverse) Athena Nike seated on an aeroplane, with a hawk rising from her hand. Originally undated, but the date 1918 was added to the reverse with the advent of the George VI obverse. The medal is suspended by a pair of wings from a straight bar.

Comments: *Introduced at the same time as the DFC, it was awarded to NCOs and men of the RAF for courage or devotion to duty while flying on active operations against the enemy. During the Second World War it was extended to the equivalent ranks of the Army and Fleet Air Arm personnel engaged in similar operations. First World War medals have the names of recipients impressed in large seriffed lettering, whereas Second World War medals are rather coarsely engraved. Approximately 150 medals have been awarded since 1945. After WWII it was expanded to include aviation officers of other services. As a result of the 1993 Review of gallantry awards and resultant changes to the operational gallantry award system, this award has been replaced by the DFC which is now available both to officers and other ranks.*

VALUE:

		Miniature
George V uncrowned head 1918–30 (105)	£4500–6500	£18–20
George V crowned head 1930–38	£8000–12,000	£70–100
George VI IND IMP 1938–49 (6500)	£2500–3500	£10–12
George VI 2nd type 1949–53	£5000–7000	£25–40
Elizabeth II	£6000–10,000	£10–12

(in silver add £5)

ᴏH . STUBBINGTON . H

Example of WWI impressed naming

SGT. W.H. HITCHCOCK · R A.

WWII engraved naming.

57. AIR FORCE MEDAL

Second award bar

Pre-1919

Post-1919

Instituted: 1918.

Ribbon: Originally horizontal narrow stripes of white and crimson but since July 1919 diagonal narrow stripes of the same colours.

Metal: Silver.

Size: 42mm tall; 32mm wide.

Description: An oval medal with a laurel border. (Obverse) the sovereign's effigy; (reverse) Hermes mounted on a hawk bestowing a laurel wreath. The medal is suspended by a pair of wings from a straight bar, like the DFM.

Comments: *Instituted at the same time as the AFC, it was awarded to NCOs and men of the RAF for courage or devotion to duty while flying, but not on active operations against the enemy. About 100 medals and 2 first bars were awarded during the First World War, 106 medals and 3 bars between the wars and 259 medals during the Second World War. After WWII it was expanded to include aviation officers of other services. After the 1993 Review of gallantry awards the AFM was discontinued; the AFC is now available both to officers and other ranks.*

VALUE:

		Miniature
George V uncrowned head 1918–30	£2000–2500	£25–30
George V crowned head 1930–38	£4000–6000	£80–100
George VI IND IMP 1939–49	£2500–3000	£15–20
George VI 2nd type 1949–53	£2500–3000	£30–40
Elizabeth II	£2500–3000	£15–20

(in silver add £5)

58. CONSTABULARY MEDAL (IRELAND)

1st type obv.

2nd type obv.

Instituted: 1842.

Ribbon: Originally light blue, but changed to green in 1872.

Metal: Silver.

Size: 36mm.

Description: (Obverse) a crowned harp within a wreath of oak leaves and shamrocks, with REWARD OF MERIT round the top and IRISH CONSTABULARY round the foot. In the first version the front of the harp took the form of a female figure but later variants had a plain harp and the shape of the crown and details of the wreath were also altered. These changes theoretically came in 1867 when the Constabulary acquired the epithet Royal, which was then added to the inscription round the top, although some medals issued as late as 1921 had the pre-1867 title. (Reverse) a wreath of laurel and shamrock, within which are engraved the recipient's name, rank, number, date and sometimes the location of the action.

Comments: *Originally awarded for gallantry and meritorious service by members of the Irish Constabulary. From 1872, however, it was awarded only for gallantry. It was first conferred in 1848 and became obsolete in 1922 when the Irish Free State was established. Bars for second awards were authorised in 1920. About 315 medals and 7 bars were awarded (or, in some cases, second medals—the records are inconclusive), mostly for actions in connection with the Easter Rising of 1916 (23) or the subsequent Anglo-Irish War of 1920 (180) and 1921 (55).*

VALUE:		Miniature
First type	£8000–12,000	—
Second type	£8000–12,000	£200–250

Original ribbon

Post-1872 ribbon

59. INDIAN POLICE MEDAL

1st type

2nd type (after 1944)

Instituted: 23 February 1932.

Ribbon: Crimson flanked by stripes of dark blue and silver grey. From 1942 onwards additional narrow silver stripes appeared in the centre of the blue stripe intended for the gallantry medal.

Metal: Bronze.

Size: 36mm.

Description: (Obverse) the King Emperor; (reverse) a crowned wreath inscribed INDIAN POLICE, with the words FOR DISTINGUISHED CONDUCT across the centre. In December 1944 the reverse was re-designed in two types, with the words FOR GALLANTRY or FOR MERITORIOUS SERVICE in place of the previous legend.

Comments: *Intended for members of the Indian police forces and fire brigades as a reward for gallantry or meritorious service. The medal became obsolete in 1948 when India became a republic.*

VALUE:

		Miniature
George V	£500–650	£35–45
George VI Distinguished Conduct	£500–650	£35–45
George VI for Gallantry	£750–900	£45–55
George VI for Meritorious Service	£500–600	£35–45

From 1942 for gallantry

Second award bar.

60. BURMA POLICE MEDAL

Instituted: 14 December 1937.
Ribbon: A wide central blue stripe flanked by broad black stripes and white edges.
Metal: Bronze.
Size: 36mm.
Description: (Obverse) the effigy of George VI; (reverse) similar to the Indian medal (first type) and inscribed FOR DISTINGUISHED CONDUCT, irrespective of whether awarded for gallantry or distinguished service.
Comments: *Introduced following the separation of Burma from India, it was abolished in 1948. All ranks of the police, frontier force and fire brigades, both European and Burmese, were eligible.*

VALUE:

For Gallantry (53)	£1950–2500
For Meritorious Service (80)	£1200–1700
Miniature	£60–75

61. COLONIAL POLICE MEDAL

Instituted: 10 May 1938.
Ribbon: Blue with green edges and a thin silver stripe separating the colours, but the gallantry award had an additional thin red line through the centre of each green edge stripe.
Metal: Silver.
Size: 36mm.
Description: (Obverse) the sovereign's effigy; (reverse) a policeman's truncheon superimposed on a laurel wreath. The left side of the circumference is inscribed COLONIAL POLICE FORCES and the right either FOR GALLANTRY or FOR MERITORIOUS SERVICE.
Comments: *Intended to reward all ranks of the police throughout the Empire for acts of conspicuous bravery or for meritorious service. The number to be issued was limited to 150 in any one year. Only 450 were awarded for gallantry (with nine second award bars), whilst almost 3000 were issued for meritorious service. As from June 14, 2012 this medal was renamed the Overseas Territories Police Medal.*

Second award bar.

Ribbon for gallantry award

VALUE:		*Miniature*
George VI GRI for Gallantry	£850–1250	£40–50
George VI GRI for Meritorious Service	£375–475	£30–40
George VI GVIR for Gallantry	£850–1250	£40–50
George VI GVIR for Meritorious Service	£375–475	£30–40
Elizabeth II 1st type for Gallantry	£850–1250	£40–50
Elizabeth II 1st type for Meritorious Service	£375–475	£30–40
Elizabeth II 2nd type for Gallantry	£850–1250	£40–50
Elizabeth II 2nd type for Meritorious Service	£375–475	£30–40

62. COLONIAL FIRE BRIGADE MEDAL

Instituted: 10 May 1938.
Ribbon: As above.
Metal: Silver.
Size: 36mm.
Description: (Obverse) the effigy of the reigning sovereign; (reverse) a fireman's helmet and axe, with the inscription COLONIAL FIRE BRIGADES FOR GALLANTRY or FOR MERITORIOUS SERVICE.
Comments: *This medal was intended to reward all ranks of the Colonial fire brigades for gallantry or meritorious service but very few were awarded for gallantry. As from June 14, 2012 this medal was renamed the Overseas Territories Fire Brigade Medal.*

VALUE:		*Miniature*
George VI GRI for Gallantry	Rare	£40–50
George VI GRI for Meritorious Service	Rare	£30–40
George VI GVIR for Gallantry	Rare	£40–50
George VI GVIR for Meritorious Service	£350–500	£30–40
Elizabeth II 1st type for Gallantry	From £750	£40–50
Elizabeth II 1st type for Meritorious Service	£350–500	£30–40
Elizabeth II 2nd type for Gallantry	£600–800	£40–50
Elizabeth II 2nd type for Meritorious Service	£300–450	£30–40

63. QUEEN'S GALLANTRY MEDAL

Instituted: 20 June 1974.

Ribbon: Blue with a central pearl-grey stripe bisected by a narrow rose-pink stripe.

Metal: Silver.

Size: 36mm.

Description: (Obverse) the Queen's effigy; (reverse) St. Edward's crown above THE QUEEN'S GALLANTRY MEDAL flanked by laurel sprigs.

Comments: *Awarded for exemplary acts of bravery. Although intended primarily for civilians, it is also awarded to members of the armed forces for actions which would not be deemed suitable for a military decoration. With the introduction of the QGM the gallantry awards in the Order of the British Empire came to an end. To date, about 1,000 QGMs have been awarded, including 18 bars. A bar is added for a second award. A post-1990 SAS QGM and bar group sold at a recent auction for £26,000.*

Second award bar.

VALUE:		Miniature
Service award	From £3500	£10–12
Civilian award	From £2500	

64. ALLIED SUBJECTS' MEDAL

Instituted: November 1920.

Ribbon: Bright red with a light blue centre, flanked by narrow stripes of yellow, black and white (thus incorporating the Belgian and French national colours).

Metal: Silver or bronze.

Size: 36mm.

Description: (Obverse) the effigy of King George V; (reverse) designed by C. L. J. Doman, the female allegory of Humanity offering a cup to a British soldier resting on the ground, with ruined buildings in the background.

Comment: *Shortly after the cessation of the First World War it was proposed that services rendered to the Allied cause, specifically by those who had helped British prisoners of war to escape, should be rewarded by a medal. The decision to go ahead was delayed on account of disagreement between the War Office and the Foreign Office, but eventually the first awards were announced in November 1920, with supplementary lists in 1921 and 1922. Medals were issued unnamed and almost half of the total issue, namely 56 silver and 247 bronze medals, were issued to women.*

VALUE:		Miniature
Silver (134)	£1000–1250	£40–50
Bronze (574)	£500–600	£45–55

NB These prices are for unattributable awards.

65. KING'S MEDAL FOR COURAGE IN THE CAUSE OF FREEDOM

Instituted: 23 August 1945

Ribbon: White with two narrow dark blue stripes in the centre and broad red stripes at the edges.

Metal: Silver.

Size: 36mm.

Description: (Obverse) the crowned profile of King George VI; (reverse) inscribed, within a chain link, THE KING'S MEDAL FOR COURAGE IN THE CAUSE OF FREEDOM.

Comments: *Introduced to acknowledge acts of courage by foreign civilians or members of the armed services "in the furtherance of the British Commonwealth in the Allied cause" during the Second World War. Like its First World War counterpart, it was intended mainly to reward those who had assisted British escapees in enemy-occupied territories. About 3200 medals were issued, commencing in 1947.*

VALUE: £250–350 (unattributable)   *Miniature* £30–40

66. KING'S MEDAL FOR SERVICE IN THE CAUSE OF FREEDOM

Instituted: 23 August 1945.

Ribbon: White with a central red stripe flanked by dark blue stripes.

Metal: Silver.

Size: 36mm.

Description: (Obverse) effigy of King George VI; (reverse) a medieval warrior in armour carrying a broken lance, receiving nourishment from a female.

Comments: *Introduced at the same time as the foregoing, it was intended for foreign civilians who had helped the Allied cause in other less dangerous ways, such as fund-raising and organising ambulance services. 2490 medals were issued.*

VALUE: £250–350 (unattributable)　　　*Miniature* £15–20

67. SEA GALLANTRY MEDAL

Instituted: 1855, under the Merchant Shipping Acts of 1854 and 1894.

Ribbon: Bright red with narrow white stripes towards the edges.

Metal: Silver or bronze.

Size: 58mm or 33mm.

Description: (Obverse) Profile of the reigning monarch; (reverse) a family on a storm-tossed shore reviving a drowning sailor. Both obverse and reverse were sculpted by Bernard Wyon.

Comments: *Exceptionally, this group of medals was authorised not by Royal Warrant but by Parliamentary legislation, under the terms of the Merchant Shipping Acts of 1854 and 1894. The 1854 Act made provision for monetary rewards for life saving at sea, but in 1855 this was transmuted into medals, in gold, silver or bronze, in two categories, for gallantry (where the rescuer placed his own life at risk) and for humanity (where the risks were minimal). The gold medal, if ever awarded, must have been of the greatest rarity. These medals, issued by the Board of Trade, were 58mm in diameter and not intended for wearing. The only difference between the medals lay in the wording of the inscription round the circumference of the obverse. In 1903 Edward VII ordered that the medal be reduced to 1.27 inches (33mm) in diameter and fitted with a suspension bar and ribbon for wearing. Both large and small medals were always issued with a minimum of the recipient's name and date of rescue round the rim. The last medal was awarded in 1989 and appears to have fallen into disuse although the award has not been cancelled. Only one second award clasp has ever been issued—that to Ch.Off. James Whiteley in 1921.*

VALUE:

	Silver	Bronze	*Miniature*
Victoria Gallantry	£750–1000	£450–550	£100–150
Victoria Humanity (to 1893)	£850–1250	£1000–1500	
Edward VII Gallantry (large)	£1750–2000	£1500–1650	
Edward VII Gallantry (small)	£850–1000	£550–650	£100–150
Edward VII (2nd small type)	£750–950	£450–550	
George V	£500–650	£350–450	£50–75
George VI 1st type	£1200–1500	—	
George VI 2nd type	—	—	
Elizabeth II	—	—	

68. SEA GALLANTRY MEDAL (FOREIGN SERVICES)

Type 4 rev.

Instituted: 1841.

Ribbon: Plain crimson till 1922; thereafter the same ribbon as the SGM above.

Metal: Gold, silver or bronze.

Size: 36mm or 33mm.

Description: The large medal had Victoria's effigy (young head) on the obverse, but there were five reverse types showing a crowned wreath with PRESENTED BY (or FROM) THE BRITISH GOVERNMENT inside the wreath. Outside the wreath were the following variants:

1. Individually struck inscriptions (1841-49 but sometimes later).
2. FOR SAVING THE LIFE OF A BRITISH SUBJECT (1849-54)
3. FOR ASSISTING A BRITISH VESSEL IN DISTRESS (1849-54)
4. FOR SAVING THE LIVES OF BRITISH SUBJECTS (1850-54)

There are also unissued specimens or patterns with a Latin inscription within the wreath VICTORIA REGINA CUDI JUSSIT MDCCCXLI.

The small medal, intended for wear, has five obverse types combined with four reverse types: as 2 above (1854-1906), as 3 above (1854-1918), as 4 above (1854-1926), or FOR GALLANTRY AND HUMANITY (1858 to the present day).

Comments: *Although intended to reward foreigners who rendered assistance to British subjects in distress some early awards were actually made for rescues on dry land. Originally a special reverse was struck for each incident, but this was found to be unnecessarily expensive, so a standard reverse was devised in 1849. Medals before 1854 had a diameter of 45mm and were not fitted with suspension. After 1854 the diameter was reduced to 33mm and scrolled suspension bars were fitted. Of the large medals about 100 gold, 120 silver and 14 bronze were issued, while some 10 gold and 24 bronze specimens have been recorded. The small bronze medal is actually the rarest of all, only six medals being issued.*

Original ribbon

Post-1922 ribbon

VALUE:	Gold	Silver	Bronze
Victoria large	—	£550–750	£450–550
Victoria small	£1500–1800	£300–450	—
Edward VII	£1500–2000	£450–550	—
George V	£1500–1800	£350–450	—
George VI	—	—	—
Elizabeth II	—	—	—
Miniature			£175–225

69. BRITISH NORTH BORNEO COMPANY'S BRAVERY CROSS

Instituted: 1890.

Ribbon: Gold (later yellow) watered silk 34mm.

Metal: Silver or bronze.

Size: 36mm.

Description: The cross pattée has a central medallion bearing a lion passant with the Company motto PERGO ET PERAGO (I carry on and accomplish) within a garter. The arms of the cross are inscribed BRITISH NORTH BORNEO with FOR BRAVERY in the lower limb. Three crosses have been recorded with the lower inscription for bravery omitted.

Comments: *Manufactured by Joseph Moore of Birmingham. The silver version bears the Birmingham hallmark for 1890. The reverse of the bronze medal is smooth. The cross was awarded for bravery in some 17 actions between 1883 and 1915, to the Company's Armed Constabulary. Several of these actions involved fewer than 40 combatants, but at the other extreme 144 men took*

69. BRITISH NORTH BORNEO COMPANY'S BRAVERY CROSS *continued*

part in the major battle at Tambunan in 1900. Only five silver and four bronze crosses are known to have been awarded. Jemadar Natha Singh was the only officer to win both bronze (1892) and silver (1897). Examples with the word STERLING on the reverse are modern copies.

VALUE:

Silver	£800–1000	*Not known in miniature.*
Bronze	£400–500 (but much more in either case if attributable)	
Specimens/Copies	£100–150	

70. KING'S MEDAL FOR NATIVE CHIEFS

Instituted: 1920.

Ribbon: Yellow with two white central stripes (silver-gilt) or a single white stripe (silver).

Metal: Silver or silver-gilt.

Size: Oval 40mm x 34mm or circular 36mm x 32mm.

Description: Originally an oval badge with collar. (Obverse) the crowned effigy of the monarch; (reverse) a warship, symbolic of imperial power. The medals of Elizabeth II come in two versions: the original larger size with collar and the smaller size (1955) fitted with a plain ring for suspension from a yellow watered silk ribbon with or without a narrow central white stripe.

Comments: *Various large silver medals were struck for award to native chiefs in various parts of the world, from the eighteenth century onwards, and of these the awards to American Indian chiefs are probably the best known. In 1920, however, a standard King's Medal for Chiefs was instituted. It was awarded exceptionally in silver-gilt (first class), and usually in silver (second class). The oval medal was worn round the neck from a silver collar. The more modern issues, however, are smaller and intended for wear with a ribbon from the breast. The medal is normally returned on the death of the recipient.*

VALUE:	Silver-gilt	Silver
George V		
First (couped) type	£1000–1200	£700–800
Second (larger bust) type	£1000–1200	£650–750
George VI	£1000–1200	£600–700
Elizabeth II		
First type	£1000–1200	£600–700
Second (small) type	£350–400	£300–400

MENTIONS
and Commendations

A description of the various emblems denoting Mentions in Despatches and King's (or later Queen's) Commendations was published as a Supplement to the London Gazette, July 27, 1951. A special emblem to signify a Mention in Despatches was instituted during World War I and continued to be awarded for active service up to August 10, 1920. It was worn on the ribbon of the Victory Medal (no. 170) or the British War Medal if no Victory Medal is awarded and consisted of a bronze spray of oak leaves.

For Mentions in Despatches after August 10, 1920, or a King's Commendation for Brave Conduct or Valuable Service in the Air, a bronze emblem consisting of a single oak leaf was worn on the appropriate medal ribbon, either a General Service Medal or the War Medal, 1939–45. King's or Queen's Commendations for Brave Conduct or Valuable Service in the Air, in cases where no campaign or war medal was awarded, were worn on the breast in the position where an appropriate medal ribbon would have been worn, generally on the uniform tunic after any medal ribbons.

King's or Queen's Commendations in respect of bravery, granted to civilians for acts during or since the Second World War, are denoted by a silver emblem in the form of a spray of laurel leaves (this was originally a plastic oval badge). The emblem was worn on the ribbon of the Defence Medal (no. 185) for bravery in situations earning the medal. Where no medal was awarded, it was sewn directly on to the coat. For civilians the King's or Queen's Commendation for Valuable Service in the Air, during the Second World War and subsequently, consisted of an oval silver badge, worn on the coat below any medals or medal ribbons, or in civil airline uniform, on the panel of the left breast pocket.

Since 2003 all MiD, QCB, QCBA and QCVS emblems may be worn on UK, UN, NATO or EC/EU medal ribbons.

Mention in Despatches emblem 1914–20

Mention in Despatches emblem 1920–94

King's Commendation for Brave Conduct plastic badge for civilians (1942–45).

King's Commendation for Valuable Service in the Air silver badge for civilians (1942–93).

The emblems for Mentions and Commendations were revised in 1994, as shown in the table below.

FOR GALLANTRY			FOR VALUABLE SERVICE
IN ACTION WITH THE ENEMY (ALL ENVIRONMENTS)	NOT IN ACTION WITH THE ENEMY or OUT OF THEATRE (EXCEPT FLYING)	NOT IN ACTION WITH THE ENEMY or OUT OF THEATRE (FLYING)	IN-THEATRE BUT NOT IN ACTION WITH THE ENEMY
MENTION IN DESPATCHES	QUEEN'S COMMENDATION FOR BRAVERY	QUEEN'S COMMENDATION FOR BRAVERY IN THE AIR	QUEEN'S COMMENDATION FOR VALUABLE SERVICE
A single oak leaf in SILVER	A spray of laurel leaves in SILVER	A new emblem in SILVER	A spray of oak leaves in SILVER

CAMPAIGN
Medals

The evolution of medals struck to commemorate, and later to reward participants in, a battle or campaign was a very gradual process. The forerunner of the modern campaign medal was the Armada Medal, cast in gold or silver, which appears to have been awarded to naval officers and distinguished persons after the abortive Spanish invasion of 1588. The obverse bears a flattering portrait of Queen Elizabeth (thought to have been designed by Nicholas Hilliard, the celebrated miniaturist) with a Latin inscription signifying "enclosing the most precious treasure in the world" (i.e. the Queen herself). On the reverse, the safety of the kingdom is represented by a bay tree growing on a little island, immune from the flashes of lightning which seem to strike it. This medal, and a similar type depicting the Ark floating calmly on a stormy sea, bore loops at the top so that a chain or cord could be passed through it for suspension from the neck of the recipient.

The Civil War produced a number of gallantry medals, mentioned in the previous section; but in 1650 Parliament authorised a medal which was struck in silver, bronze or lead to celebrate Cromwell's miraculous victory over the Scots at Dunbar. This was the first medal granted to all the participants on the Parliamentary side, and not restricted to high-ranking officers, or given for individual acts of heroism.

The Dunbar Medal thus established several useful precedents, which were eventually to form the criteria of the campaign medal as we know it today. After this promising start, however, the pattern of medals and their issue were much more restrictive. Naval medals were struck in gold for award to admirals and captains during the First Dutch War (1650–53), while the battle of Culloden (1746) was marked by a medal portraying the "Butcher" Duke of Cumberland, and granted to officers who took part in the defeat of the Jacobites.

In the second half of the eighteenth century there were a number of medals, but these were of a private or semi-official nature. The Honourable East India Company took the lead in awarding medals to its troops. These medals were often struck in two sizes, and in gold as well as silver, for award to different ranks. The siege of Gibraltar (1779–83) was marked by an issue of medals to the defenders, but this was made on the initiative (and at the expense) of the garrison commanders, Generals Eliott and Picton, themselves.

During the French Revolutionary and Napoleonic Wars several medals were produced by private individuals for issue to combatants. Alexander Davison and Matthew Boulton were responsible for the medals granted to the officers and men who fought the battles of the Nile (1798) and Trafalgar (1805). Davison also produced a Trafalgar medal in pewter surrounded by a copper rim; it is recorded that the seamen who received it were so disgusted at the base metal that they threw it into the sea! At the same time, however, Government recognition was given to senior officers who had distinguished themselves in certain battles and engagements and a number of gold

medals were awarded. The events thus marked included the capture of Ceylon (1795–96) and the battles of Maida, Bagur and Palamos.

Towards the end of the Napoleonic Wars an Army Gold Medal was instituted in two sizes—large (generals) and small (field officers). Clasps for second and third battles and campaigns were added to the medal, but when an officer became eligible for a third clasp the medal was exchanged for a Gold Cross with the names of the four battles engraved on its arms. Clasps for subsequent campaigns were then added to the cross (the Duke of Wellington receiving the Gold Cross with nine clasps). A total of 163 crosses, 85 large and 599 small medals was awarded, so that, apart from their intrinsic value, these decorations command very high prices when they appear in the saleroom.

The first medal awarded to all ranks of the Army was the Waterloo Medal, issued in 1816 shortly after the battle which brought the Napoleonic Wars to an end. No action was taken to grant medals for the other campaigns in the Napoleonic Wars until 1847 when Military and Naval General Service Medals were awarded retrospectively to veterans who were then still alive. As applications were made, in some cases, in respect of campaigns more than fifty years earlier, it is hardly surprising that the number of medals awarded was comparatively small, while the number of clasps awarded for certain engagements was quite minute. The Military General Service Medal was restricted to land campaigns during the Peninsular War (1808–13), the American War (1812–14) and isolated actions in the West Indies, Egypt and Java, whereas the Naval GSM covered a far longer period, ranging from the capture of the French frigate La Cleopatra by HMS Nymphe in June 1793, to the naval blockade of the Syrian coast in 1840, during the British operations against Mehemet Ali. Thus Naval Medals with the clasp for Syria are relatively plentiful (7057 awarded) while in several cases clasps were awarded to one man alone, and in seven cases there were no claimants for clasps at all. It is worth bearing in mind that applications for the medals and clasps resulted mainly from the publicity given by printed advertisements and notices posted up all over the country. With the poor general standard of literacy prevalent at the time, many people who were entitled to the medals would have been quite unaware of their existence.

The Naming of Medals

The Military and Naval GSMs, with their multitudinous combinations of clasps, have long been popular with collectors, but the other campaign medals of the past century and a half have a strong following as well. With the exception of the stars and medals awarded during World War II, all British campaign medals have usually borne the name of the recipient and usually his (or her) number, rank and regiment, unit or ship as well. This brings a personal element into the study of medals which is lacking in most other branches of numismatics. The name on a medal is very important for two reasons. It is a means of testing the genuineness, not only of the medal itself, but its clasp combination, and secondly it enables the collector to link the medal not only with the man who earned it, but with his unit or formation, and thus plays a vital part in the development of naval or military history, if only a small part in most cases.

Much of the potential value of a medal depends on the man who won it, or the unit to which he belonged. To form a coherent collection as opposed to a random accumulation of medals, the collector would be well advised to specialise in some aspect of the subject, restricting his interests perhaps to one medal (the Naval GSM) or a single group (British campaigns in India), or to medals awarded to the men of a particular regiment. The information given on the rim or back of a medal is therefore important in helping to identify it and assign it to its correct place. Even this has to be qualified to some extent. Some regiments are more popular than others with collectors and much depends on the part, active or passive, played by a unit in a particular battle or campaign for which the medal was awarded. Then again, the combination of event with the corps or regiment of the recipient must also be considered.

At one extreme we find the Royal Regiment of Artillery living up to its motto Ubique (everywhere) by being represented in virtually every land action (and not a few naval actions, as witness the Atlantic Star worn by former Maritime Gunners), so that a comprehensive collection of medals awarded to the RA would be a formidable feat.

At the other extreme one finds odd detachments, sometimes consisting of one or two men only, seconded from a regiment for service with another unit. The Indian IGS medal with clasp Hazara 1891, was also issued to five men of the 1st Dragoon Guards, these men were part of the "Government Telegraph Department", Punjab Division, whose names appear on Roll WO100/75 page 269, together with other soldiers serving as Signallers from other regiments. Whereas a specimen of the IGS medal with this clasp is not hard to find named to a soldier in one of the Bengal units, it constitutes a major rarity when awarded to one of the "odd men" and its value is correspondingly high.

As the personal details given on a medal regarding the recipient are so important, it is necessary for the collector to verify two facts—that the person whose name is on the medal was actually present at the action for which either the medal or its clasps were awarded, and secondly, that the naming of the clasp and the attachment of the clasps is correct and not tampered with in any way. As regards the first, the National Archives at Kew, London, is a goldmine of information for all naval and military campaigns. Apart from despatches, reports and muster rolls covering the actions, there are the medal rolls compiled from the applications for medals and clasps. Transcriptions of the medal rolls are held by regimental museums and also by such bodies as the Military Historical Association and the Orders and Medals Research Society and, of course, many of these can be found on-line. Details of these and other clubs and societies devoted to medal collecting can be found in the later chapters.

The presence of a name on the roll does not mean that a medal or clasp was inevitably awarded; conversely authenticated medals are known to exist named to persons not listed on the medal roll. There are often divergences between the muster and medal rolls. Moreover, discrepancies in the spelling of recipients' names are not uncommon and clasps are sometimes found listed for regiments which were not even in existence when the battle was fought! This is explained, however, by the fact that a man may have been serving with one unit which took part in the campaign and subsequently transferred to another regiment. When claiming his medal he probably gave his present unit, rather than the one in which he was serving at the time of the action.

Unfortunately cases of medals having been tampered with are by no means rare, so it is necessary to be able to recognise evidence of fakery. A common device of the faker is to alter the name and personal details of the recipient and to substitute another name in order to enhance the medal's value. This is done simply by filing the inscription off the rim and adding a new one. In order to check for such alterations a similar medal of proven genuineness should be compared with a pair of fine callipers. Take the measurements at several points round the rim so that any unevenness should soon be apparent.

We cannot stress too much the importance of being closely familiar with the various styles of naming medals. Over the past 150 years an incredible variety of lettering—roman, italic, script, sans-serif, seriffed in all shapes and sizes—has been used at one time or another. In some cases the inscription was applied by impressing in raised relief; in others the inscription was punched in or engraved by hand. If a medal is normally impressed and you come across an engraved example you should immediately be on your guard. This is not an infallible test, however, as medals have been known with more than one style of naming, particularly if duplicates were issued at a much later date to replace medals lost or destroyed.

A rather more subtle approach was adopted by some fakers in respect of the Naval GSM. The three commonest clasps—Algiers (1362), Navarino (1137) and Syria (7057)—were awarded to many recipients possessing common names such as Jones or Smith which can be matched with recipients of some very rare clasps. In the case of the Naval GSM the ship on which the recipient served is not given, thus aiding the fraudulent substitution of clasps. It is necessary, therefore, to check the condition of clasps, even if the naming appears to be correct. Points to watch for are file or solder marks on the rivets which secure the clasps to each other and to the suspender of the medal. This test is not infallible as clasps do occasionally work loose if subject to constant wear (particularly if the recipient was a cavalryman, for obvious reasons). But clasps whose rivets appear to have been hammered should automatically be suspect, until a check of the medal rolls pass them as authentic. Examples of the earlier medals, particularly those awarded to officers may be found with unorthodox coupling. Major L. L. Gordon in his definitive British Battles and Medals, mentions a Naval GSM awarded to one of his ancestors with clasps for Guadaloupe and Anse la Barque in a large rectangular style which must have been unofficial. The medal is quite authentic, so it must be presumed that officers were allowed a certain degree of latitude in the manner in which they altered their medals.

Medals with clasps awarded for participation in subsequent engagements are invariably worth much more than the basic medal. In general, the greater number of clasps, the more valuable the medal, although, conversely, there are a few instances in which single-clasp medals are scarcer than twin-clasp medals. There is no short answer to this and individual rare clasps can enhance the value of an otherwise common medal out of all proportion. Thus the Naval GSM with clasp for Syria currently rates about £1000, but one of the two medals known to have been issued with the Acheron clasp of 1805 would easily rate 12 times as much. Again, relative value can only be determined by reference to all the circumstances of the award.

The person to whom a medal was issued has considerable bearing on its value. If the recipient belonged to a regiment which played a spectacular part in a battle, this generally rates a premium. The rank of the recipient also has some bearing; in general the higher the rank, the more valuable the medal. Medals to commissioned officers rate more than those awarded to NCOs and other ranks, and the medals of British servicemen rate more as a rule than those awarded to native troops. Medals granted to women usually command a relatively good premium. Another grim aspect is that medals issued to personnel who were wounded or killed in the campaign also rate more highly than those issued to servicemen who came through unscathed.

With the collector of British campaign medals the person to whom the medal was awarded tends to become almost as important as the medal itself. It is often not sufficient to collect the medal and leave it at that. The collector feels that he must investigate it and delve into the archives to find out all that he can about the recipient. Nowadays there is a plethora of information available on-line and the National Archives and regimental museums have already been mentioned, but do not overlook the usefulness of such reference tools

as the monumental Mormon International Genealogical Index (now on microfiche and available in good public libraries and county record offices). All of these should help you to flesh out the bare bones of the details given in the muster and medal rolls.

Medal Groups

Apart from the combination of clasps on a medal and the significance of the recipient, there is a third factor to be considered in assessing the value of medals, namely the relationship of one medal to another in a group awarded to one person. Just as the number of clasps on a medal is not in itself a significant factor, so also the number of medals in a group is not necessarily important per se. Groups of five or more medals, whose recipient can be identified, are by no means uncommon. For example, a fairly common five medal group would consist of 1914–15 Medal, War Medal and Victory Medal (for World War I) and the Defence Medal and War Medal (for World War II). Thousands of men served throughout the first war survived to do duty, in a less active role, during a part at least of the second, long enough to qualify for the latter pair of medals.

It should be noted that none of the medals awarded for service in World War II was named to the recipient, so that groups comprising such medals alone cannot be readily identified and are thus lacking in the interest possessed by those containing named medals. Six-medal groups for service in World War II are not uncommon, particularly the combination of 1939–45 Star, Africa Star, Italy Star, France and Germany Star, Defence Medal and War Medal awarded to Army personnel who served from any time up to late 1942 and took part in the campaigns of North Africa and Europe.

Conversely it would be possible for troops to have served over a longer period and seen more action and only been awarded the 1939–45 Star, Burma Star (with Pacific clasp) and the War Medal. Naval groups consisting of the 1939–45 Star, Atlantic Star (with clasp for France and Germany), Italy Star and War Medal are less common and therefore more desirable (with, of course, the rider that it must be possible to identify the recipient), while the most desirable of all is the three-medal group of 1939–45 Star (with Battle of Britain clasp), Air Crew Europe Star (with clasp for France and Germany) and the War Medal. Such a group, together with a Distinguished Flying Cross awarded to one of The Few, is a highly coveted set indeed, providing, as always, that one can prove its authenticity. In any event, the addition of a named medal to a World War II group (e.g. a long service award, a gallantry medal, or some other category of medal named to the recipient), together with supporting collateral material (citations, log-books, pay-books, service records, newspaper cuttings, etc), should help to establish the provenance of the group.

71. LOUISBURG MEDAL

Date: 1758.

Campaign: Canada (Seven Years War).

Branch of Service: British Army and Navy.

Ribbon: 32mm half yellow, half blue, although not originally intended for wear and therefore not fitted with suspension or ribbon.

Metals: Gold, silver or bronze.

Size: 42mm.

Description: (Obverse) the globe surrounded by allegorical figures of victory and flanked by servicemen; (reverse) burning ships in the harbour.

Comments: *More in the nature of a decoration, this medal was only given to certain recipients for acts of bravery or distinguished service in the capture in July 1758 of Louisburg in Canada during the Seven Years War. James Wolfe and Jeffrey Amherst commanded the land forces and Edward Boscawen the fleet.*

VALUE:

Gold	Rare
Silver	£4000–5000
Bronze	£1500–2000

72. CARIB WAR MEDAL

Date: 1773.

Campaign: Carib rebellion, St Vincent.

Branch of Service: Local militia or volunteers.

Ribbon: None.

Metal: Silver.

Size: 52mm.

Description: (Obverse) bust of George III in armour; (reverse) Britannia offering an olive branch to a defeated Carib, the date MDCCLXXIII in the exergue.

Comments: *The Legislative Assembly of St Vincent in the West Indies instituted this award to members of the militia and volunteers who served in the campaign of 1773 which put down a native rebellion that had been fomented by the French.*

VALUE:

Silver	£2000–2500

73. DECCAN MEDAL

Date: 1784.

Campaign: Western India and Gujerat 1778-84.

Branch of Service: HEIC forces.

Ribbon: Yellow cord.

Metals: Gold or silver.

Size: 40.5mm or 32mm.

Description: (Obverse) a rather languid Britannia with a trophy of arms, thrusting a laurel wreath towards a distant fort. (Reverse) an inscription in Farsi signifying "As coins are current in the world, so shall be the bravery and exploits of these heroes by whom the name of the victorious English nation was carried from Bengal to the Deccan. Presented in AH 1199 [1784] by the East India Company's Calcutta Government".

Comments: *The first medals struck by order of the Honourable East India Company were conferred on Indian troops for service in western India and Gujerat under the command of Warren Hastings. They were struck at Calcutta in two sizes; both gold and silver exist in the larger size but only silver medals in the smaller diameter.*

VALUE:

40.5mm gold	£4000–6000
40.5mm silver	£1800–2000
32mm silver	£1200–1400

74. DEFENCE OF GIBRALTAR

Eliott's medal   Picton's medal

Date: 1783.
Campaign: Siege of Gibraltar 1779–83.
Branch of Service: British and Hanoverian forces.
Ribbon: None.
Metal: Silver.
Size: 49mm (Eliott) and 59mm (Picton) .
Description: Eliott's medal was confined to the Hanoverian troops, hence the reverse inscribed
BRUDERSCHAFT (German for "brotherhood") above a wreath containing the names of the three
Hanoverian commanders and General Eliott. The obverse, by Lewis Pingo, shows a view of the Rock and
the naval attack of 13 September 1782 which was the climax of the siege. Picton's medal, awarded to the
British forces, has a larger than usual diameter, with a map of the Rock on the obverse and a 22-line text—the
most verbose British medal—above a recumbent lion clutching a shield bearing the castle and key emblem of
Gibraltar on the reverse.
Comments: *Several medals of a private nature were struck to commemorate the defence of Gibraltar during the Franco-
Spanish siege of 1779–83, but those most commonly encountered are these silver medals which were provided by George
Augustus Eliott and Sir Thomas Picton, the military commanders.*

VALUE:
Eliott medal	£700–1000
Picton medal	£1000–1200

75. MYSORE MEDAL

Date: 1792.
Campaign: Mysore 1790-92.
Branch of Service: HEIC forces.
Ribbon: Yellow cord.
Metal: Gold or silver.
Size: 43mm or 38mm.
Description: (Obverse) a sepoy of the HEIC Army holding British and Company flags over a trophy of arms with the fortress of Seringapatam in the background; (reverse) a bilingual inscription (in English and Farsi). The medal has a ring for suspension round the neck by a cord.
Comments: *Indian officers and men who served under Marquis Cornwallis and Generals Abercromby and Meadows received this medal for service in the campaign which brought about the downfall of Tippoo Sultan of Mysore.*

VALUE:

43mm gold (subadars)	£15,000–20,000
43mm silver (jemadars)	£2500–2800
38mm silver (other ranks)	£1500–1800

76. ST VINCENTS BLACK CORPS MEDAL

Date: 1795.
Campaign: Carib rebellion 1795.
Branch of Service: Local militia volunteers.
Ribbon: None.
Metal: Bronze.
Size: 48.5mm.
Description: (Obverse) the winged figure of Victory brandishing a sword over a fallen foe who has abandoned his musket; (reverse) native holding musket and bayonet, BOLD LOYAL OBEDIENT around and H.G.FEC. in exergue.
Comments: *Awarded to the officers and NCOs of the Corps of Natives raised by Major Seton from among the island's slaves for service against the rebellious Caribs and French forces.*

VALUE:

Bronze	£1000–1200

77. CAPTURE OF CEYLON MEDAL

Date: 1796.
Campaign: Ceylon 1795.
Branch of Service: HEIC forces.
Ribbon: Yellow cord.
Metal: Gold or silver.
Size: 50mm.
Description: The plain design has an English inscription on the obverse, and the Farsi equivalent on the reverse.
Comments: *Awarded for service in the capture of Ceylon (Sri Lanka) from the Dutch during the French Revolutionary Wars. It is generally believed that the gold medals were awarded to Captains Barton and Clarke while the silver medals went to the native gunners of the Bengal Artillery.*

VALUE:

Gold (2)	—	
Silver (121)	£1500–2000 (original striking)	£400–500 (later striking)

78. DAVISON'S NILE MEDAL

Date: 1798.
Campaign: Battle of the Nile 1798.
Branch of Service: Royal Navy.
Ribbon: None, but unofficially 32mm, deep navy blue.
Metal: Gold, silver, gilt-bronze and bronze.
Size: 47mm.
Description: (Obverse) Peace caressing a shield decorated with the portrait of Horatio Nelson; (reverse) the British fleet at Aboukir Bay. The edge bears the lettering "A TRIBUTE OF REGARD FROM ALEX^r DAVISON, ESQ^r ST JAMES'S SQUARE=".
Comments: *Nelson's victory at the mouth of the Nile on 1 August 1798 was celebrated in a novel manner by his prize agent, Alexander Davison, whose name and London address appear in the edge inscription of the medal designed by Kuchler. Originally issued without a suspender, many recipients added a ring to enable the medal to be worn. Admiral Nelson's medal was stolen in 1900 and is believed to have been melted down. Prices quoted below are for unnamed specimens, contemporary engraved medals are usually worth about twice as much.*

VALUE:			
Gold (Nelson and his captains)	£8000–10,000	**Gilt-bronze (petty officers)**	£550–650
Silver (junior officers)	£1500–2000	**Bronze (ratings)**	£300–400

79. SERINGAPATAM MEDAL

Date: 1808.
Campaign: Seringapatam, India, 1799.
Branch of Service: HEIC forces.
Ribbon: 38mm gold.
Metal: Gold, silver-gilt, silver, bronze and pewter.
Size: 48mm or 45mm.
Description: (Obverse) the British lion defeating Tiger of Mysore (Tippoo Sultan) with the date of the capture of the fortress IV MAY MDCCXCIX (1799) in the exergue; (reverse) the assault on Seringapatam.
Comments: *The British and native troops who took part in the renewed campaign against Tippoo Sultan were awarded this medal in 1808 in various metals without suspension (a number of different types of suspenders and rings were subsequently fitted by individual recipients). The medal was designed by Kuchler and struck in England (48mm) and Calcutta, the latter version being slightly smaller (45mm). There are several different strikings of these medals.*

VALUE:

British Mint	
Gold 48mm (30)	£6500–8500
Silver-gilt 48mm (185)	£1250–1750
Silver 48mm (850)	£1000–1500
Bronze 48mm (5000)	£450–550
Pewter 48mm (45,000)	£350–450
Calcutta Mint	
Gold 45mm (83)	£3500–4500
Silver 45mm (2786)	£850–1000
Miniature	Silver £230–290

80. EARL ST. VINCENT'S MEDAL

Date: 1800.   **Campaign:** Mediterranean.
Branch of Service: Royal Navy.
Ribbon: None.
Metal: Gold or silver.   **Size:** 48mm
Description: (Obverse) left-facing bust of the Earl in Admiral's uniform; (reverse) a sailor and marine.
Comments: *A private medal presented by Earl St Vincent, when he struck his flag and came ashore in 1800, to the petty officers and men of his flagship* Ville de Paris *as a token of appreciation to his old shipmates. Contemporary engraved and named pieces with researched provenance are worth at least twice as much as unnamed specimens.*

VALUE:
Gold	£5500–6500
Silver	£750–850

81. EGYPT MEDAL 1801

Date: 1801.
Campaign: Egypt 1801.
Branch of Service: HEIC forces.
Ribbon: Yellow cord.
Metal: Gold or silver.
Size: 48mm.
Description: (Obverse) a sepoy holding a Union Jack, with an encampment in the background. A four-line Farsi text occupies the exergue; (reverse) a warship and the Pyramids.
Comments: *Issued by the Honourable East India Company to British and Indian troops in the Company's service who took part in the conquest of Egypt under Generals Baird and Abercromby.*

VALUE:
Gold (16)	—	
Silver (2200)	£1500–1650 (original striking)	£400–500 (later striking)

82. SULTAN'S MEDAL FOR EGYPT

Date: 1801.

Campaign: Egypt 1801.

Branch of Service: British forces.

Ribbon: The gold medals were originally suspended by gold hook and chain as shown. The silver medals were hung from a sand-coloured ribbon.

Metals: Gold or silver.

Size: Various (see below).

Description: The very thin discs have an elaborate arabesque border enclosing the *toughra* or sign manual of the Sultan.

Comments: *This medal was conferred by Sultan Selim III of Turkey on the British officers and NCOs who took part in the campaign against the French. It was produced in five gold versions for award to different ranks of commissioned officers, as well as one in silver for award to sergeants and corporals.*

VALUE:

Gold 54mm studded with jewels	—
Gold 54mm plain (less than 100 issued)	£6500–8500
Gold 48mm	£4500–5500
Gold 43mm	£4000–5000
Gold 36mm	£4000–4500
Silver 36mm	£2500–3500

Miniature	
Gold	£175–230
Silver	£125–175

83. HIGHLAND SOCIETY'S MEDAL FOR EGYPT 1801

Date: 1801.

Campaign: Egypt 1801.

Branch of Service: British forces.

Ribbon: None.

Metals: Gold, silver and bronze.

Size: 49mm.

Description: The medal was designed by Pidgeon. (Obverse) the right-facing bust of General Sir Ralph Abercromby, with a Latin inscription alluding to his death in Egypt; (reverse) a Highlander in combat with the Gaelic inscription NA FIR A CHOISIN BUAIDH SAN EPHAIT(These are the heroes who achieved victory in Egypt) and the date 21 MAR 1801. On the edge is the inscription "On choumun Chaeleach D'on Fhreiceadan Dubh Na XLII RT" (From the London Highland Society to the Black Watch or 42nd Regt.).

Comments: *The Highland and Agricultural Society (now Royal) was founded in 1784 to promote the development of agriculture in Scotland generally and the Highlands in particular. General Abercromby (born at Tullibody, 1734) commanded the British expedition to Egypt, and the landing at Aboukir Bay on 2 March 1801 in the face of strenuous French opposition, is justly regarded as one of the most brilliant and daring exploits of all time. The French made a surprise attack on the British camp on the night of 21 March and Abercromby was struck by a ricochet; he died aboard the flagship seven days later. Medals in gold were presented to the Prince Regent and Abercromby's sons, but silver and bronze medals were later struck and awarded to senior officers of the expedition as well as soldiers who had distinguished themselves in the campaign.*

VALUE:

Gold	—
Silver	£650–850
Bronze	£250–300

84. BOULTON'S TRAFALGAR MEDAL

Date: 1805.
Campaign: Battle of Trafalgar 1805.
Branch of Service: Royal Navy.
Ribbon: None, but unofficially 32mm navy blue (originally issued without suspension).
Metals: Gold, silver, white metal, gilt-bronze or bronze.
Size: 48mm.
Description: (Obverse) bust of Nelson; (reverse) a battle scene.
Comments: *Matthew Boulton of the Soho Mint, Birmingham, originally struck about 15,000 examples of this medal in white metal on his own initiative for presentation to the survivors of the battle of Trafalgar, but bronze and gilt-bronze specimens also exist. It was subsequently restruck on at least two occasions, the first and second strikings have the inscription impressed in large capitals around the rim TO THE HEROES OF TRAFALGAR FROM M:BOULTON, the later having the inscription omitted. As the original dies were used for each striking, they had to be polished before reuse, so the fine detail on Nelson's uniform and in the battle scene is less pronounced in the second and subsequent strikings. Examples of the original striking can sometimes be found engraved in various styles, but great care should be taken over checking the authenticity of such pieces. All gold specimens are restrikes. Silver medals were later ordered from Boulton's successors by officers who wished to have a medal to form a group with the 1848 NGS.*

VALUE:

Gold (c. 1905)	£4000–5000	Gilt-bronze	£650–800
Silver (1820–50)	£1500	Bronze	£250–500
White metal	£450–600		

NB These prices are based on medals issued from the original striking and are dependent on attribution and generally in EF to Mint condition.

85. DAVISON'S TRAFALGAR MEDAL

Date: 1805.
Campaign: Battle of Trafalgar 1805.
Branch of Service: Royal Navy.
Ribbon: None, but unofficially 32mm navy blue.
Metal: Pewter with a copper rim.
Size: 52mm.
Description: (Obverse) bust of Nelson; (reverse) a man-of-war with an appropriate biblical quotation from Exodus "The Lord is a Man-of-War".
Comments: *Alexander Davison, Nelson's prize agent, had this medal struck for award to the ratings of HMS Victory who took part in the battle.*

VALUE: £1750-2000

86. CAPTURE OF RODRIGUEZ, ISLE OF BOURBON AND ISLE OF FRANCE

Date: 1810.
Campaign: Indian Ocean 1809-10.
Branch of Service: HEIC forces.
Ribbon: Yellow cord.
Metal: Gold or silver.
Size: 49mm.
Description: (Obverse) a sepoy in front of a cannon with the Union Jack; (reverse) a wreath with inscriptions in English and Farsi.
Comments: *The East India Company awarded this medal to native troops of the Bengal and Bombay Armies for the capture of three French islands in the Indian Ocean (the latter two being better known today as Mauritius and Reunion) between July 1809 and December 1810.*

VALUE:	Original striking	Later striking
Gold (50)	£8500–10,000	—
Silver (2200)	£2000–2500	£550–650

87. BAGUR AND PALAMOS MEDAL

Date: 1811.
Campaign: Peninsular War 1810.
Branch of Service: Royal Navy.
Ribbon: Red with yellow edges (illustration at right has faded ribbon).
Metal: Gold or silver. **Size:** 45mm.
Description: (Obverse) the conjoined crowned shields of Britain and Spain in a wreath with ALIANZA ETERNA (eternal alliance) round the foot; (reverse) inscription in Spanish GRATITUDE OF SPAIN TO THE BRAVE BRITISH AT BAGUR 10 SEPT. 1810, PALAMOS 14 SEPT. 1810.
Comments: *Awarded by the Captain General of Catalonia to General Sir Charles Doyle and the Royal Marines and a limited number of officers and seamen from the British frigate* Cambrian, *for two actions on the coast of Catalonia in September 1810. Only awarded to those who actually went ashore: General Doyle, the Royal Marines, Captain Francis Fane and three of his officers received the medal for their participation in the attack on Bagur, while Lieutenant Benjamin Baynton and the launch crew received the medal for their participation at Palamós. Awarded in gold to officers and silver to other ranks.*

VALUE: Gold (8) £6500–10,000 Silver (72+) £2500–3000

88. JAVA MEDAL

Date: 1811.
Campaign: Java 1811.
Branch of Service: HEIC forces.
Ribbon: Yellow cord.
Metals: Gold or silver.
Size: 49mm.
Description: (Obverse) the assault on Fort Cornelis; (reverse) inscriptions in English and Farsi.
Comments: *Awarded by the HEIC for the seizure of Java from the Dutch. The 750 British officers and men who took part in the operation were not only awarded this medal but were eligible for the Military GSM with Java clasp, issued 38 years later. Senior officers of the Company were given the gold medal, while junior officers, NCOs and sepoys received the silver version.*

VALUE:	Original striking	Later striking
Gold (133)	£8000–10,000	£3000–3500
Silver (6519)	£1600–1800	£500–600

89. NEPAL MEDAL

Date: 1816.
Campaign: Nepal 1814-16.
Branch of Service: HEIC native troops.
Ribbon: Yellow cord.
Metal: Silver.
Size: 51mm.
Description: (Obverse) a fortified mountain-top with a cannon in the foreground; (reverse) Farsi inscription.
Comments: *This medal marked the campaign to pacify Nepal led by Generals Marley, Ochterlony and Gillespie (the last named being killed in action). At the conclusion of the war Ochterlony began recruiting Gurkha mercenaries, a policy which has continued in the British Army to this day. The clasp "Nepaul" was granted with the Army of India Medal to British forces in 1851.*

VALUE: Original striking £1800–2000   Later striking £450–500
(as illustrated)

90. CEYLON MEDAL

Date: 1818.
Campaign: Ceylon (Sri Lanka) 1818.
Branch of Service: British and HEIC forces.
Ribbon: 38mm deep navy blue.
Metal: Gold or silver.
Size: 35mm.
Description: The very plain design has "Ceylon 1818" within a wreath (obverse) and REWARD OF MERIT at top and bottom of the reverse, the personal details being engraved in the centre.
Comments: *Awarded by the Ceylon government for gallant conduct during the Kandian rebellion. Only selected officers and men of the 19th, 73rd and 83rd Foot, the 1st and 2nd Ceylon Regiments and 7th, 15th and 18th Madras Native Infantry received this medal.*

VALUE:

Gold (2)	—
Silver (45)	£2000–3000

91. BURMA MEDAL

Date: 1826.
Campaign: Burma 1824-26.
Branch of Service: HEIC native forces.
Ribbon: 38mm crimson edged with navy blue.
Metals: Gold or silver.
Size: 39mm.
Description: (Obverse) the Burmese elephant kneeling in submission before the British lion; (reverse) the epic assault on Rangoon by the Irrawaddy Flotilla.
Comments: *Granted to native officers and men who participated in the campaign for the subjugation of Burma. This was the first of the HEIC campaign medals in what was to become a standard 1.5 inch (38mm) diameter. The medal was fitted with a large steel ring for suspension and issued unnamed. British troops in this campaign were belatedly (1851) given the clasp "Ava" to the Army of India Medal.*

VALUE:

		Miniature
Gold (750)	£3500–4500	—
Silver-gilt	£1500–1800	—
Silver (24,000)	£800–1200	£300–350

92. COORG MEDAL

Date: 1837.
Campaign: Coorg rebellion 1837.
Branch of Service: HEIC loyal Coorg forces.
Ribbon: Yellow cord.
Metals: Gold, silver or bronze.
Size: 50mm.
Description: (Obverse) a Coorg holding a musket, with kukri upraised; (reverse) weapons in a wreath with the inscription FOR DISTINGUISHED CONDUCT AND LOYALTY TO THE BRITISH GOVERNMENT COORG APRIL 1837, the equivalent in Canarese appearing on the obverse.
Comments: *Native troops who remained loyal during the Canara rebellion of April-May 1837 were awarded this medal by the HEIC the following August. Bronze specimens were also struck but not officially issued and may have been restrikes or later copies. Bronzed and silvered electrotype copies are also known.*

VALUE:	Original striking	Later striking
Gold (44)	£5000–8000	—
Silver (300)	£1500–1800	£400–500
Bronze	£300–400	—

93. NAVAL GOLD MEDAL

Date: 1795.
Campaign: Naval actions 1795-1815.
Branch of Service: Royal Navy.
Ribbon: 44mm white with broad dark blue edges.
Metal: Gold.
Size: 51mm and 38mm.
Description: The medals were glazed on both sides and individually engraved on the reverse with the name of the recipient and details of the engagement in a wreath of laurel and oak leaves. (Obverse) the winged figure of Victory bestowing a laurel wreath on the head of Britannia standing in the prow of a galley with a Union Jack shield behind her, her right foot on a helmet, her left hand holding a spear.
Comments: *Instituted in 1795, a year after Lord Howe's naval victory on "the glorious First of June", this medal was awarded continually till 1815 when the Order of the Bath was expanded into three classes. Large medals were awarded to admirals and small medals went to captains. As medals were awarded for separate actions it was possible for officers to wear more than one; Lord Nelson himself had three. Two miniatures are recorded and would probably fetch at least £1000 if they came onto the market.*

VALUE:

Large medal (22)	From £80,000	
Small medal (117)	From £50,000	*Miniature £350–450*

94. NAVAL GENERAL SERVICE MEDAL

Date: 1847.

Campaign: Naval battles and boat actions 1793-1840.

Branch of Service: Royal Navy.

Ribbon: 32mm white with dark blue edges.

Metal: Silver.

Size: 36mm.

Description: (Obverse) the Young Head profile of Queen Victoria by William Wyon; (reverse) Britannia with her trident seated on a sea horse.

Clasps: No fewer than 230 different clasps for major battles, minor engagements, cutting-out operations and boat service were authorised. These either have the name or date of the action, the name of a ship capturing or defeating an enemy vessel, or the words BOAT SERVICE followed by a date. No fewer than 20,933 medals were awarded but most of them had a single clasp. Multi-clasp medals are worth very considerably more. The greatest number of clasps to a single medal was seven (three awards made); four medals had six clasps and 26 medals had five clasps. For reasons of space only those clasps which are met with fairly often are listed below. At the other end of the scale it should be noted that only one recipient claimed the clasps for *Hussar* (17 May 1795), *Dido* (24 June 1795), *Spider* (25 August 1795), *Espoir* (7 August 1798), *Viper* (26 December 1799), *Loire* (5 February 1800), *Louisa* (28 October 1807), *Carrier* (4 November 1807), *Superieure* (10 February 1809), *Growler* (22 May 1812) and the boat actions of 15 March 1793, 4 November 1803, 4 November 1810 and 3-6 September 1814. In several cases no claimants came forward at all. The numbers of clasps awarded are not an accurate guide to value, as some actions are rated more highly than others, and clasps associated with actions in the War of 1812 have a very strong following in the USA as well as Britain. Clasps for famous battles, such as Trafalgar, likewise command a high premium out of all proportion to the number of clasps awarded. A medal to HMS *Victory* would be worth in excess of £15,000.

Comments: *Instituted in 1847 and issued to surviving claimants in 1848, this medal was originally intended to cover naval engagements of the French Revolutionary and Napoleonic Wars (1793-1815) but was almost immediately extended to cover all naval actions of a more recent date, down to the expedition to Syria in 1840. It was fitted with a straight suspender.*

VALUE (for the most commonly encountered clasps):

v.	1 June 1794 (583)	£3500–4500
ix.	14 March 1795 (114)	£3500–4500
xv.	23 June 1795 (200)	£3500–4500
xxxi.	St Vincent (364)	£3500–4500
xxxiv.	Camperdown (336)	£3500–4500
xxxvi.	Mars 21 April 1798 (26)	£6500–8500
xxxviii.	Lion 15 July 1798 (23)	£6500–8500
xxxix.	Nile (351)	£3500–4000
xli.	12 Octr 1798 (79)	£4000–5000
xlv.	Acre 30 May 1799 (50)	£4500–5500
lxii.	Egypt (618)	£2000–2500
lxiii.	Copenhagen (545)	£4500–6000
lxv.	Gut of Gibraltar (144)	£4000–5000
lxxv.	Trafalgar (1,710)	£7500–8500
lxxvi.	4 Novr 1805 (297)	£3000–4000
lxxvii.	St Domingo (406)	£3500–4500
lxxix.	London 13 March 1806 (27)	£5000–6000
lxxxv.	Curacao 1 Jany 1807 (67)	£4000–5000
xcvii.	Stately 22 March 1808 (31)	£5000–6000
cxiii.	Martinique (506)	£2000–2500
cxvii.	Basque Roads (551)	£3000–3500

cxxviii.	Guadaloupe (484)	£1500–2000
cxli.	Lissa (124)	£3000–3500
cxlvi.	Java (695)	£2000–2500
clxi.	Shannon wh Chesapeake (42)	£6000–7000
clxiii.	St Sebastian (288)	£4000–5000
clxv.	Gluckstadt 5 Jany 1814 (45)	£5000–6500
clxxvi.	Gaieta 24 July 1815 (89)	£4500–5000
clxxvii.	Algiers (1,362)	£1500–2500
clxxviii.	Navarino (1,137)	£1500–2500
clxxix.	Syria (7,057)	£1000–1500

Boat Service

cxcii.	16 July 1806 (52)	£3500–4500
ccvi.	1 Novr 1809 (110)	£3000–4000
ccx.	28 June 1810 (27)	£4500–5500
ccxxiii.	29 Sepr 1812 (25)	£4500–5500
ccxxvii.	Ap and May 1813 (51)	£4500–5500
ccxxviii.	2 May 1813 (48)	£4500–5500
ccxxix.	April 1814 (24)	£5000–6500
ccxxx.	24 May 1814 (14)	£6000–7500
ccxxxiii.	14 Decr 1814 (205)	£2500–3000

Miniature

Without clasp   £115–175, for each clasp add £75+ depending on the action.

Below are listed all of the clasps authorised for wear on the Naval General Service Medal. As they were not issued until some years after the events, in some cases very few were ever claimed and in some instances there were no claimants at all. The numbers issued are indicated in brackets.

i.	Nymphe 18 June 1793 (4)		lxiv.	Speedy 6 May 1801 (7)
ii.	Crescent 20 Octr 1793 (12)		lxv.	Gut of Gibraltar 12 July 1801 (144)
iii.	Zebra 17 March1794 (2)		lxvi.	Sylph 28 Septr 1801 (2)
iv.	Carysfort 29 May 1794 (0)		lxvii.	Pasley 28 Octr 1801 (4)
v.	1 June 1794 (583)		lxviii.	Scorpion 31 March 1804 (4)
vi.	Romney 17 June 1794 (2)		lxix.	Beaver 31 March 1804 (0)
vii.	Blanche 4 Jany 1795 (5)		lxx.	Centurion 18 Septr 1804 (12)
viii.	Lively 13 March 1795 (6)		lxxi.	Arrow 3 Feby 1805 (8)
ix.	14 March 1795 (114)		lxxii.	Acheron 3 Feby 1805 (2)
x.	Astraea 10 April 1795 (2)		lxxiii.	San Fiorenzo 14 Feby 1805 (13)
xi.	Thetis 17 May 1795 (2)		lxxiv.	Phoenix 10 Aug 1805 (29)
xii.	Hussar 17 May 1795 (1)		lxxv.	Trafalgar (1,710)
xiii.	Mosquito 9 June 1795 (0)		lxxvi.	4 Novr 1805 (297)
xiv.	17 June 1795 (42)		lxxvii.	St. Domingo (406)
xv.	23 June 1795 (200)		lxxviii.	Amazon 13 March 1806 (30)
xvi.	Dido 24 June 1795 (1)		lxxix.	London 13 March 1806 (27)
xvii.	Lowestoffe 24 June 1795 (6)		lxxx.	Pique 26 March 1806 (8)
xviii.	Spider 25 August 1795 (1)		lxxxi.	Sirius 17 April 1806 (20)
xix.	Port Spergui (4)		lxxxii.	Blanche 19 July 1806 (22)
xx.	Indefatigable 20 April 1796 (8)		lxxxiii.	Arethusa 23 Aug 1806 (17)
xxi.	Unicorn 8 June 1796 (4)		lxxxiv.	Anson 23 Aug 1806 (11)
xxii.	Santa Margarita 8 June 1796 (3)		lxxxv.	Curacoa 1 Jany 1807 (67)
xxiii.	Southampton 9 June 1796 (8)		lxxxvi.	Pickle 3 Jany 1807 (2)
xxiv.	Dryad 13 June 1796 (6)		lxxxvii.	Hydra 6 Aug 1807 (12)
xxv.	Terpsichore 13 Oct 1796 (3)		lxxxviii.	Comus 15 Aug 1807 (9)
xxvi.	Lapwing 3 Decr 1796 (2)		lxxxix.	Louisa 28 Octr 1807 (1)
xxvii.	Minerve 19 Decr 1796 (4)		xc.	Carrier 4 Novr 1807 (1)
xxviii.	Blanche 19 Decr 1796 (4)		xci.	Ann 24 Novr 1807 (0)
xxix.	Indefatigable 13 Jany 1797 (8)		xcii.	Sappho 2 March 1808 (4)
xxx.	Amazon 13 Jany 1797 (6)		xciii.	San Fiorenzo 8 March 1808 (17)
xxxi.	St Vincent (364)		xciv.	Emerald 13 March 1808 (10)
xxxii.	San Fiorenzo 8 March 1797 (8)		xcv.	Childers 14 March 1808 (4)
xxxiii.	Nymphe 8 March 1797 (5)		xcvi.	Nassau 22 March 1808 (31)
xxxiv.	Camperdown (336)		xcvii.	Stately 22 March 1808 (31)
xxxv.	Phoebe 21 Decr 1797 (5)		xcviii.	Off Rota 4 April 1808 (19)
xxxvi.	Mars 21 April 1798 (26)		xcix.	Grasshopper 24 April 1808 (7)
xxxvii.	Isle St. Marcou (3)		c.	Rapid 24 April 1808 (1)
xxxviii.	Lion 15 July 1798 (23)		ci.	Redwing 7 May 1808 (7)
xxxix.	Nile (351)		cii.	Virginie 19 May 1808 (21)
xl.	Espoir 7 Aug 1798 (1)		ciii.	Redwing 31 May 1808 (7)
xli.	12 Octr 1798 (79)		civ.	Seahorse wh Badere Zaffer (32)
xlii.	Fisgard 20 Octr 1798 (9)		cv.	Comet 11 Aug 1808 (4)
xliii.	Sybille 28 Feby 1799 (12)		cvi.	Centaur 26 Aug 1808 (42)
xliv.	Telegraph 18 March 1799 (0)		cvii.	Implacable 26 Aug 1808 (44)
xlv.	Acre 30 May 1799 (50)		cviii.	Cruizer 1 Novr 1808 (4)
xlvi.	Schiermonnikoog 12 Aug 1799 (9)		cix.	Amethyst wh Thetis (31)
xlvii.	Arrow 13 Sept 1799 (2)		cx.	Off the Pearl Rock 13 Decr 1808 (16)
xlviii.	Wolverine 13 Sept 1799 (0)		cxi.	Onyx 1 Jany 1809 (5)
xlix.	Surprise wh Hermione (7)		cxii.	Confiance 14 Jany 1809 (8)
l.	Speedy 6 Novr 1799 (3)		cxiii.	Martinique (506)
li.	Courier 22 Novr 1799 (3)		cxiv.	Horatio 10 Feby 1809 (13)
lii.	Viper 26 Decr 1799 (2)		cxv.	Supérieure 10 Feby 1809 (1)
liv.	Harpy 5 Feby 1800 (4)		cxvi.	Amethyst 5 April 1809 (27)
lv.	Fairy 5 Feby 1800 (4)		cxvii.	Basque Roads 1809 (551)
lvi.	Peterel 21 March 1800 (2)		cxviii.	Recruit 17 June 1809 (7)
lvii.	Penelope 30 March 1800 (11)		cxix.	Pompee 17 June 1809 (47)
lviii.	Vinciego 30 March 1800 (2)		cxx.	Castor 17 June 1809 (13)
lix.	Capture of the Désirée (24)		cxxi.	Cyane 25 and 27 June 1809 (5)
lx.	Seine 20 August 1800 (7)		cxxii.	L'Espoir 25 and 27 June 1809 (5)
lxi.	Phoebe 19 Feby 1801 (6)		cxxiii.	Bonne Citoyenne wh Furieuse (12)
lxii.	Egypt (618)		cxxiv.	Diana 11 Septr 1809 (8)
lxiii.	Copenhagen 1801 (545)		cxxv.	Anse la Barque 18 Decr 1809 (51)

cxxvi.	Cherokee 10 Jany 1810 (4)		cliii.	Griffon 27 March 1812 (3)
cxxvii.	Scorpion 12 Jany 1810 (8)		cliv.	Northumberland 22 May 1812 (63)
cxxviii.	Guadaloupe (484)		clv.	Growler 22 May 1812 (1)
cxxix.	Thistle 10 Feby 1810 (0)		clvi.	Malaga 29 May 1812 (18) (the date should have been 29 April 1812)
cxxx.	Surly 24 April 1810 (1)			
cxxxi.	Firm 24 April 1810 (1)		clvii.	Off Mardoe 6 July 1812 (47)
cxxxii.	Sylvia 26 April 1810 (1)		clviii.	Sealark 21 July 1812 (4)
cxxxiii.	Spartan 3 May 1810 (30)		clix.	Royalist 29 Decr 1812 (4)
cxxxiv.	Royalist May and June 1810 (3)		clx.	Weasel 22 April 1813 (8)
cxxxv.	Amanthea 25 July 1810 (23)		clxi.	Shannon wh Chesapeake (42)
cxxxvi.	Banda Neira (68)		clxii.	Pelican 14 Aug 1813 (4)
cxxxvii.	Staunch 18 Septr 1810 (2)		clxiii.	St. Sebastian (288)
cxxxviii.	Otter 18 Septr 1810 (8)		clxiv.	Thunder 9 Octr 1813 (9)
cxxxix.	Boadicea 18 Septr 1810 (15)		clxv.	Gluckstadt 5 Jany 1814 (45)
cxl.	Briseis 14 Octr 1810 (2)		clxvi.	Venerable 16 Jany 1814 (42)
cxli.	Lissa (124)		clxix.	Cyane 16 Jany 1814 (7)
cxlii.	Anholt 27 March 1811 (40)		clxx.	Eurotas 25 Feby 1814 (32)
cxliii.	Arrow 6 April 1811 (0)		clxxi.	Hebrus wh L'Etoile (40)
cxliv.	Off Tamatave 20 May 1811 (87)		clxxii.	Phoebe 28 March 1814 (36)
cxlv.	Hawke 18 Aug 1811 (6)		clxxiii.	Cherub 28 March 1814 (7)
cxlvi.	Java (695)		clxxiv.	The Potomac 17 Aug 1814 (108)
cxlvii.	Skylark 11 Novr 1811 (4)		clxxv.	Endymion wh President (58)
cxlviii.	Locust 11 Novr 1811 (2)		clxxvi.	Gaieta 24 July 1815 (89)
cxlix.	Pelagosa 29 Novr 1811 (74)		clxxvii.	Algiers (1,362)
cl.	Victorious wh Rivoli (67)		clxxviii.	Navarino (1,137)
cli.	Weasel 22 Feby 1812 (6)		clxxix.	Syria (7,057)
clii.	Rosario 27 March 1812 (7)			

BOAT SERVICE

These clasps have the words BOAT SERVICE separating the month and the years of the dates. They were only awarded for actions which culminated in an officer or the senior member present being promoted.

clxxx.	15 March 1793 (1)		ccvii.	13 Decr 1809 (9)
clxxxi.	17 March 1794 (29)		ccviii.	13 Feby 1810 (20)
clxxxii.	29 May 1797 (3)		ccix.	1 May 1810 (15)
clxxxiii.	9 June 1799 (4)		ccx.	28 June 1810 (27)
clxxxiv.	20 Decr 1799 (3)		ccxi.	27 Sept 1810 (36)
clxxxv.	29 July 1800 (4)		ccxii.	4 Novr 1810 (1)
clxxxvi.	29 Aug 1800 (25)		ccxiii.	23 Novr 1810 (42)
clxxxvii.	27 Octr 1800 (5)		ccxiv.	24 Decr 1810 (6)
clxxxviii.	21 July 1801 (7)		ccxv.	4 May 1811 (10)
clxxxix.	27 June 1803 (5)		ccxvi.	30 July 1811 (4)
cxc.	4 Novr 1803 (2)		ccxvii.	2 Aug 1811 (9)
cxci.	4 Feby 1804 (11)		ccxviii.	20 Sept 1811 (6)
cxcii.	4 June 1805 (10)		ccxix.	4 Decr 1811 (19)
cxciii.	16 July 1806 (52)		ccxx.	4 April 1812 (4)
cxciv.	2 Jan 1807 (3)		ccxxi.	1st Sept 1812 (21)
cxcv.	21 Jan 1807 (8)		ccxxii.	17 Sept 1812 (11) (Bars are known dated 17 Decr 1812 in error)
cxcvi.	19 April 1807 (0)			
cxcvii.	13 Feby 1808 (2)		ccxxiii.	29 Sept 1812 (25)
cxcviii.	10 July 1808 (8)		ccxxiv.	6 Jany 1813 (25)
cxcix.	11 Aug 1808 (17)		ccxxv.	21 March 1813 (3)
cc.	28 Novr 1808 (2)		ccxxvi.	29 April 1813 (2)
cc.	7 July 1809 (35)		ccxxvii.	Ap and May 1813 (51)
cci.	14 July 1809 (7)		ccxxviii.	2 May 1813 (48)
ccii.	25 July 1809 (36)		ccxxix.	8 April 1814 (24)
cciii.	27 July 1809 (10)		ccxxx.	24 May 1814 (14)
cciv.	29 July 1809 (11)		ccxxxi.	Aug and Septr 1814 (1)
ccv.	28 Aug 1809 (15)		ccxxxii.	3 and 6 Septr 1814 (1)
ccvi.	1 Novr 1809 (100)		ccxxxiii.	14 Decr 1814 (205)

95. ARMY GOLD CROSS

Date: 1813.
Campaigns: Napoleonic and Peninsular War.
Branch of Service: British Army.
Ribbon: 38mm crimson edged with dark blue.
Metal: Gold. **Size:** 38mm.
Description: A cross pattée with a laurel border having a rose at the centre on each of the four flat ends. At the centre of the cross appears a British lion statant. The scrolled top of the cross is fitted with an elaborate ring decorated with laurel leaves looped through a plain swivel ring fitted to the suspender. The arms of the cross on both obverse and reverse bear the names of four battles in relief.
Clasps: Large borders of laurel leaves enclosing the name of a battle in raised relief within an elliptical frame, awarded for fifth and subsequent battles.
Comments: *Arguably the most prestigious award in the campaign series, the Army Gold Cross was approved by the Prince Regent in 1813. It was granted to generals and officers of field rank for service in four or more battles of the Peninsular War. Four crosses were also awarded for Maida, seven Martinique and three Guadeloupe. A total of 164 crosses and 244 clasps were awarded. Three crosses had six clasps, two had seven, while the Duke of Wellington himself had the unique cross with nine clasps, representing participation in thirteen battles.*

VALUE:

Gold cross without clasp (61)	From £25,000
Miniature	£520–635

The Battle of Waterloo

96. MAIDA GOLD MEDAL

Date: 1806.
Campaign: Battle of Maida 1806.
Branch of Service: British Army.
Ribbon: 38mm crimson edged with navy blue.
Metal: Gold.
Size: 39mm.
Description: (Obverse) laureated profile of George III; (reverse) winged figure of Victory hovering with a laurel wreath over the head of Britannia, shield upraised, in the act of throwing a spear. The name and date of the battle appears on Britannia's left, with the *trinacria* or three-legged emblem on the right.
Clasps: None.
Comments: *This small gold medal was authorised in 1806 and awarded to the thirteen senior officers involved in the battle of Maida in Calabria when a small British force under General Sir John Stuart defeated a much larger French army with heavy loss. A small unknown number of gold and silver specimens are known to exist.*

VALUE: **From £45,000**

97. ARMY GOLD MEDAL

Date: 1810.
Campaigns: Peninsular War 1806-14 and War of 1812.
Branch of Service: British Army.
Ribbon: 38mm crimson edged with navy blue.
Metal: Gold.
Size: 54mm and 33mm.
Description: (Obverse) Britannia seated on a globe, holding a laurel wreath over the British lion and holding a palm branch in her left hand while resting on a shield embellished with the Union Jack. The name of the first action is generally engraved on the reverse.
Clasps: For second and third actions.
Comments: *The Maida medal (no. 96) established a precedent for the series of medals instituted in 1810. The name of the battle was inscribed on the reverse, usually engraved, though that for Barossa was die-struck. These medals were struck in two sizes, the larger being conferred on generals and the smaller on officers of field rank. Second or third battles were denoted by a clasp appropriately inscribed, while those who qualified for a fourth award exchanged their medal and bars for a gold cross. The award of these gold medals and crosses ceased in 1814 when the Companion of the Bath was instituted.*

VALUE*:
Large medal	From £30,000
Small medal	From £17,500

*Medals to British officers in the Portuguese Service generally sell for 20% less. Only one miniature is known to exist.

98. MILITARY GENERAL SERVICE MEDAL

Date: 1847.

Campaigns: French Revolutionary and Napoleonic Wars 1793-1814.

Branch of Service: British Army.

Ribbon: 31mm crimson edged with dark blue.

Metal: Silver.

Size: 36mm.

Description: (Obverse) the Wyon profile of Queen Victoria; (reverse) a standing figure of the Queen bestowing victor's laurels on a kneeling Duke of Wellington. The simple inscription TO THE BRITISH ARMY appears round the circumference, while the dates 1793-1814 are placed in the exergue. Despite this, the earliest action for which a clasp was issued took place in 1801 (Abercromby's Egyptian campaign).

Clasps: Only 29 battle or campaign clasps were issued but multiple awards are much more common than in the naval medal, the maximum being fifteen. While it is generally true to say that multi-clasp medals are worth more than single-clasp medals, there are many in the latter category (noted below) which command higher prices. The figures quoted below are based on the commonest regiments. Clasps awarded to specialists and small detached forces rate more highly than medals to the principal regiment in a battle or campaign. In particular, it should be noted that one naval officer, Lieut. Carroll, received the Military GSM and clasp for Maida, while a few other officers of the Royal Navy and Royal Marines received the medal with the clasps for Guadaloupe, Martinique or Java, and these, naturally, are now very much sought after. Paradoxically, the clasps for Sahagun and Benevente alone are very much scarcer than the clasp inscribed Sahagun and Benevente, awarded to surviving veterans who had participated in both battles. The clasps are listed below in chronological order. Medals to officers rate a premium.

Comments: *Like the Naval GSM, this medal was not sanctioned till 1847 and awarded the following year. Unlike the Naval medal, however, the Military GSM was confined to land actions up to the defeat of Napoleon in 1814 and the conclusion of the war with the United States. The regiment is now having a bearing on price, with medals to the 52nd, 88th or 95th Foot worth a good premium.*

VALUE:

i.	Egypt	£1250–1500	xxi.	Chateauguay	£4000–5000
ii.	Maida	£1300–1550	xxii.	Chrystler's Farm	£4000–5000
iii.	Roleia	£1150–1250	xxiii.	Vittoria	£1000–1250
iv.	Vimiera	£1000–1250	xxiv.	Pyrenees	£1000–1100
v.	Sahagun	£1750–2000	xxv.	St Sebastian	£1100–1200
vi.	Benevente	£4500–6000	xxvi.	Nivelle	£1000–1250
vii.	Sahagun and Benevente	£1750–2000	xxvii.	Nive	£950–1000
viii.	Corunna	£1000–1250	xxviii.	Orthes	£950–1000
ix.	Martinique	£1000–1250	xxix.	Toulouse	£950–1000
x.	Talavera	£1100–1200	2 clasps		from £1000
xi.	Guadaloupe	£1000–1250	3 clasps		from £1250
xii.	Busaco	£1000–1250	4 clasps		from £1500
xiii.	Barrosa	£1000–1250	5 clasps		from £1750
xiv.	Fuentes D'Onor	£1000–1250	6 clasps		from £2000
xv.	Albuhera	£1250–1400	7 clasps		from £2500
xvi.	Java	£1000–1250	8 clasps		from £3000
xvii.	Ciudad Rodrigo	£1000–1250	9 clasps		from £3500
xviii.	Badajoz	£1300–1400	10 clasps		from £4000
xix.	Salamanca	£1000–1250	11 clasps		from £4500
xx.	Fort Detroit	£5000–6500	12 or more clasps		from £7500

Miniature **without clasp** £125–175, **for each clasp add £75+ depending on the action.**

99. WATERLOO MEDAL

Date: 1815.

Campaign: Waterloo 1815.

Branch of Service: British Army.

Ribbon: 38mm, crimson edged in dark blue.

Metal: Silver.

Size: 37mm.

Description: (Obverse) the profile of the Prince Regent; (reverse) the seated figure of Victory above a tablet simply inscribed WATERLOO with the date of the battle in the exergue.

Comments: *This was the first medal awarded and officially named to all ranks who took part in a particular campaign. It was also issued, however, to those who had taken part in one or more of the other battles of the campaign, at Ligny and Quatre Bras two days earlier. The ribbon was intended to be worn with an iron clip and split suspension ring but many recipients subsequently replaced these with a more practical silver mount which would not rust and spoil the uniform. Some 39,000 medals were issued. The value of a Waterloo medal depends to a large extent on the regiment of the recipient. Medals awarded to those formations which saw the heaviest action and bore the brunt of the losses are in the greatest demand, whereas medals named to soldiers in General Colville's reserve division which did not take part in the fighting, are the least highly rated.*

VALUE:

Heavy Cavalry	£3500–4500
Scots Greys	£8000–10,000
Light Cavalry	£2500–3500
Royal Artillery	£2000–2500
Royal Horse Artillery	£2000–2500
Foot Guards	£2250–2800
1st, 27th, 28th, 30th, 42nd, 44th, 52nd, 73rd, 79th, 92nd, 95th Foot	£3500–4500
Other Foot regiments	£2000–2500
Colville's division (35th, 54th, 59th, 91st Foot)	£1500–2000
King's German Legion	£1400–1600

Miniature
Original | £60–250

100. BRUNSWICK MEDAL FOR WATERLOO

Date: 1817.

Campaign: Battle of Waterloo 1815.

Branch of Service: Brunswick troops.

Ribbon: 38mm wide, yellow with light blue stripes towards the edges.

Metal: Bronze.

Size: 35mm.

Description: (Obverse) Duke Friedrich Wilhelm of Brunswick who was killed in the battle; (reverse) a wreath of laurel and oak leaves enclosing the German text "Braunschweig Seinen Kriegern" (Brunswick to its warriors) and the names of Quatre Bras and Waterloo.

Comments: *The Prince Regent authorised this medal for issue to the contingent from the Duchy of Brunswick.*

VALUE: | £600–800
| Casualty £2000–2500

Miniature | —

101. HANOVERIAN MEDAL FOR WATERLOO

Date: 1818.
Campaign: Battle of Waterloo 1815.
Branch of Service: Hanoverian troops.
Ribbon: Maroon edged with light blue.
Metal: Silver.
Size: 35mm.
Description: (Obverse) the Prince Regent, his name and title being rendered in German. (Reverse) a trophy of arms below the legend HANNOVERISCHER TAPFERKEIT (Hanoverian bravery), with the name and date of the battle wreathed in the centre.
Comments: *The Prince Regent authorised this medal on behalf of his father George III in his capacity as Elector of Hanover and this was conferred on survivors of the battle. Suspension was by iron clip and ring similar to the British Waterloo Medal.*

VALUE:	£700–800
Miniature	£125–175

102. NASSAU MEDAL FOR WATERLOO

Date: 1815.
Campaign: Battle of Waterloo 1815.
Branch of Service: Nassau forces.
Ribbon: Dark blue edged in yellow.
Metal: Silver.
Size: 28mm.
Description: (Obverse) Duke Friedrich of Nassau; (reverse) the winged figure of Victory crowning a soldier with laurels, the date of the action being in the exergue.
Comments: *Friedrich Duke of Nassau distributed this medal on 23 December 1815 to all of his own troops who had been present at the battle.*

VALUE:	£400–500

103. SAXE-GOTHA-ALTENBURG MEDAL

Date: 1816.
Campaign: Germany and Waterloo 1814-15.
Branch of Service: Saxe-Gotha-Altenburg Foreign Legion.
Ribbon: Green with black edges and gold stripes.
Metal: Gilt bronze or bronze.
Size: 42mm.
Description: (Obverse) a crown with the legend IM KAMPFE FUER DAS RECHT (in the struggle for the right); (reverse) an ornate rose motif with the name of the duchy and the dates of the campaign in roman numerals.
Comments: *Gilded medals were issued to officers, NCOs received bronze medals with gilt raised points and other ranks a bronze version.*

VALUE:	
Gilt-bronze	£1000–1200
Bronze	£650–750

104. ARMY OF INDIA MEDAL

Date: 1851.
Campaigns: India 1803–26.
Branch of Service: British and HEIC troops.
Ribbon: 32mm pale blue.
Metal: Silver.
Size: 35mm.
Description: (Obverse) the Wyon profile of Queen Victoria; (reverse) the seated figure of Victory beside a palm tree, with a wreath in one hand and a laurel crown in the other. The medal is fitted with an ornamental scroll suspender.
Clasps: The medal was not awarded without a campaign clasp and, unusually, in multi-clasp medals, the last clasp awarded was mounted closest to the medal itself, so that the battle roll has to be read downwards. There were two dies of the reverse, leading to the long- or short-hyphen varieties, both of comparable value. In all, some 4500 medals were awarded, but there is a very wide divergence between the commonest and rarest bars. Multi-clasp medals are rare, and medals awarded to Europeans are much scarcer than those to Indian troops.
Comments: *The last of the medals authorised in connection with the Napoleonic Wars, it was instituted and paid for by the Honourable East India Company in March 1851 for award to surviving veterans of the battles and campaigns in India and Burma between 1803 and 1826. Despite the dates 1799–1826 in the exergue, the medal was in fact awarded for service in one or other of four wars: the Second Mahratta War (1803–4), the Nepal War (1814–16), the Pindaree or Third Mahratta War (1817–18) and the Burmese War (1824–26), together with the siege of Bhurtpoor (1825–26). The medal is scarce, and examples with the clasps for the Second Mahratta War are much sought after, partly because few veterans were still alive 48 years after the event to claim medals, and partly because of the war's association with Arthur Wellesley, the Duke of Wellington, who died in the very year in which the medal was awarded. Medals to the Royal Navy with the Ava clasp are very rare.*

Rev. die a, short hyphen

Rev. die b, long hyphen

VALUE:

Prices for medals bearing the following clasps are for European recipients. Medals to Indians are generally less expensive.

i.	Allighur (66)	£3000–3500
ii.	Battle of Delhi (40)	£3500–4500
iii.	Assye (87)	£3000–3500
iv.	Asseerghur (48)	£3500–4500
v.	Laswarree (100)	£3000–3500
vi.	Argaum (126)	£2500–3000
vii.	Gawilghur (110)	£3000–3500
viii.	Defence of Delhi (5)	—
ix.	Battle of Deig (47)	£3500–4500
x.	Capture of Deig (103)	£3000–3500
xi.	Nepaul (505)	£1500–1800
xii.	Kirkee (5)	—
xiii.	Poona (75)	£3000–3500
xiv.	Kirkee and Poona (88)	£3000–3500
xv.	Seetabuldee (2)	—
xvi.	Nagpore (155)	£2500–3000
xvii.	Seetabuldee and Nagpore (21)	£6000–8000
xviii.	Maheidpoor (75)	£3000–3500
xix.	Corygaum (4)	£6000–10,000
xx.	Ava (2325)	£1000–1200
xxi.	Bhurtpoor (1059)	£1200–1500
	2 clasps (300)	from £2500
	3 clasps (150)	from £7000
	4 clasps (23)	from £10,000
	5 or more clasps (10 x 5, 2 x 6, 1 x 7)	—
	Glazed gilt specimen	£750–1000

*Miniature**
One clasp Ava	£200–275
Further clasps	£125–175 each

Note there are many silver reproductions and clasps on the market, value £10–20.

105. GHUZNEE MEDAL

Date: 1839.

Campaign: Ghuznee 1839.

Branch of Service: British and HEIC forces.

Ribbon: 35mm half crimson, half dark green (originally green and yellow)

Metal: Silver.

Size: 37mm.

Description: (Obverse) the impressive gateway of the fortress of Ghuznee; (reverse) a mural crown enclosed in a laurel wreath with the date of capture.

Comments: *This was the second medal awarded for a particular campaign (after Waterloo) and was granted to both British and Indian troops who took part in the assault on Ghuznee in July 1839 which brought the first Afghan War to a close, overthrew the pro-Russian Dost Mohamed and restored Shah Soojah who instituted the Order of the Dooranie Empire (awarded to British generals and field officers) in appreciation. The Ghuznee medal was issued unnamed by the Honourable East India Company, but many recipients subsequently had their names impressed or engraved in various styles. No clasps were issued officially, but unauthorised clasps are occasionally encountered.*

VALUE:

British recipient	£800–1000
Indian recipient	£750–850
Unnamed as issued	£500–600
Miniature	£175–330

Original type ribbon.

Taking the Ghuznee fortress.

105A. BRITISH LEGION MEDAL

Date: 1836.

Campaign: First Carlist War.

Branch of Service: British Auxiliary Legion, plus a battalion of Royal Artillery seconded to the forces loyal to Queen Isabella.

Ribbon: Broad blue with narrow yellow stripes towards the edges.

Metal: Silver or white metal.

Size: 36mm.

Description: (Obverse) A cross pattee with the word TUJO in a laurel wreath at the centre; (reverse) ESPANA / AGRADECIDA (Grateful Spain) with a British lion enclosed by the cordon of the Golden Fleece. The medal is fitted with a ring for suspension from a double-looped bar and has a brooch fitment at the top of the ribbon. The medal was struck in Birmingham.

Comments: *The British Auxiliary Legion, commanded by General Sir George De Lacey Evans (1787-1870), volunteered for service in Spain in support of Isabella II who, at the age of three (1833) succeeded her father as monarch. Her uncle, Don Carlos, opposed this and triggered off a war which lasted till 1840 and was largely fought in the northern provinces. The inscription on the obverse alludes to the battle at Laguna del Tujo near Castilla la Mancha.*

VALUE:	Silver	£400–450
	(one Continental size miniature example with engraved details to reverse is known)	
	White metal	£150–200

106. ST. JEAN D'ACRE MEDAL

Date: 1840.

Campaign: Syria 1840.

Branch of Service: Royal Navy, Royal Marines and British Army.

Ribbon: Red with white edges.

Metal: Gold (22gms), silver or copper (bronzed).

Size: 30mm.

Description: (Obverse) a fortress flying the Ottoman flag, with six five-pointed stars round the top. A commemorative inscription and date in Arabic appear at the foot; (reverse) the Toughra of the Sultan in a laurel wreath.

Comments: *Awarded by the Sultan of Turkey to British, Austrian and Turkish forces under Sir Charles Napier, taking part in the liberation of this important city on the Syrian coast after eight years of Egyptian occupation. The medal has a plain ring suspension. The clasp "Syria" to the Naval GSM was awarded in 1848 in respect of this operation, and this medal generally accompanies the St Jean d'Acre medal.*

VALUE:		Miniature
Gold (captains and field officers)	£4500–5000	—
Silver (junior officers)	£400–450	£150–200
Copper (petty officers, NCOs and other ranks)	£200–250	—

107. CANDAHAR, GHUZNEE, CABUL MEDAL

Date: 1842.

Campaign: Afghanistan 1841–42.

Branch of Service: British and HEIC troops.

Ribbon: 40mm watered silk of pink, white, yellow, white and blue representing an eastern sky at sunrise.

Metal: Silver.

Size: 36mm.

Description: Although the medals have a uniform obverse, a profile of the Queen captioned VICTORIA VINDEX, reverses are inscribed with the names of individual battles, or combinations thereof, within wreaths surmounted by a crown.

Comments: *The Honourable East India Company instituted this series of medals in 1842 for award to both HEIC and British troops who took part in the First Afghan War. The issue of this medal to units of the British Army, to Europeans serving in the Company's forces, and to Indian troops is further complicated by the fact that unnamed medals are generally common. In addition, the medal for Cabul is known in two versions, with the inscription CABUL or CABVL, the latter being a major rarity as only fifteen were issued. Only 160 medals with Candahar reverse were issued to Europeans. Beware of modern copies of the Candahar and Cabul medals.*

VALUE:	Imperial Regiments	Indian Units	Unnamed
i. Candahar	£850–1000	£500–650	£400–550
ii. Cabul	£650–800	£450–650	£400–550
iii. Cabvl (15)	—	—	—
iv. Ghuznee/Cabul	£800–950	£500–650	£400–550
v. Candahar/Ghuznee/ Cabul	£850–1000	£500–650	£400–550
Miniature	from £265 (depending on reverse)		

108. JELLALABAD MEDALS

Type 1

Date: 1842.

Campaign: Afghanistan 1841-42.

Branch of Service: British and HEIC forces.

Ribbon: 44mm watered silk red, white, yellow, white and blue representing an eastern sky at sunrise.

Metal: Silver.

Size: 39mm and 35mm.

Description: There are two different types of this medal, awarded by the HEIC to surviving defenders of the fortress of Jellalabad between 12 November 1841 and 7 April 1842. The first, struck in Calcutta, has a mural crown and JELLALABAD on the obverse, with the date of the relief of the garrison on the reverse; the second type shows the Wyon profile of Victoria (obverse) and the winged Victory with mountain scenery in the background and JELLALABAD VII APRIL round the top and the year in roman numerals in the exergue (reverse).

Comments: *The first type, struck in Calcutta, was considered to be unsuitable and holders were invited to exchange their medals for the second, more attractive, issue which was produced in London, although very few recipients took up the offer. The latter type was also awarded to the next of kin of soldiers killed in action.*

VALUE:	Imperial Regiments	Indian Units	Unnamed	*Miniature*
i. First type (Crown)	£850–1000	£750–850	£600-800	£350–400
ii. Second type (Victory)	£1200–1500	—	£900–1000	£250–350

109. MEDAL FOR THE DEFENCE OF KELAT-I-GHILZIE

Date: 1842.

Campaign: Afghanistan 1842.

Branch of Service: European and native troops, HEIC.

Ribbon: 40mm watered silk red, white, yellow, white and blue representing an eastern sky at sunrise.

Metal: Silver.

Size: 36mm.

Description: (Obverse) a shield bearing the name of the fort, surmounted by a mural crown and encircled by laurels; (reverse) a trophy of arms above a tablet inscribed INVICTA (unbeaten) and the date in roman numerals.

Comments: *Awarded to those who took part in the defence of the fort at Kelat-i-Ghilzie in May 1842, it is the rarest medal of the First Afghan War. No British imperial regiments took part, but 55 Europeans in the Company's service received the medal. It was also awarded to 877 native troops (including a contingent supplied by Shah Soojah) but few of their medals appear to have survived.*

VALUE:

European recipients	£5500–6500
Indian recipients	£3000–3500
Unnamed	£1500–1800
Miniature	£345–475

110. CHINA WAR MEDAL

Issued reverse

Date: 1842.

Campaign: China 1841-42.

Branch of Service: British and HEIC forces.

Ribbon: 39mm crimson with deep yellow edges the heraldic colours of Britain and China respectively.

Metal: Silver.

Size: 35mm.

Description: The medal has the usual Wyon obverse, but the reverse was to have shown a British lion with its forepaws on a dragon. This was deemed to be offensive to the Chinese and was replaced by an oval shield bearing the royal arms and a palm tree flanked by a capstan, anchor and naval cannon representing the Royal Navy (left) and a field gun, drum and regimental flag representing the Army (right), with the Latin motto ARMIS EXPOSCERE PACEM (to pray for peace by force of arms) round the top and CHINA 1842 in the exergue.

Comments: *Originally intended for issue to all ranks of the Honourable East India Company, it was subsequently awarded by the British government in 1843 to all who had taken part in the campaign in China popularly known as the First Opium War which ended with the seizure of Nanking.*

VALUE:

Royal Navy	£700–800
Indian and Bengal marine units	£550–650
British imperial regiments	£650–800
Indian Army	£500–600
Specimens of the original reverse	£800–1000
Miniature	£175–275

111. SCINDE MEDAL

Date: 1843.
Campaign: Scinde 1843.
Branch of Service: HEIC forces and 22nd Foot.
Ribbon: 44mm watered silk red, white, yellow, white and blue representing an eastern sky at sunrise.
Metal: Silver.
Size: 36mm.
Description: The usual Wyon profile obverse was married to three different reverse types showing a crowned laurel wreath inscribed with the name of one or two campaigns and the date.
Comments: *Authorised in September 1843, this silver medal marked Sir Charles Napier's conquest of Scinde. The two major battles in the campaign, at Meeanee and Hyderabad, accomplished the complete rout of the forces of the Amirs of Scinde. The medals were originally issued with steel suspenders but the commanding officer of the 22nd Foot had the medals awarded to his men fitted with silver suspenders, at his own expense. Medals to the Indus Flotilla are particularly sought after by collectors.*

VALUE:

	22nd Foot	Indian units	HEIC ships
i. Meeanee	£1000–1200	£650–750	£1750–2500 (38)
ii. Hyderabad	£1000–1200	£650–750	£1750–2500 (52)
iii. Meeanee/Hyderabad	£1000–1250	£650–750	
Miniature	£175–275		

112. GWALIOR STAR

Date: 1843.
Campaign: Gwalior 1843.
Branch of Service: British and HEIC forces.
Ribbon: 44mm watered silk red, white, yellow, white and blue representing an eastern sky at sunrise.
Metals: Bronze, with a silver centre.
Size: Max. width 45mm; max. height 52mm.
Description: Six-pointed bronze star with a silver centre star. The silver stars in the centre bear the name of one or other of the battles and the date 29 December 1843 on which both battles were fought. The plain reverse bears the name and regiment of the recipient.
Comments: *Bronze from guns captured at the battles of Maharajpoor and Punniar during the Gwalior campaign was used in the manufacture of these stars, thus anticipating the production of the Victoria Cross in the same manner. They were presented by the Indian government to all ranks who took part in these actions. When first issued, these stars were fitted with hooks to be worn like a breast decoration, but later ornate bar or ring suspensions were fitted to individual fancy and worn with the standard Indian ribbon of the period.*

VALUE:

			Miniature
i.	Maharajpoor	£650–750	£200–250
ii.	Punniar	£650–750	£250–350

*Awards to Indian recipients are usually marginally less.

113. SUTLEJ MEDAL

Date: 1846.
Campaign: Sutlej 1845-46.
Branch of Service: British and HEIC forces.
Ribbon: Dark blue with crimson edges.
Metal: Silver.
Size: 36mm.
Description: (Obverse) Wyon profile of Queen Victoria; (reverse) standing figure of Victory holding aloft a laurel crown, with a pile of captured weapons at her feet. The legend ARMY OF THE SUTLEJ appears round the top. The medal was fitted with an ornamental scroll suspender.
Clasps: Mounted above the suspender with roses between: Ferozeshuhur, Aliwal or Sobraon.
Comments: *The practice of issuing medals inscribed with different battles now gave way to the style of medals with specific battle or campaign clasps which set the precedent for the Naval and Military GSMs and later awards. As a compromise, however, the exergue of the reverse bears the name and date of the action for which the medal was first granted, and thus several different types are known.*

VALUE:	British regiments	Europeans in HEIC units	Indian units
i. Moodkee	£400–475	£300–500	£325–375
Moodkee 1 clasp	£500–575	£400–550	£375–425
Moodkee 2 clasps	£700–825	£600–750	£475–575
Moodkee 3 clasps	£1200–1500	£950–1150	£750–950
ii. Ferozeshuhur	£400–475	£300–400	£325–375
Ferozeshuhur 1 clasp	£500–575	£400–500	£375–425
Ferozeshuhur 2 clasps	£700–825	£600–750	£475–575
iii. Aliwal	£350–425	£300–400	£325–375
Aliwal 1 clasp	£500–575	£400–550	£375–475
iv. Sobraon	£400–525	£350–450	£375–475
Glazed gilt specimen	£500–750		
Miniature	£125–175, for each clasp add £50		

114. PUNJAB MEDAL

Date: 1849.
Campaign: Punjab 1848-49.
Branch of Service: British and HEIC forces.
Ribbon: Dark blue with yellow stripes towards the edges.
Metal: Silver.
Size: 36mm.
Description: (Obverse) Wyon profile of Queen Victoria; (reverse) Sir Walter Gilbert receiving the Sikh surrender. TO THE ARMY OF THE PUNJAB appears round the top and the year in roman numerals in the exergue. The medal has a scroll suspender.
Clasps: Mooltan, Chilianwala, Goojerat. Unusually the clasps read downwards from top to bottom
Comments: *This medal was granted to troops taking part in the campaigns which ended in the annexation of the Punjab. Unlike the Sutlej medal, however, this silver medal had a standard design. Large numbers of this medal were awarded to native troops, however many were melted down and therefore surprisingly few remain on the market in comparison with medals to European recipients.*

VALUE:	British units	Europeans in HEIC units	Indian units
No clasp	£400–450	£400–450	£350–375
i. Mooltan	£450–550	£400–450	£375–400
ii. Chilianwala	£450–550	£400–450	£375–400
iii. Goojerat	£450–550	£400–450	£375–400
iv. Mooltan/Goojerat	£650–750	£650–700	£475–550
v. Chilianwala/Goojerat	£650–750	£650–700	£475–550
24th Foot casualty at Chilianwala	£1000–1500	—	—
Glazed gilt specimen	£350–500		
Miniature	£90–125, for each clasp add £25		

115. SOUTH AFRICA MEDAL

Date: 1854.

Campaigns: Southern Africa 1834–53.

Branch of Service: Royal Navy and Army.

Ribbon: Gold with broad and narrow deep blue stripes towards each end.

Metal: Silver.   **Size:** 36mm.

Description: (Obverse) Wyon profile of Queen Victoria; (reverse) an African lion crouching in submission beside a protea shrub, the date 1853 being in the exergue.

Clasps: None.

Comments: *Authorised in November 1854, this medal was awarded in respect of three campaigns in southern Africa: 1834–35, 1846–47 and 1850–53, but as the medal was issued with a standard reverse and no campaign clasps it is impossible to tell when and where the recipient served without reference to the medal rolls. The majority of recipients were British troops but several hundred sailors of the Royal Navy also received the medal and a much smaller number of local forces. Medals to proven recipients who took part in well-known sieges or battles such as the siege of Port Natal (1842), Fort Cox (1850) or the battles of Zwartkopje (1845) or Boomplaats (1848) for example, are worth a considerable premium. Also of particular interest are medals awarded to men who survived the sinking of the troopship* Birkenhead *on its way to the Eastern Cape from Simons Town and medals awarded to those in clashes with Boer forces.*

VALUE:

British Army	£550–650
Royal Navy	£475–575
HMS *Birkenhead*	From £2000
Local forces (levies, burghers and colonial units)	From £1000
Miniature	£90–125

116. SIR HARRY SMITH'S MEDAL FOR GALLANTRY

Date: 1851.

Campaign: Eighth Kaffir War 1850-51.

Branch of Service: Army and Colonial Forces.

Ribbon: Dark blue with crimson edges.

Metal: Silver.

Size: 34mm.

Description: (Obverse) British lion passant gardant with a laurel wreath over its head; date 1851 in the exergue. (Reverse) PRESENTED BY round top and FOR GALLANTRY IN THE FIELD round the foot. HIS EXCELLENCY SIR H. G. SMITH and the name of the recipient appear across the centre.

Comments: *Sir Harry Smith (1787–1860) served with distinction in the Kaffir War of 1834–35, gained his KCB in the Gwalior campaign and a baronetcy for his decisive victory at Aliwal in the Sikh War. In 1847 he returned to South Africa as governor of Cape Colony. Although short of troops he conducted the eighth Kaffir War (1850–53) with great resourcefulness but was recalled to England in 1852 before the Xhosas had been subdued. Harrismith in the Orange Free State was named in his honour, while Ladysmith in Natal was named after his beautiful and spirited Spanish wife Juanita, the forces' sweetheart of her day. Sir Harry had this medal struck at his own expense and, according to unconfirmed accounts, awarded to troopers of the Cape Mounted Rifles who took part in the epic ride through the enemy lines from Fort Cox to Kingwilliamstown in 1851. Only 31 medals were presented, of which 22 are believed to be still extant.*

VALUE:

Unnamed	£3000–4000
Named and appearing on 1853 medal roll or muster rolls	£7000–10,000

One contemporary miniature example is known

117. INDIA GENERAL SERVICE MEDAL

Date: 1854.

Campaigns: Indian 1854-95.

Branch of Service: British and Indian forces.

Ribbon: Three crimson and two dark blue stripes of equal width.

Metal: Silver or bronze.

Size: 36mm.

Description: (Obverse) Wyon profile of Queen Victoria; (reverse) Victory crowning a semi-nude seated warrior.

Clasps: 24 (see below).

Comments: *This medal was the first of four general service medals issued to cover minor campaigns in India. It was instituted in 1854 and continued for forty-one years, retaining the original Wyon profile of Queen Victoria throughout the entire period. Although the medal itself is quite common, some of its clasps are very rare, notably* Kachin Hills 1892–93 *awarded to the* Yorkshire Regiment *and* Chin Hills 1892–93 *awarded to the* Norfolk Regiment. *The maximum number of clasps to one medal recorded is seven. At first the medal was awarded in silver to all ranks regardless of race or branch of the services, but from 1885 onwards it was issued in bronze to native support personnel such as bearers, sweepers and drivers.*

VALUE:		RN/RM	British Army	Indian Army	Bronze
i.	Pegu	£320–350	£300–350	£250–275*	—
ii.	Persia	—	£600–800	£350–400	—
iii.	Northwest Frontier	—	£300–360	£200–250	—
iv.	Umbeyla	—	£325–375	£200–250	—
v.	Bhootan	—	£360–385	£200–250	—
vi.	Looshai	—	—	£400–550	—
vii.	Perak	£320–350	£360–385	£250–275	—
viii.	Jowaki 1877–8	—	£285–325	£200–250	—
ix.	Naga 1879–80	—	—	£375–450	—
x.	Burma 1885–7	£320–350	£185–250	£150–175	£150–185
xi.	Sikkim 1888	—	£380–440	£175–200	£200–250
xii.	Hazara 1888	—	£235–260	£175–200	£160–200
xiii.	Burma 1887–89	—	£200–230	£165–185	£160–200
xiv.	Burma 1887–9	—	£225–275	—	—
xv.	Chin Lushai 1889–90	—	£300–350	£200–250	£220–275
xvi.	Lushai 1889–92	—	£600–650	£225–275	£425–500
xvii.	Samana 1891	—	£300–350	£185–200	£175–200
xviii.	Hazara 1891	—	£250–300	£185–200	£175–200
xix.	NE Frontier 1891	—	£385–425	£175–200	£175–200
xx.	Hunza 1891	—	—	£500–550	£850–1000
xxi.	Burma 1889–92	—	£200–250	£175–200	£150–185
xxii.	Chin Hills 1892–93	—	£850–1000	£385–475	£875–1000
xxiii.	Kachin Hills 1892–93	—	£850–1000	£400–500	£875–1000
xxiv.	Waziristan 1894–95	—	£275–300	£175–200	£175–200

Miniature   £25–35, for each clasp add £15–20 (*Hunza, Chin Hills* and *Kachin Hills* clasps are rare)

* In addition a number of Indian ships were present—medals to Indian naval or marine recipients are rare.

118. BALTIC MEDAL

Date: 1856.

Campaign: Baltic Sea 1854–55.

Branch of Service: Royal Navy, Royal Marines and Royal Sappers and Miners.

Ribbon: Yellow with light blue edges.

Metal: Silver.

Size: 36mm.

Description: (Obverse) Wyon profile of Queen Victoria; (reverse) Britannia seated on a plinth decorated by a cannon, with a coastal scene in the background and BALTIC round the top.

Comments: *Authorised in 1856, this medal was granted to officers and men of the Royal Navy and Royal Marines for operations against Russia in the Baltic at the same time as the war in the Crimea. It was also awarded to about 100 members of the Royal Sappers and Miners engaged in the demolition of Russian fortifications of Bomarsund and Sveaborg. Medals were generally issued unnamed but often privately named afterwards, the exception being medals to the Sappers and Miners which were officially impressed.*

VALUE:

Unnamed	£185–250
Privately named	£200–250
Officially impressed to Sappers and Miners	£800–1000
Miniature	£50–75

119. CRIMEA MEDAL

Date: 1854.

Campaign: Crimea 1854–56.

Branch of Service: Royal Navy and Marines, British Army.

Ribbon: Pale blue with yellow edges.

Metal: Silver.

Size: 36mm.

Description: (Obverse) Wyon profile of Queen Victoria; (reverse) a Roman soldier, armed with circular shield and short sword, being crowned by a flying Victory.

Clasps: Unusually ornate, being shaped like oak leaves with acorn finials: Alma, Balaklava, Inkerman, Sebastopol, Azoff, but the maximum found on any medal is four. Recipients of the Balaklava clasp were invariably entitled to other clasps. Unofficial clasps for Traktir, Mamelon Vert, Malakoff, Mer d'Azoff and Kinburn are sometimes found on medals awarded to French troops.

Comments: *Medals may be found unnamed, unofficially or regimentally named, or officially impressed. Medals awarded to participants in the most famous actions of the war—the Thin Red Line (93rd Foot) and the Charge of the Light and Heavy Brigades—rate a very high premium. The prices quoted are for medals named to the Army. Clasps awarded to the Royal Navy and Royal Marines (Azoff, Balaklava, Inkerman, Sebastopol) rate a good premium, especially those named to personnel on board HM Ships* London, Niger, Rodney *and* Wasp.* *No fewer than 19 VCs were awarded for gallantry at Inkerman alone, the largest number for a single action.*

VALUE :	Unnamed	Engraved	Regimentally impressed	Officially impressed Army
No clasp	£150–200	£175–200	£175–200	£200–250
i. Alma	£150–200	£200–250	£200–250	£225–300
ii. Balaklava	£200–250	£200–250	£200–250	£325–400
93rd Foot*	—	£500–575	£800–1000	£1000–1250
Heavy Brigade*	—	£750–1000	£1000–1500	£1500–2000
Light Brigade (Charger)*	—	£2500–2750	£4500–5500	£10,000–15,000
iii. Inkerman	£175–200	£200–250	£200–250	£225–275
iv. Sebastopol	£175–200	£200–250	£200–250	£275–350
v. Azoff	£300–375	£350–400	—	£525–650
2 clasps	£250–300	£300–350	£300–375	£425–550
3 clasps	£325–400	£400–450	£400–475	£700–900
4 clasps	£400–500	£500–750	£565–700	£1250–1750
Miniature	£25–35, for each clasp add £15			

*It is always difficult to price scarce or rare medals such as those marked * as we have seen many engraved or Depot-style impressing that were probably named in the past 30 to 40 years. Also an engraved Crimea, together with a Mutiny and/or LS&GC would be worth considerably more than the prices indicated. Buyer beware!*

120. TURKISH CRIMEA MEDAL

Date: 1855.
Campaign: Crimea 1855-56.
Branch of Service: British, French and Sardinian forces.
Ribbon: Crimson with green edges (originally 18mm wide).
Metal: Silver.
Size: 36mm.
Description: (Obverse) a cannon, weapons and the four Allied flags with the name and date in the exergue; (reverse) the Toughra and Arabic date according to the Moslem calendar.
Clasps: None.
Comments: *Instituted by the Sultan of Turkey, this silver medal was conferred on troops of the three Allies who fought in the Crimea. The obverse types differed in the arrangement of the flags, corrsponding with the inscription in English, French or Italian in the exergue. Although the medals were intended to be issued to British, French and Sardinian troops respectively, they were issued haphazardly due to most of the British version being lost at sea. They were unnamed, but many were privately engraved or impressed later. There are a number of dangerous copies known to be circulating.*

VALUE:		*Miniature*
i. CRIMEA (British Issue)	£140–160	£45–50
ii. LA CRIMEE (French Issue)	£220–250	Not seen
iii. LA CRIMEA (Sardinia Issue)	£120–140	£35–45

120A. TURKISH MEDAL FOR GLORY

Date: 1853.
Campaign: Crimea.
Branch of Service: British forces.
Ribbon: Crimson with green edges.
Metal: Gold or silver.
Size: 31mm.
Description: (Obverse) the Sultan's cypher in a beaded ring below a star and crescent with flags and wreath around; (reverse) a star with a smaller star in the centre, an arabic inscription below which reads "Medal for Glory". With ring suspension.
Clasps: None.
Comments: *Instituted by the Sultan of Turkey, it was awarded to officers and men of British forces who fought in the war against Russia, at Silistria and Giurgevo. Gold medals were awarded to high ranking officers and silver to others.*

VALUE:	
Gold	£1000–1500
Silver	£500–750

120B. TURKISH MEDAL FOR THE DEFENCE OF SILISTRIA

Date: 1854.
Campaign: Crimea.
Branch of Service: British and Turkish forces.
Ribbon: Crimson with green edges.
Metal: Gold or silver.
Size: 36mm.
Description: (Obverse) the Sultan's cypher within in a wreath; (reverse) a depiction of the fortress of Silistria with a flag flying from the ramparts with the river Danube in the foreground, an inscription in Turkish script below which reads "Silistria 1271 AH (1854)". With ring suspension
Clasps: None.
Comments: *Instituted by the Sultan of Turkey, it was awarded to officers and men of British forces who were present during the actual siege by 30,000 Russian troops. Only seven British officers were there at the time and qualified for the medal but the medal was issued unnamed.*

VALUE:
Gold	£1000–1500
Silver	£500–750

120C. TURKISH MEDAL FOR THE DEFENCE OF KARS

Date: 1855.
Campaign: Crimea.
Branch of Service: British and Turkish forces.
Ribbon: Crimson with green edges.
Metal: Silver.
Size: 36mm.
Description: (Obverse) the Sultan's cypher within in a wreath; (reverse) a depiction of the city of Kars with a flag flying from the citadel and the words "Kars 1272 AH (1855)" in Turkish script below. With simple ring suspension.
Clasps: None.
Comments: *Instituted by the Sultan of Turkey, it was awarded to officers and men of British forces who were present at the siege of Kars by 50,000 Russian troops. The silver medal was awarded to the British officers present including the British Commissioner, Brigadier General Sir William Fenwick Williams. Lt C. C. Teesdale was sawarded the VC for his part in the action. The medals were issued unnamed.*

VALUE: £2000–3000

121. INDIAN MUTINY MEDAL

Date: 1858.

Campaign: Sepoy Mutiny, India 1857–58.

Branch of Service: Royal Navy, British Army and Indian forces. It was also awarded to many civilians who took part in suppressing the Mutiny.

Ribbon: White with two red stripes, representing blood and white bandages.

Metal: Silver.

Size: 36mm.

Description: (Obverse) Wyon profile of Queen Victoria; (reverse) the standing figure of Britannia bestowing victor's laurels, with the British lion alongside. INDIA appears round the top with the dates 1857–1858 in the exergue.

Clasps: Delhi, Defence of Lucknow, Relief of Lucknow, Lucknow, Central India. The maximum recorded for a single medal is four (Bengal Artillery) or three (imperial troops, 9th Lancers).

Comments: *This medal was awarded to troops who took part in operations to quell the Sepoy mutiny which had been the immediate cause of the uprising, although it also served to focus attention on the Honourable East India Company's conduct of affairs and led directly to the transfer of the administration of India to the Crown. Medals with the clasp for the defence of Lucknow awarded to the original defenders rate a considerable premium, as do medals awarded to members of the Naval Brigade which witnessed most of the fighting in the mopping-up operations. Medals to Indian recipients although scarcer on the market, generally bring a little less than their British counterparts although verified four-clasp medals to the Bengal Artillery are much sought after.*

VALUE:

	Royal Navy	British Army	Miniature
No clasp	£800–1000*	£250–350	£30–405
i. Delhi	—	£500–550	£45–50
ii. Defence of Lucknow			
original defender	—	£1600–1800	£50–55
first relief force	—	£800–1000	
iii. Relief of Lucknow	£800–1000	£450–550	£35–45
iv. Lucknow	£800–1000	£450–550	£45–50
v. Central India	—	£450–550	£45–50, add
2 clasps	£1000–1200	£550–700	£15 for each
3 clasps (9th Lancers)	—	£1500–1800	additional clasp
4 clasps (Bengal Arty.)	—	£3500–4500	

66 medals to HMS Shannon and 253 to HMS Pearl.

122. SECOND CHINA WAR MEDAL

Date: 1861.
Campaign: Second China War 1857-60.
Branch of Service: Royal Navy and British Army.
Ribbon: 33mm crimson with yellow edges (originally five equal stripes of green, white, red, yellow and blue, edged with red).
Metal: Silver.
Size: 36mm.
Description: As the First China War Medal (no. 110), but without the year 1842 at the foot.
Clasps: Fatshan 1857, Canton 1857, Taku Forts 1858, Taku Forts 1860, Pekin 1860.
Comments: *This medal was awarded to British sevicemen who took part, alongside the French, in the campaign against China which had been provoked by hostile acts against European nationals. The Royal Navy, under Admiral Sir Michael Seymour, destroyed a Chinese flotilla at Fatshan Creek, preparing the way for the attack on Canton whose capture brought the first phase to an end in June 1858. Reinforcements were meanwhile diverted to help put down the Indian mutiny. Fighting broke out again and this time large numbers of troops were involved in the assault on the Taku forts and the sack of Pekin (Beijing). Examples of the China medal of 1842, with or without clasps for 1857-60, have been recorded to recipients who fought in the Second China War. Medals may be found unnamed or with names officially engraved (Indian Army) or impressed (British Army, Indian Navy). Although those to the Navy were all issued unnamed, they are occasionally encountered unofficially named.*

Original ribbon.

Second type ribbon.

VALUE:

	Unnamed	Army/Navy officially impressed	Miniature
No clasp	£150–180	£185–200	£45–50
i. China 1842	—	—	£130–160
ii. Fatshan 1857	£185–225	£325–375	£60–70
iii. Canton 1857	£185–225	£300–350	£60–70
iv. Taku Forts 1858	£185–225	£300–350	£50–60
v. Taku Forts 1860	£185–225	£300–350	£50–60
vi. Pekin 1860	£185–225	£300–350	£50–60
2 clasps	£300–350	£400–500	For each
3 clasps	£350–450	£500–650	clasp add
4 clasps	£450–500	—	£15
5 clasps	£600–700	—	

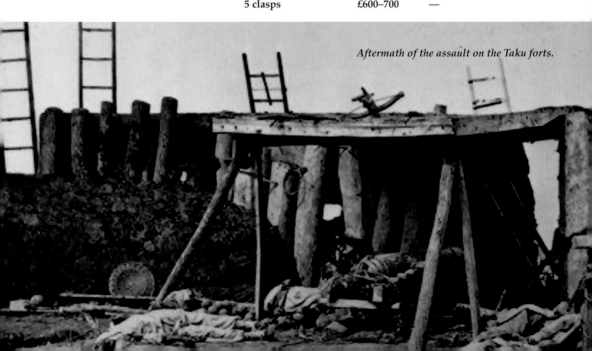

Aftermath of the assault on the Taku forts.

123. NEW ZEALAND MEDALS

Date: 1869.

Campaigns: First and Second Maori Wars 1845–47 and 1860–66.

Branch of Service: Army, Navy and local volunteers.

Ribbon: Blue with a central orange stripe.

Metal: Silver.

Size: 36mm.

Description: (Obverse) Veiled head of Queen Victoria. (Reverse) Date of service in a wreath, with NEW ZEALAND round the top and VIRTUTIS HONOR (honour of valour) round the foot. Suspender ornamented with New Zealand fern fronds.

Comments: *These medals were unusual in having the recipient's dates of service die-struck on the centre of the reverse, though medals were also issued without dates. As the medal was only awarded to surviving veterans, the numbers issued in respect of the earlier conflict are understandably small. Many of the dates are very scarce, especially those issued to naval personnel in the first war when only naval personnel received dated medals. A hitherto unknown 1845-dated medal appeared at auction in January 2010 when it sold for a hammer price of £12,800. This medal was named to Captain David Robertson, HMS* Hazard.

VALUE:		Army	RN/RM
First war			
i.	Undated	£450–500	—
ii.	1845–46 (155)	—	£1300–1600
iii.	1845–47 (36)	—	£1400–1700
iv.	1846–47 (69)	—	£1300–1600
v.	1846 (10)	—	£1500–2000
vi.	1847 (20)	£800–1000	£1500–2000
Second war			
vii.	Undated	£375–475	—
viii.	1860	£700–800	—
ix.	1860–61	£475–525	£650–750
	(to Australians)	£2000–2300	—
x.	1860–63	From £1550	—
xi.	1860–64	£450–500	—
xii.	1860–65	£450–500	—
xiii.	1860–66	£450–500	—
xiv.	1861	—	—
xv.	1861–63	—	—
xvi.	1861–64	£450–500	—
xvii.	1861–65	—	—
xviii.	1861–66	£450–500	—
xix.	1861–66		
	(Waikato Regt issues)	From £750	—
xx.	1862–66	—	—
xxi.	1863	£450–500	—
xxii.	1863–64	£450–500	£650–750
xxiii.	1863–65	£450–500	—
xxiv.	1863–66	£450–500	—
xxv.	1864	£450–500	—
xxvi.	1864–65	£450–500	—
xxvii.	1864–66	£450–500	—
xxviii.	1865	£450–500	£650–750
xxvix.	1865–66	£450–500	—
xxx.	1866	£450–500	—

Miniature		
Undated		£100–125
Dated		£85–£95

124. ABYSSINIAN WAR MEDAL

Date: 1869.
Campaign: Abyssinia (Ethiopia) 1867–68.
Branch of Service: Royal Navy, British and Indian Armies.
Ribbon: Red with broad white edges.
Metal: Silver.
Size: 33mm diameter.
Description: (Obverse) the veiled portrait of Victoria framed by a zigzag pattern with floral ornament alternating with the letters of the name ABYSSINIA. The recipient's name and unit were embossed in the centre of the reverse except most to Indian troops which were impressed. Suspension is by a ring via a large crown standing proud from the top of the medal.
Clasps: None.
Comments: *The imprisonment of British subjects by King Theodore of Abyssinia precipitated a punitive expedition under General Sir Robert Napier involving ships of the Royal Navy, a naval brigade and troops of the British and Indian armies. Because casualties were unusually light (only two killed and 27 wounded), medals from this campaign are not so highly rated as those from other nineteenth century wars.*

VALUE:

British troops	£375–450
Royal Navy	£375–450
RN Rocket Brigade	£575–650
Indian troops	£300–375
Miniature	£125–175

125. CANADA GENERAL SERVICE MEDAL

Date: 1899.
Campaign: Canada 1866–70.
Branch of Service: Royal Navy, British Army and Canadian units.
Ribbon: Three equal stripes of orange-red, white and orange-red.
Metal: Silver.
Size: 36mm.
Description: (Obverse) crowned and veiled Old Head bust of Queen Victoria by Sir Thomas Brock (reflecting the very late issue of the medal). (Reverse) Canadian flag surrounded by maple leaves.
Clasps: Fenian Raid 1866, Fenian Raid 1870, Red River 1870.
Comments: *This medal was not authorised until January 1899, thirty years after the event, and was issued by the Canadian government to British and Canadian local forces who took part in operations to put down the Fenian raids of 1866 and 1870 and the Red River rebellion of the latter year. Of the 16,100 medals awarded, 15,000 went to local forces. Naval medals command a premium.*

VALUE:

	Canadian forces	British Army	Royal Navy	*Miniature*
i. Fenian Raid 1866	£350–400	£450–550	£550–650	£65–70
ii. Fenian Raid 1870	£350–400	£450–550	—	£70–75
iii. Red River 1870	£1500–1800	£2000–2500	£1000–1500	£90–115
2 clasps*	£675–850	£950–1000	—	£85–110
3 clasps	Rare	—	—	—

*Two 2-clasp medals were awarded to men of the 1st Bn 60th Foot (KRRC) and ten to the 4th Bn.

126. ASHANTEE MEDAL

Date: 1874.
Campaign: Gold Coast 1873–74.
Branch of Service: Royal Navy, Army and native troops.
Ribbon: Yellow with black stripes at the sides and two narrow black stripes towards the centre.
Metal: Silver.   **Size:** 36mm.
Description: The obverse and reverse are similar to the East and West Africa Medal of 1887–1900, differing solely in thickness and the method of naming. The veiled profile of Victoria graces the obverse while the reverse, designed by Sir Edwin Poynter, shows a skirmish in the jungle between British soldiers and Ashantee warriors.
Clasps: Coomassie.
Comments: *All ranks who took part in operations against King Kalkali of Ashantee, Gold Coast, were awarded this medal, approved in June 1874. The campaign was fought in difficult and hostile terrain, requiring the building of a road through dense rain forest, the construction of many staging posts, camps, bridges and a telegraph. The movement of troops and supplies was met with skirmishes and ferocious battles developed as the column approached Kumasi in the final four weeks and resulted in the award of four VCs. There was also a very high incidence of sickness and disease among the troops, notably the naval contingent. Unusually the medals are named in engraved capitals filled in with black.*

VALUE	Royal Navy	Army	Natives	Miniature
No clasp	£350–400	£350–400	£250–300	£50–55
i. Coomassie	£450–550	£450–550	£300–350	£70–75

127. SOUTH AFRICA MEDAL

Date: 1879.
Campaign: South Africa 1877–79.
Branch of Service: Royal Navy, Army and colonial units.
Ribbon: Gold with broad and narrow deep blue stripes towards each end.
Metal: Silver.
Size: 36mm.
Description: The same design as no. 115, except that the date 1853 in the exergue is replaced by a Zulu shield and four crossed assegais.
Clasps: 1877, 1877–8, 1877–9, 1877–8–9, 1878, 1878–9, 1879.
Comments: *The campaign began in 1877 with an attack on the Fingoes by the Galeka and Gaika tribes and culminated in the showdown between the Zulus and the British when Lord Chelmsford's column was annihilated at Isandhlwana. When the 3,000 Zulus advanced on Rorke's Drift, however, they were checked with heavy losses by a tiny garrison of 139 men. During the defence no fewer than eleven VCs were won—a very large number for a single action. The campaign concluded with the defeat of Cetshwayo's warriors at Ulundi. A number of recipients of the medal stayed on in the country and took part in the first Anglo-Boer War of 1880–81. Medals confirmed to these men, particularly those who took part in the sieges of Wakkerstroom, Rustenburg, Standerton, Marabastadt or Lydenburg or well-known battles such as Swartkoppies, are worth a considerable premium.*

VALUE:	RN	Army	Colonial	Miniature
No clasp	£400–450	£450–500	£450–500	£35–40
i. 1877	—	Unique	£3500–4500	£110–160
ii. 1877–8	£900–1000	£800–1000	£750–850	£70–80
iii. 1877–9	—	Unique	£4500–6000	—
iv. 1877–8–9	£800–1000	£850–1000	£750–850	£70–80
v. 1878	—	£850–1000	£750–850	£70–80
vi. 1878–9	—	£850–1000	£750–850	£70–80
vii. 1879	£800–1000	£850–1000	£750–850	£75–85

Isandhlwana casualty	£9000–12,000	
Isandhlwana escapee	£10,000–12,000	
Rorke's Drift participant	£50,000–80,000	

128. AFGHANISTAN MEDAL

Date: 1881.

Campaign: Afghanistan 1878–80.

Branch of Service: British and Indian Armies.

Ribbon: Dark green, the sacred colour of the prophet with broad crimson edges, the heraldic colour of Britain.

Metal: Silver.

Size: 36mm.

Description: (Obverse) veiled profile of Queen Victoria. (Reverse) a column on the march, with an elephant carrying cannon. The dates 1878–79–80 appear in the exergue.

Clasps: Ali Musjid, Peiwar Kotal, Charasia, Kabul, Ahmed Kel, Kandahar. Maximum number of clasps per medal is four.

Comments: *This medal was awarded to all who took part in the campaigns against Afghanistan known as the Second Afghan War. In 1877 the Amir refused to accept a British resident and the following year raised an army which began harrassing the Indian frontier. A treaty with Russia, however, granting it protective rights in Afghanistan, precipitated an armed response from Britain. In 1880 General Roberts led a column from Kabul to Kandahar to relieve General Burrows and the resulting battle led to the defeat of the Afghans and the conclusion of the war. Medals awarded to the 66th Foot (Berkshire Regiment) and E Battery of B Brigade, Royal Artillery rate a high premium as these units sustained the heaviest casualties at the battle of Maiwand in July 1880.*

VALUE:	British units	Indian units	Miniature
No clasp silver	£250–300	£150–175	£25–35
i. Ali Musjid	£350–400	£200–275	£35–45
ii. Peiwar Kotal	£350–400	£200–275	£35–45
iii. Charasia	£350–400	£200–275	£35–45
iv. Kabul	£350–400	£200–275	£30–35
v. Ahmed Khel	£350–400	£200–275	£35–45
vi. Kandahar	£350–400	£200–275	£30–35
2 clasps	£500–600	£300–375	£60–70
3 clasps	£600–750	£375–475	£80–90
4 clasps	£750–1000	£475–600	£95–100
Maiwand casualties:			
66th Foot	£3000–3500	—	
E Bty, B Bde RHA	£2500–3000	—	

Richard Caton Woodville's famous depiction of Saving the Guns at Maiwand.

129. KABUL TO KANDAHAR STAR

Date: 1881.
Campaign: Afghanistan 1878–80.
Branch of Service: British and Indian Armies.
Ribbon: 40mm watered silk of pink, white, yellow, white and blue representing an eastern sky at sunrise.
Metal: Bronze from captured guns.
Size: Height 60mm, width 45mm.
Description: (Obverse) a rayed five-pointed star surmounted by a crown with a ring for suspension. The centre is inscribed KABUL TO KANDAHAR with 1880 at the foot and the VRI monogram of the Queen Empress in the centre. Stars were either issued unnamed, or had the recipient's name impressed (to British) or engraved (to Indian troops) on the reverse.
Clasps: None.
Comments: *This star, struck by Jenkins of Birmingham, was awarded to those who took part in the epic 300-mile march from the Afghan capital to Kandahar, led by General Roberts to relieve the beleaguered forces of General Burrows.*

VALUE:

Unnamed	£150–180
Impressed (British troops)	£350–400
Engraved (Indian troops)	£250–275

Miniature	Early pierced crown £75–85
	Later solid crown £50–65

130. CAPE OF GOOD HOPE GENERAL SERVICE MEDAL

Date: 1900.
Campaign: Uprisings in Transkei, Basutoland and Bechuanaland 1880-97.
Branch of Service: Local forces and volunteers.
Ribbon: Dark blue with a central yellow stripe.
Metal: Silver.
Size: 36mm.
Description: (Obverse) Jubilee bust of Queen Victoria by Sir Joseph Boehm; (reverse) arms of Cape Colony.
Clasps: Transkei, Basutoland, Bechuanaland.
Comments: *Instituted by the Cape government, this medal acknowledged service in putting down the Transkei (September 1880–May 1881), Basutoland (September 1880–April 1881) and Bechuanaland (December 1896–July 1897) rebellions in those areas. The medal was awarded, with one or more campaign clasps, to local forces and volunteer regiments. Recent research has shown that the medal could not be awarded without a clasp. The previously held notion that ten medals were awarded without clasps, was brought about by an error in transcribing the medal rolls.*

VALUE:

			Miniature
i.	Transkei (562)	£375–450	£50–60
ii.	Basutoland (1589)	£250–350	£50–60
iii.	Bechuanaland (2483)	£225–300	£50–60
	2 clasps (585)	£350–475	£65–80
	3 clasps (23)	£3000–4000	—

131. EGYPT MEDAL 1882–89

Date: 1882.
Campaign: Egypt 1882–89.
Branch of Service: Royal Navy and Army.
Ribbon: Three blue and two white stripes, (the Blue and White Niles).
Metal: Silver.
Size: 36mm.
Description: (Obverse) the veiled profile of Queen Victoria; (reverse) the Sphinx.
Clasps: 14, listed below. Maximum number for one medal is 7, but only one such award was made. Common two-clasp combinations are denoted below by /.
Comments: *British involvement in Egypt deepened after the opening of the Suez Canal in 1869, many British officers being seconded to the Khedive's Army. When the Army mutinied in 1882 and triggered off a general anti-European uprising, an Anglo-French expedition was mounted. Subsequently the French withdrew before a landing was effected. Trouble erupted in the Sudan (under Anglo-Egyptian administration) in 1884 where General Gordon was besieged at Khartoum. Further campaigns aimed at the overthrow of the Mahdi and the reconquest of the Sudan. These prolonged operations created immense logistical problems. Nile transportation in particular was a matter resolved only when Canadian* voyageurs *were recruited to handle the river-boats. In addition, a contingent of troops from New South Wales "answered the Empire's call" and medals awarded to them for the Suakin campaign of 1885 are much sought after. Except where noted, the prices quoted below are for medals awarded to British Army personnel. Medals awarded to Indian or Egyptian troops are generally worth about 25 per cent less than comparable awards to British Army units.*

Dated rev.

Undated rev.

VALUE:

			Miniature
i.	No clasp (dated)	£120–175	£30–35
ii.	No clasp (undated)	£120–175	£30–35
iii.	Alexandria 11th July	£250–300	£45–50
iv.	Tel-el-Kebir	£250–300	£45–50
v.	El-Teb	£325–375	£45–50
vi.	Tamaai	£325–375	£45–50
vii.	El-Teb–Tamaai	£300–350	£45–50
viii.	Suakin 1884	£250–300	£45–50
ix.	The Nile 1884-85	£250–300	£45–50
x.	The Nile 1884-85/Abu Klea	£700–1000	£45–50
xi.	The Nile 1884-85/Kirbekan	£350–400	£45–50
xii.	Suakin 1885	£250–300	£45–50
xiii.	Suakin 1885/Tofrek	£350–400	£45–50
xiv.	Gemaizah 1888	£280–325	£45–55
xv.	Toski 1889	£450–650	£55–65
xvi.	Gemaizah 1888-Toski 1889		
	Egyptian troops	£260–300	
	20th Hussars	£350–450	
2 clasps		£250–300	Add £15
3 clasps		£350–450	for each
4 clasps		£450–550	clasp
5 clasps		£1250–2000	—
Canadian boatmen		£1500–2000	
NSW units (Suakin 1885)		£3500–4000	

132. KHEDIVE'S STAR

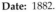

Date: 1882.
Campaign: Egypt 1882–91.
Branch of Service: Royal Navy and Army.
Ribbon: 37mm deep blue.
Metal: Bronze.
Size: Height 60mm; width 45mm.
Description: A five-pointed star with a circular centre showing the Sphinx and Pyramids surrounded by a band inscribed EGYPT followed by a year round the top, with "Khedive of Egypt" and the year in the Moslem calendar in Arabic at the foot. (Reverse) the Khedive's monogram surmounted by a crown. The star is suspended by a ring from an ornamental clasp in the centre of which is a star and crescent.
Clasps: Tokar.
Comments: *This star, struck by Jenkins of Birmingham, was conferred by Khedive Tewfik of Egypt on those who qualified for the Egypt medal and it was invariably worn alongside, to the detriment of the silver medal which suffered abrasion from the points of the star. There was also an undated version found with or without a campaign clasp for Tokar, awarded in 1891. These stars were issued unnamed.*

VALUE:

			Miniature
i.	1882	£65–100	£15–20
ii.	1884	£65–100	£14–18
iii.	1884-86	£65–100	£20–25
iv.	Undated	£65–100	£20–25
v.	Undated with Tokar bar	£200–250	£75-120

133. GENERAL GORDON'S STAR FOR THE SIEGE OF KHARTOUM

Date: 1884.
Campaign: Mahdist uprising, Sudan 1884.
Branch of Service: British and Sudanese forces.
Ribbon: Deep blue or red.
Metal: Silver or pewter.
Size: Height 80mm; maximum width 54mm.
Description: Star with three concentric circles and seven groups of rays on which are superimposed seven crescents and stars. Suspension by a ring from a Crescent and Star ornament.
Clasps: None.
Comments: *To boost the morale of the defenders Charles Gordon, commanding the garrison at Khartoum, had this star cast locally in a sand mould, using his own breast star of the Order of Mejidieh as the model. Exceptionally, recipients had to purchase their medals, the proceeds going to a fund to feed the poor.*

VALUE:

Silver gilt	£1000–1200
Silver	£750–1000
Pewter	£600–800

134. NORTH WEST CANADA MEDAL

Date: 1885.

Campaign: Riel's rebellion 1885.

Branch of Service: Mainly local forces.

Ribbon: Blue-grey with red stripes towards the edges.

Metal: Silver.

Size: 36mm.

Description: (Obverse) bust of Queen Victoria; (reverse) the inscription NORTH WEST CANADA 1885 within a frame of maple leaves.

Clasps: Saskatchewan,

Comments: *Paradoxically, while the medal for the Fenian Raids of 1866–70 was not sanctioned till 1899, this medal for service in the North West was authorised immediately after the conclusion of operations against the Metis led by Louis Riel. It was issued unnamed, with or without the clasp for Saskatchewan where the bulk of the action took place. Of particular interest are medals to officers and men aboard the steamship Northcote involved in a boat action; exceptionally, their medals were impressed. Other medals may be encountered with unofficial naming. The medal was awarded to sixteen British staff officers but the majority of medals (5600 in all) went to local forces.*

VALUE:

			Miniature
i.	No clasp	£450–500	£55–65
ii.	Saskatchewan	£850–1000	£70–80
	Northcote recipient	£2800–3200	

135. ROYAL NIGER COMPANY'S MEDAL

Date: 1899.

Campaign: Nigeria 1886–97.

Branch of Service: Officers and men of the Company's forces.

Ribbon: Three equal stripes of yellow, black and white.

Metal: Silver or bronze.

Size: 39.5mm.

Description: (Obverse) the Boehm bust of Queen Victoria; (reverse) the Company's arms in a laurel wreath.

Clasps: Nigeria 1886-97 (silver), Nigeria (bronze).

Comments: *This medal was issued in silver to Europeans and bronze to natives for service in the vast territories administered by the Royal Niger chartered company. Silver medals were impressed in capitals, but those in bronze were more usually stamped with the recipient's service (constabulary) number. Specimens of both versions were later struck from the original dies but these lack name or number.*

VALUE:

		Miniature
Silver named (85)	£3000–4000	no clasp £175–220
Silver specimen	£80–100	—
Bronze oficially numbered (250)	£650–850	Nigeria clasp £210–260
Bronze specimen	£60–80	—

136. IMPERIAL BRITISH EAST AFRICA COMPANY'S MEDAL

Date: 1890.
Campaign: East Africa (Kenya and Uganda) 1888–95.
Branch of Service: Company forces.
Ribbon: Plain dark blue.
Metal: Silver.
Size: 40mm.
Description: (Obverse) the Company badge, a crowned and radiant sun, with a Suaheli inscription in Arabic round the foot signifying "the reward of bravery"; (reverse) plain except for a wreath. Suspension is by a plain ring or an ornamental scroll.
Comments: *The rarest of the medals awarded by the chartered companies, this medal was originally intended solely as a gallantry award; but after the BEA Company was wound up in 1895 further issues were authorised by the Foreign Office for service in Witu (1890) and the Ugandan civil war (1890-91). Fewer than thirty medals are known.*

VALUE: £4000–5000   *Miniature* £330–460

137. EAST AND WEST AFRICA MEDAL

Date: 1892.
Campaigns: East and West Africa 1887–1900.
Branch of Service: Royal Navy, Army and native forces.
Ribbon: As 126.
Metal: Silver or bronze.
Size: 36mm.
Description: As the Ashantee Medal (no. 126), distinguished only by its clasps.
Clasps: 22 (see below). A 22nd operation (Mwele, 1895–96) was denoted by engraving on the rim of the medal.
Comments: *This medal was awarded for general service in a number of small campaigns and punitive expeditions. Though usually awarded in silver, it was sometimes struck in bronze for issue to native servants, bearers and drivers. British regiments as such were not involved in any of the actions, but individual officers and NCOs were seconded as staff officers and instructors and their medals bear the names of their regiments. Units of the Royal Navy were also involved in many of the coastal or river actions. Especially sought after are naval medals with the bar for Lake Nyassa 1893 in which the ships* Pioneer *and* Adventure *were hauled in sections overland through 200 miles of jungle.*

VALUE:		Royal Navy	Europeans	Natives	Miniature
i.	1887–8	£850–1250	£425–625	£400–450	£45–50
ii.	Witu 1890	£200–250	£200–250	£150–180	£50–55
iii.	1891–2	£225–275	£200–250	£150–180	£50–55
iv.	1892	£1250–1500	£200–250	£150–180	£50–55
v.	Witu August 1893	£225–250	—	£150–180	£65–75
vi.	Liwondi 1893	£2250–2500	—	—	—
vii.	Juba River 1893	£2250–2500	—	—	—
viii.	Lake Nyassa 1893	£2500–3500	—	—	—
ix.	1893–94	£750–900	£200–250	£150–180	£55–65
x.	Gambia 1894	£325–375	—	£150–180	£55–65
xi.	Benin River 1894	£350–400	£200–250	£150–180	£45–55
xii.	Brass River 1895	£325–375	—	—	£50–55
xiii.	M'wele 1895–6 (Bronze)	£400–450	£300–350	£200–250 £800–1000	£110
xiv.	1896–98	—	£375–475	£220–300	£35–50
xv.	Niger 1897	—	£375–425	£220–300	£50–60
xvi.	Benin 1897	£300–350	£200–250	£220–300	£40–50
xvii.	Dawkita 1897	—	—	—	£110
xviii.	1897–98	—	£325–425	£220–250	£50–55
xix.	1898	£725–950	£325–425	£220–250	£50–55
xx.	Sierra Leone 1898–9	£225–275	£325–425	£220–250	£50–55
xxi.	1899	£925–1250	£325–375	£220–250	£50–55
xxii.	1900	—	£325–375	£220–250	£50–55
	2 clasps	£475–525	£325–375	£250–300	
	3 clasps	£575–675	—	£350–400	—
	4 clasps	—	—	£450–500	—

138. BRITISH SOUTH AFRICA COMPANY'S MEDAL

1st type rev.

Mashonaland (2nd) rev.

Date: 1896.
Campaign: South Africa 1890-97.
Branch of Service: British Army and colonial units.
Ribbon: Seven equal stripes, four yellow and three dark blue.
Metal: Silver.
Size: 36mm.
Description: (Obverse) the Old Head bust of Queen Victoria; (reverse) a charging lion impaled by a spear, with a mimosa bush in the background and a litter of assegais and a shield on the ground.
Clasps: Mashonaland 1890, Matabeleland 1893, Rhodesia 1896, Mashonaland 1897.
Comments: *Originally instituted in 1896 for award to troops taking part in the suppression of the Matabele rebellion of 1893, it was later extended to cover operations in Rhodesia (1896) and Mashonaland (1897). The medal, as originally issued, had the inscription MATABELELAND 1893 at the top of the reverse. The medal was re-issued with RHODESIA 1896 or MASHONALAND 1897 inscribed on the reverse, but holders of medals for their first campaign only added clasps for subsequent campaigns. Rather belatedly, it was decided in 1927 to issue medals retrospectively for the Mashonaland campaign of 1890; in this instance the name and date of the campaign were not inscribed on the reverse though the details appeared on the clasp. Although 705 men were entitled, only 200 claimed the medal and clasp. An unusually ornate suspender has roses, thistles, shamrocks and leeks entwined. Only two medals are known with all four clasps, while only fifteen medals had three clasps.*

VALUE:

		Miniature
a. Undated reverse with		
Mashonaland 1890 clasp	£850–1000	£55–65
i. Matabeleland 1893	Rare	—
ii. Rhodesia 1896	Rare	—
iii. Mashonaland 1897	Rare	—
b. Matabeleland 1893 rev.	£300–350	£45–50
ii.Rhodesia 1896	£450–500	£55–65
iii. Mashonaland 1897	£450–500	£55–65
with 2 clasps	£650–850	£70–80
c. Rhodesia 1896 rev.	£300–350	£55–65
iii. Mashonaland 1897	£560–600	£65–75
d. Mashonaland 1897	£300–350	£55–65

Shangani Patrol confirmed member £1800–2200

139. HUNZA NAGAR BADGE

Date: 1891.
Campaign: Hunza and Nagar 1891.
Branch of Service: Jammu and Kashmir forces.
Ribbon: Large (46mm x 32mm) with a broad red diagonal band and white centre stripe and green upper left and lower right corners.
Metal: Bronze.
Size: 55mm x 27mm.
Description: A uniface rectangular plaque featuring three soldiers advancing on the crenellated hill fort of Nilt, with mountains in the background. The inscription HUNZA NAGAR 1891 appears lower right. It was intended to be worn as a brooch at the neck but subsequently many were fitted with a suspender for wear with a red and green ribbon. The reverse is impressed "Woodstock St."
Clasps: None.
Comments: *Gurney of London manufactured this badge which was awarded by the Maharajah of Jammu and Kashmir to his own troops who served in the operation against the border states of Hunza and Nagar and qualified for the Indian general service medal with clasp for Hunza 1891. The punitive expedition was led by Colonel A. Durand in response to the defiant attitude of the Hunza and Nagar chiefs towards the British agency at Gilgit.*
VALUE: £500–650

140. CENTRAL AFRICA MEDAL

Date: 1895.
Campaigns: Central Africa 1891–98.
Branch of Service: Mainly local forces.
Ribbon: Three equal stripes of black, white and terracotta representing the Africans, Europeans and Indians.
Metal: Silver or bronze.
Size: 36mm.
Description: Obverse and reverse as the East and West Africa (Ashantee) medal, distinguished only by its ribbon.
Clasps: Originally issued without a clasp but one for Central Africa 1894–98 was subsequently authorised.
Comment: *Though generally issued in silver, a bronze version was awarded to native servants. The first issue of this medal had a simple ring suspension and no clasp. For the second issue a clasp, Central Africa 1894–98 was authorised and the medal was issued with a straight bar suspender, which is very rare.*

VALUE:		Miniature
Without clasp (ring suspension)		£75–100
To natives	£600–800	
To Europeans	£2000–3000	
With clasp (ring suspension)		£85–120
To natives	£1200–1500	
To Europeans	£2500–3500	
With clasp (bar suspension)	£1200–1500	£85–120
To Navy native	£2500–3000	
Bronze, unnamed	From £500	—

141. HONG KONG PLAGUE MEDAL

Date: 1894.
Campaign: Hong Kong, May-September 1894.
Branch of Service: Royal Navy, Royal Engineers, KSLI and local personnel.
Ribbon: Red with yellow edges and two narrow yellow stripes in the centre.
Metal: Silver.
Size: 36mm.
Description: (Obverse) a Chinese patient lying on a trestle table being supported by a man warding off the winged figure of Death while a woman tends the sick man. The year 1894 appears on a scroll in the exergue, while the name of the colony in Chinese pictograms is inscribed on the left of the field. (Reverse) inscribed PRESENTED BY THE HONG KONG COMMUNITY round the circumference, and FOR SERVICES RENDERED DURING THE PLAGUE OF 1894 in seven lines across the centre. It was fitted with a plain ring for suspension.
Clasps: None.
Comments: *The colonial authorities in Hong Kong awarded this medal to nurses, civil servants, police, British Army and Royal Navy personnel who rendered assistance when the crown colony was stricken by a severe epidemic of bubonic plague in May 1894. Despite stringent measures, over 2500 people died in the ensuing three months. About 400 medals were issued in silver and awarded to 300 men of the King's Shropshire Light Infantry, 50 petty officers and ratings of the Royal Navy and NCOs and other ranks of the Royal Engineers, as well as about the same number of police and junior officials, while 45 were struck in gold for award to officers, nursing sisters and senior officials. However, the medal was not authorised for wear on uniform by British troops.*

VALUE:		Miniature
		£225–310
Gold (45)	£6500–10,000	£175–250
Silver (400)	£1600–1800	

142. INDIA MEDAL

Date: 1896.
Campaign: India 1895–1902.
Branch of Service: British and Indian forces.
Ribbon: Crimson with two dark green stripes—the heraldic colour of Britain and the sacred colour of the prophet.
Metal: Silver or bronze.
Size: 36mm.
Description: Issued with two different obverses, portraying Queen Victoria (1895–1901) and King Edward VII in field marshal's uniform (1901–02). (Reverse) British and Indian soldiers supporting a standard. The Edward VII reverse is undated.
Clasps: Seven, mainly for actions on the North West Frontier (see below).
Comments: *This medal replaced the India GSM which had been awarded for various minor campaigns over a period of four decades from 1854. Combatant troops were given the medal in silver but native bearers and servants received a bronze version. Although the clasp Waziristan 1901–2 is rare to British recipients it was awarded to a number of regiments.*

VALUE:

	British regiments	Indian Army	Bronze	Miniature
i. Defence of Chitral 1895	—	£200–300	£300–400	£90–110
ii. Relief of Chitral 1895	£200–225	£160–185	£135–185	£30–35
iii. Punjab Frontier 1897–98	£200–225	£160–185	£110–160	£25–30
iv. Malakand 1897*	£500–700	£195–260	£160–210	£55–65
v. Samana 1897*	£200–225	£185–210	£110–160	£40–45
vi. Tirah 1897–98*	£200–250	£185–210	£110–160	£50–55
vii. Waziristan 1901–2	£350–450	£185–210	£110–160	£60–70
3 clasps	£275–350	£260–310	£185–260	£55–65
4 clasps	—	£300–350	—	£65–85

*These clasps are always paired with clasp iii.

143. JUMMOO AND KASHMIR MEDAL

Date: 1895.
Campaign: Defence of Chitral 1895.
Branch of Service: Native levies.
Ribbon: White with red stripes at the edges and a central green stripe.
Metal: Bronze, silver.
Size: 35mm high; 38mm wide.
Description: This medal, by Gurney of London, has a unique kidney shape showing the arms of Jummoo (Jammu) and Kashmir on the obverse. (Reverse) a view of Chitral fort with troops in the foreground.
Clasps: Chitral 1895.
Comments: *Awarded by the Maharajah of Jummoo (Jammu) and Kashmir to the Indian troops who participated in the defence of Chitral (a dependency of Kashmir) during the siege of 4 March to 20 April by Chitralis and Afghans led by Umra Khan and Sher Afzul.*

VALUE:

Named	£500–700
Unnamed	£400–600
Silver	—

144. ASHANTI STAR

Date: 1896.
Campaign: Gold Coast 1896.
Branch of Service: British forces.
Ribbon: Yellow with two black stripes.
Metal: Bronze.
Size: 44mm.
Description: A saltire cross with a four-pointed star in the angles, surmounted by a circular belt inscribed ASHANTI 1896 around a British crown. The plain reverse is simply inscribed FROM THE QUEEN.
Clasps: None.
Comments: *Issued unnamed, but the colonel of the West Yorkshire Regiment had the medals of the second battalion engraved at his own expense. Some 2000 stars were awarded to officers and men serving in the expedition led by Major-General F.C. Scott against the tyrannical King Prempeh. It is believed that the star was designed by Princess Henry of Battenberg whose husband died of fever during the campaign.*

VALUE:

Unnamed	£200–250
Named to West Yorkshire Regiment	£600–700
In attributable group	£750–900
Miniature	£50–60

145. QUEEN'S SUDAN MEDAL

Date: 1899.
Campaign: Reconquest of the Sudan 1896–97.
Branch of Service: Royal Navy, Army and local forces.
Ribbon: Half-yellow and half-black representing the desert and the Sudanese nation, divided by a thin crimson stripe representing the British forces.
Metal: Silver or bronze.
Size: 36mm.
Description: (Obverse) the Jubilee bust of Queen Victoria. (Reverse) a seated figure of Victory holding palms and laurels with flags in the background, the word SUDAN appearing on a tablet at her feet.
Clasps: None.
Comments: *Unusually, no clasps were granted for individual actions which included the celebrated battle of Omdurman in which young Winston Churchill charged with the cavalry. Medals named to the 21st Lancers are especially desirable on that account.*

VALUE:

Bronze	
unnamed	£250–300
named	£300–350
Silver	
unnamed	£200–250
named to British Regt	£350–400
Indian Regt	£300–350
21st Lancers	£2500–3000
Confirmed charger*	£3000–3500
RN/RM (46)	£3000–3500
War correspondent	£1500–2000

* *Dependent on which Company the recipient served in.*

Miniature	£40–50

146. KHEDIVE'S SUDAN MEDAL 1896–1908

(reverse)

Date: 1897.
Campaign: Sudan 1896-1908.
Branch of Service: Royal Navy and British and Egyptian Armies.
Ribbon: 38mm yellow with a broad central deep blue stripe, symbolising the desert and the River Nile.
Metal: Silver or bronze.
Size: 39mm.
Description: (Obverse) an elaborate Arabic inscription translating as 'Abbas Hilmi the Second' and the date 1314 (AD 1897); (reverse) an oval shield surrounded by flags and a trophy of arms. Bar suspender.
Clasps: Fifteen (see below) but medals with more than the two clasps 'The Atbara' and 'Khartoum' are unusual. Inscribed in English and Arabic to British recipients.
Comments: *Instituted by the Khedive of Egypt in February 1897 and granted to those who served in the reconquest of Dongola province in the Sudan (1896-8) as well as in subsequent operations for the pacification of the southern provinces. It was awarded to officers and men of the British and Egyptian Armies and Royal Navy personnel who served on the Nile steamboats. In addition, the crews of the Royal Naval ships HMS Melita (139) and HMS Scout (149) were awarded silver medals with no clasps for Dongola 1896 (but were not awarded the Queen's Sudan Medal 1896–98). Medals to Royal Naval personnel with clasps are rare and command a high premium: Hafir (16), The Atbara (6), Sudan 1897 (12), Khartoum (33), Gedaref (9), Gedid (5) and Sudan 1899 (6).*

VALUE:

No clasp silver		
Unnamed	£130–150	
named to British regt	£185–210	
named to Indian regt	£160–185	
named to Royal Navy	£360–460	
No clasp bronze	£160–185	
i. Firket	£160–185	
ii. Hafir	£160–185	
iii. Abu Hamed	£160–185	
iv. Sudan 1897	£160–185	
v. The Atbara	£155–175	
vi. Khartoum	£225–260	
vii. Gedaref	£160–185	
viii. Gedid	£160–185	
ix. Sudan 1899	£160–185	
x. Bahr-el-Ghazal 1900–2	£195–235	
xi. Jerok	£160–185	
xii. Nyam-Nyam	£185–210	
xiii. Talodi	£185–210	
xiv. Katfia	£185–210	
xv. Nyima	£185–210	
2 clasps	£200–250	
3 clasps	£225–260	
4 clasps	£260–300	
5 clasps	£360–450	
6 clasps	£385–450	
7 clasps	£450–500	
8 clasps	£475–550	

Miniature

No clasp silver	£40–55
With any single clasp	£55–85
Add £15 for each additional clasp	

A young, fresh-faced Winston Churchill aged 24 poses in his brand new 4th Hussars dress uniform. He was to be involved in action in the Sudan and his detailed accounts of his experiences there provide an important eye-witness view of this turbulent time in the history of the British Empire.

147. EAST AND CENTRAL AFRICA MEDAL

Date: 1899.
Campaigns: East and Central Africa 1897–99.
Branch of Service: British, Indian and local forces.
Ribbon: Half yellow, half red.
Metal: Silver or bronze.
Size: 36mm.
Description: (Obverse) the Jubilee bust of Queen Victoria; (reverse) a standing figure of Britannia with the British lion alongside.
Clasps: Four (see below).
Comments: *Instituted for service in operations in Uganda and the southern Sudan, it was awarded in silver to combatants and in bronze to camp followers. Most of the medals were awarded to troops of the Uganda Rifles and various Indian regiments. The few British officers and NCOs were troop commanders and instructors seconded from their regiments and their medals are worth very much more than the prices quoted, which are for native awards.*

VALUE:

	Europeans	Natives	*Miniature*
No clasp			
silver	—	£260–285	£50–60
bronze	—	£335–435	—
i. Lubwa's (with clasp			
Uganda 1897-98)	—	£385–485	£80–90
ii. Uganda 1897-98	£800–1000	£335–435	£70–80
iii. 1898 (silver)	—	£335–435	£70–80
iv. 1898 (bronze)	—	£535–635	—
v. Uganda 1899	—	£335–435	£70–80

147A. UGANDA STAR

Instituted: 1897–98.
Campaign: Mutiny of Sudanese troops in Uganda.
Branch of Service: African civilians and soldiers.
Ribbon: None.
Metal: Silver.
Description: An eight-pointed uniface star surmounted by a crown, with the dates 1897 and 1898 on a circular rim enclosing the Old Head or Veiled Bust of Queen Victoria. Brooch-mounted. Manufactured by Carrington of London and issued in a blue plush-lined case.
Comments: *This award, approved by the Foreign Office and sanctioned by Queen Victoria, acknowledged the loyalty of African tribal leaders but, in a few cases, was also awarded to Sudanese troops (one, in fact, a Tunisian) who fought gallantly in quelling the serious mutiny of Sudanese troops of the Uganda Rifles. It was for this action that British, Indian and Local forces were awarded the East and Central Africa Medal with the bar for Lubwa's (see above). Only 39 stars were awarded.*

VALUE: From £2500

148. BRITISH NORTH BORNEO COMPANY'S MEDAL 1888–1916

Instituted: 1897.

Campaign: North Borneo (now Sabah, Malaysia), 1897-1916.

Ribbon: Initially gold (later yellow) watered silk 32mm, replaced in 1917 by a 32mm ribbon with maroon edges, two yellow stripes and a dark blue central stripe. The central stripe was originally 6mm wide but modern ribbons have a 10mm stripe.

Metal: Silver or bronze.

Size: 38mm, with a thickness of 5mm.

Description: (Obverse) the shield of the Company, supported by a warrior on either side. The Company motto at the foot is PERGO ET PERAGO (I carry on and accomplish); (reverse) the British lion facing left, standing in front of a bush adorned with the Company flag, with a small wreath in the exergue.

Clasps: Punitive Expedition (1897), Punitive Expeditions (1898-1915), Rundum (1915). The Punitive Expeditions clasp was awarded to those who took part in two or more actions, but it also replaced the earlier single Expedition clasp in due course.

Comments: *These medals were awarded for service in the 15 minor expeditions between 1883 and 1915, excluding the major action at Tambunan. The manufacturers, Spink, supplied 12 silver medals in 1898–9 for award to officers (only three being named). In 1906 a further 74 silver medals were issued, to be exchanged for the bronze medals initially awarded to other ranks. A further 11 silver medals were supplied later on, all unnamed. A total of 75 bronze medals were supplied, 25 of them stamped with a name and sometimes rank and number as well, and issued, both stamped and engraved, to other ranks.*

First type ribbon.   *Second type ribbon.*

VALUE:

		Type	Officially Named	Unnamed original	Spink copy	Stamped "Specimen"	Miniature
i.	Punitive Expedition	Silver	£1500–2000	£350–500	£50–60	£60–80	£180–200
		Bronze	£1500–2000	£350–500	£50–60	£60–80	
ii.	Punitive Expeditions	Silver	£1500–2000	£350–500	£50–60	£60–80	£180–200
		Bronze	£1500–2000	£350–500	£50–60	£60–80	
iii.	Rundum	Silver	£1500–2000	£350–500	£50–60	£60–80	£180–200

148A. BRITISH NORTH BORNEO COMPANY'S MEDAL 1899–1900

Instituted: 1900.
Campaign: The final expedition in the Tambunan Valley against Mat Salleh.
Ribbon: 32mm yellow with a 10mm green stripe down the centre.
Metal: Silver or bronze.
Size: 38mm. Officially named medals are 5mm thick.
Description: (Obverse) the shield of the British North Borneo Company with BRITISH NORTH BORNEO round the top and the date 1900 below; (reverse) a wreath enclosing a device of one clothed and one naked arm supporting the Company's flag. The motto PERGO ET PERAGO is inscribed outside the wreath. The inscription SPINK & SON, LONDON appears in very tiny lettering at the foot.
Clasps: Tambunan.
Comments: *Instituted for award to those officers and men who took part in the expedition of January-February 1900 against Mat Salleh who had roused the Tegas against the Tiawan Dusuns in the Tambunan Valley. Salleh was killed on February 1, 1900 when Company forces stormed his stronghold and his followers were dispersed or killed. Eight silver medals were originally awarded to officers, but in 1906 some 106 were issued to be exchanged for the bronze medals initially issued to other ranks. A further 22 silver medals were later supplied, unnamed. A total of 125 bronze medals were supplied, 118 of them stamped with a name and sometimes also a rank and number, and issued, both stamped and engraved, to other ranks. Only 36 are recorded as replaced by silver medals, but it is known that some of these bronze medals were not returned to the authorities.*

VALUE:

Type	Officially Named	Unnamed original	Spink copy	Stamped "Specimen"
Silver	£1800–2000	£300–500	£50–60	£60–80
Bronze	£1000–1500	£300–500	£50–60	£60–80
Miniature	£175–200			

149. SULTAN OF ZANZIBAR'S MEDAL

Date: 1896.
Campaign: East Africa 1896.
Branch of Service: Sultan's forces.
Ribbon: Plain bright scarlet.
Metal: Silver.
Size: 36mm.
Description: (Obverse) a facing bust of Sultan Hamid bin Thwain surrounded by a Suaheli inscription in Arabic; (reverse) same inscription set in four lines.
Clasps: Pumwani, Jongeni, Takaungu, Mwele (inscribed only in Arabic).
Comments: *Awarded to the Zanzibari contingent who served under Lieut. Lloyd-Matthews RN in East Africa alongside British and Imperial forces.*

VALUE: £400–500   *Miniature* £580–680

150. QUEEN'S SOUTH AFRICA MEDAL

Date: 1899.

Campaign: Anglo-Boer War 1899-1902.

Branch of Service: British and Imperial forces.

Ribbon: Red with two narrow blue stripes and a broad central orange stripe.

Metal: Silver or bronze.

Size: 36mm.

Description: (Obverse) the Jubilee bust of Queen Victoria; (reverse) Britannia holding the flag and a laurel crown towards a large group of soldiers, with warships offshore. The words SOUTH AFRICA are inscribed round the top.

Clasps: 26 authorised but the maximum recorded for a single medal is nine to the Army and eight to the Navy.

Comments: *Because of the large number of British and imperial forces which took part and the numerous campaign and battle clasps awarded, this is one of the most popular and closely studied of all medals, offering immense scope to the collector. A total of 250,000 medals were awarded. Numerous specialist units were involved for the first time, as well as locally raised units and contingents from India, Canada, Australia and New Zealand. Of particular interest are the medals awarded to war correspondents and nurses which set precedents for later wars. Although nurses received the medal they were not issued with clasps to which they were entitled. A small number of bronze medals without a clasp were issued to bearers and servants in Indian units. The original issue of the QSA depicts Britannia's outstretched hand pointing towards the R of AFRICA and bears the dates 1899–1900 on the reverse field. Less than 70 of these were issued to Lord Strathcona's Horse who had returned to Canada before the war ended, but as the war dragged on the date was removed before any other medals were issued, although some medals can be found with a "ghost" of this date still to be seen. On the third type reverse there is again no date but Britannia's hand points towards the F. The prices for clasps given overleaf are for*

clasps issued in combination with others. Some clasps are much scarcer when issued singly than combined with other clasps and conversely some clasps are not recorded on their own. Verified ten-clasp medals to South African units are known. It is important to note that the following list is very basic and represents the value of straightforward medals and clasps. Confusion can sometimes occur as single clasps and combinations of two or three clasps can command higher premiums than medals with a greater number of clasps. It is beyond the remit of this book to give the value of every possible combination of clasps. A very rough guide would be to take the most valuable clasp as a starting point and add 25% of this value for each Battle clasp and 10% for each State clasp, however, this is by no means infallible. An example would be to take a three-clasp medal which has Elandslaagte (£350–400), Belfast (£80–90) and Relief of Kimberley (£80–100) which as a simple 3-clasp medal would be valued at £100–130—however, on the rough guide system it would be valued at c. £550. Certain clasp combinations will always command a higher premium, for example Relief of Ladysmith/ Relief of Mafeking, Defence of Ladysmith/Relief of Mafeking, Elandslaagte/Defence of Ladysmith, Defence of Kimberley/Paardeberg, etc. Clasps for Natal and Cape Colony cannot appear on the same medal.

1st type rev.

2nd type rev.
(occasionally ghost dates can be seen)

3rd type rev.

150. QUEEN'S SOUTH AFRICA MEDAL *continued*

VALUE:	RN	British Army	SA/Indian	Aus/NZ	Canadian
No clasp bronze	—	—	£150–250	—	—
No clasp silver	£150–160	£75–85	£75–85	£125–175	£125–175
i. Cape Colony	£180–200	£75–85	£80–100	£125–175	£125–175
ii. Rhodesia	£1000–1250	£350–400	£300–350	£350–400	£350–400
iii. Relief of Mafeking	—	—	£350–450	£400–500	£400–450
iv. Defence of Kimberley	—	£300–325	£220–250	—	—
v. Talana	—	£350–400	£250–350	—	—
vi. Elandslaagte	—	£350–450	£300–350	—	—
vii. Defence of Ladysmith	£750–850	£300–350	£200–250	—	—
viii. Belmont	£300–350	£125–150	—	£250–300	—
ix. Modder River	£300–350	£125–150	—	£250–300	—
x. Tugela Heights	£300–350	£100–125	—	—	—
xi. Natal	£300–350	£100–160	£120–150	—	£220–250
xii. Relief of Kimberley	£750–950	£125–150	£80–100	£125–175	—
xiii. Paardeberg	£250–300	£100–125	£80–100	£125–175	£175–200
xiv. Orange Free State	£180–225	£85–125	£65–85	£125–175	£175–200
xv. Relief of Ladysmith	£250–300	£100–135	£80–100	—	—
xvi. Driefontein	£240–260	£85–125	—	£125–175	£225–275
xvii. Wepener	—	£600–800	£400–450	—	—
xviii. Defence of Mafeking	—	—	£1000–1750	—	—
xix. Transvaal	£450–600	£85–100	£65–85	£100–150	£225–275
xx. Johannesburg	£250–300	£85–100	£80–90	£125–175	£125–175
xxi. Laing's Nek	£500–650	£85–100	—	—	—
xxii. Diamond Hill	£250–300	£85–100	£80–90	£125–175	£200–225
xxiii. Wittebergen	£1000–1200	£85–100	£80–90	£125–175	—
xxiv. Belfast	£250–300	£85–100	£80–90	£125–175	£125–175
xxv. South Africa 1901	£125–150	£75–90	£65–75	£85–125	£100–150
xxvi. South Africa 1902	£750–850	£75–90	£60–65	£85–125	£100–150
2 clasps *(see Comment above)*	£180–220	£95–150	£85–95	£175–200	£175–200
3 clasps "	£250–280	£100–165	£120–145	£185–225	£185–225
4 clasps	£300–350	£125–175	£120–150	£225–275	£225–275
5 clasps*	£380–450	£135–185	£120–155	£275–300	£225–275
6 clasps*	£550–650	£155–200	£180–200	£325–375	£325–375
7 clasps*	£800–900	£450–500	£400–450	£850–1000	—
To Royal Marines	£1600–1800				
8 clasps*	£1800–2000	£800–1000	£2000–3000	—	—
9 clasps	—	—	£3500–4000	—	—
Relief dates on reverse (Lord Strathcona's Horse)	—	—	—	—	£3000–3800
Nurses	—	£350–500	—	—	—
War Correspondents	—	£1150–1250	—	—	—

* excluding date clasps

Miniature
From £20 with no clasp to £50 with 6 fixed clasps—"slip-on" style clasps approx. 20% less.
With dated reverse £125–175

151. QUEEN'S MEDITERRANEAN MEDAL

Date: 1899.
Campaign: Mediterranean garrisons 1899-1902.
Branch of Service: British militia forces.
Ribbon: Red with two narrow dark blue stripes and a central broad orange stripe (as for Queen's South Africa Medal).
Metal: Silver.
Size: 36mm.
Description: Similar to the Queen's South Africa Medal but inscribed MEDITERRANEAN at the top of the reverse.
Clasps: None.
Comments: *Awarded to officers and men of the militia battalions which were sent to Malta and Gibraltar to take over garrison duty from the regular forces who were drafted to the Cape.*

VALUE:

Silver (5000)	£300–375	*Miniature*	£75–85

152. KING'S SOUTH AFRICA MEDAL

Date: 1902.
Campaign: South Africa 1901–02.
Branch of Service: British and imperial forces.
Ribbon: Three equal stripes of green, white and orange.
Metal: Silver.
Size: 36mm.
Description: (Obverse) bust of King Edward VII in field marshal's uniform; (reverse) as for Queen's medal.
Clasps: Two: South Africa 1901, South Africa 1902.
Comments: *This medal was never issued without the Queen's medal and was awarded to all personnel engaged in operations in South Africa in 1901–02 when fighting was actually confined to numerous skirmishes with isolated guerrilla bands. Very few medals were awarded to RN personnel as the naval brigades had been disbanded in 1901. Apart from about 600 nurses and a few odd men who received the medal without a clasp, this medal was awarded with two clasps—most men were entitled to both clasps, single clasp medals being very rare. Only 137 were awarded to New Zealand troops.*

VALUE:

No clasp (Conductors and associated ranks in the ASC (106) and nurses (587))	£300–400
Two clasps:	
i. South Africa 1901	
ii. South Africa 1902	
RN (33)	£1500–1800
Army	£85–125
Canada (160)	£125–175
Australia (*not issued on its own, in a pair with any QSA to an Australian*)	£2500–2600
New Zealand	£300–350
South African units	£85–125
St John Ambulance Brigade (12)	£300–350
Single clasp 1902 (ii) (502 to Imperial troops, none known for Colonial troops)	From £200
Miniature	
No clasp	£15–20
2 clasps	£20–25

152A. ST ANDREW'S AMBULANCE ASSOCIA-TION MEDAL FOR SOUTH AFRICA

Date: 1902.
Campaign: South Africa 1899–1902.
Branch of Service: St Andrew's Ambulance Association.
Ribbon: Plain white silk.
Metal: Silver.
Size: 31x20mm.
Description: An oval medal: (obverse) the Geneva cross surmounted on a rayed star in red enamel with SOUTH AFRICA above and 1900 below surrounded by the inscription SCOTTISH NATIONAL RED CROSS HOSPITAL; (reverse) the arms of the Association: St Andrew in front of the cross, with ST ANDREW'S AMBULANCE ASSOCIATION around.
Clasps: None.
Comments: *This small medal was awarded in 3 classes, Bronze, Silver and Gold. The Gold medal was given to senior staff of the 160-strong Scottish Hospital, including Sir George Cayley (late IMS) who commanded; the Silver to Officers, Nurses, and Civil Surgeons and the Bronze to the OR's who served. The Bronze variety has been seen named in small impressed capitals on the rim at 6 o'clock. All Varieties of the medal are rare.*
VALUE: Rare *Miniature* —

153. ST JOHN AMBULANCE BRIGADE MEDAL FOR SOUTH AFRICA

Date: 1902.
Campaign: South Africa 1899–1902.
Branch of Service: St John Ambulance Brigade.
Ribbon: Black with narrow white edges.
Metal: Bronze.
Size: 37mm.
Description: (Obverse) King Edward VII; (reverse) the arms of the Order and SOUTH AFRICA and the dates 1899 and 1902 with the legend in Latin around.
Clasps: None.
Comments: *Issued by the Order of St John of Jerusalem to the members of its ambulance brigade who served during the Boer War or who played an active part in the organisation, mobilisation and supply roles. Medals were engraved on the edge with the recipient's name and unit. It is most often associated with the two South Africa medals, but 14 members who went on from South Africa to serve during the Boxer Rebellion were also awarded the China Medal.*

VALUE: Bronze (1,871) £350–450 *Miniature* **£175–200** *(in silver slightly less)*

153A. NATIONAL FIRE BRIGADE'S UNION MEDAL FOR SOUTH AFRICA

Date: 1902.
Campaign: South Africa 1899–1902.
Branch of Service: National Fire Brigade's Union.
Ribbon: Red with narrow orange edges and two orange stripes near the centre.
Metal: Silver.
Size: 36mm.
Description: (Obverse) King Edward VII; (reverse) A bust of a helmeted fireman with a Geneva cross in the sky above. Around the circumference a spray of laurel leaves between the dates 1899 and 1902 and SOUTH AFRICA at top.
Comments: *Awarded to a small detachment of volunteers of the National Fire Brigades Union (Ambulance Department) who served in South Africa as stretcher bearers and ambulance personnel. Each volunteeer also received the St John Ambulance Medal for South Africa and the Queen's South Africa Medal with the clasp Cape Colony. Only 42 were awarded.*
VALUE: £1200–1500 *Miniature (silver)* **£220–350**

154. KIMBERLEY STAR

Date: 1900.
Campaign: Defence of Kimberley 1899–1902.
Branch of Service: British and local forces.
Ribbon: Half yellow, half black, separated by narrow stripes of red, white and blue.
Metal: Silver.
Size: Height 43mm; max. width 41mm.
Description: A six-pointed star with ball finials and a circular centre inscribed KIMBERLEY 1899–1900 with the civic arms in the middle. (Reverse) plain, apart from the inscription MAYOR'S SIEGE MEDAL 1900. Suspended by a plain ring from a scrolled bar.
Clasps: None
Comments: *The Mayor and council of Kimberley awarded this and the following medal to the defenders of the mining town against the Boer forces. Two medals were struck in gold but about 5000 were produced in silver. Those with the "a" Birmingham hallmark for 1900 rate a premium over stars with later date letters.*

VALUE:

Hallmark "a"	£350–400	*Miniature*	£145–175
Later date letters	£300–350		

155. KIMBERLEY MEDAL

Date: 1900.
Campaign: Defence of Kimberley 1899–1900.
Branch of Service: Local forces.
Ribbon: As above.
Metal: Silver
Size: 38mm.
Description: (Obverse) the figure of Victory above the Kimberley Town Hall, with the dates 1899–1900 in the exergue. (Reverse) two shields inscribed INVESTED 15 OCT. 1899 and RELIEVED 15 FEB. 1900. The imperial crown appears above and the royal cypher underneath, with the legend TO THE GALLANT DEFENDERS OF KIMBERLEY round the circumference.
Comments: *Although awarded for the same purpose as MY154, this silver medal is a much scarcer award.*

VALUE: £1400–1800

156. YORKSHIRE IMPERIAL YEOMANRY MEDAL

Date: 1900.
Campaign: South Africa 1900–02.
Branch of Service: Yorkshire Imperial Yeomanry.
Ribbon: Dark blue with a central yellow stripe.
Metal: Silver.
Size: 38mm.
Description: Three versions were produced. The first two had the numeral 3 below the Prince of Wales's feathers and may be found with the dates 1900–1901 or 1901–1902, while the third type has the figures 66, denoting the two battalions involved. The uniform reverse has the white rose of Yorkshire surmounted by an imperial crown and enclosed in a laurel wreath with the legend A TRIBUTE FROM YORKSHIRE.
Comments: *Many medals were produced locally and awarded to officers and men of county regiments. The medals struck by Spink and Son for the Yorkshire Imperial Yeomanry, however, are generally more highly regarded as they were much more extensively issued, and therefore more commonly met with.*

VALUE:

		Miniature
3rd Battalion 1900–1901	£250–300	£130–150
3rd Battalion 1901–1902	£250–300	£110–130
66th Company 1900–1901	£250–300	Not seen

157. MEDAL FOR THE DEFENCE OF OOKIEP

Date: 1902.
Campaign: Defence of Ookiep 1902.
Branch of Service: British and colonial forces.
Ribbon: Dark brown with a central green stripe.
Metal: Silver or bronze.
Size: 36mm.
Description: (Obverse) a miner and copper-waggon, with the Company name and date of foundation (1888) round the circumference; (reverse) a thirteen-line text. Fitted with a scroll suspender.
Clasps: None.
Comments: *Commonly known as the Cape Copper Co. Medal, this medal was awarded by the Cape Copper Company to those who defended the mining town of Ookiep in Namaqualand when it was besieged from 4 April to 4 May 1902 by a Boer commando led by Jan Christian Smuts, later Field Marshal, Prime Minister of South Africa and a member of the Imperial War Cabinet. The defence was conducted by Lt-Col W. A. D. Shelton, DSO, and Maj J. L. Dean of the Namaqualand Town Guard, the Company's manager. The garrison consisted of 206 European miners, 660 Cape Coloureds, 44 men of the 5th Warwickshire militia and twelve men of the Cape Garrison Artillery.*

VALUE:

Silver (officers)	£6000–8000
Bronze (other ranks)	£1000–1200

158. CHINA WAR MEDAL 1900

Date: 1901.
Campaign: Boxer Rebellion 1900.
Branch of Service: British and imperial forces.
Ribbon: Crimson with yellow edges.
Metal: Silver or bronze.
Size: 36mm.
Description: (Obverse) bust of Queen Victoria; (reverse) trophy of arms, similar to the 1857-60 China Medal but inscribed CHINA 1900 at the foot.
Clasps: Taku Forts, Defence of Legations, Relief of Pekin.
Comments: *Instituted for service during the Boxer Rebellion and the subsequent punitive expeditions, this medal was similar to that of 1857-60 with the date in the exergue altered to 1900. There are three types of naming: in small, impressed capitals for European troops, in large impressed capitals for naval recipients, and in engraved cursive script for Indian forces. The medal was issued in silver to combatants and in bronze to native bearers, drivers and servants. The international community was besieged by the Boxers, members of a secret society, aided and abetted by the Dowager Empress. The relieving force, consisting of contingents from Britain, France, Italy, Russia, Germany and Japan, was under the command of the German field marshal, Count von Waldersee. The British Legation Guard, comprising 80 Royal Marines and a number of 'odd men', won the clasp for Defence of Legations, the most desirable of the campaign bars in this conflict.*

VALUE:	Royal Navy	Army	Indian units	*Miniature*
Silver no clasp	£220–280	£200–280	£130–175	£25–30
Australian naval forces	£2500–3000 (approx. 550 issued)			
Bronze no clasp	—	—	£175–235	—
i. Taku Forts	£600–700	—	—	£35–45
ii. Defence of Legations	£5000–6000	—	—	£55–65
iii. Relief of Pekin:				
Silver	£400–500	£700–750	£275–350	£30–35
Bronze	—	—	£300–350	—
2 clasps	£700–800	—	—	£45–55
No-clasp medal to a nurse	£1500–2000			
To a war correspondent (9)	£1500–2000			
ditto Relief of Pekin (1)	Rare			

159. TRANSPORT MEDAL

Date: 1903.
Campaigns: Boer War 1899-1902 and Boxer Rebellion 1900.
Branch of Service: Mercantile Marine.
Ribbon: Red with two blue stripes.
Metal: Silver.
Size: 36mm.
Description: (Obverse) bust of King Edward VII in the uniform of an Admiral of the Fleet; (reverse) HMST *Ophir* below a map of the world with a Latin inscription at the foot OB PATRIAM MILITIBUS PER MARE TRANSVECTIS ADJUTAM (For carrying troops across the sea).
Clasps: S. Africa 1899-1902, China 1900.
Comments: *The last of the medals associated with the major conflicts at the turn of the century, it was instituted for award to the officers of the merchant vessels used to carry troops and supplies to the wars in South Africa and China. The medal was discontinued as from August 4, 1914.*

VALUE:

		Miniature
i. South Africa 1899–1902 (1219)	£650–750	£80–110
ii. China 1900 (322)	£900–1000	£80–110
Both clasps (178)	£1200–1400	£110–160

160. ASHANTI MEDAL

Date: 1901.
Campaign: Gold Coast 1900.
Branch of Service: British and local forces.
Ribbon: Black with two broad green stripes.
Metal: Silver or bronze.
Size: 36mm.
Description: (Obverse) bust of King Edward VII in field marshal's uniform. (Reverse) a lion on the edge of an escarpment looking towards the sunrise, with a native shield and spears in the foreground. The name ASHANTI appeared on a scroll at the foot.
Clasps: Kumassi.
Comments: *A high-handed action by the colonial governor provoked a native uprising and the siege of the garrison at Kumassi. The medal was awarded to the defenders as well as personnel of the two relieving columns. Very few Europeans were involved as most were in South Africa fighting the Boers. The medal was awarded in silver to combatants and bronze to native transport personnel and servants.*

VALUE:

	Silver	**Bronze**	*Miniature*
No clasp	£300–350	£400–500	£45–65
i. Kumassi	£550–650	Rare	£65–80

161. AFRICA GENERAL SERVICE MEDAL

Date: 1902.
Campaigns: Minor campaigns in Africa 1902 to 1956.
Branch of Service: British and colonial forces.
Ribbon: Yellow with black edges and two thin central green stripes.
Metal: Silver or bronze.
Size: 36mm.
Description: (Obverse) effigies of Edward VII, George V and Elizabeth II; (reverse) similar to that of the East and Central Africa medal of 1897–99, with AFRICA in the exergue.
Clasps: 34 awarded in the reign of Edward VII, ten George V and only one Elizabeth II (see below).

continued overleaf

161. AFRICA GENERAL SERVICE MEDAL *continued*

Comments: *This medal replaced the East and West Africa Medal 1887–1900, to which 21 clasps had already been issued. In turn, it remained in use for 54 years, the longest-running British service medal. Medals to combatants were in silver, but a few bronze medals were issued during the 1903–04 operations in Northern Nigeria and the Somaliland campaigns of 1902 and 1908 to transport personnel and these are now much sought after, as are any medals with the effigy of George V on the obverse. With the exception of the 1902–04 Somali campaign and the campaign against the Mau Mau of Kenya (1952–56) European troops were not involved in any numbers, such personnel consisting mostly of detached officers and specialists.*

VALUE:		RN	British units	African/Indian regiments
i.	N. Nigeria	—	—	£200–225
ii.	N. Nigeria 1902	—	—	£180–200
iii.	N. Nigeria 1903	—	—	£170–190
iv.	N. Nigeria 1903–04	—	—	£240–280
v.	N. Nigeria 1903–04 (bronze)	—	—	£230–250
vi.	N. Nigeria 1904	—	—	£225–250
vii.	N. Nigeria 1906	—	—	£200–225
viii.	S. Nigeria	—	—	£280–320
ix.	S. Nigeria 1902	—	—	£240–280
x.	S. Nigeria 1902–03	—	—	£240–280
xi.	S. Nigeria 1903	—	—	£220–260
xii.	S. Nigeria 1903–04	—	—	£280–320
xiii.	S. Nigeria 1904	—	—	£210–230
xiv.	S. Nigeria 1904–05	—	—	£280–320
xv.	S. Nigeria 1905	—	—	£400–500
xvi.	S. Nigeria 1905–06	—	—	£240–280
xvii.	Nigeria 1918	—	—	£180–200
xviii.	East Africa 1902	—	—	£380–420
xix.	East Africa 1904	—	—	£300–350
xx.	East Africa 1905	—	—	£240–280
xxi.	East Africa 1906	—	—	£280–320
xxii.	East Africa 1913	—	—	£280–320
xxiii.	East Africa 1913–14	—	—	£220–240
xxiv.	East Africa 1914	—	—	£280–320
xxv.	East Africa 1915	—	—	£250–270
xxvi.	East Africa 1918	—	—	£220–250
xxvii.	West Africa 1906	—	—	£250–300
xxviii.	West Africa 1908	—	—	£250–300
xxix.	West Africa 1909–10	—	—	£320–370
xxx.	Somaliland 1901	—	—	£320–370
xxxi.	Somaliland 1901 (bronze)	—	—	£300–350
xxxii.	Somaliland 1902–04	£175–225	£220–280	£160–190
xxxiii.	Somaliland 1902–04 (bronze)	—	—	£300–350
xxxiv.	Somaliland 1908–10	£175–225	—	£150–175
xxxv.	Somaliland 1908–10 (bronze)	—	—	£250–300
xxxvi.	Somaliland 1920	£300–350	—	£170–200
	as above but RAF (225 awarded)	—	£700–900	—
xxxvii.	Jidballi (with Somaliland 1902–04)	—	£350–450	£210–270
xxxviii.	Uganda 1900	—	—	£250–300
xxxix.	B.C.A. 1899–1900	—	—	£250–300
xl.	Jubaland	£300–350	—	£210–250
xli.	Jubaland (bronze)	—	—	£550–650
xlii.	Jubaland 1917–18	—	—	£230–250
xliii.	Jubaland 1917–18 (bronze)	—	—	£250–300
xliv.	Gambia	£600–800	—	£300–350
xlv.	Aro 1901–1902	£800–900	—	£250–300
xlvi.	Lango 1901	—	—	£350–400
xlvii.	Kissi 1905	—	—	£400–450
xlviii.	Nandi 1905–06	—	—	£200–250
xlix.	Shimber Berris 1914–15	—	—	£300–350
l.	Nyasaland 1915	—	—	£250–300
li.	Kenya	£350–500	£150–175	£75–125
lii.	Kenya (to RAF)	—	£175–200	—
	2 clasps	£250–300	£350–400	£175–300
	3 clasps	—	—	£250–450
	4 clasps	—	—	£350–500
	5 clasps	—	—	£450–650
	6 clasps	—	—	£850–1200
	Medal to war correspondent	£1200–1500		

Miniature
Range from £35 to £90 depending upon clasp. "Slip-on" clasps are approx. 20% cheaper. Add £15 for each additional clasp.

162. TIBET MEDAL

Date: 1905.
Campaign: Tibet 1903–04.
Branch of Service: British and Indian regiments.
Ribbon: Green with two white stripes and a broad maroon central stripe.
Metal: Silver or bronze.
Size: 36mm.
Description: (Obverse) bust of King Edward VII; (reverse) the fortified hill city of Lhasa with TIBET 1903–04 at the foot.
Clasps: Gyantse.
Comments: *The trade mission led by Colonel Sir Francis Younghusband to Tibet was held up by hostile forces, against whom a punitive expedition was mounted in 1903. This medal was awarded mainly to Indian troops who took part in the expedition, camp followers being awarded the medal in bronze. A clasp was awarded to those who took part in the operations near Gyantse between 3 May and 6 July 1904.*

VALUE:

	British	Indian	Bronze	*Miniature*
Without clasp	£500–700	£350–400	£125–150	£45–55
i. Gyantse	£850–1000	£550–650	£350–450	£65–75

163. NATAL REBELLION MEDAL

Date: 1907.
Campaign: Natal 1906.
Branch of Service: Local forces.
Ribbon: Crimson with black edges.
Metal: Silver.
Size: 36mm.
Description: (Obverse) right-facing profile of King Edward VII. (Reverse) an erect female figure representing Natal with the sword of justice in her right hand and a palm branch in the left. She treads on a heap of Zulu weapons and is supported by Britannia who holds the orb of empire in her hand. In the background, the sun emerges from behind storm clouds.
Clasp: 1906.
Comments: *The Natal government instituted this medal for services in the operations following the Zulu rebellion. Local volunteer units bore the brunt of the action and it is interesting to note that one of the recipients was Sergeant-Major M. K. Gandhi who later led India to independence. Medals to officers are engraved in running cursive script.*

VALUE:

		Miniature
No clasp (2000)	£175–200	£45–55
i. 1906 (8000)	£225–275	£55–70
Natal Naval Corps		
without clasp (67)	£175–250	
clasp 1906 (136)	£275–300	

163A. MESSINA EARTHQUAKE COMMEMORATIVE MEDAL

Date: 1908.

Campaign: Messina earthquake relief.

Branch of Service: Royal Navy.

Ribbon: Green with white edges and central white stripe.

Metal: Silver.

Size: 31.5mm.

Description: (Obverse) left-facing profile of King Victor Emanuel III; (reverse) A wreath of oak leaves within which are the words MEDAGLIA COMMEMORATIVA / TERREMOTO CALABRO SICULO 28 DICEMBRE 1908.

Comments: *The King of Italy rewarded Royal Naval and other personnel who went to the aid of victims of the tragic earthquake that hit Messina in December 1908 with this silver medal. Officers and men serving on certain ships were eligible for the award as well as members of the Mercantile Marine and others who were engaged in relief operations. The Admiralty's published list of RN ships is as follows: HMS Duncan, HMS Euralyus, HMS Exmouth, HMS Lancaster, HMS Minerva and HMS Sutlej. However 52 medals were also awarded to personnel from HMS Boxer, which was omitted from the original list and a further 35 medals were awarded to the officers and men of HMS Philomel who had actually "been engaged in work which was directly attributable to the rescue operations". The medal was issued unnamed. In addition to the commemorative medal a special Messina Earthquake Merit Medal was awarded in two sizes (40mm and 30mm) bronze, silver and gold to organisations, vessels and various key individuals who played a part in the rescue operations and examples are known in miniature, in silver.*

VALUE:

		Miniature
Unattributed single medal	£100–150	£65–85
Royal Navy (c. 3500)	£125–175	
Royal Marines (481)	£150–200	
Mercantile Marine (c. 400)	£150–200	
Other	£200–300	
Merit Medal	£200–300	£105–£155

164. INDIA GENERAL SERVICE MEDAL

Date: 1909.

Campaigns: India 1908 to 1935.

Branch of Service: British and Indian forces.

Ribbon: Green with a broad blue central stripe.

Metal: Silver.

Size: 36mm.

Description: Three obverse types were used: Edward VII (1908–10), George V Kaisar-i-Hind (1910–30) and George V Indiae Imp (1930–35). (Reverse) the fortress at Jamrud in the Khyber Pass, with the name INDIA in a wreath at the foot.

Clasps: Twelve, plus two in bronze (see below).

Comments: *This medal was awarded for a number of minor campaigns and operations in India before and after the First World War. The medals were struck at the Royal Mint in London and by the Indian government in Calcutta, the only difference being in the claw suspenders, the former being ornate and the latter plain. Medals with the clasps North West Frontier 1908 and Abor 1911–12 were also issued in bronze to native bearers.*

continued overleaf

164. INDIA GENERAL SERVICE MEDAL *continued*

VALUE:

		British Army	RAF	Indian regiments	*Miniature*
i.	North West Frontier 1908	£150–200	—	£80–100	£25–30
	bronze	— —	£80–125	—	
ii.	Abor 1911–12	— —	£200–250	£25–30	
	bronze	— —	£275–350	—	
iii.	Afghanistan NWF 1919	£85–100	£150–180	£45–65	£20–25
iv.	Waziristan 1919–21	£120–150	£180–200	£45–65	£20–25
iv*a**	Mahsud 1919–20	£120–150	£550–650 (175)	£60–85	£20–25
v.	Malabar 1921–22	£175–200	—	£110–155	£35–40
vi.	Waziristan 1921–24	£75–100	£150–180	£45–55	£20–25
vii.	Waziristan 1925 (254)	—	£1000–1500	—	£25–30
viii.	NW Frontier 1930–31	£85–100	£150–160	£45–55	£20–25
ix.	Burma 1930–32	£100–150	£1000–1500	£65–90	£20–25
x.	Mohmand 1933	£200–250	£500–600	£40–60	£20–25
xi.	NW Frontier 1935	£85–100	£150–200	£45–55	£25–30

*Usually found in combination with Waziristan 1919-21, but 10 medals were awarded either with this clasp alone or with the Afghanistan NWF clasp.

Royal Mint striking.

Calcutta striking.

165. KHEDIVE'S SUDAN MEDAL 1910

Date: 1911.
Campaign: Sudan 1910 to 1922
Branch of Service: British and Egyptian forces.
Ribbon: Black with thin red and green stripes on either side.
Metal: Silver or bronze.
Size: 36mm.
Description: (Obverse) an Arabic inscription signifying the name of Khedive Abbas Hilmi and the date 1328 in the Moslem calendar (1910 AD) (type I). He was deposed in December 1914 when Egypt was declared a British protectorate, and succeeded by his nephew who was proclaimed Sultan. Sultan Hussein Kamil changed the Arabic inscription and date to AH 1335 (1916–17) on later issues of the medal (type II) . (Reverse) a lion poised on a plinth with the sunrise in the background.
Clasps: 16, inscribed in English and Arabic.
Comments: *Introduced in June 1911 as a replacement for the previous Khedive's Sudan medal of 1896–1908, it was awarded for minor operations in the southern Sudan between 1910 and 1922. The silver medal was issued with clasps to combatants, and without a clasp to non-combatants, while the bronze version was granted to camp followers. The medal is usually found unnamed although a few British recipients' medals are found named in small impressed capitals or Arabic script. The prices below are for unnamed examples.*

VALUE:

Silver without clasp type I		£200–250
Silver without clasp type II		£180–200
Bronze without clasp type I		£400–450
Bronze without clasp type II		£300–350
i.	Atwot	£400–500
ii.	S. Kordofan 1910	£400–500
iii.	Sudan 1912	£400–500
iv.	Zeraf 1913-14	£400–500
v.	Mandal	£400–500
vi.	Miri	£400–500
vii.	Mongalla 1915-16	£400–500
viii.	Darfur 1916	£400–500
ix.	Fasher	£400–500
x.	Lau Nuer	£400–500
xi.	Nyima 1917-18	£400–500
xii.	Atwot 1918	£400–500
xiii.	Garjak Nuer	£400–500
xiv.	Aliab Dinka	£400–500
xv.	Nyala	£400–500
xvi.	Darfur 1921	£450–550
2 clasps		£500–600
Miniature		
Silver type I		£40–60
Silver type II		£40–60
With any single clasp		£60–95

For each additional clasp add £15–30 (slip-on clasps approx. 20% less)

165A. BRITISH RED CROSS SOCIETY MEDAL FOR THE BALKAN WARS 1912–13

Date: 1913.
Campaign: Balkan Wars 1912–13.
Branch of Service: British Red Cross Society.
Ribbon: White with a central red stripe.
Metal: Silver gilt.
Size: 30mm.
Description: (Obverse) an enamelled design of a red cross on a white shield with the legend THE BRITISH RED CROSS SOCIETY around; (Reverse) blank for naming and hallmark. Ribbon suspended from a top white enamel brooch with indented ends and BALKAN WAR 1912–13. The medal has a swivel scroll bar suspender
Clasps: White enamelled Bulgaria, Greece, Montenegro, Servia, Turkey.
Comments: *This medal, manufactured by J. R. Gaunt of Birmingham, was given to all members of the Society who rendered first aid service to the belligerents also to others who gave help to those units. A total of 198 medals were awarded to members of the Society and a further 72 to others for services rendered. An additional 14 medals were awarded to Turkish nationals but these carried the Red Crescent emblem in place of the Red Cross. A complete roll of all recipients is held by the BRCS.*

VALUE: £250–300

FIRST WORLD WAR MEDALS

As we go to press with this year's edition of the YEARBOOK the commemorations of the 100th anniversary of the outbreak of World War I are well underway and over the next four years we are sure to see a great deal more with regard to the various battles and campaigns of the war as well as the lead up to the final armistice. The increased popularity in family history research, accompanied by the vast digitisation of records and the on-line resources such as *Ancestry, Find My Past* etc., has gone a long way to encouraging more and more people to find out about their ancestors' military service and as World War I was the first war that touched every family there is plenty of interest in this conflict out there. This interest is inevitably reflected in the prices of World War I medals that have, despite the recession in recent years, held firm and whilst the prices we have quoted in this year's edition of the *Yearbook* are broadly similar to last year's there are instances of World War I medals being offered for far more than listed here—whether they actually make that amount is a matter of conjecture and certainly on a well-known on-line auction site the money that has been asked for a "simple" pair or trio just because we have got to the centenary has, at times, been quite staggering! Certain medals will command a premium, of course, as with all medals a connection to the more famous actions, in this case particularly the Somme, Gallipoli, the Retreat from Mons, and the battles of Loos and Jutland will increase the price of the group (the prices paid for First Day of the Somme casualties continue to amaze) and gallantry and complete "sets" to casualties all continue to sell exceptionally well. It should also be noted that medals to Imperial forces, particularly Australian, Canadian and New Zealanders will fetch a considerable premium. As always in the MEDAL YEARBOOK the prices listed in this section are intended as a guide for a non-casualty private in a line regiment. The medals to an officer killed on the First Day of the Somme for example will, of course, be worth more.

166. 1914 STAR

Date: 1917.
Campaign: France and Belgium 1914.
Branch of Service: British forces.
Ribbon: Watered silk red, white and blue.
Metal: Bronze.
Size: Height 50mm; max. width 45mm.
Description: A crowned four-pointed star with crossed swords and a wreath of oak leaves, having the royal cypher at the foot and a central scroll inscribed AUG NOV 1914. Uniface, the naming being inscribed incuse on the plain reverse.
Clasps: 5th Aug.–22nd Nov. 1914. The clasp was sewn on to the ribbon of the medal, the first of this type. A silver rosette is worn on the ribbon strip if the bar was awarded.
Comments: *Awarded to all those who had served in France and Belgium between 5 August and 22 November 1914. In 1919 King George V authorised a clasp bearing these dates for those who had actually been under fire during that period. The majority of the 400,000 recipients of the star were officers and men of the prewar British Army, the "Old Contemptibles" who landed in France soon after the outbreak of the First World War and who took part in the retreat from Mons, hence the popular nickname of Mons Star by which this medal is often known. Approximately 1000 were awarded to members of the Royal Flying Corps of which about 300 received the bar, hence they command a premium.*

VALUE:		Miniature
1914 Star	From £70	£5–10
To RN	£200–300	
RM	£100–150	
RND	£150–200	
1914 Star/BWM/Victory trio		
Corps	From £100	
British Regiments	From £180	
Canadian Regiments	From £850	
Australian Regiments	From £1500	
1914 trio with plaque (no. 172)		
Corps	£180–250	
Regiments	£300–450	
RFC	£1500–2000	
i. 5th Aug.–22nd Nov. 1914 ("Mons") clasp	£100–150	£5–7
Clasp alone	£50–60	

167. 1914–15 STAR

Date: 1918.
Campaign: First World War 1914–15.
Branch of Service: British and imperial forces.
Ribbon: Watered silk red, white and blue (as above).
Metal: Bronze.
Size: Height 50mm; max. width 45mm.
Description: As above, but AUG and NOV omitted and scroll across the centre inscribed 1914–15.
Clasps: None.
Comments: *Awarded to those who saw service in any theatre of war between 5 August 1914 and 31 December 1915, other than those who had already qualified for the 1914 Star. No fewer than 2,350,000 were awarded, making it the commonest British campaign medal up to that time.*

VALUE:

1914–15 Star	from £25	*Miniature* £5–8
1914–15 Star/BWM/Victory trio		
Corps	From £55	
RN	From £75	
Regiments	From £85	
Trio with plaque (no. 172)		
Corps	£150–225	
Regiments	£250–350	
RN	£250–350	

168. BRITISH WAR MEDAL 1914–20

Date: 1919.
Campaign: First World War, 1914–20.
Branch of Service: British and imperial forces.
Ribbon: Orange watered centre with stripes of white and black at each side and borders of royal blue.
Metal: Silver or bronze.
Size: 36mm.
Description: (Obverse) the uncrowned left-facing profile of King George V by Sir Bertram Mackennal. (Reverse) St George on horseback trampling underfoot the eagle shield of the Central Powers and a skull and cross-bones, the emblems of death. Above, the sun has risen in victory. The figure is mounted on horseback to symbolise man's mind controlling a force of greater strength than his own, and thus alludes to the scientific and mechanical appliances which helped to win the war.
Clasps: None.
Comments: *This medal was instituted to record the successful conclusion of the First World War, but it was later extended to cover the period 1919–20 and service in mine-clearing at sea as well as participation in operations in North and South Russia, the eastern Baltic, Siberia, the Black Sea and Caspian. Some 6,500,000 medals were awarded in silver, but about 110,000 in bronze were issued mainly to Chinese, Indian and Maltese personnel in labour battalions. It was originally intended to award campaign clasps, but 79 were recommended by the Army and 68 by the Navy, so the scheme was abandoned as impractical. The naval clasps were actually authorised (7 July 1920) and miniatures are known with them, though the actual clasps were never issued.*

VALUE:

		Miniature
Silver (6,500,000)	From £15*	£5–10
Bronze (110,000)	£100–135	£15–20
BWM/Victory pair		
Corps	From £30	
Regiments/RN	From £45	
Pair with plaque (no. 172)		
Corps	From £140	
Regiment/RN	From £200	

* Current prices are being dictated by world silver markets. The BWM being 1oz of silver, as the price of silver fluctuates so will the minimum price of the BWM.

169. MERCANTILE MARINE WAR MEDAL

Date: 1919.
Campaign: First World War 1914–18.
Branch of Service: Mercantile Marine.
Ribbon: Green and red with a central white stripe, symbolising port and starboard masthead steaming lights.
Metal: Bronze.
Size: 36mm.
Description: (Obverse) Mackennal profile of King George V; (reverse) a steamship ploughing through an angry sea, with a sinking submarine and a sailing vessel in the background, the whole enclosed in a laurel wreath.
Clasps: None.
Comments: *Awarded by the Board of Trade to members of the Merchant Navy who had undertaken one or more voyages through a war or danger zone.*

VALUE:

Bronze (133,000)	£35–45
To women	£200–300
BWM/Mercantile Marine pair	From £75
To Australians	From £150
To South Africans	From £175
With plaque (no. 172)	From £450
Miniature	£25–40

170. VICTORY MEDAL

Date: 1919.
Campaign: First World War 1914–19.
Branch of Service: British and imperial forces.
Ribbon: 38mm double rainbow (indigo at edges and red in centre).
Metal: Yellow bronze.
Size: 36mm.
Description: (Obverse) the standing figure of Victory holding a palm branch in her right hand and stretching out her left hand. (Reverse) a laurel wreath containing a four-line inscription THE GREAT WAR FOR CIVILISATION 1914–1919.
Clasps: None.
Comments: *Issued to all who had already got the 1914 or 1914–15 Stars and most of those who had the British War Medal, some six million are believed to have been produced. It is often known as the Allied War Medal because the same basic design and double rainbow ribbon were adopted by thirteen other Allied nations (though the USA alone issued it with campaign clasps). The Union of South Africa produced a version with a reverse text in English and Dutch (not Afrikaans as is often stated).*

VALUE:

British pattern	£12–25
South African pattern	£25–35
Dark "Chocolate" colour issue	£20–25
Miniature	
Normal	£5–6
"CIVILIZATION" variety	£25–30
South African pattern	£75–85

171. TERRITORIAL FORCE WAR MEDAL

Date: 1919.
Campaign: First World War 1914–19.
Branch of Service: Territorial forces.
Ribbon: Watered gold silk with two dark green stripes towards the edges.
Metal: Bronze.
Size: 36mm.
Description: (Obverse) effigy of King George V; (reverse) a wreath enclosing the text FOR VOLUNTARY SERVICE OVERSEAS 1914–19.
Clasps: None.
Comments: *Awarded to all those serving with the Territorial Forces on 4 August 1914, or those who had completed four years service before this date and rejoined on or before 30 September 1914, who served overseas during the course of World War I. Those who had already qualified for the 1914 or 1914–15 Stars, however, were excluded. Around 34,000 medals were awarded, making it by far the scarcest of the First World War medals. The value of individual medals depends on the regiment or formation of the recipient. The totals awarded given below are from "The Great War Medal Collector's Companion" courtesy of Howard Williamson.*

VALUE:

Infantry/Corps (23,762)	£200–300
Artillery (6460)	£175–250
Yeomanry (3271)	£400–500
Cavalry (95)	£850–1000
RFC, RAF, RNAS (505)	£850–1000
Nurses (277)	£650–750
Miniature	£25–35

171A. BRITISH RED CROSS SOCIETY MEDAL FOR WAR SERVICE

Date: 1920.
Campaign: First World War.
Branch of Service: Members of the British Red Cross Society.
Ribbon: Plain white.
Metal: Bronze-gilt.
Size: 31mm.
Description: (Obverse) the Geneva Cross surrounded by a laurel wreath, with the legend BRITISH RED CROSS SOCIETY: FOR WAR SERVICE: 1914–1918 around; (reverse) a wreath enclosing the text INTER/ARMA/CARITAS ("Amidst the arms, charity").
Clasps: None.
Comments: *Granted to all members of the BRCS including Voluntary Aid Detachments who had performed one year or 1,000 hours voluntary service during the war and who did not receive any British War Medal for services rendered in respect of Red Cross war work. The medal was unnamed for wear only on Red Cross or similar uniform.*

VALUE: £15–25   *Miniature* £25–35

172. MEMORIAL PLAQUE

Date: 1919.
Campaign: First World War.
Branch of Service: British forces.
Ribbon: None.
Metal: Bronze.
Size: 120mm.
Description: The plaque shows Britannia bestowing a laurel crown on a rectangular tablet bearing the full name of the dead in raised lettering. In front stands the British lion, with dolphins in the upper field, an oak branch lower right, and a lion cub clutching a fallen eagle in the exergue. The inscription round the circumference reads HE (or SHE) DIED FOR FREEDOM AND HONOVR. A parchment scroll was issued with each plaque giving the deceased's name and unit.
Comments: *Given, with a parchment scroll, to the next of kin of those who lost their lives on active service during the War. Originally it was thought that Naval and Army plaques differed because of the width of the "H" in "HE" however examples of narrow "H" plaques found to Army units and wide "H" plaques to the Navy indicates this to be incorrect. The most likely reason for the narrower "H" is the later decision to add an "S" to allow for female casualty plaques.*

VALUE:	"He died" (1,355,000)	From £60
	"She died" (600)	From £3000
	Parchment scroll (male)	From £35
	ditto (female)	From £1500–2500
Miniature:	Uniface/unnamed (Contemporary casting)	£40–50

172A. SILVER WAR BADGE

Date: 12 September 1916.
Campaign: First World War.
Ribbon: None.
Metal: Silver.
Size: 33mm.
Description: A brooch-mounted circular badge with the crowned royal monogram in the centre and edge inscription FOR KING AND EMPIRE + SERVICES RENDERED +.
Comments: *Awarded to service personnel who sustained a wound or contracted sickness or disability in the course of the war as a result of which they were invalided out. It was worn on the lapel in civilian clothes. Each badge was numbered on the reverse. The purpose of the badge was to prevent men of military age but not in uniform from being harassed by women pursuing them with white feathers. Later in the War medical restrictions altered and some men re-enlisted and could wear the badge in uniform. Recently records for these badges have become publicly available and this research potential has inevitably had an effect on prices.*

VALUE:	From £30–40	*Miniature:*	£20–25

172B. CEYLON VOLUNTEER SERVICE MEDAL

Date: 1919.
Campaign: First World War.
Branch of Service: Ceylon volunteer forces.
Ribbon: None.
Metal: Bronze.
Size: 48mm x 44mm.
Description: An upright oval medal. (Obverse) a seated female figure bestowing a laurel crown on a kneeling soldier, with a radiant sun on the horizon; above, a six-line inscription: PRESENTED BY THE GOVERNMENT OF CEYLON TO THOSE WHO VOLUNTARILY GAVE THEIR SERVICES OVERSEAS IN THE GREAT WAR OF with the dates 1914 1919 in two lines on the right of the field; (reverse) the winged figure of Victory seated on a throne above a tablet inscribed with the name of the recipient.
Comments: *Awarded to volunteers from the Ceylon forces who served abroad during the war. Ceylon (now Sri Lanka) was the only British colony to issue such a medal for war service.*

VALUE: £100–150

173. NAVAL GENERAL SERVICE MEDAL 1909–62

Date: 1915.
Campaigns: Naval actions 1909 to 1962.
Branch of Service: Royal Navy.
Ribbon: White with broad crimson edges and two narrow crimson stripes towards the centre.
Metal: Silver.   **Size:** 36mm.
Description: (Obverse) effigy of the reigning monarch (see below). (Reverse) Britannia and two seahorses travelling through the sea.
Clasps: 17 (see below).
Comments: *Instituted for service in minor operations for which no separate medal might be issued. Five different obverses were employed: George V (1915-36), George VI Ind Imp (1936-49), George VI Fid Def (1949-52), Elizabeth II Br Omn (1952-53) and Elizabeth II Dei Gratia (1953-62). Medals issued with the first clasp include the name of the recipient's ship but this lapsed in later awards. The MALAYA clasp was issued with three types of medal: the George VI Fid Def and Elizabeth II Dei Gratia being the most common. The clasp BOMB & MINE CLEARANCE 1945–46 is very rare as it was apparently only awarded to the Royal Australian Navy. The clasp CANAL ZONE was instituted in October 2003 for service between October 1951 and October 1954.*

Bomb & Mine Clearance 1945–53 clasp

VALUE:			Miniature
			(in silver add £5)
i.	Persian Gulf 1909-1914		
	RN (7,127)	£185–225	
	Army (37)	£800–1000	£20-30
ii.	Iraq 1919-20 (116)	£2000–2500	£20-30
iii.	NW Persia 1919–20 (4)*	Rare	£35–75
iv.	Palestine 1936–39 (13,600)	£125–155	£20-30
v.	SE Asia 1945–46 (2,000)	£250–300	£20-30
vi.	Minesweeping 1945–51 (4,750)	£200–250	£20-30
vii.	Palestine 1945–48 (7,900)	£150–185	£20-30
viii.	Malaya (George VI, Elizabeth II		
	2nd type) (7,800)	£125–155	£20-30
	(Elizabeth II 1st type)	£145–175	£20-30
ix.	Yangtze 1949 (1,450)	£850–1250	£20-30
	to HMS *Amethyst*	£1550–2500	
x.	Bomb & Mine Clearance 1945–53 (145)	£850–1000	£40–60
xi.	Bomb & Mine Clearance 1945–46	Very rare	£40–60
xii.	Bomb & Mine Clearance		
	Mediterranean (60)	£2000–2500	£40–60
xiii.	Cyprus (4,300)	£155–200	£20-30
xiv.	Near East (17,800)	£100–125	£20-30
xv.	Arabian Peninsula (1,200)	£225–275	£20-30
xvi.	Brunei (900)	£275–350	£20-30
xvii.	Canal Zone	£250–350	—

* The clasp NW Persia 1920 was withdrawn in favour of the clasp NW Persia 1919–20. Recipients were supposed to return their first clasp in exchange for the latter.

174. GENERAL SERVICE MEDAL 1918–62

Date: 1923.

Campaigns: Minor campaigns 1918 to 1962.

Branch of Service: Army and RAF.

Ribbon: Purple with a central green stripe.

Metal: Silver.

Size: 36mm

Description: (Obverse) six different effigies of the reigning monarch [George V coinage head (1918–30), George V crowned and robed bust (1931–36), George VI Ind Imp (1937–49), George VI Fid Def (1949–52), Elizabeth II Br Omn (1952–54) and Elizabeth II Dei Gratia (1955–62)]. (Reverse) a standing figure of Victory in a Greek helmet and carrying a trident, bestowing palms on a winged sword.

Clasps: 18 (see below).

Comments: *Awarded to military and RAF personnel for numerous campaigns and operations that fell short of full-scale war. It did not cover areas already catered for in the Africa and India general service medals. The George V crowned and robed bust was used only on the medal for Northern Kurdistan in 1931. The clasp CANAL ZONE was instituted in October 2003 for service between October 1951 and October 1954. On 29 July 2014 it was confirmed that those who served in Cyprus between 1955 and 1959 qualify for the clasp CYPRUS, also aircrew who assisted with at least one day's service in the operation between 20 June 1948 and 6 October 1948 qualify for the clasp BERLIN AIRLIFT.*

VALUE:

		British units	RAF	Indian and local units	Miniature *(in silver add £5)*
i.	S. Persia (Brit. officers)	£250–300	£3000–3500	£60–90	£20-30
ii.	Kurdistan	£125–150	£250–300	£60–90	£20-30
iii.	Iraq	£100–125	£200–250	£60–90	£20-30
iv.	N.W. Persia	£125–150	£300–350	£60–90	£20-30
v.	Southern Desert Iraq	—	£600–700	—	£20–30
vi.	Northern Kurdistan	£350–450	£1000–1200	—	£90–100
vii.	Palestine	£150–175	£150–200	£75–100	£20-30
viii.	S.E. Asia 1945–46	£120–150	£100–150	£45–65	£20-30
ix.	Bomb and Mine Clearance 1945–49	£600–650	£450–500	—	£40–60
x.	Bomb and Mine Clearance 1945–56	—	—	£475–550*	£40–60
xi.	Palestine 1945–48	£85–100	£75–95	£85–100	£20-30
xii.	Malaya (George VI)	£85–125	£75–95	£55–65	£20-30
xiii.	Malaya (Elizabeth II)	£85–100	£75–95	£55–65	£20-30
xiv.	Cyprus	£85–100	£75–95	£55–65	£20-30
xv.	Near East	£85–125	£80–120	—	£20-30
xvi.	Arabian Peninsula	£85–125	£70–90	£65–70	£20-30
xvii.	Brunei	£200–250	£180–220	£125–155	£20-30
xviii.	Canal Zone	£200–300	£200–300	—	£15–25
xvix.	Berlin Airlift	£85–100	£85–100	—	£20–30

*Australian units

174A. IRAQ ACTIVE SERVICE MEDAL

Date: May 1926.
Campaign: Iraq, 1924–38.
Branch of Service: Army and RAF.
Ribbon: 31mm in equal stripes of green, white and green.
Metal: Bronze.
Size: 38mm.
Description: (Obverse) a crescent forming the lower part; with an Arabic inscription above signifying "General Service" in two laurel branches. The medal is superimposed on crossed rifles, with rays in the arc between the muzzles, to which is joined a flattened loop suspender. (Reverse) The name of King Faisal I in Arabic and the date (AH) 1344 (i.e. 1926).
Clasps: Dates 1930–31, 1932, 1935 or 1936 in Arabic numerals with an Arabic inscription on the left.
Comments: *Also known as King Faisal's War Medal, it was awarded to British Army and RAF personnel stationed in Iraq or serving with the Iraq Levies. It was originally issued without a clasp, but clasps denoted subsequent actions or periods of service. By 1931, however, medals were issued with appropriate clasps from the outset.*

VALUE:

Without clasp	£85–125	*Miniature*	£50–80
With clasp	£100–150		

175. INDIA GENERAL SERVICE MEDAL 1936–39

Date: 1938.
Campaign: India 1936–39.
Branch of Service: British and Indian Armies and RAF.
Ribbon: Stone flanked by narrow red stripes, with broad green stripes at the edges.
Metal: Silver.
Size: 36mm
Description: (Obverse) crowned effigy of King George VI; (reverse) a tiger with the word INDIA across the top.
Clasps: North-West Frontier 1936–37, North-West Frontier 1937–39.
Comments: *The fourth and last of the IGS series, it was introduced when the change of effigy from George V to George VI became necessary, anticipating a similarly long life. It was not awarded after the outbreak of the Second World War, while the partition and independence of the Indian sub-continent afterwards rendered it obsolete. The medal was struck at the Royal Mint, London for award to British Army troops and RAF personnel, but the Calcutta Mint struck the medals awarded to the Indian Army.*

VALUE:

	British Army	RAF	Indian Army	*Miniature*
North West Frontier				
i. 1936-37	£100–150	£120–150	£45–50	£20–25
ii. 1937-39	£100–150	£120–150	£45–50	£20–30
2 clasps	£150–200	£180–200	£55–75	£20–35

(slip-on clasps deduct 20%)

176. BRITISH NORTH BORNEO COMPANY'S GENERAL SERVICE MEDAL 1937–1941

Instituted: 1937.

Campaign: British North Borneo (now Sabah), 1937–41.

Branch of Service: British North Borneo Company staff, Constabulary and various civilians.

Ribbon: 35mm, half dark green, half yellow. Gallantry awards were denoted by a thin red central stripe.

Metal: Silver. Copies were made in bronze.

Size: 38mm diameter, with a thickness of 3mm.

Description: (Obverse) the shield of the Company flanked by warriors as supporters. Above the shield are two arms, one clothed and the other naked, supporting the Company's flag. Below the shield is the motto PERGO ET PERAGO (I carry on and accomplish); (reverse) the seated figure of Britannia facing right, holding a trident in her left hand, with her right hand resting on a shield which bears the Union flag. NORTH BORNEO GENERAL SERVICE MEDAL is inscribed round the top and in the exergue is a branch with 11 leaves.

Clasps: None.

Comments: *Only one gallantry award was ever made, to Leong Yew Pong, aged 15, gazetted August 3, 1939. For specially valuable or long and meritorious services 44 were issued, gazetted in 1937, 1938, 1939 and 1941, with one replacement in 1947. Recipients were government officials, armed constabulary, rubber planters, the Archdeacon of North Borneo, the Chairman of the Chamber of Commerce, railway managers, businessmen and local dignitaries.*

VALUE

Medal	Type	Officially named	Unnamed original	Spink copy	Specimen
For Gallantry	Silver	Unique	Rare	£250–300	£300–350
For Service	Silver	£1500–1750	Rare	£150–200	£150–200
Miniature	£210–230				

Ribbon with red stripe denoting gallantry

176A. SUDAN DEFENCE FORCE GENERAL SERVICE MEDAL

Instituted: November 1933.

Campaign: Minor campaigns in the Sudan after 1933.

Branch of Service: Sudan Defence Force (SDF) and Police.

Ribbon: Central stripe of royal blue, edged by two yellow stripes and two black stripes at the edges.

Metal: Silver.

Size: 36mm.

Description: (Obverse) the seal of the Governor-General of the Sudan; (reverse) a stationary group of Sudanese soldiers, with "The Sudan" in Arabic below.

Clasps: None.

Comments: *The medal was awarded on the recommendation of the Kaid el'Amm (SDF Commander) to native personnel of the SDF, Police and other approved Sudanese who served in the field on such operations as might be considered by the Governor-General as being of sufficient importance to warrant the grant of the medal. It was also awarded for action against Italian forces in the southern Sudan from June 1940 to November 1941. About 9,000 were issued.*

VALUE: £175–£250

SECOND WORLD WAR STARS

Nine different campaign stars were issued for the Second World War. Apart from some Commonwealth issues notably Australia, Pakistan and South Africa, these were issued unnamed. In the cases of the Pacific Star, Burma Star and Italy Star naval personnel must have earned the 1939–45 Star before eligibiliuty for those Stars begins. This is the same for the RAF in respect of the Air Crew Europe Star. It was decided that the maximum number of stars that could be earned by any one person was five, while those who qualified for more received a clasp to be sewn on the ribbon of the appropriate star. Only one clasp per ribbon was permitted which was the first to be earned after qualifying for that star, but this rule has been relaxed for the 1939–45 Star to allow for the new Bomber Command clasp. Thus the stars could bear the following clasps:

1. 1939–45 Star   Battle of Britain *and/or* Bomber Command
2. Atlantic Star   Air Crew Europe *or* France and Germany
3. Arctic Star   None
4. Air Crew Europe Star   Atlantic *or* France and Germany
5. Africa Star   North Africa 1942–43, 8th Army *or* 1st Army
6. Pacific Star   Burma
7. Burma Star   Pacific
8. Italy Star   None
9. France and Germany Star   Atlantic

Most of the ribbons are believed to have been designed by King George VI personally and have symbolic significance in each case. When ribbons alone are worn, the clasp is usually denoted by a silver rosette. However, the Battle of Britain clasp is represented by a gilt rosette and the 8th Army and 1st Army clasps by small silver numerals. As the clasps were sewn on to the ribbon and the stars issued unnamed, it is difficult to put valuations on examples with campaign clasps, however, the prices quoted are for medals with the *original* clasps. When purchasing expensive groups it is advisable that the medals be supported by documentary provenance or form part of a group in which at least one of the medals is named to the recipient.

Many of the medals and stars of the Second World War are still being officially produced, therefore there are a number of different die varieties available. There are also a number of dangerous copies in existence so care should be taken when purchasing expensive items. In the past few years a number of lapel badges or emblems have also been produced for award to veterans—see MYB nos. 242C et seq.

177. 1939–45 STAR

Date: 1945.
Campaign: Second World War 1939–45.
Branch of Service: British and Commonwealth forces.
Ribbon: Equal stripes of dark blue, red and light blue symbolising the Royal and Merchant Navies, Army and RAF respectively. The 1939–43 ribbon was authorised in November 1943 and worn by those awarded this proposed Star which became the 1939–45 Star when finally issued.
Metal: Bronze.
Size: Height 44mm; max. width 38mm.
Description: The six-pointed star has a circular centre with the GRI/VI monogram, surmounted by a crown and inscribed THE 1939-1945 STAR round the foot.
Clasps: Battle of Britain, Bomber Command, sewn directly on to the ribbon.
Comments: *The first in a series of nine bronze stars issued for service in the Second World War, it was awarded to personnel who had completed six months' service in specified operational commands overseas, between 3 September 1939 and 2 September 1945, though in certain cases the minimum period was shortened. Any service curtailed by death, injury or capture overseas also qualified, as did the award of a decoration or a mention in despatches. Clasps were awarded to RAF aircrew who took part in the Battle of Britain and, as a result of constant lobbying, in 2013 a clasp was also granted to aircrew members of Bomber Command. The clasps are denoted by a gilt rosette when the ribbon is worn alone. Surprisingly RAF ground crews who kept the Battle of Britain fighters in the air did not qualify for the 1939–45 Star, although those who assisted with the evacuation of troops from the beaches of Dunkirk did qualify.*

VALUE:

		Miniature
1939–45 Star	£10–15	£5–7
Battle of Britain clasp	£1800–2000	£8–10
Bomber Command clasp	£40–60	£6–8

178. ATLANTIC STAR

Campaign: Atlantic 1939-45.
Branch of Service: Mainly Royal and Commonwealth Navies.
Ribbon: Watered silk blue, white and green representing the ocean.
Metal: Bronze.
Size: Height 44mm; max. width 38mm.
Description: As above, but inscribed THE ATLANTIC STAR.
Clasps: Air Crew Europe, France and Germany.
Comments: *This star was awarded in the Royal Navy for six months' service afloat between 3 September 1939 and 8 May 1945 in the Atlantic or home waters, and to personnel employed in the convoys to North Russia and the South Atlantic. Personnel must have already qualified for the 1939–45 Star with the qualifying period for this not counting towards the Atlantic Star. Merchant Navy personnel also qualified, as did RAF and Army (maritime gunners and air crews—the latter only requiring 2 months service) who served afloat. In the last six months of operational service up to 8 May 1945, the Atlantic Star was awarded but not the 1939–45 Star. Entitlement to the France and Germany or Air Crew Europe stars was denoted by clasps to that effect, if the Atlantic Star was previously awarded. Only one clasp could be worn. Only two awards were made to WRNS: to an officer and a rating.*

VALUE:		Miniature
Atlantic Star	£30–35	£5–7
Air Crew Europe clasp	Add £60-80	£8–10
France and Germany clasp	Add £20–25	£8–10

178A. ARCTIC STAR

Campaign: Arctic convoys 1939–45.
Branch of Service: British and Commonwealth forces.
Ribbon: A central white stripe with fine black edging bordered either side by equal stripes of pale blue, dark blue and red.
Metal: Bronze.
Size: Height 44mm; max. width 38mm.
Description: As above, but inscribed THE ARCTIC STAR.
Clasps: None.
Comments: *As the direct result of constant lobbying by veterans and associated organisations over the years, the Government finally agreed to issue the Arctic Star retrospectively from March 2013. Huge numbers of surviving veterans or their next of kin are expected to apply for the medal. The Star is intended primarily to commemorate those who assisted or saw service on the ships of the convoys that sailed to North Russia in support of the Russian allies. Any member of the Royal Navy or Merchant Navy, as well as members of the Army and the RAF and certain civilian units are eligible if they served on or over the Arctic Circle for any length of time.*

VALUE:		Miniature
Arctic Star	£50–75	£8–10

179. AIR CREW EUROPE STAR

Campaign: Air operations over Europe 1939-44.
Branch of Service: RAF and Commonwealth aircrew.
Ribbon: Pale blue (the sky) with black edges (night flying) and a narrow yellow stripe on either side (enemy searchlights).
Metal: Bronze.
Size: Height 44mm; max. width 38mm.
Description: As above, but inscribed THE AIR CREW EUROPE STAR.
Clasps: Atlantic or France and Germany.
Comments: *Awarded for operational flying from UK bases over Europe, for a period of two months between 3 September 1939 and 4 June 1944. Entitlement to either the Atlantic Star or France and Germany Star was denoted by the appropriate bar. This star is by far the most coveted of all the Second World War stars. Officially named stars to South Africans are the rarest of all the Second World War medals.*

VALUE:		Miniature
Air Crew Europe Star	£250–300	£3–5
Atlantic clasp	Add £90	£6–8
France and Germany clasp	Add £20–25	£6–8

180. AFRICA STAR

Campaign: Africa 1940-43.
Branch of Service: British and Commonwealth forces.
Ribbon: Pale buff symbolising the sand of the desert, with a broad red central stripe, a dark blue stripe on the left and a light blue stripe on the right symbolising the three services.
Metal: Bronze.
Size: Height 44mm; max. width 38mm.
Description: As above, but inscribed THE AFRICA STAR.
Clasps: North Africa 1942-43, 8th Army, 1st Army.
Comments: *Awarded for entry into an operational area in North Africa between 10 June 1940 (the date of Italy's declaration of war) and 12 May 1943 (the end of operations in North Africa), but service in Abyssinia (Ethiopia), Somaliland, Eritrea and Malta also qualified for the award. A silver numeral 1 or 8 worn on the ribbon denoted service with the First or Eighth Army between 23 October 1942 and 23 May 1943. A clasp inscribed North Africa 1942-43 was awarded to personnel of the Royal Navy Inshore Squadrons and Merchant Navy vessels which worked inshore between these dates. RAF personnel also qualified for this clasp, denoted by a silver rosette on the ribbon alone.*

VALUE:

		Miniature
Africa Star	£20–25	£3–5
8th Army clasp	Add £20	£8–10
1st Army clasp	Add £20	£8–10
North Africa 1942–43 clasp	Add £20	£10–12

181. PACIFIC STAR

Campaign: Pacific area 1941-45.
Branch of Service: British and Commonwealth forces.
Ribbon: Dark green (the jungle) with a central yellow stripe (the beaches), narrow stripes of dark and light blue (Royal Navy and RAF) and wider stripes of red (Army) at the edges.
Metal: Bronze.
Size: Height 44mm; max. width 38mm.
Description: As above, but inscribed THE PACIFIC STAR.
Clasps: Burma.
Comments: *Awarded for operational service in the Pacific theatre of war from 8 December 1941 to 15 August 1945. Service with the Royal and Merchant navies in the Pacific Ocean, Indian Ocean and South China Sea and land service in these areas also qualified. Personnel qualifying for both Pacific and Burma Stars got the first star and a clasp in respect of the second.*

VALUE:

		Miniature
Pacific Star	£35–40	£3–5
Burma clasp	Add £40	£6–8

182. BURMA STAR

Campaign: Burma 1941-45.
Branch of Service: British and Commonwealth forces.
Ribbon: Three equal bands of dark blue (British forces), red (Commonwealth forces) and dark blue. The dark blue bands each have at their centres a stripe of bright orange (the sun).
Metal: Bronze.
Size: Height 44mm; max. width 38mm.
Description: As above, but inscribed THE BURMA STAR.
Clasps: Pacific.
Comments: *Qualifying service in the Burma campaign counted from 11 December 1941 and included service in Bengal or Assam from 1 May 1942 to 31 December 1943, and from 1 January 1944 onwards in these parts of Bengal or Assam east of the Brahmaputra. Naval service in the eastern Bay of Bengal, off the coasts of Sumatra, Sunda and Malacca also counted.*

VALUE:

		Miniature
Burma Star	£25–30	£3–5
Pacific Clasp	Add £40	£6–8

183. ITALY STAR

Campaign: Italy 1943-45.
Branch of Service: British and Commonwealth forces.
Ribbon: Five equal stripes of red, white, green, white and red (the Italian national colours).
Metal: Bronze.
Size: Height 44mm; max. width 38mm.
Description: As above, but inscribed THE ITALY STAR.
Clasps: None.
Comments: *Awarded for operational service on land in Italy, Sicily, Greece, Yugoslavia, the Aegean area and Dodecanese islands, Corsica, Sardinia and Elba at any time between 11 June 1943 and 8 May 1945.*

VALUE:		Miniature
Italy Star	£20–25	£3–5

184. FRANCE AND GERMANY STAR

Date: 1945.
Campaign: France and Germany 1944-45.
Branch of Service: British and Commonwealth forces.
Ribbon: Five equal stripes of blue, white, red, white and blue (the national colours of the United Kingdom, France and the Netherlands).
Metal: Bronze.
Size: Height 44mm; max. width 38mm.
Description: As above, but inscribed THE FRANCE AND GERMANY STAR.
Clasps: Atlantic.
Comments: *Awarded for operational service in France, Belgium, the Netherlands or Germany from 6 June 1944 to 8 May 1945. Service in the North Sea, English Channel and Bay of Biscay in connection with the campaign in northern Europe also qualified. Prior eligibility for the Atlantic or Air Crew Europe Stars entitled personnel only to a bar for France and Germany. Conversely a first award of the France and Germany Star could earn an Atlantic bar.*

VALUE:		Miniature
France and Germany Star	£20–25	£3–5
Atlantic clasp	Add £90	£6–8

185. DEFENCE MEDAL

Date: 1945.
Campaign: Second World War 1939-45.
Branch of Service: British and Commonwealth forces.
Ribbon: Two broad stripes of green (this green and pleasant land) superimposed by narrow stripes of black (the black-out), with a wide stripe of orange (fire-bombing) in the centre.
Metal: Cupro-nickel or silver.
Size: 36mm.
Description: (Obverse) the uncrowned effigy of King George VI; (reverse) two lions flanking an oak sapling crowned with the dates at the sides and wavy lines representing the sea below. The words THE DEFENCE MEDAL appear in the exergue.
Clasps: None, but the King's Commendation for Brave Conduct emblem is worn on the ribbon.
Comments: *Awarded to service personnel for three years' service at home, one year's service in a non-operational area (e.g. India) or six months' service overseas in territories subjected to air attack or otherwise closely threatened. Personnel of Anti-Aircraft Command, RAF ground crews, Dominion forces stationed in the UK, the Home Guard, Civil Defence, National Fire Service and many other civilian units* qualified for the medal. The medal was generally issued unnamed in cupro-nickel, but the Canadian version was struck in silver.*

VALUE:		Miniature
Cupro-nickel (32g)	£15–20	£8–10
Silver (Canadian) (36g)	£25–30	£12–15

*The definitive list of eligible recipients was published by the Ministry of Defence in 1992—Form DM1/DM2 and Annexe. This lists 50 different organisations and 90 sub-divisions of eligible personnel.

186. WAR MEDAL 1939–45

Date: 1945.
Campaign: Second World War 1939-45.
Branch of Service: British and Commonwealth forces.
Ribbon: Narrow red stripe in the centre, with a narrow white stripe on either side, broad red stripes at either edge and two intervening stripes of blue.
Metal: Cupro-nickel or silver.
Size: 36mm.
Description: (Obverse) effigy of King George VI; (reverse) a triumphant lion trampling on a dragon symbolising the Axis powers.
Clasps: None.
Comments: *All fulltime personnel of the armed forces wherever they were serving, so long as they had served for at least 28 days between 3 September 1939 and 2 September 1945 were eligible for this medal. It was granted in addition to the campaign stars and the Defence Medal. A few categories of civilians, such as war correspondents and ferry pilots who had flown in operational theatres, also qualified. No clasps were issued with this medal but a bronze oak leaf denoted a mention in despatches. The medal was struck in cupro-nickel and issued unnamed, but those issued to Australian and South African personnel were officially named with SA prefixes (see MYB189). The Canadian version of the medal was struck in silver.*

VALUE:

		Miniature
Cupro-nickel (32g)	£10–15	£8–10
Officially named	£20–25	
Silver (Canadian) (36g)	£25–35	£12–15

186A. KING'S BADGE

Date: 1941.
Campaign: Second World War.
Ribbon: None.
Metal: Silver.
Size: 26mm.
Description: A circular buttonhole badge with the crowned monogram GRI in script capitals in the centre, inscribed FOR LOYAL SERVICE.
Comments: *Awarded to personnel who had been invalided out of the services and were in receipt of a war disablement pension. The badges are not numbered or named. For further information see MEDAL NEWS, September 2008.*

VALUE:	£15–20	Miniature	£15–20

187. INDIA SERVICE MEDAL

Date: 1945.
Campaign: India 1939-45.
Branch of Service: Indian forces.
Ribbon: Dark blue with two wide and one central thin pale blue stripes. The colours of the Order of the Indian Empire and the Order of the Star of India
Metal: Cupro-nickel.
Size: 36mm.
Description: (Obverse) the effigy of the King Emperor; (reverse) a map of the Indian sub-continent with INDIA at the top and 1939–45 at foot.
Clasps: None.
Comments: *Awarded to officers, men and women of the Indian forces for three years' non-operational service in India. In effect, it took the place of the Defence Medal in respect of Indian forces.*

VALUE:	£15–20	Miniature	£10–12

188. CANADIAN VOLUNTEER SERVICE MEDAL

Date: 22 October 1943.
Campaign: Second World War 1939-45.
Branch of Service: Canadian forces.
Ribbon: Narrow stripes of green and red flanking a broad central stripe of dark blue.
Metal: Silver.
Size: 36mm.
Description: (Obverse) seven men and women in the uniforms of the various services, marching in step; (reverse) the Canadian national arms.
Clasps: Maple leaf clasp to denote overseas service. A clasp inscribed DIEPPE and surmounted by the Combined Operations emblem, was instituted on 28 April 1994 for award to all servicemen who took part in the Dieppe raid of 19 August 1942. A clasp inscribed Hong Kong, with the letters HK entwined within a circle, was instituted on 28 April 1994 for award to those involved in the Battle of Hong Kong, 8–25 December 1941. A clasp showing an ascending heavy bomber was instituted on 11 April 2013 to be awarded to members of an air crew and non-flying personnel for operational service with a Bomber Command squadron engaged in or supported bombing operations over Continental Europe from September 3, 1939 to May 8, 1945.

Comments: *Awarded for eighteen months' voluntary service in the Canadian forces from 3 September 1939 to 1 March 1947. The seven marching personnel are based on real people taken from National Defence photographs, representing the land, sea and air forces plus a nurse. The individuals are: first row: centre, 3780 Leading Seaman P. G. Colbeck, RCN; left, C52819 Pte D. E. Dolan, 1 Can. Para Bn; right, R95505 F/Sgt K. M. Morgan, RCAF. Second row: centre, W4901 Wren P. Mathie, WRCNS; left, 12885 L/Cpl J. M. Dann, CWAC; right, W315563 LAW O. M. Salmon, RCAF; back row: Lt N/S E. M. Lowe, RCAMC. 650,000 have been awarded including 525,500 with the overseas clasp.*

VALUE:		Miniature
Silver medal	£30–35	£8–10
i. Maple Leaf clasp	£30–35	£12–15
ii. Dieppe clasp	£35–45	£15–18
iii. Hong Kong clasp	£35–45	

188A. CANADIAN MEMORIAL CROSS

Instituted: 1 December 1919.
Branch of Service: Relatives of deceased Canadian forces.
Ribbon: Violet 11mm with ring suspension only.
Metal: Dull silver.
Size: 32mm.
Description: A Greek cross with the royal cypher at the centre, superimposed on another with arms slightly flared at the ends. Maple leaves adorn three of the arms while the top arm has a crown surmounted by a suspension ring. (Reverse) The service number, rank, initials and name of the person being commemorated are engraved. There is also a sterling mark on the lower arm. Four versions of the cross exist: the original, with GRI cypher (1914–19), with GVIR cypher and ring suspension (1940–45), GVIR cypher with suspension bar (1945–52) and an EIIR version for Korea and later conflicts.
Comments: *Issued to wives and mothers of servicemen who had died during World War I. A second version was introduced in August 1940 for award to widows and mothers of World War II servicemen, but this was extended to include those of merchant seamen and civilian firefighters. Newfoundland service personnel became eligible after April 1, 1949. The current version was introduced in 1950 for the Korean War and peacekeeping operations. All service-related deaths since 7 October 2001 are eligible and up to three Crosses are now granted to persons previously designated by the deceased.*

VALUE:	Named	Unnamed
GVR, ring suspension (58,500)	From £120	£55–65
GVIR, ring suspension } (32,500)	From £120	£55–65
GVIR, bar suspension	From £120	£55–65
EIIR, bar suspension (1,000)	From £150	£65–75

Miniature   £70–90

189. AFRICA SERVICE MEDAL

Date: 1943.
Campaign: Second World War 1939-45.
Branch of Service: South African forces.
Ribbon: A central orange stripe, with green and gold stripes on either side.
Metal: Silver.
Size: 36mm.
Description: (Obverse) a map of the African Continent, inscribed AFRICA SERVICE MEDAL on the left and AFRIKADIENS-MEDALJE on the right; (reverse) a leaping Springbok.
Clasps: None, but a Protea emblem is worn on the ribbon by recipients of the King's Commendation.
Comments: *Awarded to Union service personnel who served at home and abroad during the War for at least thirty days. Medals were fully named and gave the service serial number of the recipient, prefixed by various letters, for example N (Native Military Corps), C (Cape Corps), M (Indian and Malay Corps), etc., no prefix indicated a white volunteer.*

VALUE:

Silver medal (190,000)	£25–45	*Miniature* £10–12

Protea emblem.

190. AUSTRALIA SERVICE MEDAL 1939–45

Date: 1949.
Campaign: Second World War 1939-45.
Branch of Service: Australian forces.
Ribbon: Dark blue representing the Royal Australian Navy, Khaki representing the Army, light blue representing the R.A.A.F and red representing the Mercantile Marine.
Metal: Cupro-nickel.
Size: 36mm.
Description: (Obverse) the effigy of King George VI; (reverse) the Arms of the Commonwealth of Australia surrounded by the inscription "THE AUSTRALIA SERVICE MEDAL 1939–45".
Clasps: None.
Comments: *Awarded to all Australian personnel who had seen at least 18 months' full time or three years part-time service. The medals were named to the recipients. In the case of Army personnel, their service numbers were prefixed by the initial of their state or territory of enlistment: D (Northern Territory), N (New South Wales), NG (New Guinea), P (Papua), Q (Queensland), S (South Australia), T (Tasmania), V (Victoria) and W (Western Australia). X prefix is for Volunteer Overseas Services, that is service with the 2nd AIF (Second Australian Imperial Force). In 1996 time served for eligibility was reduced to 30 days full-time, 90 days part-time.*

VALUE:
    Cupro-nickel medal (600,000)   £55–65   *Miniature* £12–15

191. NEW ZEALAND WAR SERVICE MEDAL

Date: 1946.
Campaign: Second World War 1939-45.
Branch of Service: New Zealand forces.
Ribbon: Black with white edges.
Metal: Cupro-nickel.
Size: 36mm.
Description: (Obverse) effigy of King George VI; (reverse) the text FOR SERVICE TO NEW ZEALAND 1939-45 with a fern leaf below. Suspension was by a pair of fern leaves attached to a straight bar.
Clasps: None.
Comments: *Issued unnamed, to all members of the New Zealand forces who completed one month full-time or six months part-time service between September 1939 and September 1945, provided the applicant carried out the prescribed training or duties. This included Home Guard service and Naval Auxiliary Patrol service.*

VALUE:
    Cupro-nickel medal (240,000)   £30–35   *Miniature* £7–10

191A. NZ MEMORIAL CROSS

Instituted: 1960.
Campaign: Second World War, 1939–45.
Branch of Service: Relatives of deceased New Zealand forces personnel.
Ribbon: 12mm royal purple
Metal: Dull Silver.   **Size:** 32 mm.
Description: A cross surmounted by a St Edward Crown, with fern leaves on each arm, in the centre, within a wreath, the Royal Cypher; (reverse) details of the person in respect of whose death the cross is granted.
Comments: *First announced in the New Zealand Gazette dated at Wellington, September 12, 1947 and approved by the King but not instituted until August 16, 1960. Originally granted to the next-of-kin of persons who had lost their lives on active service with the New Zealand forces during the Second World War, or who had subsequently died of wounds or illness contracted during that conflict. Provision was made for the grant of crosses to the parent(s) as well as the wife or eldest surviving daughter or son. It was subsequently awarded in respect of postwar campaigns: Korea (47), Malaya, South Vietnam (37), and East Timor (3).*

VALUE: **Officially named**   **Unnamed**
        From £100   £75–85

192. SOUTH AFRICAN MEDAL FOR WAR SERVICES

Date: 1946.
Campaign: Second World War 1939–46.
Branch of Service: South African forces.
Ribbon: Three equal stripes of red, white and blue, the South African national colours.
Metal: Silver.
Size: 36mm.
Description: (Obverse) South African arms; (reverse) a wreath of protea flowers enclosing the dates 1939 and 1945. Inscribed in English and Afrikaans: SOUTH AFRICA FOR WAR SERVICES on the left and SUID AFRIKA VIR OORLOGDIENSTE on the right.
Clasps: None.
Comments: *Men and women who served for at least two years in any official voluntary organisation in South Africa or overseas qualified for this medal so long as the service was both voluntary and unpaid. Those who already had the Africa Service Medal were ineligible, but exceptions exist. The medals are unnamed but were issued with a named certificate.*

VALUE: Silver (17,500)   £40–50   *Miniature   £15–18*

192A. SOUTH AFRICAN MEMORIAL PLAQUE

Date: 1946.
Campaign: Second World War 1939–46.
Branch of Service: South African forces.
Metal: Bronze.
Size: Wood backing 135x106.4mm.
Description: The South African arms in a wreath superimposed on a Maltese cross with torches in the angles. Below is a separate panel containing the details of the deceased. Mounted on a wooden panel.
Comments: *The plaque was given to the next of kin to personnel who lost their lives whilst on active service. The name and the cause of death are inscribed thereon. A numbered brooch of a similar design was also issued. Plaques to personnel killed in famous actions or in well-known theatres of war are worth a considerable premium, as are those named to SAAF aircrew, SANF personnel or plaques named to women. Plaques bearing the Star of David signifying that the person was of the Jewish faith are extremely rare.*

VALUE: Plaque from £50, brooch from £25

193. SOUTHERN RHODESIA SERVICE MEDAL

Date: 1946.
Campaign: Second World War 1939-45.
Branch of Service: Southern Rhodesian forces.
Ribbon: Dark green with black and red stripes at each edge.
Metal: Cupro-nickel.
Size: 36mm.
Description: (Obverse) King George VI; (reverse) the Southern Rhodesian national arms. FOR SERVICE IN SOUTHERN RHODESIA round the top and the dates 1939-1945 at the foot.
Clasps: None.
Comments: *This very scarce medal was awarded only to those who served in Southern Rhodesia during the period of the War but who were ineligible for one of the campaign stars or war medals. 5,000 medals were struck but only 3,908 were awarded.*

VALUE:
Cupro-nickel (3908)   £300–350   *Miniature   £25–30*

194. NEWFOUNDLAND VOLUNTEER WAR SERVICE MEDAL

Date: 1981.
Campaign: Second World War 1939-45.
Branch of Service: Newfoundland forces.
Ribbon: Deep claret with edges of red, white and blue.
Metal: Bronze.
Size: 37mm
Description: (Obverse) the royal cypher of George VI surmounted by a crown topped by a caribou, the Newfoundland national emblem; (reverse) Britannia on a scallop shell background guarded by two lions.
Comments: *While the Second World War was being fought, Newfoundland was still a separate British colony which did not enter the Canadian Confederation till 1949. Consequently Newfoundland servicemen did not qualify for the Canadian Volunteer Service medal, and this deficiency was not remedied until July 1981 when the Newfoundland provincial government instituted this medal. Those who had served with the Canadian forces, on the other hand, and already held the Canadian medal, were not eligible for this award. The medal could be claimed by next-of-kin of those who died in or since the war.*

VALUE: Bronze (7500)   £450–550   *Miniature*   £65–75

194A. THE ELIZABETH CROSS

Instituted: 2009.
Campaign: Post World War II.
Branch of Service: Relatives of deceased UK forces personnel.
Ribbon: None.
Metal: Oxidised silver.
Size: 31 mm.
Description: A Greek cross superimposed on another cross, with a crowned Royal cypher at its centre, within a wreath. The arms of the outer cross bear the national emblems of the British Isles: the Rose (England), Thistle (Scotland), Shamrock (Ireland) and the Daffodil (Wales).
Comments: *The Cross was first announced in July 2009 and complements the existing Canadian Memorial Cross (MYB 188A) and the New Zealand Memorial Cross (MYB 191A). Only one Cross will be available to the next of kin of any service personnel who died whilst on operational duty or as a consequence of an act of terrorism. Awards of the Cross have been back-dated to 1 January 1948 to cover deaths that occurred after World War II or as a result of service in Palestine since 27 September 1945. It is accompanied by a memorial scroll, except in the case of Korean War casualties, as a scroll has already been issued for that conflict—in this instance the Cross alone will be issued. Crosses are named to the individual commemorated.*

VALUE: From £400

195. KOREA MEDAL

Date: July 1951.
Campaign: Korean War 1950-53.
Branch of Service: British and Commonwealth forces.
Ribbon: Yellow, with two blue stripes .
Metal: Cupro-nickel or silver.
Size: 36mm.
Description: (Obverse) Right-facing bust of Queen Elizabeth II by Mary Gillick; there are two obverse types, with or without BRITT: OMN; (reverse) Hercules wrestling with the Hydra, KOREA in the exergue.
Clasps: None.
Comments: *Awarded to all British and Commonwealth forces who took part in the Korean War between July 1950 and July 27, 1953. British and New Zealand medals were issued in cupro-nickel impressed in small capitals, medals to Australian forces were impressed in large capitals and the Canadian version was struck in silver and has CANADA below the Queen's bust. Particularly prized are medals issued to the "Glorious Gloucesters" who played a gallant part in the battle of the Imjin River.*

VALUE:		Miniature
British		
Regiments	£250–350	£12–15
Corps/RN	£150–200	
RAF	£600–850	
To Gloucester Regiment	£550–750	
Australian or New Zealand naming	£250–300	
Canadian, silver (over 20,000)	£100–150	£15–20

196. SOUTH AFRICAN MEDAL FOR KOREA

Date: 1953.
Campaign: Korea 1950-53.
Branch of Service: South African forces.
Ribbon: Sky blue central stripe flanked by dark blue stripes and edges of orange.
Metal: Silver.
Size: 38mm.
Description: (Obverse) maps of South Africa and Korea with an arrow linking them and the words VRYWILLIGERS and VOLUNTEERS in the field. (Reverse) the then South African arms surmounted by the crowned EIIR.
Clasps: None.
Comments: *Awarded to the 800 personnel in the contingent sent to Korea by the Union of South Africa. Suspension is by a ring and claw.*

VALUE:			
Silver (800)	£450–550	*Miniature*	£40–50
Pilot's issue	£1500–2000		

197. UNITED NATIONS KOREA MEDAL

Date: December 1950.
Campaign: Korea 1950-53.
Branch of Service: All UN forces.
Ribbon: Seventeen narrow stripes alternating pale blue and white.
Metal: Bronze.
Size: 35mm.
Description: (Obverse) the wreathed globe emblem of the UN;
   (reverse) inscribed FOR SERVICE IN DEFENCE OF THE
   PRINCIPLES OF THE CHARTER OF THE UNITED NATIONS.
Clasps: Korea.
Comments: *National variants were produced, but the British type was
   granted to all personnel of the British and Commonwealth forces who
   had served at least one full day in Korea or in support units in Japan.
   Moreover, as those who served in Korea after the armistice in July 1953
   were also entitled to the UN medal it is sometimes found in groups without
   the corresponding British medal. The award was extended to cover the
   period up to July 27, 1954, the first anniversary of the Panmunjom Truce.
   Issues to Australian, South African and Canadian personnel were named
   on the rim.*

VALUE: £20–25   *Miniature*   £8–10

198. GENERAL SERVICE MEDAL 1962–2007

Date: 1964.
Campaign: Campaigns and operations since 1962.
Branch of Service: British forces.
Ribbon: Deep purple edged with green.
Metal: Silver.
Size: 36mm.
Description: (Obverse) a crowned bust of Queen Elizabeth II; (reverse)
   an oak wreath enclosing a crown and the words FOR CAMPAIGN
   SERVICE. It has a beaded and curved suspension above which are
   mounted campaign clasps.
Clasps: 14. The maximum number of clasps awarded appears to be six.
Comments: *This medal, also commonly known as the Campaign Service
   Medal 1962, was instituted for award to personnel of all services, and thus
   did away with the need for separate Army and Navy general service medals.
   Awards range from a mere 70 for South Vietnam to over 130,000 for service
   in Northern Ireland. The eligibility for the Northern Ireland clasp ceased at
   midnight on 31 July 2007—the eligibility period having been from 14 August
   1969, almost 38 years, the longest period for any individual clasp. In July 2014
   it was confirmed that those who served between 21 December 1963 and 26
   March 1964 qualify for the clasp CYPRUS 1963–64.*

VALUE:			Miniature
i.	Borneo	£85–100	£12–15
ii.	Radfan	£90–120	£12–15
iii.	South Arabia	£75–100	£12–15
iv.	Malay Peninsula	£75–100	£12–15
v.	South Vietnam	Rare	£15–20
vi.	Northern Ireland	£75–100	£12–15
vii.	Dhofar	£175–225	£12–15
viii.	Lebanon	£800–900	£12–15
ix.	Mine Clearance, Gulf of Suez (250)	£1600–1800	£12–15
x.	Gulf	£250–300	£12–15
xi.	Kuwait	£400–450	£12–15
xii.	N. Iraq & S. Turkey	£375–475	£12–15
xiii.	Air Operations Iraq	£350–450	£15–20
	2 clasps	£100–125	£15–20
	3 clasps	£150–200	£25–30
	4 clasps	£250–300	£30–35
xiv.	Cyprus 1963–64	£75–95	£15–25

198A. OPERATIONAL SERVICE MEDAL 2000

Date: 1999.
Campaign: Operations after May 5, 2000.
Branch of Service: All branches of the armed forces.
Ribbon: Broad central red stripe, flanked by royal blue and light blue with green edge stripes (Sierra Leone), buff edge stripes (Afghanistan) or ochre edge stripes (Congo). The colours represent the three services.
Metal: Silver.
Size: 36mm.
Description: (Obverse) crowned profile of Queen Elizabeth; (reverse) an eight-pointed star with different crowns impaled on each alternate point, the centre having the Union flag in a circle surrounded by the inscription FOR OPERATIONAL SERVICE. The medal has a scrolled suspender with ornamental finials.
Clasp: Afghanistan, D.R.O.C. (Congo), silver rosette.
Comments: *Intended for minor campaigns for which a separate medal is not awarded. It replaces the General Service Medal 1962–2007, except for Northern Ireland and Air Operations Iraq. It has so far been awarded for operations in Afghanistan (from 11 September 2001), Sierra Leone (5 May 2000–31 July 2002) and the Democratic Republic of the Congo (14 June–10 September 2003). The award of a clasp is denoted by a silver rosette on the ribbon when only the ribbon is worn. For operations Maidenly and Barras (Sierra Leone) a "South Atlantic" type rosette is worn with the medal, and a smaller version on the ribbon alone. The D.R.O.C. clasp is especially sought after.*

Sierra Leone

Congo

Afghanistan

VALUE:				
	Cavalry	£400–600	*Miniature*	£12–15
	Line regiment	£250–350		
	Corps	£200–300		
	Royal Marines	£300–500		
	RAF	£300–500		

198B. ACCUMULATED CAMPAIGN SERVICE MEDAL

Instituted: January 1994.
Branch of Service: All branches of the armed services.
Ribbon: Purple with green edges and a central gold stripe.
Metal: Silver.
Size: 36mm.
Description: (Obverse) crowned effigy of Queen Elizabeth; (reverse) the inscription FOR ACCUMULATED CAMPAIGN SERVICE set within a four-part ribbon surrounded by a branch of oak leaves with laurel and olive leaves woven through the motto ribbon.
Comments: *The ACSM was awarded for aggregated service since August 14, 1969 in those theatres of operations where the General Service Medal (GSM) 1962 with clasp was awarded. The GSM (MYB198) has subsequently been replaced by the Operational Service Medal. The following medals count towards the award: Iraq Medal, GSM 1962–2007 with the clasps for Northern Ireland, Dhofar, Lebanon, Mine Clearance–Gulf of Suez, Gulf, Kuwait, Northern Iraq and Southern Turkey, Air Operations Iraq; the Operational Service Medal awarded since 2000 for Sierra Leone, Afghanistan and the Democratic Republic of Congo. Further periods of 36 months accumulated campaign service are denoted by a clasp, indicated as a silver rosette when the ribbon alone is worn. A gilt rosette is worn on the ribbon alone to denote the award of four silver clasps. A further gilt rosette was awarded for a further three silver clasps and a third gilt rosette for another two silver clasps. Service on UN, NATO EC or EU missions is not allowed to count towards the qualifying service. This was the first British medal put out to competitive tendering, a contract won by the Royal Mint. As such, the medal is not only silver but hallmarked (believed to be the first medal, although hallmarking is a feature of certain decorations and orders). In July 2011 the medal was superseded by the Accumulated Campaign Service Medal 2011 (MYB 198C).*

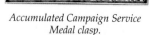

Accumulated Campaign Service Medal clasp.

VALUE:	£300–350	*Miniature*	£10–12

198C. ACCUMULATED CAMPAIGN SERVICE MEDAL 2011

Instituted: July 2011.
Branch of Service: All branches of the armed services.
Ribbon: Purple with green edges and two central gold stripes.
Metal: Silver.
Size: 36mm.
Description: (Obverse) crowned effigy of Queen Elizabeth; (reverse) the inscription FOR ACCUMULATED CAMPAIGN SERVICE set within a four-part ribbon surrounded by a branch of oak leaves with laurel and olive leaves woven through the motto ribbon.

Comments: *On July 1, 2011 the Accumulated Campaign Service Medal (no. 198B) was superseded by the Accumulated Campaign Service Medal 2011, with the qualifying time to be reduced from 36 months (1,080 days) to 24 months (720 days). Although the medal design remains identical to the previous issue it will not be hallmarked on the rim and the ribbon carries two gold stripes. The range of qualifying service has also been amended to reflect the current operational conditions and the need for medallic recognition. The new medal will mean that holders of an existing operational service medal (whether military, MOD civilian or Contractors on Deployed Operations) or other specifically designated multi-national campaign medal, who are or were serving on or after January 1, 2008 (whether currently serving or retired), are eligible for the ACSM 11 provided they have completed more than 24 months (720 days) campaign service. Bars are to be awarded for each additional period of 720 days approved operational service.*

The following campaign service counts towards the ACSM 11 and holders of the following medals, if they have completed enough service, may be eligible for the new medal: General Service Medal: Northern Ireland August 14, 1969–July 31, 2007; Dhofar October 1, 1969–September 30, 1976; Lebanon February 7, 1983–March 9, 1984; Mine Clearance Gulf of Suez August 15, 1984–October 15, 1984; Gulf November 17, 1986–February 28, 1989; Kuwait March 8, 1991–September 30, 1991; N Iraq & S Turkey April, 6, 1991–July 17, 1991; Air Operations Iraq (South) July 16, 1991–March 18, 2003, and Iraq (North) July 16, 1991–April 30, 2003. Operational Service Medal: Sierra Leone May 5, 2000–July 31, 2002; Afghanistan September 11, 2001 to a date to be decided; Democratic Republic of Congo June 14, 2003– September 10, 2003. The Iraq Medal January 20, 2003–May 22, 2011. And any Multinational campaign medals approved since April 1, 2000. Certain service does not count towards the ACSM 11, this includes any service prior to August 14, 1969, service in Kuwait during Op TELIC after August 10, 2003; service in the Balkans; service in the British Embassy in Iraq; service on Op BANDOG with the exception of Afghanistan; service in the First Gulf War and service in the Falklands Conflict.

VALUE:	£300–350	*Miniature*	£10–15

198D. GENERAL SERVICE MEDAL 2008

Date: 2016.
Campaign: Campaigns and Operations since 2008.
Branch of Service: British forces.
Ribbon: 32mm, green with two 5mm purple stripes 5mm from the edges.
Metal: Silver .
Size: 36mm.
Clasps: Southern Asia, Arabian Peninsula, Northern Africa, Western Africa, Eastern Africa.
Description: (Obverse) Ian Rank-Broadley effigy of Her Majesty the Queen; with the legend REGINA FID DEF ELIZABETH II DEI GRATIA around; (reverse) A standing figure of Britannia holding a shield and trident, in front of a lion with the words FOR CAMPAIGN SERVICE below, the whole surrounded by a wreath of oak.

Comments: *Instituted for minor campaigns since 2008 the first awards were made by the Secretary of State for Defence, Michael Fallon, in June 2016. The clasps are named for geographic locations as opposed to specific Operations with Southern Asia, Arabian Peninsula and East Africa each covering two Operations to date. The Western Africa clasp at present covers service there in the period January 13 2013-May 22 2013 with the Northern Africa clasp covering service in that region from November 1 2012 onwards.*

VALUE: —

199. UNITED NATIONS EMERGENCY FORCE MEDAL

Date: 1957.
Campaign: Israel and Egypt 1956–57.
Branch of Service: All UN forces.
Ribbon: Sand-coloured with a central light blue stripe and narrow dark blue and green stripes towards each edge.
Metal: Bronze.
Size: 35mm.
Description: (Obverse) the UN wreathed globe emblem with UNEF at the top; (reverse) inscribed IN THE SERVICE OF PEACE. Ring suspension.
Clasps: None.
Comments: *Awarded to all personnel who served with the UN peace-keeping forces on the border between Israel and Egypt following the Sinai Campaign of 1956. These medals were awarded to troops from Brazil, Canada, Colombia, Denmark, Finland, Indonesia, Norway, Sweden and Yugoslavia.*

VALUE:

Bronze original issue	£35–45	*Miniature*	£6–8

200. VIETNAM MEDAL

Date: July 1968.
Campaign: Vietnam 1964-73.
Branch of Service: Australian and New Zealand forces.
Ribbon: A broad central stripe of bright yellow surmounted by three thin red stripes (the Vietnamese national colours) and bordered by broader red stripes, with dark and light blue stripes at the edges, representing the three services.
Metal: Silver.
Size: 36mm.
Description: (Obverse) the crowned bust of Queen Elizabeth II; (reverse) a nude male figure pushing apart two spheres representing different ideologies.
Clasps: None.
Comments: *Awarded to personnel who served in Vietnam a minimum of one day on land or 28 days at sea after 28 May 1964. The medal was impressed in large capitals (Australian) or small capitals (New Zealand).*

VALUE:

Australian recipient	£200250
New Zealand recipient (3,312)	£250–300
Miniature	£10–12

200A. VIETNAM LOGISTIC AND SUPPORT MEDAL

Instituted: 1993.
Campaign: Vietnam 1964–68.
Branch of Service: Australian forces.
Ribbon: A broad central stripe of yellow with three narrow red stripes superimposed. On the left are stripes of red and dark blue and on the right stripes of dark brown and light blue.
Metal: Nickel-silver.
Size: 36mm.
Description: (Obverse) crowned effigy of Queen Elizabeth and titles; (reverse) as MYB200 above but with a cartouche containing a ram's head (Royal Australian Mint's mark) near the man's right foot. With a straight bar suspension.
Clasps: None.
Comments: *Awarded to personnel who served in the Vietnam War but who did not qualify for the Vietnam Medal. It is estimated that about 20,000 individuals are eligible for this award. Recipients include Qantas air crew who took troop flights to Saigon, and civilian entertainers.*

VALUE: Australian recipient (5,121)

201. SOUTH VIETNAM CAMPAIGN MEDAL

Date: May 12, 1964.
Campaign: Vietnam 1964–72.
Branch of Service: Allied forces in Vietnam.
Ribbon: White with two broad green stripes towards the centre and narrow green edges.
Metal: Bronze.
Size: Height 42mm; max. width 36mm.
Description: A six-pointed star, with gold rays in the angles. The gilt enamelled centre shows a map of Vietnam engulfed in flames; (reverse) a Vietnamese inscription in the centre.
Clasps: 1960 (bronze, cupro-nickel or silver gilt).
Comments: *Awarded by the government of South Vietnam to Australian and New Zealand forces who served at least six months in Vietnam from March 1, 1961. The original issue, of Vietnamese manufacture, was relatively crude and issued unnamed. Subsequently medals were produced in Australia and these are not only of a better quality but bear the name of the recipient. A third version, made in the USA, has the suspension ring a fixed part of the medal. The medal was always issued with a clasp.*

VALUE:
Unnamed	£15–20
Named	£25–35
Miniature	enamels £10–15, painted £5–8

202. RHODESIA MEDAL

Date: 1980.
Campaign: Rhodesia 1979–80.
Branch of Service: British and Rhodesian forces.
Ribbon: Sky blue, with a narrow stripe of red, white and dark blue in the centre.
Metal: Rhodium-plated cupro-nickel.
Size: 36mm.
Description: (Obverse) the crowned bust of Queen Elizabeth II; (reverse) a sable antelope with the name of the medal and the year of issue.
Clasps: None.
Comments: *This medal was awarded to personnel serving in Rhodesia for fourteen days between 1 December 1979 and 20 March 1980, pending the elections and the emergence of the independent republic of Zimbabwe, known as Opration Agila. Medals were issued unnamed or named in impressed capitals. It was officially named to the armed forces and RAF personnel but unnamed to participating British Police. Examples with the word COPY in raised capitals immediately below the suspension fitment are believed to have been issued as replacements for lost medals, although examples with "R" for replacement are also known to exist.There has been some discussion over whether this medal is actually a campaign medal. It seems that the Ministry of Defence includes it in its list of campaign medals whereas the Central Chancery does not include it as a campign medal but rules that it should be worn after long service awards. Further research may clarify the situation.*

VALUE:
Cupro-nickel (2500)	£450–550	*Miniature*	£35–55

203. SOUTH ATLANTIC MEDAL

Date: 1982.
Campaign: Falkland Islands and South Georgia 1982.
Branch of Service: British forces.
Ribbon: Watered silk blue, white, green, white and blue.
Metal: Cupro-nickel.
Size: 36mm.
Description: (Obverse) crowned profile of Queen Elizabeth II; (reverse) laurel wreath below the arms of the Falkland Islands with SOUTH ATLANTIC MEDAL inscribed round the top.
Clasps: None, but a rosette denoting service in the combat zone.
Comments: *Awarded to all personnel who took part in operations in the South Atlantic for the liberation of South Georgia and the Falkland Islands following the Argentinian invasion. To qualify, the recipient had to have at least one full day's service in the Falklands or South Georgia, or 30 days in the operational zone including Ascension Island. Those who qualified under the first condition were additionally awarded a large rosette for wear on the ribbon. As a result of the Sir John Holmes' Independent medal review in 2012 the 30 day qualifying period for the award of the South Atlantic Medal was extended from 12 July to 21 October 1982. Those who qualify under this condition are not entitled to wear the rosette*

VALUE:

	With rosette	Without
Army (7000)	£750–850	£550–750
Scots & Welsh Guards	£1000–1500	
Parachute Regiment	£1750–2500	
Royal Navy (13,000)	£650–750	£500–650
Royal Marines (3700)	£1200–1500	£750–1000
Royal Fleet Auxiliary (2000)	£475–550	£300–400
RAF (2000)	£550–750	£350–450
Merchant Navy and civilians (2000)	£500–700	£350–450
Gurkhas	£650–850	£500–650
Miniature	£15–20	

203A. SOVIET 40th ANNIVERSARY MEDAL

40th anniversary

Date: 1985.
Campaign: Second World War.
Branch of Service: British and Canadian forces who served mainly in RN or MN ships on Arctic convoys.
Ribbon: One half red, the other orange with three black stripes, edged with pale blue. Later issues have no blue edges. Worn in the Russian style.
Metal: Bronze.
Size: 32mm.
Description: (Obverse) Group of servicemen and women in front of a five-pointed star flanked by oak leaves and the dates 1945–1985 above; (reverse) 40th anniversary of the Victory in the Great Patriotic War 1941–1945, in Russian.
Clasps: None.
Comments: *In 1994 Her Majesty the Queen approved the wearing of this medal, first awarded by the Soviet Government, to selected ex-Servicemen, mostly surviving veterans of the Arctic convoys of World War II. Similar medals have also been issued for the 50th and subsequent five year anniversaries.*

VALUE:	British striking	£15–20
	Russian striking	£10–15
	Miniature	£10–15

203AA. USHAKOV MEDAL

Date: 2013.
Campaign: Second World War.
Branch of Service: Allied forces who served on the Arctic convoys.
Ribbon: Pale blue moire edged with narrow stripes of white and dark blue. Worn in the Russian style.
Metal: Silver.
Size: 36mm.
Description: (Obverse) Central couped portrait of Marshal Ushakov with Cyrillic wording around and laurel leaves below, the circular medal surmounted on an anchor; (reverse) anchor with serial number.
Clasps: None.
Comments: *Copies of the original Soviet medal were awarded by the Russian Government, on application, to surviving veterans of the Arctic convoys of World War II. Permission to wear was granted in 2013 by HM the Queen.*

VALUE: £35–50

203B. PINGAT JASA MALAYSIA MEDAL

Instituted: 2005.
Ribbon: Central red stripe, flanked by dark blue and yellow.
Metal: Base metal (brass)-coated nickel silver.
Size: 38mm
Description: (Obverse) arms of the Republic of Malaysia with JASA MALAYSIA below; (reverse) map of Malaysia with P.J.M. below, attached to a scrolled suspension bar by two crossed fern fronds.
Comments: *Awarded by the Malaysian Government to members of the British and Commonwealth Armed Forces who were posted on strength of unit or formation and served in the prescribed operational area of Malaysia and Singapore during the "Confrontation" and "Emergency" periods in direct support of operations for: 90 days or more, in Malaysia between August 31, 1957 and December 31 1966 or Singapore between August 31, 1957 and August 9, 1965; or for 180 days for ADF outside the area but in support of operations for the first two dates. Permission to wear was officially granted in time for veterans to wear their medals at the Remembrance Day ceremonies in 2011. Several types are known, with later strikings being of poorer quality than the original and with various minor alterations to the original design.*

VALUE: £35–55   *Miniature* £10–15

Late striking

203C. KING HUSSEIN MEDAL

Date: 1970.
Campaign: Jordan Civil War.
Branch of Service: British military medical teams.
Ribbon: Plain crimson.
Metal: Silver with red enamel emblem.
Description: (Obverse) Emblem of the Red Cross and Red Crescent. THE HASHEMITE KINGDOM OF JORDAN and its Arabic equivalent, with the date 1970 and Arabic equivalent at the sides; (rev) seven-line inscription across the centre.
Comments: *Awarded to British and American personnel involved in relief operations codenamed Operation Shoveller during and after the Civil War of September 1970. At the end of the deployment all personnel were presented with the medal by King Hussein. Permission to wear it has never been granted.*

VALUE: £50–70

204. GULF MEDAL

Date: 1992.
Campaign: Kuwait and Saudi Arabia 1990-91.
Branch of Service: British forces.
Ribbon: Sand-coloured broad central stripe flanked by narrow stripes of dark blue, red and light blue (left) or light blue, red and dark blue (right) representing the sands of the desert and the three armed services.
Metal: Cupro-nickel.
Size: 36mm.
Description: (Obverse) crowned profile of Queen Elizabeth II; (reverse) an eagle and automatic rifle superimposed on an anchor, symbolising the three armed services. The dates of the Gulf War appear at the foot.
Clasps: 2 Aug 1990, 16 Jan–28 Feb 1991.
Comments: *Awarded to personnel who had thirty days continuous service in the Middle East (including Cyprus) between 2 August 1990 and 7 March 1991, or seven days between 16 January 1991 and 28 February 1991, or service with the Kuwait Liaison Team on 2 August 1990, the date of the Iraqi invasion. Two clasps were sanctioned and awarded to personnel who qualified for active service with the Liaison Team or in the operations to liberate Kuwait. A rosette is worn on the ribbon alone to denote the campaign clasps. Naming is in impressed capitals. More than 45,000 medals were awarded. See also the Kuwait and Iraq-Turkey clasps awarded to the General Service Medal 1962. About 1,500 civilians, including members of British Aerospace working at Dahran, also received the medal with the clasp 16 Jan to 28 Feb 1991.*

VALUE:

No clasp	£200–250
i. 2 Aug 1990	£2000–3000
ii. 16 Jan to 28 Feb 1991	
Regiments/RN/RAF	£250–350
Corps and Artillery	£200–250
Civilians	£200–250
Miniature	£15–20

204A. BRUNEI GENERAL SERVICE MEDAL

Date: 1968.
Campaign: Service in Brunei.
Branch of Service: British personnel on loan service.
Ribbon: Blue with red edges and a central red stripe.
Description: A radiate star with a central medallion inscribed GENERAL SERVICE MEDAL and its equivalent Pingkat Laila Tugas in Arabic script, the royal insignia of the sultanate appearing in the centre. This insignia has changed several times over the years so varieties are seen. The original versions have a white enamel cross on the star (as illustrated) but the later version has the insignia surrounded by a laurel wreath. Suspended by a plain bar.
Comments: *Awarded to British personnel who completed a minimum of 12 months service. The Queen has granted unrestricted permission to entitled members of the British forces.*

VALUE: £100–150   *Miniature*   £20–25

204AA. SIERRA LEONE GENERAL SERVICE MEDAL

Date: 1965.
Campaign: Service in Sierra Leone and neighbouring countries.
Branch of Service: British forces on secondment to the Royal Sierra Leone Military Forces.
Ribbon: Broad central red stripe bordered with narrow green, white and dark blue stripes.
Metal: Bronze.
Size: 36mm.
Description: (Obverse) crowned effigy of Queen Elizabeth; (reverse) arms of Sierra Leone with inscription FOR GENERAL SERVICE / SIERRA LEONE. Fitted with a ring for suspension and a brooch bar at the top of the ribbon.
Clasps: Congo.
Comments: *Worn after medals previously earned and before the United Nations' Congo Medal and Sierra Leone Long Service and Independence medals, with restricted permission. UK personnel qualified for this medal if not eligible for any other general service medal for the same service. British personnel who served in the Congo between January 26, 1962 and February 28, 1963 qualified for the clasp.*

VALUE: £45–55   *Miniature*   £15–25

204B. IRAQ MEDAL

Date: 2004.

Campaign: Operation TELIC (the Iraq War).

Branch of Service: All military and civilian personnel, including embedded media, involved in the operations for the liberation of Iraq and the overthrow of Saddam Hussein.

Ribbon: Central narrow stripes of black, white and red (symbolising the Iraq national flag) flanked by broad sand-coloured edges.

Metal: Cupro-nickel.

Size: 36mm.

Description: (Obverse) crowned effigy of Queen Elizabeth; (reverse) image of a Lamassu (ancient Assyrian statue) over the word IRAQ.

Clasps: 19 Mar to 28 Apr 2003.

Comments: *This medal was awarded to all military and civilian personnel involved in Operation TELIC in Kuwait and Iraq from January 20, 2003. Those who took part in the actual combat from March 19, 2003 were awarded the clasp, denoted by a silver rosette on the ribbon alone. The medal is currently awarded to those who have served for 30 days continuously or an aggregate 45 days.*

VALUE:		*Miniature*
i. With clasp		*£10–20*
Corps	£300–350	
Regiments/RAF/Navy	£350–400	
Cavalry	£400–450	
ii. No clasp		*£10–15*
Corps	£150–175	
Regiments/RAF/Navy	£175–250	
Cavalry	£300–350	

204C. IRAQ RECONSTRUCTION SERVICE MEDAL

Instituted: January 2007.

Branch of Service: Civilians and members of the Armed Forces who have seen service in Iraq but do not qualify for the Iraq Medal.

Ribbon: Sand-coloured with a broad green central stripe and narrow blue stripes towards the edges.

Metal: Rhodium-plated cupro-nickel.

Size: 36mm.

Description: (Obverse) Rank-Broadley effigy of the Queen; (reverse) cuneiform tablet translated as 'land bringing forth life' with stylised depiction of two rivers, based on a relief carving from Mesopotamia in the British Museum.

Comments: *The qualifying period for the medal was set at 40 days continuous service since March 19, 2003, or 40 days of service on working visits within Iraq aggregated over a period of one calendar year, for a minimum of 48 hours each.The medal was decommissioned in July 2013.*

VALUE: £300—£450   *Miniature*   £15–25

204D. THE CIVILIAN SERVICE MEDAL (AFGHANISTAN)

Instituted: April 2011.
Branch of Service: Civilian.
Ribbon: As 204C but lighter blue stripes.
Metal: Rhodium-plated cupro-nickel.
Size: 36mm.
Description: (Obverse) Rank-Broadley effigy of the Queen; (reverse) a stylised depiction of the mountains of Afghanistan with the name of the country, both in English and Afghan surrounding it.
Comments: *Awarded to recognise the role of civilians and others involved in the transition of Afghanistan to democracy. The qualifying period is thirty days continuous or 45 days aggregate service provided that takes place within a single calendar year and the visits are of at least 48 hours each. Those whose service is curtailed by death or injury also eligible. Eligible persons include any Crown Servant (including Members of Her Majesty's UK Armed Forces), under Operational Control of the Foreign and Commonwealth Office (but NOT those under the command of the UK joint task force), Police and Contractors. Locally employed civilians are not eligible.*

VALUE: £300—£400

205. SAUDI ARABIAN MEDAL FOR THE LIBERATION OF KUWAIT

Original type

Date: 1991.
Campaign: Gulf War 1991.
Branch of Service: British and Allied forces.
Ribbon: Green with edges of red, black and white (the Saudi national colours). The ribbon bar has a gold state emblem (palm tree over crossed scimitars).
Metal: White metal.
Size: approx. 45mm across
Description: The white metal medal has a star of fifteen long and fifteen short round-tipped rays, surmounted by a bronze circle bearing a crowned and enwreathed globe on which appears a map of Arabia. Above the circle is a palm tree with crossed scimitars, the state emblem of Saudi Arabia. A scroll inscribed in Arabic and English LIBERATION OF KUWAIT appears round the foot of the circle.
Clasps: None.
Comments: *Awarded by the government of Saudi Arabia to all Allied personnel who took part in the campaign for the liberation of Kuwait, although only a few of the 45,000 British servicemen were subsequently given permission by the Foreign and Commonwealth Office to wear it. The contract for production was shared between Spink and a Swiss company, but subsequently a flatter version, more practicable for wear with other medals, was manufactured in the United States.*

VALUE:	Original type	£35–55	*Miniature*	£15–20
	US "flat" type	£25–35		

205A. MULTINATIONAL FORCE AND OBSERVERS MEDAL

Date: March 1982.
Campaign: Sinai Peninsula.
Ribbon: 36mm orange with central white stripe flanked by 3mm dark green stripes. The civilian award ribbon is orange with two green 8mm stripes and central 8mm white stripe
Metal: Bronze.
Size: 30mm.
Description: (Obverse) a dove clutching an olive branch surrounded by the inscription MULTINATIONAL FORCE & OBSERVERS; (reverse) UNITED IN SERVICE FOR PEACE in five lines.
Comments: *Awarded to personnel of the Multinational Force and Observers (MFO) created in 1979 to monitor the peace agreement between Egypt and Israel. Eligibility for the medal was originally 90 days continuous service in the force, but this was raised to 170 days in March 1985. Subsequent awards for each completed six-month tour are indicated by a silver numeral affixed to the ribbon. It was originally awarded personally by the MFO's first commander, the Norwegian General Fredrik Bull-Hansen. The Force has 3,000 personnel drawn from the armed services of Australia, Canada, Colombia, Fiji, France, Italy, the Netherlands, New Zealand, UK, USA and Uruguay.*

VALUE: £25–30   *Miniature* £10–15

Civilian

206. KUWAITI LIBERATION MEDALS

4th grade

Date: 1991.
Campaign: Liberation of Kuwait 1991.
Branch of Service: Allied forces.
Ribbon: Equal stripes of green, white and red with a black quadrilateral at the upper edge, representing the Kuwait national flag.
Metal: Various.
Size: Various.
Description: The circular medals have different decorative treatments of the Kuwaiti state emblem on the obverse, enshrined in a five-petalled flower (Second Grade), a five-pointed star with radiate background (Third Grade) and a plain medallic treatment (Fourth Grade). All grades, however, have a straight bar suspender of different designs.
Clasps: None.
Comments: *This medal was issued in five grades and awarded according to the rank of the recipient. The Excellent Grade was only conferred on the most senior Allied commanders, the First Grade went to brigadiers and major-generals, the Second Grade to officers of field rank (colonels and majors), the Third Grade to junior officers (captains, lieutenants and equivalent ranks in the other services), and the Fourth Grade to all other ranks. HM Government has decreed that British personnel may accept their medals as a keepsake but permission to wear them in uniform has so far been refused. The Canadian Government has followed the same policy, but the personnel of other Allied nations are permitted to wear their medals.*

VALUE:		*Miniature*
First Grade	£100–150	£25–30
Second Grade	£40–50	£20–25
Third Grade	£20–30	£20–25
Fourth Grade	£20–30	£20–25 *(silver)*

206A. NATO SERVICE MEDALS

Instituted: December 1994.

Campaigns: Any theatre or area of operations in the service of the North Atlantic Treaty Organization.

Branch of Service: NATO military and service personnel.

Ribbon: NATO blue with narrow white stripes having central metal threads: For engagements in NATO-led Article 5 operations (gold thread): Eagle Assist (central stripe), Active Endeavour (two stripes towards the edges), Non-Article 5 (central stripe with silver thread, from January 2011 two stripes towards the edges with silver thread denote operations) with clasps.

Metal: Bronze.

Size: 36mm.

Description: (Obverse) the NATO star emblem set in a wreath of olive leaves; (reverse) the title NORTH ATLANTIC TREATY ORGANIZATION and the words IN SERVICE OF PEACE AND FREEDOM in English and French. Two versions of this medal have been recorded: (a) light bronze, broad leaves in wreath, (b) dark bronze, narrow leaves.

Clasps: Former Yugoslavia, Kosovo, Non-Article 5 (superseding the first two clasps), Balkans (replaces last), Ex Yugoslavie, Africa*, OUP Libya/Libye*, NTM-Iraq*, AMIS*, Pakistan*, ISAF*, Article 5 (Eagle Assist & Active Endeavour). *Worn on the same ribbon. A multitour indicator was originally an Arabic numeral, currently it is a bronze square with the number inside.

Comments: *The NATO medal was first instituted to reward personnel who took part in the Alliance operations in the former Yugoslavia. Any person serving under NATO command or operational control is eligible for the award. UK Service personnel cannot qualify for the NATO Medal and the UNPROFOR Medal (no. 207) in respect of the same period of service. The qualifying period for the medal is to be designated by the Secretary-General, however, for the operations in the former Yugoslavia the period has been set as 30 days continuous or accumulated service within the theatre of operations inside the former Yugoslavia and the Adriatic, or 90 days within the area of operations but outside the territory of the former Yugoslavia. The medal takes precedence equal to the General Service Medal in order of date of award. Bronze Arabic numerals are worn on the ribbon to denote multiple tours. The Non-Article 5 medal (ribbon) replaces the three other NATO medals (ribbons) for services anywhere in the Balkans, commencing December 3, 2002. Article 5 of the NATO Charter states that an attack on one member state is an attack on the whole Alliance. Non-Article 5 operations are therefore those outside NATO territory. No clasp was issued for the service in Macedonia (Former Yugoslavia) due to objections from Greece which does not recognise the independent sovereignty of that country. The clasps for Kosovo and Former Yugoslavia have now been superseded by the Non Article 5 clasp. The clasp for Afghanistan bears the initials of the International Security Assistance Force. Those serving more than one tour of duty are authorised to wear a bronze Arabic numeral on their ribbon to indicate this. Eagle Assist, Active Endeavour, Afghanistan and Iraq medals are not approved or authorised for wear by UK personnel, either in full size or in miniature. If presented they may be retained as keepsake(s). NATO ISAF has now been approved for wear by Australian Forces (military and police). Service on awards for these medal(s) does not count as qualifying service towards the Accumulated Campaign Service Medal. Additionally a NATO Meritorious Service Medal has been instituted—see MYB291AA.*

Former Yugoslavia.

Kosovo.

Macedonia.

Eagle Assist.

Active Endeavour.

Non-Article 5.

Afghanistan (ISAF), Africa, Sudan (AMIS), Pakistan, Balkans, Iraq (NATO Training Mission) — denoted by clasp on ribbon.

VALUE: £25–£35 *Miniature* £10–12

206B. EUROPEAN COMMUNITY MONITORING MISSION MEDAL

Date: 1995.
Campaigns: Former Yugoslavia.
Branch of Service: EC Community Peacekeeping.
Ribbon: Navy with stripes of white and red and thin yellow.
Metal: Silver.
Size: 36mm.
Description: (Obverse) Outline map of Yugoslavia surmounted by the words EC MONITOR MISSION surrounded by a ring of stars; (reverse) a dove of peace.
Comments: *Awarded for 21 days service between July 27, 1991 and June 30, 1993, in and around the former Yugoslavia. Service for this medal does not count as qualifying service towards the Accumulated Campaign Service Medal.*

VALUE: £30–£35   *Miniature*   £10–15

206C. WESTERN EUROPEAN UNION MISSION SERVICE MEDAL

Date: 1997.
Campaigns: Operations in the Former Yugoslavia.
Branch of Service: Personnel serving with the Western European Union forces.
Ribbon: Bright blue with central broad bright yellow stripe.
Metal: Silver.
Size: 36mm.
Description: (Obverse) capital letters WEU arranged horizontally with U and O above and below the E to signify "Western European Union" and its French equivalent "Union de l'Europe Occidentale". Ten five-pointed stars are ranged around the lower half of the circumference; (reverse) PRO PACE UNUM ("United for peace") in three lines. A clasp signifying the area of service is worn on the ribbon.
Clasp: Ex Yugoslavie.
Comments: *This medal was instituted to award service with missions under the auspices of the Western European Union. It was awarded to personnel who had served at least 30 days in the former Yugoslavia or 90 days in the Adriatic, Hungary or Rumania. The first British recipients (March 6, 1997) were 27 police officers who had served with the WEU Police Force in Bosnia-Herzegovina. A total of 15,982 medals had been awarded by September 2000. This medal is also known as the European Union Police Mission Medal. Service for these medal(s) does not count as qualifying service towards the Accumulated Campaign Service Medal.*

VALUE: £50–£70   *Miniature*   £10–15

206D. EUROPEAN SECURITY AND DEFENCE POLICY SERVICE MEDAL

Reverse

Date: 2004.

Campaigns: Any military operations involving the European Union.

Branch of Service: Police.

Ribbon: Bright blue with central yellow stripe for HQ and Forces or with central white stripe for Planning and Support personnel, with an emblem denoting area of service.

Metal: Silver.

Size: 36mm.

Description: (Obverse) Twelve five-pointed stars in a circle; (reverse) PRO PACE UNUM in three lines (roughly translated as "United for peace"). The medal is fitted with a large ring for suspension. A clasp signifying the area of service is worn on the ribbon.

Clasps: Artemis, Concordia, Proxima, Althea, EUPM, EU Copps, EU NAVFOR Atalanta, EUSEC South Sudan, EUBAM Rafah, EUCAP Nestor, EUFOR RD Congo, EUFOR Tchad/RCA, EUPOL-AFG (Afghanistan), EUPOL Copps, EUSEC RD Congo, EUTM Mali, EUTM Somalia, EUMM Georgia, Kosovo (for EULEX Kosovo Mission) AMIS (for AMIS EU Mission).

Comments: *This medal has been awarded to police and security personnel serving in any military operation under the auspices of the European Union. It has also been awarded to civilian police missions, as well as Canadian personnel (2005). The clasps denote service in the Democratic Republic of Congo from June to September 2003 (Artemis), with the EU Police mission in Bosnia since January 2003, for service in the former Yugoslav republic of Macedonia from March to December 2003 (Concordia) or December 2003 to December 2004 (Proxima), service in Bosnia since December 2004 (Althea) and Afghanistan since June 2007. Those serving more than one tour of duty are authorised to wear an Arabic numeral on their ribbon to indicate this. Service for these medal(s) does not count as qualifying service towards the Accumulated Campaign Service Medal. The ESDP Medal with clasp Althea has been approved for unrestricted acceptance and wearing by UK personnel—headquarters and units serving in Bosnia and Herzegovina, on this operation. The ESDP medal for planning and support for Operation Althea is not approved for acceptance or wear. Those presented may be retained as a keepsake.*

VALUE: £30–35   *Miniature* £10–15

207. UNITED NATIONS MEDAL

Style of lettering for clasps.

For the various ribbons for the medal see ribbon charts.

Date: 1951.

Campaigns: Various supervisory or observation roles since 1948.

Branch of Service: UN forces.

Ribbons: Various (see below).

Metal: Bronze.

Size: 35mm.

Description: (Obverse) the wreathed globe emblem surmounted by the letters UN; (reverse) inscribed "IN THE SERVICE OF PEACE".

Clasps: CONGO, UNGOMAP, OSGAP, UNSMIH, MINUGUA, UNCRO, ONUMOZ, UNSCOM, UNAMIC, UNMIH, UNTMIH, UNOSGI, UNMONUA, UNOCHA, UNAMA.

Comments: *Apart from the UN Korea and UNEF medals, there have been numerous awards to personnel who served in one or other of the UN peace-keeping actions around the world since the end of the Second World War. The all-purpose medal has been awarded with various distinctive ribbons for service in many of the world's trouble spots. Two versions of the medal exist: globe flat (European) and globe raised (US version). Issues to South African Personnel are named. Eligibility is generally 90 days, but some missions were 180 days. Subsequent awards for each six month tour completed with the same mission are indicated by a silver numeral affixed to the ribbon. Those serving more than one tour of duty are authorised to wear an Arabic numeral on their ribbon to indicate this. Service for these medal(s) does not count as qualifying service towards the Accumulated Campaign Service Medal. The missions are listed overleaf in chronological order.*

207. UNITED NATIONS MEDAL *continued*

Reverse

UNTSO   United Nations Truce Supervision Organization (Israel, Egypt, Syria since 1948).
Blue ribbon with two narrow white stripes towards the edges.
UNOGIL   United Nations Observation Group in Lebanon (1958).
Same ribbon as UNTSO.
ONUC   Organisation des Nations Unies au Congo (1960–64).
Originally the same ribbon as UNTSO with clasp CONGO, but a green ribbon, with white and blue edges was substituted in 1963.
UNTEA   United Nations Temporary Executive Authority (Netherlands New Guinea, 1962–63).
Blue ribbon with a white central stripe bordered green.
UNMOGIP   United Nations Military Observer Group in India and Pakistan since 1949.
Dark green ribbon shading to light green with white and blue edges.
UNIPOM   United Nations India Pakistan Observation Mission (1965–66).
Ribbon as UNMOGIP.
UNYOM   United Nations Yemen Observation Mission (1963–64).
Ribbon with brown centre, yellow stripes and light blue edges.

UNFICYP   United Nations Force in Cyprus (1964–).
Pale blue ribbon with central white stripe bordered in dark blue. Initially 30, then increased to 90 days.
UNEF 2   United Nations Emergency Force 2 patrolling Israeli-Egyptian cease-fire (1973– 79).
Pale blue ribbon with sand centre and two dark blue stripes.
UNDOF   United Nations Disengagement Observer Force, Golan Heights (1974–).
Ribbon of red, white, black and pale blue.
UNIFIL   United Nations Interim Force in Lebanon (1978–).
Pale blue ribbon with green centre bordered white and red.
UNGOMAP   United Nations Good Offices in Afghanistan and Pakistan.
A bronze bar inscribed UNGOMAP was issued but as the mission was made up from observers from three other missions it can only be found on these ribbons: UNTSO, UNIFIL, UNDOF.
UNIIMOG   United Nations Iran-Iraq Monitoring Observation Group.
Pale blue with red, white and green edges (1988–91).
UNAVEM   United Nations Angola Verification Missions: I (1988–91), II (1991–95), III (1995–97).
Pale blue ribbon with yellow edges separated by narrow stripes of red, white and black (same for all three).
ONUCA   Observadores de las Naciones Unidas en Centro America (Nicaragua and Guatemala) (1989–92).
Pale blue ribbon with dark blue edges and nine thin central green or white stripes.
UNTAG   United Nations Transitional Assistance Group (Namibia, 1989–90).
Sand ribbon with pale blue edges and thin central stripes of blue, green, red, sand and deep blue.
ONUSAL   Observadores de las Naciones Unidas en El Salvador (1991–95).
Pale blue ribbon with a white central stripe bordered dark blue.
UNIKOM   United Nations Iraq Kuwait Observation Mission (1991–2003).
Sand ribbon with a narrow central stripe of pale blue.
MINURSO   Mission des Nations Unies pour la Referendum dans le Sahara Occidental (UN Mission for the Referendum in Western Sahara) (1991–).
Ribbon has a broad sandy centre flanked by stripes of UN blue.
UNAMIC   United Nations Advanced Mission in Cambodia (Oct. 1991–March 1992).
Pale blue ribbon with central white stripe bordered with dark blue, yellow and red stripes.
UNTAC   United Nations Transitional Authority in Cambodia (March 1992–Sept. 1993).
Green ribbon with central white stripe edged with red, pale blue and dark blue.
UNOSOM   United Nations Operations in Somalia (I: 1992–93 and II: 1993–95).
Pale yellow ribbon with central blue stripe edged with green.
UNMIH   United Nations Mission in Haiti (1993–96).
Pale blue ribbon with dark blue and red central stripes edged with white.
UNPROFOR   United Nations Protection Force (1992–95) operating in the former Yugoslavia, especially Bosnia. *Blue ribbon with central red stripe edged in white and green or brown edges. See also UNCRO below.*
UNOMIL   United Nations Observer Mission in Liberia (1993–97).
Pale blue ribbon flanked with white stripes with dark blue or red edges.
UNOMUR   United Nations Observer Mission in Uganda/Rwanda (1993–94).
Pale blue central stripe edged by white and flanked by equal stripes of black, orange and red.
UNOMIG   United Nations Observer Mission in Georgia (1993–2009). For 180 days service.
Pale blue central stripe flanked by equal stripes of white, green and dark blue.
UNAMIR   United Nations Assistance Mission in Rwanda (1993–96).
Pale blue central stripe edged with white and flanked by equal stripes of black, green and red.
UNHQ   General service at UN headquarters, New York.
Plain ribbon of pale blue, the UN colour.
UNPREDEP   United Nations Preventative Deployment in Yugoslavia (1995–99).
Blue ribbon with central red stripe bearing four yellow lines and flanked by white edging.

UNMOP   United Nations Mission of Observers in Pravlaka (1996–2002).
Dark blue ribbon with central yellow stripe edged with white, and two pale blue stripes.
UNTAES   United Nations Transitional Authority in Eastern Slavonia. (1996-98)
Pale blue ribbon with yellow, red edged with white, and green stripes.
UNMOT   United Nations Peacekeeping Force in Tadjikistan (1994–2000).
Blue ribbon with central green stripe flanked by white stripes.
UNMIBH   United Nations Mission in Bosnia Herzegovina (1995–2002).
Blue ribbon with white central stripe, edged with one green and one red stripe.
UNMOGUA   United Nations Military Observers in Guatemala (1997).
Blue ribbon with central pale blue stripe and two white stripes each with central green line.
UNSMIH   United Nations Support Mission in Haiti (July 1996–97).
Same ribbon as UNMIH above, but with clasp UNSMIH.
UNCRO   United Nations Confidence Restoration Operation in Croatia (1994–96).
Same ribbon as UNPROFOR above, but with clasp UNCRO.
MINUGUA   Mision de las Naciones Unidas en Guatemala (1997).
Same ribbon as UNMOGUA but clasp with initials in Spanish.
ONUMOZ   Operation des Nations Unies pour le referendum dans Mozambique (1992–94).
Pale blue ribbon edged with white and green stripes.
UNSSM   United Nations Special Service Medal.
Awarded to personnel serving at least 90 consecutive days under UN control in operations for which no other UN award is authorised. Blue ribbon with white edges. Clasps: UNOCHA, UNSCOM, UNAMA. The medal with no clasp was awarded to Operation Cheshire aircrew who had completed 100 landings at Sarajevo or ground crew who had spent 90 days at Anacona, Split or Zagreb between July 3, 1992 and January 12, 1996.
OSGAP   Office of the Secretary General for Afghanistan and Pakistan.
Silver clasp worn by Canadian personnel on the ribbons of UNTSO, UNDOF or UNIFIL.
UNOMSIL   United Nations Observer Mission in Sierra Leone. (1998–99)
Awarded for 90 days service. White ribbon with blue edges and the Sierra Leone colours (light blue flanked by green stripes) in the centre. This mission was redesignated UNAMSIL on October 1, 1999.
UNPSG   United Nations Police Support Group Medal.
A support group of 180 police monitors created in January 1998 initially to supervise the Croatian police in the return of displaced persons. 90 days qualifying service. White ribbon with a broad blue central stripe and narrow dark grey (left) and bright yellow (right) stripes towards the edges.
MINURCA   United Nations Verification Mission in the Central African Republic (1998–2000).
Mission instituted April 15, 1998 to monitor the restoration of peace following the Bangui agreement. 90 days qualifying service. Ribbon has a broad blue central stripe flanked by yellow, green, red, white and dark blue stripes on either side.
UNSCOM   United Nations Special Commission.
The UN Special Service Medal with UNSCOM clasp is awarded to personnel with a minimum of 90 days consecutive service or 180 days in all, with UNSCOM in Iraq. Ribbon is UN blue with a white stripe at each edge.
UNMIK   United Nations Mission in Kosovo (1999–).
Pale blue ribbon with wide central dark blue stripe edged with white. For 180 days service.
UNAMET   United Nations Mission in East Timor (1999).
Pale blue ribbon with wide central white stripe edged with yellow and claret.
UNTAET   United Nations Transitional Administration in East Timor (1999–2002).
Pale blue ribbon with wide central white stripe edged with yellow and claret.
UNMISET   United Nations Mission of Support in East Timor (2002–05).
Pale blue ribbon with wide central white stripe edged with yellow and claret.
MONUC   United Nations Mission in the Congo (1999–2010).
Pale blue ribbon with wide central dark blue stripe edged with yellow.
UNMEE   United Nations Mission in Ethiopia and Eritrea (2000–2008).
Pale blue with central band of sand bisected by narrow dark green stripe.
MIPONUH   United Nations Civil Police Mission in Haiti (1997–2000).
Central bands of dark blue and red, flanked by narrow silver stripes and broad blue bands
UNTMIH   United Nations Transitional Mission in Haiti (July–November 1997).
Same ribbon as MIPONUH but with a bar inscribed UNTMIH.
MICAH   International Civilian Support Mission in Haiti (March 2000–01).
Same ribbon as MIPONUH.
UNOSGI   The UN Office of the Secretary General in Iraq.
The UN Special Service Medal with UNOSGI clasp issued to a small police group assigned to Baghdad from February 1991 to December 1992.
UNHCR   United Nations High Commission for Refugees.
A clasp issued worldwide and still on-going.
UNAMSIL   United Nations Medal for Service in Sierra Leone (1999–2005).
Same ribbon as UNOMSIL.
UNAMA   United Nations Assistance Mission in Afghanistan (2002–).
This is a political mission. A clasp bearing UNAMA is worn on the UN Special Service Medal.
MINUCI   United Nations Mission in Cote d'Ivoire (Ivory Coast) (May 2003–April 2004).
Orange, white and green stripes with blue edges.
UNMIL   United Nations Mission in Liberia (September 2003–).
Pale blue with a broad central dark blue stripe edged in red and white.

207. UNITED NATIONS MEDAL *continued*

UNOCI   United Nations Operations in Cote d'Ivoire (April 2004–).
Similar to MINUCI but central stripes very narrow and blue edges correspondingly wider.
UNOB   United Nations Operations in Burundi (June 2004–07).
Central stripes of white, red, dark green and white, flanked by broad pale blue stripes.
MINUSTAH   Mission des Nations Unies Stabilisation dans Haiti (June 2004–).
Narrow central pale blue stripe, flanked by broader equal stripes of white, dark green and dark blue.
UNMIS   United Nations Mission in Sudan (March 2005–11).
UN blue with dark blue centre divided by two narrow white stripes.
UNMIT   United Nations Integrated Mission in Timor-Leste (August 2006–12)
UN blue with red centre stripe bordered each side with narrow stripes of white, dark blue and yellow.
UNAMID   African Union/United Nations Hybrid operation in Darfur (July 2007–)
Yellow with a central stripe of half blue, half white and with dark blue narrow stripes either side <u>or</u> Blue with central white stripe bordered each side by stripes of green and yellow.
MINURCAT   United Nations Mission in the Central African Republic and Chad (September 2007–10).
UN blue with five equal narrow stripes of dark blue, white, yellow, green and red.
UNGCI   A little-known United Nations Guard Contingent Mission in Iraq 1991–2003.
UN blue with orange stripes at edges divided by black stripes.
MONUSCO   United Nations Organisational Stabilisation Mission in the Democratic Republic of the Congo (2010).
Pale blue ribbon with wide central dark blue stripe edged with yellow.
UNISFA   United Nations Mission in the Republic of Sudan (2011–).
UN blue with white, green and yellow stripes with central narrow dark blue stripe .
UNMISS   United Nations Interim Security Force for Abyei, Sudan (2011–).
UN blue with central green stripe bordered by two white stripes each edged with black.
UNSMIS   United Nations Supervision Mission in Syria (2012).
Mission abandoned. Intended ribbon UN blue with red centre stripe bordered each side by thin white stripes divided by a thin green stripe.
MINUSMA   United Nations Multidimensional Integrated Stabilisation Mission in Mali (2013).
UN blue edges with central dark blue stripe bordered by thin green, yellow and red stripes at left and single pale yellow stripe at right..
MINUSCA   United Nations Multidimensional Integrated Stabilisation Mission in the Central African Republic (2014–).
UN blue with centre narrow stripes of blue, white, red, yellow, green.

VALUE:

Any current issue medal regardless of ribbon	£25–35
Original striking for Cyprus	£30–45
Miniature	£8–10

207A. INTERNATIONAL CONFERENCE ON THE FORMER YUGOSLAVIA MEDAL

Date: 1995.
Campaigns: Former Yugoslavia.
Branch of Service: UN Observers.
Ribbon: Central broad orange stripe, flanked by narrow blue and white stripes and broad red edges, mounted in the Danish style.
Metal: Silver.
Size: 38mm.
Description: (Obverse) the wreathed globe emblem of the United Nations surrounded by 15 five-pointed stars representing the member nations of the conference, with the inscription round the edge: INTERNATIONAL CONFERENCE ON THE FORMER YUGOSLAVIA; (reverse) the Drina River and the mountains of Serbia and Montenegro surmounted by a peace dove in flight, with the words OBSERVER MISSION round the foot.
Comments: *This medal was awarded to about 100 observers who monitored the 17 land and two rail crossings between Serbia and Montenegro and Bosnia-Herzegovina during September 1994.*

VALUE: £80–100   *Miniature*   £12–16

207B. INTERFET MEDAL—International Force East Timor

Instituted: March 7, 2000.

Ribbon: 32mm central thin red stripe, flanked by deep green, white and UN light blue.

Metal: Pewter coloured silver.

Size: 38mm.

Description: (Obverse) central raised stylised dove of peace over the island of Timor, surrounded by raised inscription INTERNATIONAL FORCE EAST TIMOR surmounted by Federation Star and plain suspension bar struck as one unit; (reverse) TOGETHER AS ONE FOR PEACE IN EAST TIMOR around outer circle, inner circle blank for naming.

Method of naming: Pantographed on reverse in capitals with regimental number, initials and surname.

Comments: *The Australian Prime Minister established a specific campaign medal for members of the Australian Defence Force in East Timor. Australia led the coalition of 17 nations and this is the first Australian medal issued to other countries. Awarded for 30 days service during the INTERFET stage of the conflict. 15,046 medals have been issued, including 8,690 to members of the ADF and 6,356 to members of other countries' military establishments.*

VALUE:	To Australian personnel	£500–800
	Others	£700–1000

207C. UNITAS MEDAL

Instituted: 1994.

Ribbon: 32mm, pale blue with central green stripe of 8mm edged each side by a white stripe of 4mm.

Metal: Lacquered brass.

Size: 38mm.

Description: (Obverse) a seven pointed star with central circle enclosing the Greek letter alpha; (reverse) A small embellished coat of arms of South Africa with date 1994 below. The whole is enclosed by a circle made up of the word "Unity" in all eleven official languages of the new South Africa. Suspender is uniface and struck as one piece with the medal.

Comments: *Awarded to all those who rendered service through being members of a serving force (SA Permanent Force, Citizen Force, Commandos, members of the armed forces of the former self-governing territories, the armed wing of the ANC (the MK) and APLA) during the period of South Africa's first non-racial elections and inauguration of Mr Mandela as the first black State President in South Africa between 27 April and 10 May 1994. Those medals awarded to members of the British Military Advisory Team in South Africa at the time, for which Her Majesty Queen Elizabeth II granted permission for wear, must be considered a rarity.*

VALUE:			Miniature
	SA recipient	£25–35	£12–16
	BMA recipient	From £250	

LONG

and Meritorious Service

A large, varied but until recently relatively neglected category comprises the medals awarded for long service and good conduct or meritorious service. Their common denominator is that the grant of such awards is made in respect of a minimum number of years of unblemished service—"undetected crime" is how it is often described in the armed forces. As their title implies, long service and good conduct medals combine the elements of lengthy service with no transgressions of the rules and regulations. Meritorious service, on the other hand, implies rather more. Apart from a brief period (1916–28) when awards were made for single acts of gallantry, MSMs have generally been granted to warrant officers and senior NCOs as a rather superior form of long service medal.

Long service and good conduct medals do not appear to excite the same interest among collectors as campaign medals. Perhaps this may be accounted for by their image of stolid devotion to duty rather than the romantic connotations of a medal with an unusual clasp awarded for service in some remote and all but forgotten outpost of the Empire. Nevertheless their importance should not be overlooked. Especially in regard to groups consisting primarily of the Second World War medals, they serve a useful purpose in establishing the provenance of the group, on account of the fact that they are invariably named to the recipient.

Service medals include not only such well known types as the Army LSGC (known affectionately as "the mark of the beast" on account of its high incidence on the chests of sergeant-majors), but also awards to the Territorial and Reserve forces, the auxiliary forces, the nursing services, and organisations such as the Royal Observer Corps and the Cadet Force, the Police, the Red Cross and St John's Ambulance Brigade. The Special Constabulary and Fire Brigades also have their own medals bestowed according to length of service and distinguished conduct. These medals may lack the glamour of naval and military awards but in recent years they have become increasingly fashionable with collectors and will certainly repay further study in their own right.

As many of these medals have been in use for eighty years or more with a standard reverse, variation usually lies in the obverse, changed for each successive sovereign. In addition, considerable variety has been imparted by the use of crowned or uncrowned profiles and busts, and changes in titles.

The following is a summary of the principal obverse types which may be encountered, referred to in the text by their type letters in brackets:

Queen Victoria (A) Young head by William Wyon
Queen Victoria (B) Veiled head by Leonard C. Wyon
Queen Victoria (C) Jubilee head by Sir Joseph E. Boehm
Queen Victoria (D) Old head by Sir Thomas Brock
Edward VII (A) Bareheaded bust in Field Marshal's uniform
Edward VII (B) Bareheaded bust in Admiral's uniform
Edward VII (C) Coinage profile by George W. de Saulles
Edward VII (D) Crowned profile in Coronation robes
George V (A) Bareheaded bust in Field Marshal's uniform
George V (B) Bareheaded bust in Admiral's uniform
George V (C) Crowned bust in Coronation robes
George V (D) Crowned bust in Delhi Durbar robes
George V (E) Coinage profile by Bertram Mackennal
George VI (A) Crowned profile in Coronation robes
George VI (B) Crowned profile INDIAE: IMP 1937–48
George VI (C) Crowned profile FID: DEF 1949–52
George VI (D) Coinage profile IND: IMP 1937–48
George VI (E) Coinage profile FID: DEF 1949–52
Elizabeth II (A1) Tudor crown BR: OMN 1953–54
Elizabeth II (A) Tudor crown BR: OMN omitted 1954–80
Elizabeth II (B) Coinage bust BRITT: OMN 1953–54
Elizabeth II (C) Coinage bust BRITT OMN omitted 1954–80
Elizabeth II (D) St Edward crown 1955–
Elizabeth II (E) New bust for Diamond Jubilee Medal

PRINCIPAL OBVERSE TYPES:

Queen Victoria (A) Young Head

Queen Victoria (B) Veiled Head

Queen Victoria (C) Jubilee Head

Queen Victoria (D) Old Head

Edward VII (A) Bareheaded bust in Field Marshal's uniform

Edward VII (B) Bareheaded bust in Admiral's uniform

Edward VII (C) Coinage profile by George W. de Saulles

Edward VII (D) Crowned profile in Coronation robes

George V (A) Bareheaded bust in Field Marshal's uniform

George V (B) Bareheaded bust in Admiral's uniform

George V (C) Crowned bust in Coronation robes

George V (D) Crowned bust in Delhi Durbar robes

George V (E) Coinage profile by Bertram Mackennal

George VI (B) Crowned profile with INDIAE: IMP in legend 1937–48

George VI (C) Crowned profile with FID: DEF 1949–52

George VI (D) Coinage profile with IND: IMP 1937–48

George VI (E) Coinage profile with FID: DEF 1949–52

Elizabeth II (A1) Tudor crown with BR.OMN. (1953–54)
Elizabeth II (A) BR.OMN. omitted (as above) 1954–80

Elizabeth II (B) Coinage bust with BRITT: OMN, 1953–54

Elizabeth II (C) Coinage bust without BR: OMN.

Elizabeth II (D) St Edward crown 1980–.

Second award bar.

Regular contributor to MEDAL NEWS, author of the Heroes of the Albert Medal *series, Allan Stanistreet, receiving a well-deserved long service award (as featured in "My Medals", MEDAL NEWS, April 2017).*

208. ROYAL NAVAL MERITORIOUS SERVICE MEDAL

Instituted: 14 January 1919 until 1928 by Order in Council. Reinstituted 1977.

Branch of Service: Royal Navy.

Ribbon: Crimson with three white stripes.

Metal: Silver

Size: 36mm.

Description: (Obverse) effigy of the reigning monarch; (reverse) imperial crown surmounting a wreath containing the words FOR MERITORIOUS SERVICE. The medal was named in large seriffed capitals round the rim.

Comments: *Awarded without annuity or pension to warrant and petty officers of the Royal Navy. Originally it was awarded either for specific acts of gallantry not in the presence of the enemy or for arduous and specially meritorious service afloat or ashore in action with the enemy. Bars were granted for second awards. It was superseded in 1928 by the British Empire Medal for Gallantry or Meritorious Service, but re-instated on 1 December 1977. In this guise it has been awarded to warrant and petty officers of the Royal Navy, warrant officers and senior NCOs of the Royal Marines, and equivalent ranks in the WRNS and QARNNS, who have at least 20 years service and are already holders of the LSGC medal and three good conduct badges. The medal is not awarded automatically when these criteria are satisfied, as no more than 49 medals may be awarded annually. The revived medal is identical to the Army MSM and can only be distinguished by the naming giving rank and name of ship.*

VALUE:		Miniature
George V (A)	—	—
George V (B) (1020)	£400–500	£25–35
Elizabeth II (B)	£350–450	£18–20

209. ROYAL MARINES MERITORIOUS SERVICE MEDAL

Original ribbon.

Instituted: 15 January 1849, by Order in Council (although medals dated 1848 are known).

Branch of Service: Royal Marines.

Ribbon: Plain dark blue, but later replaced by the RN MSM ribbon.

Metal: Silver.

Size: 36mm.

Description: (Obverse) effigy of the monarch; (reverse) a crowned laurel wreath enclosing the words FOR MERITORIOUS SERVICE.

Comments: *Annuities not exceeding £20 a year might be granted in addition to the medal for distinguished service. Sergeants with a minimum of 24 years service (the last fourteen as a sergeant), "with an irreproachable and meritorious character" were considered eligible for the award which was extended to discharged sergeants in 1872 when the service qualification was reduced to 21 years. The award of the MSM for gallantry was discontinued in 1874 when the Conspicuous Gallantry Medal was reconstituted. Only six MSMs for gallantry were ever awarded. The medal was identical with the Army MSM, distinguished solely by its ribbon and the naming to the recipient. Under the royal warrants of 1916-19 Marine NCOs became eligible for immediate awards of the MSM for arduous or specially meritorious service. The medals in this case were worn with crimson ribbons with three white stripes and had the obverse showing the King in the uniform of an Admiral or a Field Marshal, depending on whether the award was for services afloat, or with the naval brigades on the Western Front. The use of this medal ceased in 1928 following the institution of the BEM (MYB 19). The Royal Marines MSM was revived in 1977 solely as a long service award and is the same as the naval MSM already noted, differing only in the details of the recipient.*

VALUE:		Miniature	
Victoria (A) dated 1848	£1200–1500		£50–65
Victoria	£700–1000		£80–90
Edward VII (C)	£600–800		£80–90
George V (A)	£600–800		£45–55
George V (B)	£400–600		£45–55
Elizabeth II (B)	£400–600		£30–35

210. ARMY MERITORIOUS SERVICE MEDAL

First type ribbon.

Second type ribbon.

Third type ribbon.

Instituted: 19 December 1845.

Branch of Service: Army.

Ribbon: Plain crimson (till 1916), white edges added (1916-17), three white stripes (since August 1917).

Metal: Silver.

Size: 36mm.

Description: (Obverse) effigy of the monarch; (reverse) a crowned laurel wreath inscribed FOR MERITORIOUS SERVICE.

Comments: *A sum of £2000 a year was set aside for distribution to recipients in the form of annuities not exceeding £20, paid for life to NCOs of the rank of sergeant and above for distinguished or meritorious service. The number of medals awarded was thus limited by the amount of money available in the annuity fund, so that medals and annuities were only granted on the death of previous recipients or when the fund was increased. Until November 1902 holders were not allowed to wear the LSGC as well as the MSM, but thereafter both medals could be worn, the LSGC taking precedence. In 1979, however, the order of precedence was reversed. Until 1951 the MSM could only be awarded when an annuity became available, but since then it has been awarded without the annuity. From 1956 recipients needed at least 27 years service to become eligible, but this was reduced to 20 years in 2002. What was, in effect, a second type of MSM was introduced in October 1916 when immediate awards for exceptionally valuable and meritorious service were introduced. In January 1917 this was extended to include individual acts of gallantry not in the presence of the enemy. No annuities were paid with the immediate awards which terminated in 1928 with the institution of the Gallantry BEM. Bars for subsequent acts of gallantry or life-saving were introduced in 1916, seven being awarded up to 1928. The standard crown and wreath reverse was used but in addition to the wide range of obverse types swivelling suspension was used until 1926, and immediate and non-immediate awards may be distinguished by the presence or absence respectively of the recipient's regimental number. Recent awards of the Elizabethan second bust medals have reverted to swivelling suspension. By Royal Warrant of February 2002 the annual allocation was a maximum of 201 medals: Royal Navy (49), Royal Marines (3), Army (89) and RAF (60).*

VALUE:

		Miniature
Victoria (A) 1847 on edge (110)	£800–1000	—
Victoria (A) 1848 below bust (10)	£1500–2000	—
Victoria (A) (990)	£400–450	£35–55
Edward VII (725)	£300–400	£35–45
George V (A) swivel (1050)	£150–250	£20–30
George V (A) non-swivel (400)	£150–250	£15–25
George V (A) Immediate awards 1916–28 (26,211+7 bars):		
For Gallantry (366+1 bar)	£350–450	—
Meritorious service (25,845+6 bars)	£200–300	—
George V (E) (550)	£350–450	£20–30
George VI (B) (55)	£850–1000	£15–25
George VI (D) (1090)	£250–350	£15–25
George VI (E) (5600)	£250–350	£15–25
Elizabeth II (B) (125)	£400–650	£15–25
Elizabeth II (C) (2750+)	£350–450	£15–25

211. ROYAL AIR FORCE MERITORIOUS SERVICE MEDAL

Instituted: June 1918
Branch of Service: Royal Air Force.
Ribbon: Half crimson, half light blue, with white stripes at the centre and edges. Since 1977 the same ribbon as the Army MSM.
Metal: Silver.
Size: 36mm.
Description: (Obverse) effigy of the monarch; (reverse) a crowned laurel wreath enclosing the words FOR MERITORIOUS SERVICE. Originally medals were named in large seriffed capitals and were issued in respect of the First World War and service in Russia (1918-20), but later medals were impressed in thin block capitals. The RAF version had a swivelling suspension, unlike its military counterpart.
Comments: *Awarded for valuable services in the field, as opposed to actual flying service. This medal was replaced by the BEM in 1928, but revived in December 1977 under the same conditions as the military MSM. No more than 60 medals are awarded annually. The current issue is similar to the naval and military MSMs, differing only in the naming which includes RAF after the service number.*

Original ribbon.

VALUE:		*Miniature*
George V (E) (854)	£400–500	£25–35
Elizabeth II (C)	£350–450	£12–18

212. COLONIAL MERITORIOUS SERVICE MEDALS

For the various original ribbons see the ribbon charts at the end of this publication.

Instituted: 31 May 1895.
Branch of Service: Colonial forces.
Ribbon: According to issuing territory (see below).
Metal: Silver.
Size: 36mm.
Description: (Obverse) originally the trophy of arms as MYB 229 but later issues have the head of the reigning monarch; (reverse) as British type, but with the name of the dominion or colony round the top.
Comments: *Awarded for service in the British dominions, colonies and protectorates.*

Canada: Ribbon as for British Army MSM. CANADA on reverse till 1936; imperial version used from then until 1958. No medals with the Victorian obverse were awarded, but specimens exist.
Cape of Good Hope: Crimson ribbon with central orange stripe. Only one or two Edward VII medals issued.
Natal: Crimson ribbon with a central yellow stripe. Exceptionally, it was awarded to volunteers in the Natal Militia. Fifteen Edward VII medals awarded.
Commonwealth of Australia: Crimson ribbon with two dark green central stripes. Issued between 1903 and 1975.
New South Wales: Crimson ribbon with a dark blue central stripe. Issued till 1903.
Queensland: Crimson ribbon with light blue central stripe. Issued till 1903.
South Australia: Plain crimson ribbon. Issued till 1903.
Tasmania: Crimson ribbon with a pink central stripe. Issued till 1903.
New Zealand: Crimson ribbon with a light green central stripe. Issued since 1898 (see also NZ21).

VALUE   Rare   *Miniature* £110–220

213. INDIAN ARMY MERITORIOUS SERVICE MEDAL 1848

Instituted: 20 May 1848, by General Order of the Indian government.
Branch of Service: Forces of the Honourable East India Company and later the Indian armed services.
Ribbon: Plain crimson.
Metal: Silver.
Size: 36mm.
Description: (Obverse) the Wyon profile of Queen Victoria; (reverse) the arms and motto of the Honourable East India Company.
Comments: *Awarded with an annuity up to £20 to European sergeants, serving or discharged, for meritorious service. It was discontinued in 1873.*

VALUE: £500–600   *Miniature* £240–300

214. INDIAN ARMY MERITORIOUS SERVICE MEDAL 1888

Instituted: 1888.
Branch of Service: Indian Army.
Ribbon: Plain crimson (till 1917); three white stripes added (1917).
Metal: Silver.
Size: 36mm.
Description: (Obverse) the sovereign's effigy; (reverse) a central wreath enclosing the word INDIA surrounded by the legend FOR MERITORIOUS SERVICE with a continuous border of lotus flowers and leaves round the circumference.
Comments: *For award to Indian warrant officers and senior NCOs (havildars, dafadars and equivalent band ranks). Eighteen years of exceptionally meritorious service was the minimum requirement, subject to the availability of funds in the annuity. At first only one medal was set aside for each regiment and thereafter awards were only made on the death, promotion or reduction of existing recipients. On promotion the medal was retained but the annuity ceased. It became obsolete in 1947.*

VALUE:		*Miniature*
Victoria (B)	£200–250	£100–120
Edward VII (A)	£175–250	£100–120
George V (C) Rex Et Indiae Imp	£150–200	£100–120
George V (D) Kaisar-i-Hind	£150–200	£100–120
George VI (B)	£125–150	£100–120

Original ribbon.

215. AFRICAN POLICE MEDAL FOR MERITORIOUS SERVICE

Instituted: 14 July 1915.
Branch of Service Non-European NCOs and men of the colonial police forces in East and West Africa.
Ribbon: Sand-coloured with red edges.
Metal: Silver.
Size: 36mm.
Description: (Obverse) effigy of the sovereign; (reverse) a crown surmounted by a lion passant gardant within a palm wreath and having the legend FOR MERITORIOUS SERVICE IN THE POLICE and AFRICA at the foot.
Comments: *Awarded for both individual acts of gallantry and distinguished, meritorious or long service. In respect of the lastnamed, a minimum of 15 years exemplary service was required. It was superseded by the Colonial Police Medal in 1938.*

VALUE:
George V (A) IND: IMP 1915-31	£700–900
George V (A) INDIAE IMP 1931-7	£700–900
George VI (B) 1938	Rare
Miniature	£100–120

216. UNION OF SOUTH AFRICA MERITORIOUS SERVICE MEDAL

Instituted: 24 October 1914, by Government gazette.
Branch of Service: Service personnel of South Africa, Southern Rhodesia and Swaziland.
Ribbon: Crimson with blue edges and a central white, blue and white band.
Metal: Silver.
Size: 36mm.
Description: As British military MSM.
Comments: *A total of 46 awards were made for 21 years service and 300 meritorious service awards were made up to 1952 when the medal was discontinued. Of these only two were awarded to South Africans in the RNVR.*

VALUE:
George V (A)	Rare
George VI (B)	Rare

217. ROYAL HOUSEHOLD FAITHFUL SERVICE MEDALS

1st type obv.

Instituted: 1872 by Queen Victoria.

Branch of Service: Royal Household.

Ribbon: Originally Royal Stuart tartan; later, a different ribbon for each monarch: dark blue and red diagonal stripes descending from left to right (George V), the same but descending from right to left (George VI) or dark blue with three red stripes (Elizabeth II).

Metal: Silver.

Size: 27mm (Victoria); 29mm (later awards).

Description: (Obverse) the sovereign's effigy; (reverse) the personal details of the recipient engraved on it. The Victorian medal has a very elaborate suspension ornamented with the crowned royal monogram, with a laurel bar brooch fitting at the top. This medal was not originally intended to be worn with a ribbon, although it had a strip of Royal Stuart tartan behind it. The same medal, but struck in 22 carat gold, was presented to John Brown, the Queen's personal servant. The concept was revived by George V, a silver medal of more conventional appearance being struck with the text FOR LONG AND FAITHFUL SERVICE on the reverse. Thirty, forty and fifty year service bars were also awarded.

Comments: *Originally intended as a reward to servants of the Royal Household for long and faithful service of at least 25 years but during the reign of George V this was changed to 20 years cumulative service. A further 10 years merited a bar. Different ribbons are used for each monarch, corresponding to the crowned cypher joining the medal to the suspension bar on either side of which the recipient's years of service are inscribed.*

VALUE:

		Miniature
Victoria	From £500	Not seen
Edward VII	—	Not seen
George V (E)	From £400	£90–110
George VI (D)	From £400	£80–90
Elizabeth II (C)	From £450	£35–45

1st type rev.

Original background ribbon.

2nd type obv. (George V).

2nd type rev.

GV ribbon.

GVI ribbon.

EII ribbon.

218. ROYAL NAVAL LONG SERVICE AND GOOD CONDUCT MEDAL

1st type obv.

1st type rev.

2nd type rev. wide suspender

Later type ribbon.

Instituted: 24 August 1831, by Order in Council.
Branch of Service: Royal Navy.
Ribbon: Plain dark blue (1831); dark blue with white edges (1848).
Metal: Silver.
Size: 34mm (1831); 36mm (1848).
Description: First type: (Obverse) an anchor surmounted by a crown and enclosed in an oak wreath; (reverse) the recipient's details. Plain ring for suspension.

Second type, adopted in 1848: (Obverse) the sovereign's effigy; (reverse) a three-masted man-of-war surrounded by a rope tied at the foot with a reef knot and having the legend FOR LONG SERVICE AND GOOD CONDUCT round the circumference. This medal originally had a wide suspender bar 38mm, but a narrow suspender was substituted in 1874. Normally the obverse was undated, but about 100 medals were issued in 1849-50 with the obverse of the Naval GSM, with the date 1848 below the Queen's bust. Between 1875 and 1877 a number of medals had the years of service added to the recipient's details, either engraved or impressed on the edge—these medals (about 60 known) are now sought after by collectors. Engraved naming was used from 1875 to 1877, but from then until 1901 impressed naming was adopted. Later medals used the various obverse effigies noted below.

Comments: *Originally awarded for 21 years exemplary conduct, but the period was reduced to 10 years in 1874, then later increased to 15 years. Bars for additional periods of 15 years were instituted by George V. In March 1981 commissioned officers of the naval services became eligible after 15 years service, provided at least 12 years were served in the ranks. Under changes announced in 2015 a clasp is now awarded for every 10 years served.*

VALUE:		Miniature
Anchor type obv., 1831–47 (644)	£650–850	—
Victoria (A):		
1848–75, wide suspender (3572)	£450–550	—
Dated 1848 type (100)	£1200–1500	—
1875–77, narrow suspender,		
engraved naming (4400)	£175–250	£35–45
Year on edge variety (c. 40)	£350–450	—
1877–1901		
impressed naming (18,200)	£175–250	—
Year on edge variety (c. 20)	£350–400	—
Edward VII (B)	£75–100	—
George V (B) 1910–20 swivel	£75–100	£12–18
1920–30 non-swivelling bar	£65–85	£5–12
George V (E) 1931–36	£75–100	£10–15
George VI (D) 1937–48	£85–100	£10–15
George VI (E) 1949–52	£85–100	£10–15
Elizabeth II (B) 1953–54	£75–100	£10–15
Elizabeth II (C) 1954–	£75–100	£10–15

2nd type rev. narrow suspender

2nd type obv. George V

219. ROYAL NAVAL RESERVE DECORATION

Instituted: 1908.
Branch of Service: Royal Naval Reserve.
Ribbon: Plain green ribbon, white edges being added from 1941 onwards.
Metal: Silver and silver-gilt.
Size: Height 54mm; max. width 33mm.
Description: A skeletal badge with the royal cypher in silver surrounded by an oval cable and reef knot in silver-gilt, surmounted by a crown and suspension ring.
Comments: *Granted for 15 years commissioned service (sub-lieutenant and above) in the Royal Naval Reserve, active service in wartime counting double. Bars are awarded for additional periods of 15 years. Recipients are entitled to the letters RD after their name. This decoration was replaced by the VRSM (No. 242A) in 2000.*

VALUE:		Miniature
Edward VII	£150–175	£30–35
George V	£185–200	£30–35
George VI (GRI)	£150–175	£30–35
George VI (GVIR)	£150–175	£30–35
Elizabeth II	£175–190	£30–35

2nd type ribbon.

220. ROYAL NAVAL RESERVE LONG SERVICE AND GOOD CONDUCT MEDAL

Instituted: 1908.
Branch of Service: Royal Naval Reserve.
Ribbon: Plain green, white edges and a central white stripe being added in 1941. On the amalgamation of the RNR and RNVR in 1958 the ribbon was changed to five equal stripes of blue, white, green, white and blue.
Metal: Silver.
Size: 36mm.
Description: (Obverse) effigy of the monarch; (reverse) a battleship with the motto DIUTERNE FIDELIS (faithful for ever) at the foot.
Comments: *Awarded to petty officers and ratings of the RNR for 15 years service, war service counting double, with bars for additional 15 year periods. This medal was replaced by the VRSM (No. 242A) in 2000.*

VALUE:		Miniature
Edward VII (B)	£45–55	£30–35
George V (B)	£35–45	£30–35
George V (E)	£35–45	£30–35
George VI (D)	£55–75	£30–35
George VI (E)	£55–75	£30–35
Elizabeth II (B)	£55–75	£30–35
Elizabeth II (C)	£55–75	£30–35

2nd type ribbon.

3rd type ribbon.

221. ROYAL NAVAL VOLUNTEER RESERVE DECORATION

Instituted: 1908.

Branch of Service: Royal Naval Volunteer Reserve.

Ribbon: 38mm originally plain dark green; dark blue with a central green stripe flanked by narrow red stripes (since 1919). Dark blue represents the sea, red represents the Royal Crimson, green represents the Old Volunteer colour

Metal: Silver and silver-gilt.

Size: Height 54mm; max. width 33mm.

Description: Similar to RNR decoration.

Comments: *Awarded to commissioned officers of the RNVR. The qualifying period was 15 years, service in the ranks counting half and war service counting double. In 1966 the decoration was replaced by the RD following the merger of the RNR and RNVR. Holders were entitled to the post-nominals letters VD, until 1947 when the letters VRD were substituted. Additional bars were awarded for each 10 years service.*

VALUE:		Miniature
Edward VII	£160–185	£30–35
George V	£140–160	£30–35
George VI GRI	£140–160	£30–35
George VI GVIR	£140–160	£30–35
Elizabeth II	£160–190	£30–35

222. ROYAL NAVAL VOLUNTEER RESERVE LONG SERVICE AND GOOD CONDUCT MEDAL

Instituted: 1908.

Branch of Service: Royal Naval Volunteer Reserve.

Ribbon: Originally plain green, but subsequently a broad central green stripe edged in red with blue stripes at the ends was adopted.

Metal: Silver.

Size: 36mm.

Description: Identical to the RNR medal, but distinguished by the ribbon and the naming which includes the letters RNVR, RCNVR (Canada), RSANVR (South Africa), etc.

Comments: *Awarded to petty officers and ratings for 12 years service with the necessary training, character assessed as "very good" throughout the period. War service counted double. The award was extended to the Colonial Navies during the Second World War.*

VALUE:		Miniature
Edward VII (B)	£350–400	£30–35
George V (B)	£50–75	£30–35
George V (E)	£50–75	£30–35
George VI (D, E)	£50–75	£30–35
Elizabeth II (B, C)	£75–100	£30–35

223. ROYAL FLEET RESERVE LONG SERVICE AND GOOD CONDUCT MEDAL

Instituted: 1919.
Branch of Service: Royal Fleet Reserve.
Ribbon: Blue bordered with thin red stripes and white edges.
Metal: Silver.
Size: 36mm.
Description: Similar to the RNR LSGC but with ring suspension instead of a bar suspender.
Comments: *Awarded for 15 years service in the Fleet Reserve. This medal was discontinued in 2000.*

VALUE:		Miniature
George V (B)	£45–55	£30–35
George V (E)	£45–55	£30–35
George VI (D)	£45–55	£30–35
George VI (E)	£45–55	£30–35
Elizabeth II (B)	£55–65	£30–35
Elizabeth II (C)	£55–65	£30–35

224. ROYAL NAVAL AUXILIARY SICK BERTH RESERVE LONG SERVICE AND GOOD CONDUCT MEDAL

Instituted: 1919.
Branch of Service: Royal Naval Auxiliary Sick Berth Reserve.
Ribbon: Plain green but later green with a white central stripe and white edges.
Metal: Silver.
Size: 36mm.
Description: Identical to the RNR equivalent, but the letters RNASBR appear after the recipient's name.
Comments: *Arguably the longest title of any British medal, it continued until the RNASBR was disbanded in 1949. The Auxiliary Sick Berth Reserve was created in 1903, members being recruited from the St John Ambulance Brigade. About 780 medals were granted prior to the Second World War and a further 715 between 1939 and 1949.*

VALUE:		Miniature
George V (B)	£100–120	£30–35
George V (E)	£100–120	£30–35
George VI (D)	£100–120	£30–35

225. ROYAL NAVAL VOLUNTEER (WIRELESS) RESERVE LONG SERVICE AND GOOD CONDUCT MEDAL

Instituted: 1939.
Branch of Service: Royal Naval Volunteer Wireless Auxiliary Reserve.
Ribbon: A broad central green stripe edged in red with blue stripes at the ends.
Metal: Silver.
Size: 36mm.
Description: Identical to the RNR equivalent, but the letters RNV(W)R after the recipient's name. The last of the service medals with a battleship reverse.
Comments: *Issued till 1957 when the RNWAR was disbanded. It was awarded for 12 years service, only about 200 having been issued.*

VALUE:		Miniature
George VI (D)	£250–350	£30–35
Elizabeth II (C)	£250–350	£30–35

226. ROYAL NAVAL AUXILIARY SERVICE MEDAL

Instituted: July 1965.
Branch of Service: Royal Naval Auxiliary Service (RNXS), formerly the Royal Naval Minewatching Service, disbanded 1994.
Ribbon: Dark blue with a narrow green central stripe and broad white stripes at the edges bisected by thin dark green stripes.
Metal: Cupro-nickel.
Size: 36mm.
Description: (Obverse) the Queen's effigy; (reverse) a fouled anchor in an oak wreath surmounted by a naval crown.
Comments: *Awarded for 12 years service. A bar was awarded for each additional 12 years service. 1,710 were awarded, 131 with one bar and 2 with two bars. Interestingly this medal was the last to be issued with a pure silk ribbon.*

VALUE:	Elizabeth II (A)	£180–220	*Miniature*	£30–35

227. HM COASTGUARD LONG SERVICE AND GOOD CONDUCT MEDAL

Instituted: 1911 by the Board of Trade.
Branch of Service: Rocket Life Saving Apparatus Volunteers,
Ribbon: Originally pale blue with broad scarlet edges, in 2013 changed to scarlet with one broad central pale blue stripe and two narrow pale blue stripes.
Metal: Silver.
Size: 31mm.
Description: (Obverse) the effigy of the reigning monarch with the date below the truncation. (Reverse) exists in four types. The first refers to the Board of Trade but when that department handed over responsibility to the Ministry of Transport in 1942 the wording was amended to read ROCKET APPARATUS VOLUNTEER MEDAL round the circumference. In 1953 the inscription was changed to COAST LIFE SAVING CORPS, in 1968 to COASTGUARD AUXILIARY SERVICE and in 2012 to HM COASTGUARD.

First type reverse.

Second award bar.

First type ribbon.

Comments: *Awarded for 20 years' service.*

VALUE:		*Miniature*
George V (E)	£125–150	£55–110
George VI (D/E) BoT	£125–150	£55–110
George VI (D/E) Rocket Apparatus	£125–150	£55–110
Elizabeth II (D) Coast Life Saving	£175–200	£55–110
Elizabeth II (D) Coastguard Auxiliary	£175–200	£55–110
Elizabeth II (D) HM Coastguard	£175–200	£55–110

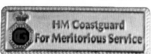

Second type ribbon.

228. HM COASTGUARD COMMENDATION

Instituted: 2000.
Branch of Service: HM Coastguard Service.
Ribbon: None.
Metal: Gilt.
Size: 35mm x 12mm.
Description: Pin badge depicting the emblem of HM Coastguard Service (left) with two-line inscription "HM Coastguard / For Meritorious Service" (right).
Comments: *Awarded to Coastguard, Auxiliary Coastguard and Coastguard rescue teams for rescuing shipwrecked mariners.*

VALUE: —

229. ARMY LONG SERVICE AND GOOD CONDUCT MEDAL

1st type obv. Trophy of Arms with badge of Hanover.

2nd type obv. with badge of Hanover omitted and swivel suspender.

Instituted: 1830.

Branch of Service: Army.

Ribbon: Plain crimson was used till 1917 when white stripes were added to the edges. Dominion and colonial medals formerly had crimson ribbons with a narrow central stripe in dark green (Commonwealth of Australia), dark blue (New South Wales), light blue (Queensland), pink (Tasmania), orange (Cape of Good Hope), yellow (Natal), white (Canada), light green (NZ). New Guinea had a scarlet ribbon with a light blue central stripe and South Australia had no central stripe on a plain crimson ribbon.

Metal: Silver.

Size: 36mm.

Description: Over the long period in which this medal has been in use it has undergone a number of changes. Until 1901 the obverse bore a trophy of arms with the royal arms in an oval shield in the centre while the reverse bore the inscription FOR LONG SERVICE AND GOOD CONDUCT. The first issue had the royal arms with the badge of Hanover on the obverse and small suspension ring with a plain crimson ribbon. A large ring was substituted in 1831. On the accession of Queen Victoria in 1837 the Hanoverian emblem was dropped from the arms. In 1855 a swivelling scroll suspension was substituted and in 1859 small lettering replaced the original large lettering on the reverse. From 1901, however, the effigy of the reigning sovereign was placed on the obverse although the reverse remained the same. In 1920 the swivelling scroll suspension gave way to a fixed suspender. In 1930 the title of the medal was changed to the Long Service and Good Conduct Medal (Military); at the same time the design was modified. A fixed suspension bar was added, bearing the words REGULAR ARMY or the name of a dominion (India, Canada, Australia, New Zealand or South Africa). This replaced the Permanent Forces of the Empire LSGC Medal (see below).

Comments: *Originally awarded to soldiers of exemplary conduct for 21 years service in the infantry or 24 years in the cavalry, but in 1854 the qualifying period was reduced to 18 years and in 1977 to 15 years. Under changes announced in 2015 a clasp is now awarded for every 10 years served. During World War II commissioned officers were permitted to acquire this medal so long as they had completed at least 12 of their 18 years service in the ranks. Canada discontinued the LSGC medal in 1950 when the Canadian Forces Decoration was instituted, while South Africa replaced it with the John Chard Medal later the same year. From 1930 onwards the lettering of the reverse inscription was in tall, thin letters. In 1940 bars for further periods of service were authorised. The LSGC is invariably named to the recipient. The William IV and early Victorian issues (to 1854) were impressed in the style of the Waterloo Medal and also bore the date of discharge and award. The 1855 issue was not dated, while lettering was impressed in the style of the Military General Service Medal. Later Victorian issues, however, were engraved in various styles, while medals from 1901 onwards are impressed in small capitals of various types. Medals to Europeans in the Indian Army are engraved in cursive script. Recent research by Irvin Mortensen, however, reveals that some medals after 1850 were issued unnamed, and this also accounts for various unofficial styles of naming found on later medals.*

VALUE:		Miniature
William IV small ring 1830–31	£850–1000	—
William IV large ring 1831–37	£750–950	—
Victoria without Hanoverian arms 1837–55	£250–350	—
Victoria swivelling scroll suspension 1855–74	£155–225	£35–45
Victoria small reverse lettering 1874–1901	£100–150	£30–35
Edward VII (A) 1902–10	£75–100	£30–35
George V (A) 1911–20	£65–85	£15–25
George V (A) fixed suspender 1920–30	£65–85	£15–25
George V (C) 1930–36, Regular Army bar	£65–85	£15–25
Commonwealth bar	From £75	£15–25
George VI (C) 1937–48, Regular Army bar	£55–80	£15–25
Commonwealth bar	From £75	£15–25
George VI (E) 1949–52, Regular Army bar	£65–85	£15–25
Elizabeth II 1953–54, Regular Army bar	£65–85	£15–25
Elizabeth II 1954–, Regular Army bar	£65–85	£15–25
Commonwealth bar	From £100	£15–25
To Royal Irish Regiment	£125–175	£15–25

GV type C obverse with fixed suspender and "Commonwealth" bar.

re-1917 ribbon.

Later ribbon, used from 1917.

230. ULSTER DEFENCE REGIMENT MEDAL FOR LONG SERVICE AND GOOD CONDUCT

Instituted: 1982.
Branch of Service: Ulster Defence Regiment.
Ribbon: Similar to the Military LSGC medal but with a central green stripe in addition.
Metal: Silver.
Size: 36mm.
Description: (Obverse) the imperial crowned bust of Queen Elizabeth II; (reverse) similar to the Military LSGC medal. Fitted with a fixed suspension bar inscribed UDR.
Comments: *Granted to personnel for 15 years exemplary service after 1 April 1970, with bars for additional 15-year periods. It is also awarded to officers provided that at least 12 of their 15 years service was in the ranks.*

VALUE:

Elizabeth II (B)	£300–450	*Miniature*	£12–18

231. VOLUNTEER OFFICER'S DECORATION

Instituted: 25 July 1892.
Branch of Service: Volunteer Force.
Ribbon: 38mm plain green, suspended from an oak bar brooch. Members of the Honourable Artillery Company were granted a distinctive ribbon in 1906, half scarlet, half dark blue with yellow edges—King Edward's racing colours.
Metal: Silver and silver-gilt.
Size: Height 42mm; max. width 35mm.
Description: An oval skeletal badge in silver and silver-gilt, with the royal cypher and crown in the centre, within a wreath of oak leaves. It is suspended by a plain ring with an oak leaf bar brooch fitted to the top of the ribbon. Although issued unnamed, many examples were subsequently engraved or impressed privately. Two versions of the Victorian decoration were produced, differing in the monogram— VR for United Kingdom recipients and VRI for recipients in the dominions and colonies.
Comments: *The basic qualification was 20 years commissioned service in the Volunteer Force, a precursor of the Territorial Army, non-commissioned service counting half. By Royal Warrant of 24 May 1894 the decoration was extended to comparable forces overseas, the qualifying period for service in India being reduced to 18 years. The colonial VD was superseded in 1899 by the Colonial Auxiliary Forces Officers Decoration and the Indian Volunteer Forces Officers Decoration. In the United Kingdom it was superseded by the Territorial Decoration, on the formation of the TF in 1908. A total of 4,710 decorations were awarded. Awards in Bermuda continued until 1930.*

VALUE:

		Miniature
Victoria VR	£150–175	£40–50
Victoria VRI	£300–350	£95–110
Edward VII	£150–175	£35–45
George V	£150–175	£30–40

HAC ribbon.

232. VOLUNTEER LONG SERVICE MEDAL

Instituted: 1894.

Branch of Service: Volunteer Force.

Ribbon: 32mm plain green, but members of the Honourable Artillery Company were granted a distinctive ribbon in 1906, half scarlet, half dark blue with yellow edges—King Edward's racing colours.

Metal: Silver.

Size: 36mm.

Description: (Obverse) effigy of the reigning monarch; (reverse) a laurel wreath on which is superimposed ribbons inscribed FOR LONG SERVICE IN THE VOLUNTEER FORCE.

Comments: *This medal was awarded for 20 years service in the ranks. Officers could also receive the medal, being eligible on account of their non-commissioned service. Many officers then gained sufficient commissioned service to be awarded either the Volunteer Decoration or (from 1908) the Territorial Decoration. The medal was extended to Colonial Forces in June 1898, the titles of the monarch being appropriately expanded for this version. This medal was superseded by the Territorial Force Efficiency Medal in 1908, although it continued to be awarded until 1930 in Bermuda, India, Isle of Man (Isle of Man Vols.) and the 7th Volunteer Battalion of the King's (Liverpool) Regiment.*

HAC ribbon.

VALUE:

		Miniature
Victoria Regina (C) (UK)	£75–100	
Unnamed	£45–50	£25–30
Victoria Regina et Imperatrix (C) (overseas)	£85–125	£25–30
Edwardus Rex (A)	£85–100	£18–30
Edwardus Rex et Imperator (A) (colonial)	£85–100	£18–30
Edwardus Kaisar-i-Hind (A) (India)	£100–120	£18–30
George V (A)		
India	£85–100	£18–25
Isle of Man	£250–300	£18–25
Bermuda	£150–200	£18–25

233. TERRITORIAL DECORATION

Instituted: 29 September 1908.

Branch of Service: Territorial Force, later Territorial Army.

Ribbon: 38mm plain dark green with a central yellow stripe suspended from an oak bar brooch. Members of the Honourable Artillery Company were granted a distinctive ribbon in 1906, half scarlet, half dark blue with yellow edges—King Edward's racing colours.

Metal: Silver and silver-gilt.

Size: Height 46mm; max. width 35mm.

Description: A skeletal badge with the crowned monogram of the sovereign surrounded by an oval oak wreath, fitted with a ring for suspension.

Comments: *Awarded for 20 years commissioned service, service in the ranks counting half and war service double. It was superseded by the Efficiency Decoration in 1930. A total of 4,783 decorations were awarded.*

VALUE:

		Miniature
Edward VII (585)	£200–250	£18–25
George V (4,198)	£175–200	£18–15

HAC ribbon.

234. TERRITORIAL FORCE EFFICIENCY MEDAL

Original ribbon.

HAC ribbon.

Instituted: 1908.
Branch of Service: Territorial Force.
Ribbon: Originally 32mm plain dark green with a central yellow stripe but members of the Honourable Artillery Company were granted a distinctive ribbon in 1906, half scarlet, half dark blue with yellow edges—King Edward's racing colours. In December 1919 the ribbon was changed to plain dark green with yellow edges.
Metal: Silver.
Size: Height 38mm; max. width 31mm.
Description: An oval medal fitted with claw and ring suspension. (Obverse) the sovereign's effigy; (reverse) inscribed with the name of the medal in four lines.
Comments: *Granted for a minimum of 12 years service in the Territorial Force. It was superseded in 1921 by the Territorial Efficiency Medal when the service was renamed. Bars were awarded for further periods of 12 years service.*

VALUE:

		Miniature
Edward VII (A) (11,800)	£140–160*	£18–25
Of these:		
With bar (537)	£200–250	
with second bars (64)	£250–300	
George V (A) (37,726)	£75–100	£18–25
George V first clasps	£130–150	

Medals to Yeomanry regiments command a higher premium.

234A. TERRITORIAL FORCE IMPERIAL SERVICE BADGE

Instituted: 1912.
Branch of Service: Members of the Territorial Force.
Ribbon: None.
Metal: Cupro-nickel or brass.
Size: 10mm x 43mm
Description: A horizontal bar surmounted by a royal crown, the bar inscribed in raised lettering IMPERIAL SERVICE.
Comments: *Awarded to members of the Territorial Force who were prepared to serve outside the United Kingdom in defence of the Empire, mainly during the First World War.*

VALUE: £12–15

235. TERRITORIAL EFFICIENCY MEDAL

Instituted: 1921.
Branch of Service: Territorial Army.
Ribbon: 32mm plain dark green with yellow edges.
Metal: Silver.
Size: Height 38mm; max. width 31mm.
Description: As above, but with the name amended and inscribed in three lines.
Comments: *Introduced following the elevation of the Territorial Force to become the Territorial Army. It was superseded by the Efficiency Medal in 1930.*

VALUE:

George V (A)	£80–100	Miniature	£10–18

236. EFFICIENCY DECORATION

Second
rd bars

Original ribbon.

Post-1969 ribbon.

HAC ribbon.

Instituted: 17 October 1930.

Branch of Service: Territorial Army (UK), the Indian Volunteer Forces and the Colonial Auxiliary Forces.

Ribbon: 38mm plain dark green with a central yellow stripe. In 1969, on the introduction of the T&AVR, the ribbon was altered to half blue, half green , with a central yellow stripe. Members of the Honourable Artillery Company wear half blue, half scarlet ribbon, with yellow edges.

Metal: Silver and silver-gilt.

Size: Height 54mm; max. width 37mm.

Description: An oval skeletal badge in silver and silver-gilt with the crowned monogram in an oak wreath, the ring for suspension being fitted to the top of the crown. It differs also from the previous decorations in having a suspender bar denoting the area of service: Territorial (UK), India, Canada, Fiji or other overseas country being inscribed as appropriate, but the previous ribbon was retained.

Comments: *Recipients in Britain were allowed to continue using the letters TD after their names, but in the Commonwealth the letters ED were used instead. The 20-year qualification was reduced to 12 years in 1949, bars for each additional 6 years being added. In 1969 the British suspender bar was changed to T & AVR, on the establishment of the Territorial and Army Volunteer Reserve. In 1982 the title of Territorial Army was resumed, so the inscription on the bar reverted to TERRITORIAL but the blue, yellow and green ribbon was retained. This decoration was superseded in the UK by the VRSM (No. 242A) in 2000. However, it is still current in some Commonwealth countries.*

VALUE:

	Territorial	T&AVR	Commonwealth
George V	£150–175	—	From £175
George VI (GRI)	£85–100	—	From £175
George VI (GVIR)	£85–100	—	—
Elizabeth II	£100–125	£120–150	From £175
Miniature	£10–18	£10–18	£55–85

237. EFFICIENCY MEDAL

Instituted: 17 October 1930.

Branch of Service: Territorial Army (UK), Indian Volunteer Forces and Colonial Auxiliary Forces.

Ribbon: 32mm green with yellow edges. In 1969, on the introduction of the T&AVR, the ribbon was altered to half blue, half green, with yellow edges. Members of the Honourable Artillery Company wear half blue, half scarlet ribbon, with yellow edges.

Metal: Silver.

Original ribbon.

Post-1969 ribbon.

HAC ribbon.

237. EFFICIENCY MEDAL *continued*

Aa

Ab

Size: Height 39mm; max. width 32mm.

Description: An oval silver medal. (Obverse) the monarch's effigy; (reverse) inscribed FOR EFFICIENT SERVICE. In place of the simple ring suspension, however, there was now a fixed suspender bar decorated with a pair of palm leaves surmounted by a scroll inscribed TERRITORIAL or MILITIA (for UK volunteer forces), while overseas forces had the name of the country.

Comments: *This medal consolidated the awards to other ranks throughout the volunteer forces of Britain and the Commonwealth. The basic qualification was 12 years continuous efficient service, but war service and peacetime service in West Africa counted double. Additional bars with a crown were awarded for further periods of six years continuous efficient service. The Militia bar was granted to certain categories of the Supplementary Reserve until the formation of the Army Emergency Reserve in 1951. In 1969 the bar inscribed T & AVR was introduced. The bar TERRITORIAL was resumed in 1982 but the half blue, half green ribbon with yellow edges was retained. For the distinctive medal awarded in the Union of South Africa see number 254. Instead of the second obverse of Queen Elizabeth II, Canada adopted a type showing the Queen wearing the Imperial Crown. This medal was superseded in the UK by the VRSM (No. 242A) in 2000, although it is still current in some Commonwealth countries.*

VALUE:	Territorial	Militia	T&AVR	Commonwealth
George V (C)	£75–100	£150–175**	—	From £85*
George VI (Aa)	£60–85	£85–100	—	From £85*
George VI (Ab)	£60–85	£85–100	—	From £85*
Elizabeth II (A1)	£75–100	—	—	From £150*
Elizabeth II (A)	£75–100	—	£85–120	From £150*
Miniature	from £18			£85–95

These prices are for the commoner Commonwealth types. However, some are extremely rare as can be seen in the table below where the issue numbers are indicated in brackets (where known).
**Only RE (176), R.Signals (94) and RAMC (42).*

GEORGE V (C)	GEORGE VI (Aa)	GEORGE VI (Ab)	ELIZABETH II (A1)	ELIZABETH II (A)
—	—	—	Antigua (3)	—
Australia	Australia	Australia	Australia	Australia
Barbados	Barbados	Barbados	Barbados	Barbados
Bermuda	Bermuda	Bermuda	Bermuda	Bermuda
British Guiana (15)	British Guiana	British Guiana	British Guiana	—
British Honduras (1)	British Honduras (23)	British Honduras (3)	British Honduras (13)—	—
—	Burma (111)	—	—	—
Canada	Canada	Canada	Canada (Rare)	Canada (Rare)
Ceylon	Ceylon	Ceylon	Ceylon (69)	—
—	Dominica (130)	—	—	—
Falkland Islands (29)	Falkland Islands (29)	—	Falkland Islands	Falkland Islands
Fiji (29)	Fiji (35)	Fiji (9)	Fiji (7)	Fiji (33)
—	—	Gibraltar (15)	Gibraltar	Gibraltar
—	Gold Coast (275)	Gold Coast (35)	—	—
—	Grenada (1)	—	—	—
—	Guernsey (3)	Guernsey (4)	Guernsey (3)	Guernsey (35)
Hong Kong (21)	Hong Kong (50)	Hong Kong (224)	Hong Kong (145)	Hong Kong (268)
India	India	—	—	—
Jamaica	Jamaica	Jamaica	Jamaica	—
—	Jersey (40)	Jersey (7)	—	Jersey (1)

237. EFFICIENCY MEDAL continued

GEORGE V (C)	GEORGE VI (Aa)	GEORGE VI (Ab)	ELIZABETH II (A)	ELIZABETH II (B)
—	Kenya (1)	Kenya (159)	Kenya (36)	—
—	Leeward Islands (49)	Leeward Islands (14)	Leeward Islands (2)	—
—	Malaya	Malaya	Malaya (54)	—
—	Malta (320)	Malta (31)	—	Malta (36)
—	—	—	Mauritius (71)	—
—	—	—	—	Montserrat (6)
New Zealand (71)	New Zealand (34)	New Zealand	New Zealand	New Zealand
Nigeria (1)	—	Nigeria (7)	Nigeria (3)	
—	—	—	Rhodesia/Nyasaland (7)	—
—	—	—	St Christopher Nevis (13)	—
—	St Lucia (2)	—	—	—
—	St Vincent (1)	—	—	—
S. Rhodesia (17)	S. Rhodesia (230)	S. Rhodesia (24)	S. Rhodesia (6)	—
—	Trinidad/Tobago (228)	Trinidad/Tobago (46)	Trinidad/Tobago (5)	—

238. ARMY EMERGENCY RESERVE DECORATION

Instituted: 17 November 1952.
Branch of Service Army Emergency Reserve.
Ribbon: 38mm dark blue with a central yellow stripe.
Metal: Silver and silver-gilt.
Size: Height 55mm; max. width 37mm.
Description: An oval skeletal badge, with the monarch's cypher surmounted by a crown in an oak wreath. Suspension is by a ring through the top of the crown and it is worn with a brooch bar inscribed ARMY EMERGENCY RESERVE.
Comments: *Awarded for 12 years commissioned service. Officers commissioned in the Army Supplementary Reserve or Army Emergency Reserve of Offices between 8 August 1942 and 15 May 1948 who transferred to the Regular Army Reserve of Officers after 10 years service were also eligible. War service counts double and previous service in the ranks counts half. The ERD was abolished in 1967 on the formation of the Territorial and Army Volunteer Reserve.*

VALUE:
Elizabeth II	£150–200	*Miniature*	£10–18

239. ARMY EMERGENCY RESERVE EFFICIENCY MEDAL

Instituted: 1 September 1953.
Branch of Service: Army Emergency Reserve.
Ribbon: 32mm dark blue with three central yellow stripes.
Metal: Silver.
Size: Height 39mm; max. width 31mm.
Description: This oval medal is similar to the Efficiency Medal previously noted but has a scroll bar inscribed ARMY EMERGENCY RESERVE.
Comments: *Awarded for 12 years service in the ranks or for service in the Supplementary Reserve between 1924 and 1948 prior to transferring to the Army Emergency Reserve. War service counted double. It was abolished in 1967 following the formation of the Territorial and Army Volunteer Reserve. .A very small number of awards were issued bearing the George VI effigy.*

VALUE:
Elizabeth II	£150–200	*Miniature*	£10–15

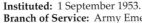

240. IMPERIAL YEOMANRY LONG SERVICE AND GOOD CONDUCT MEDAL

Instituted: December 1904, by Army Order no. 211.
Branch of Service: Imperial Yeomanry.
Ribbon: 32mm plain yellow.
Metal: Silver.
Size: Height 38mm; max. width 31mm.
Description: Upright oval. (Obverse) the sovereign's effigy; (reverse) inscribed IMPERIAL YEOMANRY round the top and the usual long service and good conduct inscription in four lines across the middle.
Comments: *Awarded to NCOs and troopers of the Imperial Yeomanry for 10 years exemplary service. It became obsolete in 1908 when the Territorial Force was created. Nevertheless 48 medals were awarded in 1909, one in 1910, one in 1914 and one in 1917. All medals were issued with the bust of King Edward VII on the obverse.*

VALUE:

Edward VII (A) (1674)	£450–500	*Miniature*	£60–80

241. MILITIA LONG SERVICE AND GOOD CONDUCT MEDAL

Instituted: December 1904, by Army Order no. 211.
Branch of Service: Militia.
Ribbon: 32mm plain light blue.
Metal: Silver.
Size: Height 38mm; max. width 31mm.
Description: An upright oval medal. (Obverse) the effigy of the monarch; (reverse) similar to the preceding but inscribed MILITIA at the top of the reverse.
Comments: *Qualifying service was 18 years and 15 annual camps. It was superseded by the Efficiency Medal with the Militia bar in 1930. A total of 1,587 medals were awarded between 1905 and 1930 (RGA 341, RE 15, RE Submarine Miners 8, Infantry 988, Channel Islands 89, Malta 131, Bermuda 15).*

VALUE:

		Miniature
Edward VII (A) (1446)	£450–500	£100–130
George V (C) (141)	£600–800	£100–130

242. SPECIAL RESERVE LONG SERVICE AND GOOD CONDUCT MEDAL

Instituted: June 1908, by Army Order no. 126.
Branch of Service: Special Reserve.
Ribbon: Dark blue with a central light blue stripe.
Metal: Silver.
Size: Height 38mm; max. width 31mm.
Description: As the foregoing but inscribed SPECIAL RESERVE round the top of the reverse.
Comments: *Awarded to NCOs and men of the Special Reserve who completed 15 years service and attended 15 camps. A total of 1,078 medals were awarded between 1908 and 1936 with solitary awards in 1947 and 1953. Summary of awards: RA, RFA, RGA 165, RE 9, Royal Anglesey RE 3, Royal Monmouthshire R. 5, RAMC 4, Labour Corps 4, MGC 1. North Irish Horse 16, South Irish Horse 31, King Edward's Horse 14, Infantry 823, Channel Islands 5. Of these, two awards (1 to the RGA, 1 to the South Irish Horse), were subsequently cancelled.*

VALUE:

		Miniature
Edward VII (A) (428)	£500–600	£110–135
George V (C) (650)	£500–600	£110–135

242A. VOLUNTEER RESERVES SERVICE MEDAL

Instituted: 1999.

Branch of Service: Volunteer reserves of all three armed services.

Ribbon: Dark green with three narrow central stripes of dark blue, scarlet and light blue, separated from the green by two narrow stripes of gold. Members of the Honourable Artillery Company wear half blue, half scarlet ribbon, with yellow edges.

Metal: Silver.

Size: Height 38mm; width 32mm.

Description: An oval medal. (Obverse) the sovereign's effigy; (reverse) inscribed FOR SERVICE IN THE VOLUNTEER RESERVES above a spray of oak.

Comments: *Awarded to all ranks of the volunteer reserves who complete ten years of reckonable qualifying service. Bars for additional five-year periods of reckonable qualifying service are also awarded. This medal replaces the Royal Naval Reserve Decoration, the Royal Naval Reserve Long Service and Good Conduct Medal, the Efficiency Decoration, the Efficiency Medal and the Air Efficiency Award. Since 2015 recipients are entitled to use the post-nominals VR, backdated to 1999.*

VALUE: £250–300   *Miniature* £10–15

HAC ribbon

242B. ROYAL MILITARY ASYLUM GOOD CONDUCT MEDAL

First type reverse.

Instituted: c.1850.

Branch of Service: Students in the Royal Military Asylum.

Ribbon: Plain red or crimson.

Metal: Silver or bronze.

Size: 36mm.

Description: (Obverse) the royal arms, garnished, crested and with supporters; (reverse) first type ROYAL MILITARY ASYLUM, second type: DUKE OF YORK'S ROYAL MILITARY SCHOOL round the circumference, enclosing a laurel wreath inscribed across the centre FOR GOOD CONDUCT. Fitted with a scrolled suspender and brooch. Engraved in upright capitals with the name of the recipient.

Comments: *The Royal Military Asylum was established for the education of the sons of soldiers who had been killed in action or who had died while in the service. It was renamed the "Duke of York's Royal Military School" in 1892 and subsequent medals are thus inscribed. The actual criteria for the award of the medal are not known.*

VALUE: "Asylum"   £125–175
            "School"   £100–150

Second type reverse.

242C. ARMED FORCES VETERAN LAPEL BADGE

Date: May 2004.
Branch of Service: Former members of HM Armed Forces, Royal Fleet Auxiliary, Cyprus Regiment, Merchant Navy who took part in a naval action, Home Guard and Polish Forces under UK command.
Ribbon: None.
Description: Badge surmounted by a gold imperial crown with VETERAN on an enamelled scroll at the foot. The badge bears the insignia of the armed services with H.M. ARMED FORCES round the top of the circumference.
Comments: *Originally available to veterans of HM Armed Forces including the Royal Fleet Auxiliary, who served up to December 31, 1954, but later extended. It is intended for any service in the Armed Forces.*

VALUE: £10–15

242D. MERCHANT SEAFARERS VETERAN LAPEL BADGE

Instituted: 2006.
Branch of Service: Personnel of the Merchant Navy.
Ribbon: None.
Description: Similar to 242C but with the badge superimposed on the Red Ensign.
Comments: *Available to surviving veterans of the Merchant Navy who contributed to HM Armed Forces military operations in World War II. Holders of this badge are not eligible for the Armed Forces Veteran badge (242C).*

VALUE: £15–20

242E. ARCTIC EMBLEM

Instituted: 2006.
Branch of Service: Personnel of the Armed Forces and the Merchant Navy
Ribbon: None.
Description: A white five-pointed star edged in gold, with a red centre, above which is a blue arc bearing the words THE ARCTIC.
Comments: *Available to surviving veterans who served north of the Arctic Circle and west of the Urals for at least one day between 3 September 1939 and 8 May 1945. The emblem is also available to the next of kin of deceased veterans.*

VALUE: £20–25

242F. BEVIN BOYS LAPEL BADGE

Date: 2007.
Branch of Service: Former Bevin Boys.
Ribbon: None.
Description: Oval badge enamelled with the outline of a pit-head winch in white on a black background, surrounded by the words BEVIN BOYS VETERANS and with a silhouette of a miner's head with helmet.
Comments: *Available to surviving veterans of the Bevin Boys of World War II.*

VALUE: £10–15

242G. WOMEN'S LAND ARMY AND TIMBER CORPS LAPEL BADGE

Date: 2007.
Branch of Service: Former members of the Women's Land Army or Women's Timber Corps.
Ribbon: None.
Description: Enamelled replica of the original WLA badge surmounted by a crown.
Comments: *Available to surviving veterans of the Women's Land Army and Women's Timber Corps of World War II.*

VALUE: £10–15

242H. AIR TRANSPORT AUXILIARY LAPEL BADGE

Date: 2008.
Branch of Service: Former members of the Air Transport Auxiliary.
Ribbon: None.
Description: Enamelled badge depicting an eagle in flight on a turquoise background surrounded by the words AIR TRANSPORT AUXILIARY on a dark blue ribbon with laurel wreath surround.
Comments: *Available to veterans of the Air Transport Auxiliary of World War II.*

VALUE: £10–15

242 I. GC & CS LAPEL BADGE

Date: 2012.
Branch of Service: Former employees at Bletchley Park and its outstations.
Ribbon: None.
Description: Enamelled badge depicting the GCHQ emblem surrounded by a laurel wreath and the dates 1939-1945, with the legend GC&CS above, BLETCHLEY PARK AND ITS OUTSTATIONS below.
Comments: *Available to surviving personnel who worked at Bletchley Park during World War II.*

VALUE: £20–25

242J. MERCHANT NAVY MEDAL

Instituted: 1 June 2005.
Branch of Service: Merchant Navy.
Ribbon: Equal halves of red and green divided by a narrow white stripe. Thin gold edge stripes were added in 2011 to avoid confusion with MYB 169 and to indicate special achievement
Metal: Rhodium plated cupro-nickel.   **Size:** 28mm.
Description: (Obverse) The bust of Admiral Nelson surrounded by the legend "THE MERCHANT NAVY MEDAL" above and "1805 - TRAFALGAR - 2005" below; (reverse) the Merchant Navy logo with the inscription "FOR MERITORIOUS SERVICE" below.
Comments: *This medal was instituted to recognise the meritorious service of British registered Merchant Seafarers. The medal was awarded annually to a maximum of 15 men or women who were judged to have made a significant contribution to merchant shipping, its operations, development, personnel, welfare or safety, or who had performed an act of bravery afloat. The names of recipients were listed in the London Gazette and the award carries the post-nominals MNM. A small silver anchor was added to the ribbon to denote an act of bravery at sea. In 2015 the medal was replaced by MYB242K.*

VALUE: —

242K. QUEEN'S MERCHANT NAVY MEDAL FOR MERITORIOUS SERVICE

Instituted: 2016.
Branch of Service: Merchant Navy.
Ribbon: Equal stripes of green, red, white, red, green.
Metal: Rhodium plated cupro-nickel.
Size: 36mm.
Description: (Obverse) coinage bust of Her Majesty the Queen by Ian Rank-Broadley with the legend ELIZABETH II DEI GRATIA REGINA FID DEF; (reverse) the Merchant Navy logo with the inscription "FOR MERITORIOUS SERVICE" below.
Comments: *Like the previous medal (MYB242J), which it replaces, this medal was instituted to recognise the meritorious service of personnel serving in the Merchant Navy or the Fishing fleets of the United Kingdom, the Isle of Man and the Channel Islands. The medal is awarded annually to a maximum of 20 men or women who are judged to have made a significant contribution to merchant shipping, its operations, development, personnel, welfare or safety and show particularly valuable devotion to duty and exemplary service so as to serve as an outstanding example to others. Recipients will typically have given 20 years of good conduct and exemplary service. The names of recipients are listed in the London Gazette and the award carries the post-nominals QMNM. .*

VALUE: —

243. INDIAN ARMY LONG SERVICE & GOOD CONDUCT MEDAL FOR EUROPEANS 1848

HEIC arms type.

Instituted: 20 May 1848, by General Order of the Indian Government.
Branch of Service: Indian Army.
Ribbon: Plain crimson.
Metal: Silver.
Size: 36mm.
Description: (Obverse) a trophy of arms, not unlike its British counterpart, but a shield bearing the arms of the Honourable East India Company was placed in the centre. (Reverse) engraved with the recipient's name and service details. In 1859 some 100 medals were sent to India by mistake, these had the Wyon profile of Queen Victoria on the obverse and a reverse inscribed FOR LONG SERVICE AND GOOD CONDUCT within an oak wreath with a crown at the top and a fouled anchor at the foot.
Comments: *Awarded to European NCOs and other ranks of the Indian Army on discharge after 21 years meritorious service. It was discontinued in 1873 after which the standard Army LSGC medal was granted.*

VALUE:		Miniature
HEIC arms	£500–650	£110–165
Victoria (A) (100)	£650–750	£90–110

Victoria type.

244. INDIAN ARMY LONG SERVICE & GOOD CONDUCT MEDAL (INDIAN)

Instituted: 1888.
Branch of Service: Indian Army.
Ribbon: Originally plain crimson but white edges were added in 1917.
Metal: Silver.
Size: 36mm.
Description: (Obverse) the sovereign's effigy; (reverse) the word INDIA set within a palm wreath surrounded by a border of lotus flowers and leaves. The inscription FOR LONG SERVICE AND GOOD CONDUCT appears between the wreath and the lotus flowers.
Comments: *Awarded to native Indian NCOs and other ranks for 20 years meritorious service. The medal became obsolete in 1947 when India achieved independence.*

VALUE:		Miniature
Victoria (B) Kaisar-i-Hind	£150–175	£100–110
Edward VII (A) Kaisar-i-Hind	£100–125	£100–110
George V (D) Kaisar-i-Hind	£55–85	£90–100
George V (C) Rex Et Indiae Imp	£55–85	£90–100
George VI (B)	£55–85	£90–100

245. INDIAN VOLUNTEER FORCES OFFICERS' DECORATION

Instituted: May 24, 1894, by extension to the Volunteer Officer Decoration (MYB 231).

Branch of Service: Indian Volunteer Forces.

Ribbon: Plain dark green (see Comments below).

Metal: Silver and silver-gilt.

Size: Height 65mm; max. width 36mm.

Description: An oval skeletal badge with the royal cipher in the centre, surrounded by a band inscribed INDIAN VOLUNTEER FORCES and surmounted by a crown. Designed for a 32mm ribbon, the decoration is fitted with a plain straight suspender behind the crown and hung from a bar brooch with an oak leaf frieze.

Comments: *Awarded for 18 years commissioned service, with service in the ranks counting half and war service double. Replacing the VD with VRI cipher in 1903, the Indian Volunteer Decoration was modelled on the Colonial Auxiliary Forces Decoration (MYB 246) and superseded by the Efficiency Decoration (MYB 236) in 1930. A total of 1,171 decorations are known to have been awarded between 1903 and 1934. Normally issued named, with the recipient's rank, name and unit engraved on the reverse. Seven styles of engraving have been observed over the life of the award. While early and late decorations may be hallmarked, the majority are not.*

VALUE:			Miniature
Edward VII	£300–350		£55–65
George V	£300–350		£35–45

246. COLONIAL AUXILIARY FORCES OFFICERS' DECORATION

Instituted: 18 May 1899.

Branch of Service: Colonial Auxiliary Forces.

Ribbon: Plain green (see Comments below).

Metal: Silver and silver-gilt.

Size: Height 66mm; max. width 35mm.

Description: Similar to the previous decoration, with an oval band inscribed COLONIAL AUXILIARY FORCES.

Comments: *Awarded to officers of auxiliary forces everywhere except in India for 20 years commissioned service. Service in the ranks counting half and service in West Africa counting double. Although issued unnamed, it was usually impressed or engraved privately. Examples to officers in the smaller colonies command a considerable premium. It became obsolete in 1930. The suspension of the medal is by a flattened loop which is only 32mm wide although it was intended to take a 38mm ribbon—the 32mm ribbon is therefore usually worn on the medal and the 38mm on the tunic.*

VALUE:			Miniature
Victoria	£300–350		£90–100
Edward VII	£200–250		£80–90
George V	£150–200		£55–65

247. COLONIAL AUXILIARY FORCES LONG SERVICE MEDAL

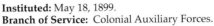

Instituted: May 18, 1899.
Branch of Service: Colonial Auxiliary Forces.
Ribbon: Plain green.
Metal: Silver.
Size: 36mm.
Description: (Obverse) the effigy of the reigning monarch; (reverse) an elaborate rococo frame surmounted by a crown and enclosing the five-line text FOR LONG SERVICE IN THE COLONIAL AUXILIARY FORCES.
Comments: *Awarded for 20 years service in the ranks, West African service counting double. It was superseded in 1930 by the Efficiency Medal with the appropriate colonial or dominion bar.*

VALUE:		Miniature
Victoria (D)	£100–125	£30–40
Edward VII (A)	£80–110	£25–30
George V (A)	£80–110	£18–25

248. COLONIAL LONG SERVICE AND GOOD CONDUCT MEDALS

Instituted: May 31, 1895.
Branch of Service: Indian and Colonial forces.
Ribbon: Crimson with a central stripe denoting the country of service (see no. 212).
Metal: Silver.
Size: 36mm.
Description: Similar to its British counterpart except that the name of the appropriate colony appeared on the reverse. The obverse of the Victorian award for the Colony of Natal depicts the Royal coat of arms.
Comments: *Awarded to warrant officers, NCOs and other ranks for meritorious service and long service and good conduct. Medals of the individual Australian colonies were superseded in 1902 by those inscribed COMMONWEALTH OF AUSTRALIA. The Colonial LSGC medal was replaced in 1909 by the Permanent Forces of the Empire Beyond the Seas LSGC award.*

VALUE:	Rare	Miniature	£85–110

249. PERMANENT FORCES OF THE EMPIRE BEYOND THE SEAS LONG SERVICE AND GOOD CONDUCT MEDAL

Instituted: 1909.
Branch of Service: Colonial and Dominion forces.
Ribbon: Maroon bearing a broad white central stripe with a narrow black stripe at its centre.
Metal: Silver.
Size: 36mm.
Description: (Obverse) the effigy of the reigning sovereign; (reverse) the legend PERMANENT FORCES OF THE EMPIRE BEYOND THE SEAS round the circumference, with FOR LONG SERVICE AND GOOD CONDUCT in four lines across the centre.
Comments: *This award replaced the various colonial LSGC medals, being itself superseded in 1930 by the LSGC (Military) Medal with appropriate dominion or colonial bar. It was awarded for 18 years exemplary service.*

VALUE:		Miniature
Edward VII (A)	£300–400	£65–90
George V (A)	£150–200	£55–65

250. ROYAL WEST AFRICA FRONTIER FORCE LONG SERVICE & GOOD CONDUCT MEDAL

Instituted: September 1903.
Branch of Service: Royal West Africa Frontier Force.
Ribbon: Crimson with a relatively broad green central stripe.
Metal: Silver.
Size: 36mm.
Description: (Obverse) the effigy of the reigning monarch. Two reverse types were used, the word ROYAL being added to the regimental title in June 1928.
Comments: *Awarded to native NCOs and other ranks for 18 years exemplary service.*

VALUE: £300–350   *Miniature*   £30–35

251. KING'S AFRICAN RIFLES LONG SERVICE AND GOOD CONDUCT MEDAL

Instituted: March 1907.
Branch of Service: King's African Rifles.
Ribbon: Crimson with a broad green central stripe.
Metal: Silver.
Size: 36mm.
Description: Very similar to the foregoing, apart from the regimental name round the top of the reverse.
Comments: *Awarded to native NCOs and other ranks for 18 years exemplary service.*

VALUE:		*Miniature*
Edward VII	£650–850	—
George V	£250–300	£55–65
George VI (B)	£250–300	£45–55
Elizabeth II	£500–750	£30–40

252. TRANS-JORDAN FRONTIER FORCE LONG SERVICE AND GOOD CONDUCT MEDAL

Instituted: 20 May 1938.
Branch of Service: Trans-Jordan Frontier Force.
Ribbon: Crimson with a green central stripe.
Metal: Silver.
Size: 36mm.
Description: Similar to the previous medals, with the name of the Force round the circumference.
Comments: *This rare silver medal was awarded for 16 years service in the ranks of the Trans-Jordan Frontier Force. Service in the Palestine Gendarmerie or Arab Legion counted, so long as the recipient transferred to the Frontier Force without a break in service. Only 112 medals were awarded before it was abolished in 1948.*

VALUE: £600–800

253. SOUTH AFRICA PERMANENT FORCE LONG SERVICE AND GOOD CONDUCT MEDAL

Instituted: 29 December 1939.
Branch of Service: South African forces.
Ribbon: Crimson with white stripes.
Metal: Silver.
Size: 36mm.
Description: (Obverse) Crowned effigy of King George VI; (reverse) FOR LONG SERVICE AND GOOD CONDUCT in four lines across the upper half and VIR LANGDURIGE DIENS EN GOEIE GEDRAG in four lines across the lower half. It also differs from its British counterpart in having a bilingual suspension bar.
Comments: *Awarded to NCOs and other ranks with a minimum of 18 years service.*

VALUE:		Miniature
George VI (B)	£120–140	£35–45
George VI (C)	£150–170	£35–45

254. EFFICIENCY MEDAL (SOUTH AFRICA)

Instituted: December 1939.
Branch of Service: Coast Garrison and Active Citizen Forces of South Africa.
Ribbon: 32mm plain dark green with yellow edges.
Metal: Silver.
Size: Height 38mm; max. width 30mm.
Description: An oval silver medal rather similar to the Efficiency Medal (number 237) but having a scroll bar inscribed UNION OF SOUTH AFRICA with its Afrikaans equivalent below. The reverse likewise bears a bilingual inscription.
Comments: *Awarded for 12 years non-commissioned service in the Coast Garrison and Active Citizen Forces. A bar, bearing in the centre a crown, was awarded for every six years of additional service. It was replaced in 1952 by the John Chard Medal.*

VALUE:	£65–75	Miniature	£35–45

254A. ROYAL HONG KONG REGIMENT DISBANDMENT MEDAL

Instituted: 1995.
Branch of Service: Royal Hong Kong Regiment (Volunteers).
Ribbon: Half red and half blue with a central yellow stripe.
Metal: Cupro-nickel.
Size: 38mm.
Description: (Obverse) Regimental badge with dates 1854 and 1995 either side and ROYAL HONG KONG REGIMENT THE VOLUNTEERS around. (Reverse) Coat of Arms of Hong Kong with DISBANDMENT MEDAL 3rd SEPTEMBER 1995 (date of disbandment) around.
Comment: *Available to those serving with the Regiment as the end of the Crown Colony became imminent. Recipients, however, had to purchase a full size and a miniature medal in a plush case.*

VALUE:	£75–100	Miniature	£55–65

255. CANADIAN FORCES DECORATION

Instituted: 15 December 1949.
Branch of Service: Canadian Forces.
Ribbon: 38mm orange-red divided into four equal parts by three thin white stripes.
Metal: Silver-gilt (George VI) or gilded tombac brass or bronze (Elizabeth II).
Size: Height 35mm; max. width 37mm.
Description: A decagonal (ten-sided) medal. The George VI issue has a suspension bar inscribed CANADA and the recipient's details engraved on the reverse, whereas the Elizabethan issue has no suspension bar, the recipient's details being impressed or engraved on the rim and the word "CANADA" appears at the base of the effigy. The reverse has a naval crown at the top, three maple leaves across the middle and an eagle in flight across the foot. The George VI version has the royal cypher superimposed on the maple leaves.
Comments: *Awarded to both officers and men of the Canadian regular and reserve forces for 12 years exemplary service. A bar, gold in colour, bearing the shield from the arms of Canada surmounted by the crown is awarded for each additional 10 years of qualifying service. Approximately 2,400 medals and 3,000 clasps are awarded annually.*

VALUE:		Miniature
George VI (E)	£75–100	£12–25
Elizabeth II (D)	£30–45	£12–25

256. VICTORIA VOLUNTEER LONG AND EFFICIENT SERVICE MEDAL

Instituted: 26 January 1881 but not given royal sanction until 21 April 1882.
Branch of Service: Volunteer Forces, Victoria.
Ribbon: White, with broad crimson stripes at the sides.
Metal: Silver.
Size: 39mm.
Description: (Obverse) the crowned badge of Victoria with LOCAL FORCES VICTORIA round the circumference; (reverse) inscribed FOR LONG AND EFFICIENT SERVICE. Two types of obverse exist, differing in the motto surrounding the colonial emblem. The first version has AUT PACE AUT BELLO (both in peace and war) while the second version is inscribed PRO DEO ET PATRIA (for God and country).
Comments: *Awarded to officers and men of the Volunteers in the colony of Victoria for 15 years efficient service. Awards to officers ended in 1894 with the introduction of the Volunteer Officers Decoration. This medal was replaced by the Commonwealth of Australia LSGC medal in 1902.*

VALUE: £800–1200   *Miniature*   £220–330

1st type obv.

257. NEW ZEALAND LONG AND EFFICIENT SERVICE MEDAL

Instituted: 1 January 1887.
Branch of Service: Volunteer and Permanent Militia Forces of New Zealand.
Ribbon: Originally plain crimson, but two white central stripes were added in 1917.
Metal: Silver.
Size: 36mm.
Description: (Obverse) an imperial crown on a cushion with crossed sword and sceptre and NZ below, within a wreath of oak-leaves (left) and wattle (right) and having four five-pointed stars, representing the constellation Southern Cross, spaced in the field; (reverse) inscribed FOR LONG AND EFFICIENT SERVICE. Plain ring suspension.
Comments: *Awarded for 16 years' continuous or 20 years' non-continuous service in the Volunteer and Permanent Militia Forces of New Zealand. It became obsolete in 1931 following the introduction of the LSGC (Military) medal with bar for New Zealand.*

VALUE: 1887–1931 £100–150   *Miniature* £45–55

258. NEW ZEALAND VOLUNTEER SERVICE MEDAL

Instituted: 1902.
Branch of Service: Volunteer Forces, New Zealand.
Ribbon: Plain drab khaki.
Metal: Silver.
Size: 36mm.
Description: (Obverse) a right-facing profile of King Edward VII with NEW ZEALAND VOLUNTEER round the top and 12 YEARS SERVICE MEDAL round the foot; (reverse) a kiwi surrounded by a wreath. Plain ring suspension.
Comments: *This rare silver medal (obsolete by 1912) was awarded for 12 years' service. Two reverse dies were used. In type I (1902–04) the kiwi's beak almost touches the ground, whereas in Type II (1905–12) there is a space between the tip of the beak and the ground. Only about 100 of Type I were produced, but 636 of Type II.*

VALUE: Type I   £250–350   *Miniature* £110–130
          Type II   £200–250

259. NEW ZEALAND TERRITORIAL SERVICE MEDAL

Instituted: 1912.
Branch of Service: Territorial Force, New Zealand.
Ribbon: Originally as above, but replaced in 1917 by a ribbon of dark khaki edged with crimson.
Metal: Silver.
Size: 36mm.
Description: (Obverse) left-facing bust of King George V in field marshal's uniform; (reverse) similar to the above.
Comments: *It replaced the foregoing on the formation of the Territorial Force on March 17, 1911, from which date the old Volunteer Force ceased to exist but became obsolete itself in 1931 when the Efficiency Medal with New Zealand bar was adopted.*

VALUE:
   George V   £80–100   *Miniature*   £35–55

261. ULSTER DEFENCE REGIMENT MEDAL

Instituted: 1982.
Branch of Service: Ulster Defence Regiment.
Ribbon: Dark green with a yellow central stripe edged in red.
Metal: Silver.
Size: 36mm.
Description: (Obverse) crowned head of Elizabeth II (B); (reverse) crowned harp and inscription ULSTER DEFENCE REGIMENT with a suspender of laurel leaves surmounted by a scroll bar bearing the regiment's initials.
Comments: *Awarded to part-time officers and men of the Ulster Defence Regiment with 12 years' continuous service since 1 April 1970. A bar for each additional six-year period is awarded. Officers are permitted to add the letters UD after their names. This medal is superseded by the Northern Ireland Home Service Medal (MYB 261B).*

VALUE:
    Elizabeth II (B)   £350–450   *Miniature* £20–25

261A. ULSTER DEFENCE REGIMENT MEDALLION

Instituted: 1987.
Branch of Service: Relatives of personnel of the Ulster Defence Regiment killed whilst on duty.
Ribbon: Dark green with a yellow central stripe edged in red, as MYB261.
Metal: Silver.
Size: 36mm.
Description: Uniface medal showing a crowned Irish harp flanked by sprays of shamrocks. Ring suspension. Ribbons of awards to widows and other female relatives mounted as a bow with a brooch fitment.
Comments: *Designed by Colour Sergeant Win Clark and struck by Spink & Son, it was commissioned by the Regiment for presentation to the families of UDR personnel killed during the conflict in Northern Ireland as a token of appreciation.*

VALUE: —

261B. NORTHERN IRELAND HOME SERVICE MEDAL

Instituted: 1992.
Branch of Service: Part time members of the Ulster Defence Regiment and the Royal Irish Regiment.
Ribbon: Dark green with a light blue central stripe.
Metal: Silver.
Size: 36mm.
Description: (Obverse) crowned head of Elizabeth II (B); (reverse) a scroll bearing the inscription FOR HOME SERVICE IN NORTHERN IRELAND surmounted by a crown, superimposed on a design of flax with harps below.
Comments: *Awarded to part-time officers and men of the Ulster Defence Regiment or Royal Irish Regiment with 12 years' continuous efficient service after 1 July 1980. A bar for each additional six-year period is awarded. Next of kin of eligible deceased members can apply for the medal.*

VALUE: £300–400   *Miniature* £15–20

262. CADET FORCES MEDAL

Instituted: February 1, 1950.

Branch of Service: Cadet Forces.

Ribbon: A broad green central band bordered by thin red stripes flanked by a dark blue stripe (left) and light blue stripe (right, with yellow edges.

Metal: Cupro-nickel.

Size: 36mm.

Description: (Obverse) the effigy of the reigning monarch; (reverse) a hand holding aloft the torch of learning with the words "THE CADET FORCES MEDAL" around. Medals are named to recipients on the rim, in impressed capitals.

Comments: *Awarded to uniformed volunteers of the Cadet Forces in recognition of long and exemplary service in the Cadet Forces. Service may reckon from September 3, 1926, with service between September 3, 1939 and September 2, 1945 counting two-fold. Until June 30, 1971, officers and non-commissioned officers only were awarded the medal, the qualification for which was 12 years' continuous service, with clasps for successive periods of 12 years' service. From July 1, 1971, cadet service over the age of 18 years of age could reckon for the medal and the qualifying period for the clasp was reduced to eight years, which need not be continuous. With effect from April 1, 1999, the qualifying period for the clasp was reduced to six years. Awards are now governed by the Royal Warrant dated November 19, 2001 which consolidates amendments to earlier Royal Warrants and extends the qualification and recognition provisions. Under JSP814 (1st edition) 2006, service for the medal did not have to be continuous; but JSP814 (final dated 31 March 2011) now states service to be continuous. Service for the clasp does not need to be continuous.*

The maximum cadet service is four years; other reckonable services includes the UK Volunteer Services, OTC, University Royal Naval Units and University Air Squadrons (maximum three years and not counted towards the Volunteer Services Medal or its predecessors), and Regular forces (maximum three years and not counted towards a long service award). When the ribbon alone is worn, the award of each clasp is denoted by a silver rose. To denote service beyond the award of three clasps, the following are to be worn: Four clasps—one gold rose, Five clasps—one gold rose and one silver rose, Six clasps—one gold rose and two silver roses, Seven clasps—two gold roses. Award of the medal and clasp is promulgated in the London Gazette. Issued to those qualifying in New Zealand under the terms of a Royal Warrant dated February 1, 1950 and the New Zealand Cadet Forces Medal Regulations dated January 13, 1954.

VALUE:		Miniature
George VI (C)	£100–125	£10–12
Elizabeth II (A1, BRITT: OMN)	£125–150	£10–12
Elizabeth II (A, DEI GRATIA)	£75–100	£10–12

263. ROYAL OBSERVER CORPS MEDAL

Long Service bar.

Instituted: 31 January 1950 but not awarded until 1953.

Branch of Service: Royal Observer Corps.

Ribbon: Pale blue with a broad central silver-grey stripe edged in dark blue.

Metal: Cupro-nickel.

Size: 36mm.

Description: (Obverse) effigy of the reigning monarch; (reverse) an artist's impression of a coast-watcher of Elizabethan times, holding a torch aloft alongside a signal fire, with other signal fires on hilltops in the background with the words "ROYAL OBSERVER CORPS MEDAL" around and the words "FOREWARNED IS FOREARMED" on a scroll below The medal hangs from a suspender of an eagle with outstretched wings. An obverse die with the effigy of George VI was engraved, but no medals were struck from it.

Comments: *Awarded to part-time officers and observers who have completed 12 years' satisfactory service and full-time members for 24 years service. A bar is awarded for each additional 12-year period. Home Office scientific officers and other non Royal Observer Corps members of the United Kingdom Warning and Monitoring Organisation were eligible for the Civil Defence Medal (no. 264) until being stood down on September 30, 1991. This entailed serving for 15 years alongside ROC members who received their own medal for 12 years' service.*

VALUE:		Miniature
Elizabeth II (B)	£300–350	—
Elizabeth II (C)	£250–300	£10–15

264. CIVIL DEFENCE LONG SERVICE MEDAL

Instituted: March 1961.
Branch of Service: Civil Defence and other auxiliary forces.
Ribbon: Blue bearing three narrow stripes of yellow, red and green.
Metal: Cupro-nickel.
Size: Height 38mm; max. width 32mm.
Description: (Obverse) the effigy of the reigning monarch; (reverse) two types. Both featured three shields flanked by sprigs of acorns and oak leaves. The upper shield in both cases is inscribed CD but the initials on the lower shields differ, according to the organisations in Britain and Northern Ireland respectively—AFS and NHSR (British) or AFRS and HSR (Northern Ireland). After 1968 a new reverse was used incorporating the words CIVIL DEFENCE and LONG SERVICE.
Comments: *Issued unnamed to those who had completed 15 years service in a wide range of Civil Defence organisations. It was extended to Civil Defence personnel in Gibraltar, Hong Kong and Malta in 1965. The medal became obsolescent in the UK after the Civil Defence Corps and Auxiliary Fire Service were disbanded in 1968, but members of the CD Corps in the Isle of Man and Channel Islands are still eligible. A bar is available for additional 15 years' service*

British reverse.

VALUE:

		Miniature
British version	£35–50	£35–45
Northern Ireland version	£85–120	£110–160
Gibraltar	£100–125	
Hong Kong	£100–125	
Malta	£100–125	
Post 1968 reverse	£75–100	

Northern Ireland reverse.

Post-1968 reverse

264A. AMBULANCE SERVICE (EMERGENCY DUTIES) LONG SERVICE AND GOOD CONDUCT MEDAL

Instituted: 5 July 1996.

Branch of Service: Ambulance services in England and Wales, Scotland, Northern Ireland, the Isle of Man and the Channel Islands.

Ribbon: Green with, on either side, a white stripe on which is superimposed a narrow green stripe.

Metal: Cupro-nickel.

Size: 36mm.

Description: (Obverse) crowned effigy of the reigning monarch, ELIZABETH II DEI GRATIA REGINA F.D.; (reverse) FOR EXEMPLARY SERVICE round the top, with either the emblem of the Ambulance Services of Scotland or the remainder of the United Kingdom in the centre below. Fitted with a ring for suspension.

Comments: *Both full- and part-time members of Ambulance Services are eligible provided they are employed on emergency duties. Service prior to 1974 in ambulance services maintained by local authorities counts. For paramedics and technicians the qualifying service is 20 years. For ambulance officers and other management grades, at least seven of their 20 years' service must have been spent on emergency duties.*

VALUE: £150–160   *Miniature* £40–45

264B. ASSOCIATION OF CHIEF AMBULANCE OFFICERS SERVICE MEDAL

Instituted: —.

Branch of Service: Members of the Ambulance Service.

Ribbon: Dark green with twin central red stripe edged with yellow.

Metal: Bronze.

Size: 36mm.

Description: (Obverse) symbol of the Association (caduceus on a wheel) surrounded by ASSOCIATION OF CHIEF AMBULANCE OFFICERS; (reverse) FOR SERVICE surrounded by a laurel wreath.

Comments: *Issued by members of the Association to ambulance personnel who have performed exemplary service.*

VALUE: £65–85   *Miniature* £55–65

264C. ROYAL FLEET AUXILIARY SERVICE MEDAL

Instituted: July 24, 2001 by Royal Warrant.
Branch of Service: Royal Fleet Auxiliary Service.
Ribbon: Central band of watered royal blue flanked by narrow stripes of cypress green, yellow-gold and purple.
Metal: Cupro-nickel.
Size: 38mm.
Description: (Obverse) the crowned effigy of the Queen; (reverse) the badge of the Royal Fleet Auxiliary Service with the inscription ROYAL FLEET AUXILIARY — FOR LONG SERVICE.
Comments: *The medal is awarded to all officers, petty officers and ratings of the RFA after 20 years' service. Clasps will be granted for a further 10 years' service. The recipient's name and rank, together with date of qualification, are impressed on the rim. The first awards of this medal were made to three petty officers in 2003, a further 400 personnel being eligible.*

VALUE: £200–250   *Miniature*   £45–55

265. WOMEN'S ROYAL VOLUNTARY SERVICE LONG SERVICE MEDAL

Instituted: 1961.
Branch of Service: Women's Royal Voluntary Service.
Ribbon: Dark green with twin white stripes towards the end and broad red edges.
Metal: Cupro-nickel.
Size: 36mm.
Description: (Obverse) the interlocking initials WVS in an ivy wreath; (reverse) three flowers, inscribed SERVICE BEYOND SELF round the circumference.
Comments: *Issued unnamed and awarded for 15 years' service. Bars for additional 15 year periods are awarded. Although the majority of the 35,000 (approx.) medals have been awarded to women there has also been a substantial number of male recipients.*

VALUE: £15–20   *Miniature*   £35–45

266. VOLUNTARY MEDICAL SERVICE MEDAL

Second award bar

Instituted: 1932.
Branch of Service: British Red Cross Society and the St Andrew's Ambulance Corps (Scotland).
Ribbon: Red with yellow and white stripes.
Metal: Originally struck in silver but since the 1960s it has been produced in cupro-nickel.
Size: 36mm.
Description: (Obverse) the veiled bust of a female holding an oil lamp, symbolic of Florence Nightingale; (reverse) the crosses of Geneva and St Andrew, with the inscription FOR LONG AND EFFICIENT SERVICE.
Comments: *Awarded for 15 years' service, with a bar for each additional period of five years. The service bars are embellished with a Geneva cross or saltire (St Andrew) cross, whichever is the more appropriate.*

VALUE:		*Miniature*
Silver	£25–35	
Cupro-nickel	£15–20	£25–35

267. SERVICE MEDAL OF THE ORDER OF ST JOHN

Instituted: 1898.

Branch of Service: The Most Venerable Order of the Hospital of St John of Jerusalem.

Ribbon: Three black and two white stripes of equal width.

Metal: Silver (1898-1947), silvered base metal (1947-60), silvered cupro-nickel (1960-66) and rhodium-plated cupro-nickel (since 1966).

Size: 38mm.

Description: (Obverse) an unusual veiled bust of Queen Victoria with her name and abbreviated Latin titles round the circumference. A new obverse was adopted in 1960 with a slightly reduced effigy of Queen Victoria and less ornate lettering. (Reverse) the royal arms within a garter surrounded by four circles containing the imperial crown, the Prince of Wales's feathers and the armorial bearings of the Order and of HRH the Prince of Wales, the first Sub-Prior of the Order. Between the circles are sprigs of St John's Wort. Round the circumference is the Latin inscription MAGNUS PRIORATUS ORDINIS HOSPITALIS SANCTI JOHANNIS JERUSALEM IN ANGLIA in Old English lettering.

Comments: *Originally awarded for 15 years' service to the Order in the United Kingdom (12 in the Dominions and 10 in the Colonies) but the qualifying period has now been reduced to 12 years' service, except that overseas service outside South Africa, New Zealand, Canada and Australia remains 10 years. The medal was designed in 1898 and first presented in 1900. A silver bar was introduced in 1911 for additional periods of five years. From then until 1924 the bar was inscribed 5 YEARS SERVICE but then a design showing a Maltese cross flanked by sprays of St John's Wort was substituted. Bars for 27 years' service were subsequently instituted in silver-gilt. Suspension by a ring was changed in 1913 to a straight bar suspender. The medal is worn on the left breast. Although awarded for long service this medal should not be solely referred to as a long service award as it can also be awarded for conspicuous service—when so awarded it was distinguished by the addition of a silver palm leaf on the ribbon. The silver palm was discontinued in 1949, after only three years. It is believed to be the only medal still issued bearing the bust of Queen Victoria (the effigy was first sculpted by HRH Princess Louise, daughter of Queen Victoria).*

Ribbon embellishments:

5-year cross

Palm leaf for conspicuous service

Voluntary Aid Detachment

Military Hospital Reserve

Ribbon bars:

5-year bar (second type)

VAD (or MHR) now obsolete

Illustrations by M. Thomas, courtesy of Roy Gould

VALUE:

		Miniature
Silver, ring suspension	£35–50	£20–25
Silver, straight bar suspension	£30–45	£15–20
Base metal, first obverse	£20–25	£10–12
Base metal, second obverse	£20–25	£10–12

268. ROYAL AIR FORCE LONG SERVICE AND GOOD CONDUCT MEDAL

Instituted: 1 July 1919.

Branch of Service: Royal Air Force.

Ribbon: Dark blue and maroon with white edges.

Metal: Silver.

Size: 36mm.

Description: (Obverse) the effigy of the reigning monarch; (reverse) the RAF eagle and crown insignia.

Comments: *Awarded to NCOs and other ranks of the RAF for 18 years' exemplary service, reduced in 1977 to 15 years. Provision for bars for further periods of service was made from 1944 onwards. Under changes announced in 2015 a clasp is now awarded for every 10 years served. Before 1945 conduct below the required standard was permitted to count if the airman had displayed higher exemplary conduct against the enemy, gallantry or some special service in times of emergency. From 1944 any prior service in the Navy and Army could be counted. Prior to this date only up to four years' service could be counted. In 1947 officers became eligible for the medal provided they had had at least 12 years' service in the ranks. Recipients' details are inscribed on the rim. The later issues are of silver-plated base metal.*

VALUE:

		Miniature			Miniature
George V (E)	£120–150	£25–35	Elizabeth II (B)	£60–65	£25–35
George VI (D)	£85–100	£25–35	Elizabeth II (C)	£60–65	£25–35
George VI (E)	£85–100	£25–35	RCAF recipient	£300–400	

269. ROYAL AIR FORCE LEVIES LONG SERVICE AND GOOD CONDUCT MEDAL

Instituted: 1948.

Branch of Service: RAF Levies, Iraq.

Ribbon: As the preceding.

Metal: Silver.

Size: 36mm.

Description: Similar to the previous type but was fitted with a clasp inscribed ROYAL AIR FORCE LEVIES IRAQ.

Comments: *Awarded to the locally commissioned officers and men of the RAF Levies in Iraq, for 18 years' service (the last 12 to be of an exemplary nature). The Iraq Levies were raised in 1919 and became the responsibility of the RAF in 1922, maintaining law and order by means of light aircraft and armoured cars. The force was disbanded in 1955 when the RAF withdrew from Iraq. 309 medals were issued, 115 to officers and 194 to airmen.*

VALUE:

George VI (E)	£800–1000
Elizabeth II (C)	£900–1100
Elizabeth II (D)	£900–1100

270. AIR EFFICIENCY AWARD

Instituted: September 1942

Branch of Service: AAF, RAAF and RAFVR.

Ribbon: Green with two light blue stripes towards the centre.

Metal: Silver.

Size: Height 38mm; max. width 32mm.

Description: An oval medal with a suspender in the form of an eagle with wings outspread. (Obverse) the effigy of the reigning monarch; (reverse) inscribed AIR EFFICIENCY AWARD in three lines.

Comments: *Granted for 10 years' efficient service in the Auxiliary and Volunteer Air Forces of the United Kingdom and Commonwealth. A bar was awarded for a further ten-year period. Officers are permitted to add the letters AE after their name. This award was replaced in 2000 by the VRSM (No. 242A).*

VALUE:

George VI (D)	£125–150
George VI (E)	£150–175
Elizabeth II (C)	£125–150
Miniature (all)	£25–35
Named to officers add £40	

Second award bar

271. POLICE LONG SERVICE AND GOOD CONDUCT MEDAL

Instituted: 14 June 1951.
Branch of Service: Police Forces.
Ribbon: Dark blue with twin white stripes towards each end.
Metal: Original issue cupro-nickel, now rhodium plated
Size: 36mm.
Description: The obverse of this medal bears the effigy of the reigning monarch while the reverse has the figure of Justice with scales in her left hand and a wreath in her right surrounded by the inscription 'FOR EXEMPLARY POLICE SERVICE'. The suspender is straight and found in both swivelling and non-swivelling formats
Comments: *Originally awarded to full-time regular police officers within any UK Constabulary for 22 years' service. However, following a national campaign by Warwickshire Police Officer Kenneth Fowler, supported by Chief Officers, the Police Federations and Members of Parliament, the award point of the medal was reduced to 20 years' service on 19 January 2010, bringing it in line with the Fire, Ambulance and Prison Long Service and Good Conduct Medals which are all awarded after 20 years' service. In 1956 this medal was extended to police officers serving in Australia, Papua New Guinea and Nauru. Australia however replaced this medal in 1976 with the National Medal.*

VALUE:		Miniature
George VI (C)	£40–50	£25–35
Elizabeth II (A)	£40–50	£25–35
Elizabeth II (D)	£40–50	£25–35

272. SPECIAL CONSTABULARY LONG SERVICE MEDAL

Special Constabulary medal.

1956 Ulster Special Constabulary medal.

Long Service bar.

Instituted: 30 August 1919.
Branch of Service: Special Constabulary.
Ribbon: A broad red stripe in the centre flanked by black and white stripes.
Metal: Bronze.
Size: 36mm.
Description: (Obverse) the effigy of the reigning monarch; (reverse) a partial laurel wreath with a six-line text inscribed FOR FAITHFUL SERVICE IN THE SPECIAL CONSTABULARY. A second reverse was introduced in 1956 for 15 years' service in the Ulster Special Constabulary, the text being modified to permit the inclusion of the word ULSTER. A third type was introduced in 1982 for 15 years' service in the RUC Reserve and is thus inscribed but, with the name change, in 2001 a fourth type inscribed Police Reserve of Northern Ireland was issued.
Comments: *Awarded to all ranks in the Special Constabulary for 9 years' unpaid service, with more than 50 duties per annum. War service with at least 50 duties counted triple. A clasp inscribed THE GREAT WAR 1914-18 was awarded to those who qualified for the medal during that conflict. Bars inscribed LONG SERVICE, with the date, are awarded for additional ten-year periods (the NI bars are not dated). To qualify during the two world wars a special constable must have served without any pay for not less than three years, and during that period have performed at least 50 duties a year, and be recommended by a chief officer of police as willing and competent to discharge the duties of special constable as required, i.e. in both world wars service counts treble.*

VALUE:		Miniature
George V (C)	£20–25	£10–12
With Great War 1914–18 clasp	£30–35	£15–20
George V (E)	£20–25	£10–12
George VI (D)	£20–25	£10–12
George VI (E)	£55–85	£15–20
Elizabeth II (B)	£55–85	£15–20
Elizabeth II (C)	£45–55	£10–12
Elizabeth II (C)		
Northern Ireland types	£250–300	£15–20

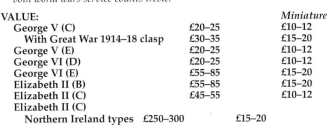

273. ROYAL ULSTER CONSTABULARY SERVICE MEDAL

Instituted: 1982.

Branch of Service: RUC and its Reserve.

Ribbon: Green, with narrow central stripes of red, black and dark blue. Following the award of the George Cross to the RUC the ribbon of this medal was modified to reflect the award. The colour of the GC ribbon is now indicated by two vertical blue stripes at the outer edges.

Metal: Cupro-nickel.

Size: 36mm.

Description: (Obverse) the effigy of Queen Elizabeth II; (reverse) the crowned harp insignia of the RUC with the words FOR SERVICE round the foot.

Comments: *Awarded for 18 months continuous service since 1 January 1971, but the award was made immediate on the recipient also being awarded a gallantry decoration or a Queen's commendation.*

VALUE:

Elizabeth II (C)	£200–250	*Miniature*	£20–25

Original ribbon.

Post-2001 ribbon.

274. COLONIAL POLICE LONG SERVICE MEDAL

Instituted: 1934.

Branch of Service: Colonial police forces.

Ribbon: Green centre bordered with white and broad blue stripes towards the edges.

Metal: Silver.

Size: 36mm.

Description: (Obverse) the effigy of the reigning monarch; (reverse) a police truncheon superimposed on a laurel wreath.

Comments: *Originally awarded to junior officers who had completed 18 years' exemplary service but latterly awarded to officers of all ranks who have the required service qualification. A bar is awarded on completing 25 years' service and a second bar after 30 years. These are represented on the ribbon bar in working dress by silver rosettes. The number (where applicable), rank and name as well as (for George VI and later issues) the relevant force in which the recipient is serving at the time of the award is engraved on the rim, often locally and therefore in a variety of styles.*

VALUE:		*Miniature*
George V (C)	£100–120	£25–35
George VI (B)	£85–100	£25–35
George VI (C)	£85–100	£25–35
Elizabeth II (A)	£85–100	£25–35
Elizabeth II (B)	£85–100	£25–35

274A. OVERSEAS TERRITORIES POLICE LONG SERVICE MEDAL

Following the renaming of this and other Colonial medals in 2012 this medal is now being issued with the inscription "Overseas Territories . . ." in place of "Colonial . . .". In all other respects this medal is identical to MYB 274 above.

275. COLONIAL SPECIAL CONSTABULARY LONG SERVICE MEDAL

Instituted: 1957.
Branch of Service: Colonial Special Constabulary.
Ribbon: Two thin white stripes on a broad green centre, with broad blue edges.
Metal: Silver.
Size: 36mm.
Description: (Obverse) the effigy of the reigning monarch; (reverse) the crowned royal cypher above the words FOR FAITHFUL SERVICE in a laurel wreath.
Comments: *Awarded for nine years' unpaid or 15 years' paid service in a colonial special constabulary. A bar is awarded for further ten-year periods Since June 2012 this medal has been renamed "Overseas Service . . .".*

VALUE:

Elizabeth II (A)	£250–300	*Miniature*	£25–35

276. CEYLON POLICE LONG SERVICE AND GOOD CONDUCT MEDAL (I)

Instituted: 1925.
Branch of Service: Ceylon Police.
Ribbon: Very similar to that of the Special Constabulary Long Service Medal—a broad red stripe in the centre flanked by black and white stripes.
Metal: Silver.
Size: 36mm.
Description: (Obverse) coinage profile of King George V by Sir Bertram Mackennal; (reverse) an elephant surmounted by a crown. Ring suspension.
Comments: *Awarded for 15 years' active service. It was superseded in 1934 by the Colonial Police Long Service Medal.*

VALUE:

George V (E)	£350–400	*Miniature*	£85–95

277. CEYLON POLICE LONG SERVICE AND GOOD CONDUCT MEDAL (II)

Instituted: 1950.
Branch of Service: Ceylon Police.
Ribbon: Dark blue edged with khaki, white and pale blue.
Metal: Cupro-nickel.
Size: 36mm.
Description: (Obverse) the effigy of the reigning monarch; (reverse) similar to the foregoing, but without the crown above the elephant, to permit the longer inscription CEYLON POLICE SERVICE. Straight bar suspender.
Comments: *Awarded for 18 years exemplary service. Bars for 25 and 30 years service were also awarded. It became obsolete when Ceylon (now Sri Lanka) became a republic in 1972.*

VALUE:

		Miniature
George VI (C)	£450–500	£35–45
Elizabeth II (A)	£400–450	£35–45

278. CEYLON POLICE MEDAL FOR MERIT

Instituted: 1950.
Branch of Service: Ceylon Police.
Ribbon: Broad central khaki stripe, flanked by narrow stripes of white, light blue and dark blue.
Metal: Silver.
Size: 36mm.
Description: (Obverse) the effigy of the reigning monarch; (reverse) an Indian elephant with the legend CEYLON POLICE SERVICE at the top and FOR MERIT at the foot.
Comments: *This medal replaced, within Ceylon, the Colonial Police Medal for Meritorious Service (no. 61). It was to be awarded for "valuable service characterised by resource and devotion to duty, including prolonged service marked by exceptional ability, merit and exemplary conduct". The number awarded each year not to exceed 10. Year of issue is included in the naming, e.g. "2/69" signifying the second award of 1969.The medal became obsolete when Ceylon (now Sri Lanka) became a republic in 1972.*

VALUE		*Miniature*
George VI	—	—
Elizabeth II	£400–500	£35–45

278A. CEYLON POLICE MEDAL FOR GALLANTRY

Instituted: 1950.
Branch of Service: Ceylon Police.
Ribbon: As for the Medal for Merit (above) but with the addition of a very narrow red stripe superimposed on the white stripes.
Metal: Silver.
Size: 36mm.
Description: Similar to the Medal of Merit (above) but reverse inscribed FOR GALLANTRY at the foot.
Comments: *The medal became obsolete when Ceylon (now Sri Lanka) became a republic in 1972.*

VALUE:		*Miniature*
George VI	—	£55–65
Elizabeth II	—	£55–65

279. CYPRUS MILITARY POLICE LONG SERVICE AND GOOD CONDUCT MEDAL

Instituted: October 1929.
Branch of Service: Cyprus Military Police.
Ribbon: Yellow, dark green and yellow in equal bands.
Metal: Silver.
Size: 36mm.
Description: (Obverse) King George V; (reverse) the title of the police round the circumference and the words LONG AND GOOD SERVICE in four lines across the middle.
Comments: *Awarded to those who had three good conduct badges, plus six years exemplary service since the award of the third badge, no more than four entries in the defaulters' book and a minimum of 15 years service. Officers who had been promoted from the ranks were also eligible. No more than 7 officers and 54 other ranks were awarded this medal during its brief life before it was superseded in 1934 by the Colonial Police Long Service Medal.*

VALUE: £800–1000

279A. ROYAL FALKLAND ISLANDS POLICE JUBILEE MEDAL

Date: 1996
Branch of Service: Royal Falkland Islands Police
Ribbon: Green with a central blue stripe edged in white.
Metal: Silver.
Size: 36mm.
Description: (Obverse) Elizabeth II (A); (reverse) arms of the colony; ROYAL FALKLAND ISLANDS POLICE round top and double dated 1846-1996 round foot. Fitted with ring suspension and a brooch clasp at the top of the ribbon.
Comments: *Awarded to all officers serving in the Royal Falkland Islands Police on 15 October 1996. Only 27 medals were awarded.*

VALUE: £1000–1500

280. HONG KONG POLICE MEDAL FOR MERIT

Instituted: May 3, 1862.
Branch of Service: Hong Kong Police.
Ribbon: Various, according to class (see below).
Metal: Gold, silver or bronze.
Size: 36mm.
Description: (Obverse) the effigy of the reigning monarch; (reverse) inscribed HONG KONG POLICE FORCE FOR MERIT within a laurel wreath and beaded circle (with various slight modifications). Examples have been recorded with the effigy of Queen Victoria as on the Abyssinian and New Zealand Medals (MY123–124), and King George V types C and E.
Comment: *Exceptionally awarded in five different classes according to the length and type of service. The 1st Class medal was struck in gold and worn with a maroon (VC) ribbon, the 2nd Class in silver with a plain yellow ribbon, the 3rd Class in bronze with a central black stripe on the yellow ribbon, the 4th Class in bronze with two central black stripes in the yellow ribbon, and the 5th Class (confined to the Police Reserve) in bronze had a green ribbon with two black central stripes. The 4th Class was engraved on the reverse above the wreath. These medals were superseded in April 1937 by the Hong Kong Police Silver Medal, only four of which were awarded before it was replaced by the Colonial Police Medal for Meritorious Service 1938.*

VALUE:	1st class	2nd class	3rd class	4th class
Victoria	—	£600–700	£500–550	£500–550
Edward VII	Rare	Rare	Rare	Rare
George V (B)	Rare	£500–550	£450–550	£450–500
George V (C)	Rare	£500–550	£450–550	£450–500

Miniature (all, silver or bronze)   Rare

1st Class.   *2nd Class.*   *3rd Class.*   *4th Class.*

280A. HONG KONG DISTRICT WATCH FORCE MERIT MEDAL

Instituted: 1868.
Branch of Service: District Watch Force.
Ribbon: Very dark green with a central deep red stripe.
Metal: Silver or bronze.
Size: 31mm with a prominent rim.
Description: (Obverse) four Chinese characters "Great Britain Hong Kong" above a watchman's lamp, superimposed on a cutlass and police baton, with the Chinese characters for "District Watch Force" and "Medal" at the sides; (reverse) DISTRICT WATCHMEN'S FORCE FOR MERIT within a laurel wreath.
Comment: *While the Hong Kong Police was principally a mixed force of Europeans and Indians, operated in the business and higher class residential areas, and was paid for out of the colony's revenues, the District Watch Force was a purely Chinese organisation, raised by prominent citizens of the colony to patrol and police the Chinese parts of the city. Its members had statutory powers, were uniformed and were trained and functioned in the style of the old parish constables, rather than in the gendarmerie style of the Hong Kong Police which was colonial in nature and imposed on society rather than integrated with it. The District Watch Force ceased to function at the time of the Japanese invasion in 1941 and was not revived on liberation.*

VALUE: £650–700

280B. ROYAL HONG KONG POLICE COMMEMORATIVE MEDAL

Instituted: 1996.
Branch of Service: Royal Hong Kong Police.
Ribbon: Black, magenta and old gold.
Metal: Silver.
Size: 38mm.
Description: (Obverse) the RHKP crest; (reverse) crossed tipstaves inside a laurel wreath with the dates 1844 and 1997.
Comment: *The medal, approved by Commissioner Eddie Hui Ki On, is available on purchase (originally HK$1,000, about £80) to those who served in the Hong Kong Police (1844–1969) and the Royal Hong Kong Police (1969–97). Purchasers' details are often found privately engraved in bold upright capitals in a variety of formats. The medal, worn on the left breast, has the same status as the Royal Hong Kong Regiment Disbandment Medal (254A).*

VALUE: £150–200   *Miniature*   £55–80

280C. ROYAL HONG KONG AUXILIARY POLICE COMMEMORATIVE MEDAL

Instituted: 1996.
Branch of Service: Royal Hong Kong Auxiliary Police.
Ribbon: Black, magenta and old gold.
Metal: Silver.
Size: 38mm.
Description: Similar to the above, but inscribed ROYAL HONG KONG AUXILIARY POLICE FORCE.
Comment: *Similar to the above this medal is available for purchase. Some 5,000 auxiliary policemen and women are eligible for the award.*

VALUE: £150–200   *Miniature*   £55-80

280D. HONG KONG MILITARY SERVICE CORPS MEDAL

Instituted: 1997.
Branch of Service: Hong Kong Military Service Corps.
Ribbon: Red, with a central yellow stripe.
Metal: Cupro-nickel.
Size: 36mm.
Description: (Obverse) a Chinese dragon on a scroll bearing the initials of the Corps. HONG KONG MILITARY SERVICE CORPS inscribed round the top and 1962-1997 at the foot; (reverse) the British royal arms with inscription round the top TO COMMEMORATE DISBANDMENT and the date 31 March 1997 at the foot.
Comments: *The Military Service Corps was a paramilitary unit formed in 1962 for defence of the Crown Colony and recruited locally. Members of the Corps were allowed to purchase this medal following its disbandment prior to the return of Hong Kong to China.*

VALUE: £100–120

281. HONG KONG ROYAL NAVAL DOCKYARD POLICE LONG SERVICE MEDAL

Instituted: 1920.
Branch of Service: Hong Kong Royal Naval Dockyard Police.
Ribbon: Yellow with two royal blue stripes towards the centre.
Metal: Gilt bronze or silver.
Size: 31mm.
Description: (Obverse) the effigy of the reigning monarch; (reverse) the title of the Police within a laurel wreath. Ring suspension (two sizes).
Comments: *Awarded for 15 years service. Although the Dockyard closed in 1961 men who transferred to other police divisions continued to be awarded the medal up to 1973. About 280 medals in all were issued.*

VALUE:		Miniature
George V (E)	£400–500	£110–160
George VI (C)	£400–500	£110–160
George VI (D)	£400–500	£110–160
Elizabeth II (C)	£400–500	£110–160

281A. HONG KONG DISCIPLINED SERVICES MEDAL

Instituted: 1986.
Branch of Service: Hong Kong Customs & Excise and Immigration Service.
Ribbon: Green bordered by vertical stripes of dark blue with a strip of sky blue at each edge.
Metal: Silver.
Size: 36mm.
Description: (Obverse) crowned effigy of Queen Elizabeth II (B); (reverse) armorial bearings of Hong Kong, with the inscription "For Long Service and Good Conduct".
Clasps: Awarded after 25 and 30 years, denoted by silver rosettes on ribband in working dress.
Comments: *Awarded after 18 years continuous service. Engraved with name and rank on rim. Some 1,739 medals were awarded between 1987 and the return of Hong Kong to China on June 30, 1997. No other long service medal to Customs officers has been awarded in the British system.*

VALUE:	Customs	Immigration
Medal	£450–£50	£500–£550
1st clasp	£500–£550	£600–£650
2nd clasp	£600–£650	Unique

281B. TIENTSIN BRITISH EMERGENCY CORPS MEDAL

Instituted: —
Branch of Service: British Municipal Emergency Corps.
Ribbon: Buff with a broad central white stripe.
Metal: Silver.
Size: 36mm.
Description: (Obverse) the arms of the colony supported by a sailor and a Chinese worker surrounded by the words TIENTSIN BRITISH MUNICIPAL EMERGENCY CORPS; (reverse) a wreath surrounding a plain panel engraved FOR LONG SERVICE in three lines, with maker's name in small lettering below: STERLING/ARNOLD.
Comments: *The British Emergency Corps was presumably a paramilitary unit recruited locally. Little is known about these medals or the unit but obviously they were awarded for long service.*

VALUE: £175–225

282. MALTA POLICE LONG SERVICE AND GOOD CONDUCT MEDAL

Instituted: 1921.
Branch of Service: Malta Police.
Ribbon: Dark blue with a narrow central silver stripe.
Metal: Silver.
Size: 36mm.
Description: (Obverse) the effigy of King George V; (reverse) an eight-pointed Maltese cross in a laurel wreath with the title of the service and FOR LONG SERVICE AND GOOD CONDUCT round the circumference.
Comments: *Awarded to sergeants and constables with 18 years exemplary service. Officers who had had 18 years in the ranks were also eligible for the award. It was superseded by the Colonial Police Long Service Medal in 1934. No more than 112 medals were awarded, although only 99 names were published in the Police Commissioner's Annual Reports and in the Malta Gazette.*

VALUE:		Miniature
George V (E)	£400–500	£110–130
George V (C)	£400–500	£110–130

282A. MAURITIUS POLICE LONG SERVICE AND GOOD CONDUCT MEDAL: I

Instituted: —.

Branch of Service: Mauritius Police.

Ribbon: Three types: (a) 36mm half black, half white; (b) 33mm white with a broad royal blue central stripe; (c) blue with two narrow white stripes towards the edges.

Metal: Bronze.

Size: Oval, 40x33mm or 39x31mm.

Description: (Obverse) crown surmounting crossed tipstaves with the motto PAX NOBISCUM (Peace be with us) and the legend POLICE DE-PARTMENT round the top and MAURITIUS at the foot; (reverse) palm fronds enclosing a three-line inscription FOR GOOD CONDUCT. Fitted with a ring for suspension. Medals with 33mm ribbon fitted at top with a pin brooch by Hunt & Roskill.

Comment: *It is believed that the different ribbons indicated different periods of service, but confirmation is sought. It is presumed that this medal was superseded by no. 282B.*

VALUE:	£200–250	*Miniature*	£80–110

First type ribbon.

282B. MAURITIUS POLICE LONG SERVICE AND GOOD CONDUCT MEDAL: II

Instituted: —.

Branch of Service: Mauritius Police.

Ribbon: Green centre flanked by white stripes and broad blue stripes towards the edges.

Metal: Silver.

Size: 36mm.

Description: (Obverse) the effigy of Queen Elizabeth II; (reverse) police truncheon on a laurel wreath.

Comments: *This medal is identical to the Colonial Police Long Service Medal (no. 274) except that the inscription substituted the name MAURITIUS for COLONIAL. It has been recorded in a medal group of 1976 and may have been introduced in or about 1968 when Mauritius attained independence.*

VALUE: £200–250

283. NEW ZEALAND POLICE MEDAL

Instituted: 1886.

Branch of Service: New Zealand Police.

Ribbon: Originally plain crimson but in 1919 it was changed to a pattern very similar to that of the Permanent Forces of the Empire Beyond the Seas LSGC medal (no. 249),

Metal: Silver.

Size: 36mm.

Description: (Obverse) identical to that of the NZ Long & Efficient Service Medal (MY257); (reverse) FOR LONG SERVICE AND GOOD CONDUCT in four lines. Issued with a ring suspender until 1919 when a bar suspender was adopted. Clasps for each additional eight years service were introduced at the same time.

Comments: *Granted to sworn police staff for 14 years service. The clasp qualifying period was reduced to seven years in 1963. This medal was rendered obsolete with the introduction, in 1976, of the New Zealand Police Long Service and Good Conduct Medal (NZ26). It seems that from September 1901 this medal was also awarded to members of the NZ Prison Service and medals have WDR in front of recipient's name.*

First type obverse.

VALUE:		*Miniature*
Regalia obverse, bar suspension	£120–150	£25–35

Second type ribbon.

283A. SEYCHELLES POLICE LONG SERVICE AND GOOD CONDUCT MEDAL

Instituted: —.
Branch of Service: Seychelles Police.
Ribbon: Crimson.
Metal: Bronze.
Size: Oval, 40x33mm.
Description: (Obverse) crown surmounting crossed tipstaves with legend POLICE DEPARTMENT round the top and SEYCHELLES at the foot; (reverse) palm fronds enclosing a three-line inscription FOR GOOD CONDUCT. Fitted with a ring for suspension.
Comments: *This medal is similar to the Mauritius Police Medal (282A) and it is presumed that this medal also became obsolete on the introduction of the Colonial Police Long Service Medal in 1934. Details of qualifying terms of service and other regulations are sought.*

VALUE: £150–200

284. SOUTH AFRICA POLICE GOOD SERVICE MEDAL

Instituted: 1923.
Branch of Service: South Africa Police.
Ribbon: Broad black centre, flanked by white stripes and green borders.
Metal: Silver.
Size: 36mm.
Description: (Obverse) South African coat of arms; (reverse) bilingual inscriptions separated by a horizontal line. Three versions of the medal have been recorded. In the first version inscriptions were in English and Dutch, the latter reading POLITIE DIENST with VOOR TROUWE DIENST (for faithful service) on the reverse. In the second, introduced in 1932, Afrikaans replaced Dutch and read POLIESIE DIENS and VIR GETROUE DIENS respectively. In the third version, current from 1951 to 1963, the Afrikaans was modified to read POLISIEDIENS and VIR TROUE DIENS.
Comments: *Awarded to other ranks for 18 years exemplary service or for service of a gallant or particularly distinguished character. In the latter instance a bar inscribed MERIT-VERDIENSTE was awarded. The medal was replaced by the South African Medal for Faithful Service.*

VALUE:		
	1st type	£35–40
	2nd type	£30–35
	3rd type	£25–30
	Miniature	£15–20

285. SOUTH AFRICAN RAILWAYS AND HARBOUR POLICE LONG SERVICE AND GOOD CONDUCT MEDAL

Instituted: 1934.
Branch of Service: South African Railways and Harbour Police.
Ribbon: Similar to the Police Good Service Medal but with the colours reversed—a green central stripe flanked by white stripes and blue edges.
Metal: Silver.
Size: 36mm.
Description: (Obverse) the Union arms with S.A.R. & H. POLICE at the top and S.A.S.- EN HAWE POLISIE round the foot, but this was changed in 1953 to S.A.S. POLISIE at the top and S.A.R. POLICE at the foot. (Reverse) six line bilingual inscription.
Comments: *Awarded for 18 years unblemished service. Immediate awards for gallant or especially meritorious service earned a bar inscribed MERIT - VERDIENSTE (later with the words transposed). The medal was superseded in 1960 by the Railways Police Good Service Medal.*

VALUE: 1st type £80–100   2nd type £75–100   *Miniature* £35–45

286. FIRE BRIGADE LONG SERVICE MEDAL

Instituted: 1 June 1954.
Branch of Service: Fire Services.
Ribbon: Red with narrow yellow stripes towards the end and yellow borders.
Metal: Cupro-nickel.
Size: 36mm.
Description: (Obverse) the Queen's effigy; (reverse) two firemen manning a hose. Ring suspension.
Comments: *Awarded to all ranks of local authority fire brigades, whether full- or part-time for 20 years exemplary service. Prior to the institution of this award most local authorities issued their own medals of individual design.*

VALUE:

Elizabeth II	£45–55	
		Miniature £12–14

286A. ASSOCIATION OF PROFESSIONAL FIRE BRIGADE OFFICERS LONG SERVICE MEDAL

Instituted: 1911.
Branch of Service: Association of Professional Fire Brigade Officers.
Ribbon: A red central stripe flanked by narrow white stripes and broad black edges (silver medal) or grey edges (bronze medal).
Metal: Silver or bronze.
Size: 38mm.
Description: (Obverse) allegorical female figure carrying a palm frond and bestowing a laurel crown on a kneeling fireman; an early fire appliance in the background; blank exergue; (reverse) an oak wreath enclosing a four-line inscription ASSOCIATION OF PROFESSIONAL FIRE BRIGADE OFFICERS FOR LONG SERVICE. Fitted with a swivelling bar suspension.
Comments: *The medal in silver was awarded to professional fire brigade officers for a minimum of 20 years full time service and in bronze for lesser periods. Engraved on the rim with the rank and name of the officer, together with the year of the award.*

VALUE: Silver £45–55   Bronze £40–50

Ribbon for silver medal.

286AA. NATIONAL FIRE BRIGADES ASSOCIATION LONG SERVICE MEDAL

Instituted: —
Branch of Service: Fire Services.
Ribbon: Red with a central dark blue stripe flanked by very thin yellow stripes.
Metal: Silver or bronze.
Size: 38mm.
Description: (Obverse) badge of the Association: a wreathed flag within a circle surmounted by a fireman's helmet and surrounded by ladders and hoses inscribed NATIONAL FIRE BRIGADES ASSOCIATION round the central motif; (reverse) LONG SERVICE in minuscule lettering inside an oak wreath with space in the centre for the recipient's name. Fitted with a plain ring for suspension from a broad bar suspender with a clasp bearing the years of service.
Comments: *The medal in silver was awarded to fire brigade officers for a minimum of 20 years full time service and in bronze for lesser periods. Engraved on the rim with the rank and number and often the name of the officer, together with the year of the award.*

VALUE: Silver £45–65   Bronze £35–55

286AB. NATIONAL FIRE BRIGADES UNION MEDAL

Instituted: 1895.

Branch of Service: Fire Services.

Ribbon: Mauve (originally with a narrow white central stripe for 20 years' service).

Metal: Silver or bronze.

Size: 38mm.

Description: (Obverse) similar to 286AA but with NATIONAL FIRE BRIGADES UNION round the central motif; (reverse) LONG SERVICE in minuscule lettering inside an oak wreath with space in the centre for the recipient's name. Service number impressed on the rim. Fitted with a suspension bar and a brooch bar denoting length of service.

Comments: *The medal in silver was awarded to fire brigade officers for a minimum of 20 years' full time service and in bronze for 10 years' service. Engraved on the rim with the rank and number and often the name of the officer.*

VALUE: Silver   £45–65   Bronze   £35–55

286B. BRITISH FIRE SERVICES ASSOCIATION MEDAL

Instituted: 1949.

Branch of Service: British Fire Services Association.

Ribbon: 33mm with a central silver-grey stripe flanked by black and white stripes and a broad red edge. However, the 10 year medal has a similar ribbon but with the white stripes to the edges to distinguish it from the 20 year ribbon.

Metal: Silver (20 years) or bronze (10 years).

Size: Originally 38mm, now 36mm.

Description: (Obverse) identical to the *obverse* of 286A, i.e allegorical female figure and fireman; (reverse) identical to the *obverse* of 286AA but with FOR LONG SERVICE & EFFICIENCY, round the central motif and THE BRITISH FIRE SERVICES ASSOCIATION round the circumference. The medal originally had an ornamental scrolled suspender with a bar inscribed BFSA, however it now has a simple straight suspender. The recipient's name and service number are engraved on the rim. A bar is added for each additional 5 years of service

Comments: *The British Fire Services Association was formed in 1949 by the amalgamation of the National Fire Brigades Association and the Professional Fire Brigades Association. This medal thus superseded 286A and 286AA. The silver medal of the BFSA was originally awarded for 15 years' service. The last silver award was made in 1953 on the institution of the Fire Brigade Medal (MYB 286).*

Original ribbon and current 20 year ribbon.

Current 10 year ribbon.

VALUE: Silver   £45–65   *Miniature*   £35–45
                 Bronze   £25–35

It should be noted that a number of authorities also issued their own medals for long service and for meritorious service by members of their fire brigades. These medals are invariably well struck and are extremely collectable. However, as they are so many and so varied it is considered that these are outside of the scope of the MEDAL YEARBOOK. For a good example see the article "For Extraordinary Bravery: The London Fire Brigade Silver Medal" by Michael Pinchen in MEDAL NEWS, June/July 2015

286C. BRITISH FIRE SERVICE ASSOCIATION MERITORIOUS SERVICE MEDAL

Instituted: —
Branch of Service: Fire service personnel.
Ribbon: Khaki with a broad central stripe edged with thin black stripes.
Metal: Silver.
Size: 45mm x 36mm.
Description: A circular medallion contained within an upright oval laurel wreath suspended from an ornamental suspender with the initials B.F.S.A. on a scroll superimposed on a laurel spray. The central medallion depicts the Union Jack in a wreath with the inscription FOR MERITORIOUS SERVICE round the circumference. Reverse is plain apart from the maker's mark (foot) and the recipient's rank and name engraved on the medallion.
Comments: *Awarded for outstanding service and gallantry in fire-fighting operations.*

VALUE: £250–350

287. COLONIAL FIRE BRIGADE LONG SERVICE MEDAL

Instituted: 1934.
Branch of Service: Colonial Fire Services.
Ribbon: Blue with twin green central stripes separated and bordered by thin white stripes.
Metal: Silver.
Size: 36mm.
Description: (Obverse) the effigy of the reigning monarch; (reverse) a fireman's helmet and axe. Ring suspension.
Comments: *Awarded to junior officers for 18 years full-time exemplary service. Bars are awarded for further periods of service. As from June 14, 2012 this medal was renamed the Overseas Territories Fire Brigade Medal.*

VALUE:		*Miniature*
George V (E)	£300–350	£35–45
George VI (D)	£300–350	£35–45
George VI (E)	£300–350	£35–45
Elizabeth II (C)	£300–350	£35–45
Elizabeth II (D)	£300–350	£35–45

288. CEYLON FIRE BRIGADE LONG SERVICE AND GOOD CONDUCT MEDAL

Instituted: 1950.
Branch of Service: Ceylon Fire Service.
Ribbon: Similar to the Police Medal (MYB277), but with a thin central white stripe through the dark blue band.
Metal: Silver.
Size: 36mm.
Description: As the Police Medal, but with a reverse inscribed CEYLON FIRE SERVICES.

VALUE:	
George VI	£300–400
Elizabeth II	£300–400

288A. NORTHERN IRELAND PRISON SERVICE MEDAL

Instituted: 25 February 2002.
Branch of Service: Northern Ireland Prison Service.
Ribbon: Green with a broad navy blue band having at its centre a sky-blue stripe. Prison grade recipients have a ribbon with an additional thin red stripe bisecting the sky-blue stripe.
Metal: Cupro-nickel.
Size: 36mm.
Description: (Obverse) the crowned profile of the Queen with her name and titles; (reverse) a ring of flax flowers with three keys at the top, enclosing a four line inscription NORTHERN IRELAND PRISON SERVICE. The medal is fitted with a plain bar for suspension. The name of the recipient is stamped on the rim.
Comments: *The medal recognises "those who have rendered professional, committed and brave service as members of and by others in support of the Northern Ireland Prison Service".*

VALUE: £150–180

288B. PRISON SERVICE MEDAL

Instituted: 17 December, 2010
Branch of Service: Operational grades in HM Prison Services of England and Wales, Northern Ireland, Jersey, Guernsey, Isle of Man and Scotland.
Ribbon: Black with twin stripes towards each end.
Metal: Cupro-nickel.
Size: 36mm.
Description: (Obverse) The effigy of the reigning monarch by Ian Rank Broadley; (reverse) a period archway with the wording "For Exemplary Service", within the archway is Her Majesty's cypher surmounted by a crown.
Comments: *Awarded to operational ranks of the Prison Service of the UK, after completing 20 years service on or after 29 April 2008. Naming includes rank, initails, surname and epaulette number, for uniformed ranks.*

VALUE: £250–300

288C. BELFAST HARBOUR POLICE MEDAL

Instituted: 1946.
Branch of Service: Belfast Harbour Police Service.
Ribbon: Deep blue with yellow edges.
Metal: Silver.
Size: 36mm.
Description: (Obverse) A mythical maritime scene—the seal of the Harbour Commissioners—with the words BELFAST HARBOUR COMMISSIONERS around; (reverse) the words WON BY across the centre above the recipient's details with BELFAST HARBOUR POLICE around the edge.
Comments: *The medal is primarily awarded for outstanding meritorious service or when awarded for gallantry a bronze anchor is worn on the ribbon. Since its inception only 16 medals have been awarded, three with the bronze anchor for gallantry, in addition four Harbour Chief Constables have received the medal for long service*

VALUE: £300–500

289. COLONIAL PRISON SERVICE LONG SERVICE MEDAL

Instituted: October 1955.
Branch of Service: Colonial Prison Services.
Ribbon: Green with dark blue edges and a thin silver stripe in the centre.
Metal: Silver.
Size: 36mm.
Description: (Obverse) Queen Elizabeth II; (reverse) a phoenix rising from the flames and striving towards the sun.
Comments: *Awarded to ranks of Assistant Superintendent and below for 18 years exemplary service. Bars are awarded for further periods of 25 or 30 years service. As from June 14, 2012 this medal was renamed the Overseas Territories Prison Service Medal.*

VALUE:
Elizabeth II   £250–300   *Miniature*   £35–45

290. SOUTH AFRICAN PRISON SERVICE FAITHFUL SERVICE MEDAL

Instituted: September 1922.
Branch of Service: South African Prison Service.
Ribbon: Broad green centre flanked by white stripes and dark blue edges.
Metal: Silver.
Size: 36mm.
Description: (Obverse) arms of the Union of South Africa, of identical design to no. 284 except with GEVANGENIS DIENST round the top and PRISONS SERVICE round the foot. (Reverse) inscribed FOR FAITHFUL SERVICE across the upper half and in Dutch VOOR TROUWE DIENST across the lower half.
Comments: *Awarded to prison officers with 18 years exemplary service. Immediate awards for gallantry or exceptionally meritorious service received the Merit bar. In 1959 this medal was superseded by a version inscribed in Afrikaans.*

VALUE: £40–50   *Miniature*   £35–45

291. SOUTH AFRICA PRISONS DEPARTMENT FAITHFUL SERVICE MEDAL

Instituted: 1959.
Branch of Service: South African Prisons Department.
Ribbon: Broad dark blue centre flanked by white stripes and green edges.
Metal: Silver.
Size: 36mm.
Description: (Obverse) arms of the Union of South Africa, of identical design to no. 284 except with DEPARTEMENT VAN GEVANGENISSE round the top and PRISONS DEPARTMENT round the foot. (Reverse) VIR TROUE DIENS across the upper half and FOR FAITHFUL SERVICE across the lower half.
Comments: *The conditions of the award were similar to the previous medal, the main difference being the change of title and the substitution of Afrikaans inscriptions for Dutch. This medal was superseded by the Prisons Department Faithful Service Medal of the Republic of South Africa, instituted in 1965.*

VALUE: £35–50   *Miniature*   £35–45

291AA. NATO MERITORIOUS SERVICE MEDAL

Date: 1994.
Branch of Service: Personnel serving with NATO forces.
Ribbon: NATO blue with white stripes at the edges each having a vertical gold and silver thread.
Metal: Silver.
Size: 36mm.
Description: Obverse and reverse as for the other NATO medals.
Clasps: Silver bar inscribed MERITORIOUS.
Comments: *Awarded for exceptional service to NATO. Not approved for wear by UK personnel either in full size or miniature. If presented it may be retained as a keepsake.*

VALUE: £45–55

291BB. EBOLA MEDAL FOR SERVICE IN WEST AFRICA

Date: 2015
Ribbon: Equal stripes of bright green, red, bright green, white, light blue each side of a central thin yellow stripe (the colours of the flags of the West African Nations affected).
Metal: Nickel silver.
Size: 36mm.
Description: (Obverse) The Rank-Broadley effigy of Her Majesty the Queen; (reverse) the eternal flame, representing the light of hope surrounded by abstract lines representing the Ebola virus. With the inscription •FOR SERVICE• WEST AFRICA EBOLA EPIDEMIC
Comments: *Awarded to an estimated 3,000 (as of July 2015) military and civilian personnel who volunteered to combat the outbreak of Ebola in Sierra Leone, Liberia, Guinea and their territorial waters. Qualification for the medal is 21 days continuous service from March 23, 2014 (the date which the World Health organisation first publicly recognised the Ebola Outbreak in West Africa) or 30 days accumulated service on working visits within the operational area provided these visits are for a minimum of 48 hours each. If qualifying service is reduced or terminated through death, serious illness, evacuation, wounding or other disability due to service in the operational area and the individual might have been expected otherwise to complete the full qualifying period then the medal will be awarded. The situation in West Africa is to be reviewed on a regular basis to determine whether the medal is still warranted.*

VALUE: —

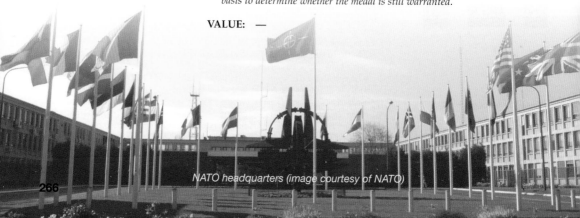

NATO headquarters (image courtesy of NATO)

CORONATION
Jubilee and other Royal medals

The first official royal medal was that cast by Henry Basse in 1547 for the accession of the young King Edward VI. It is known cast in gold or silver and is a curious example of bad design and poor workmanship for such an august occasion. No coronation medals were produced in honour of either Mary or Elizabeth I, but under James VI and I there was a small silver medal struck at the Royal Mint to mark the king's accession in 1603. These early medals celebrated the accession of the new sovereign, rather than the act of crowning itself.

To mark the coronation of James I, however, a small silver medalet was struck for distribution among the people who attended the ceremony, and this may be regarded as the forerunner of the modern series. This bore a Latin title signifying that James was Caesar Augustus of Britain and Heir to the Caesars. Thereafter medals in gold, silver or base metals were regularly struck in connection with the coronations of British monarchs. These were purely commemorative and not intended for wear, so they lack rings or bars for suspension.

By the early 19th century medals were being struck by many medallists for sale as souvenirs to the general public. At least fifteen different medals greeted the coronation of William IV in 1830 and more than twice that number appeared seven years later for the coronation of Queen Victoria. That paled into insignificance compared with the number produced for the coronation of Edward VII in 1902. On that occasion numerous civic authorities, organizations, industrial concerns and business firms issued medals in celebration — well over a hundred different medals and medalets were produced.

Sir George Frampton designed two silver medals, and one of these was mounted with a suspender and a blue ribbon with a thin white stripe and scarlet edges. This medal was distributed to notable personages attending the ceremony and established the precedent for subsequent coronation medals which came to be regarded as an award in recognition of services rendered in connection with the coronation, from the Earl Marshal of England to the private soldiers taking

part in the ceremonial parades. In more recent times the coronation medal has even been given to people who were not present at the ceremony but who performed notable public service in the coronation year.

Many other royal events have been commemorated by medals over the centuries. Royal weddings and the birth of the heir to the throne were regularly celebrated in this manner. Important anniversaries in long reigns have been the subject of numerous commemorative medals. The Golden Jubilee of George III in 1809-10, for example, resulted in over 30 different medals. Five times that number greeted the Golden Jubilee of Queen Victoria in 1887, but among them was an official medal intended for wear by those on whom it was conferred.

Even this, however, was not the first of the royal medals intended to be worn. This honour goes to a very large medal celebrating the proclamation of Victoria as Empress of India in 1877. Although fitted with a suspender bar and worn from a ribbon round the neck, it was not permitted for officers and men to wear this medal while in uniform. Later medals, however, were permitted to be worn when in uniform, but after other orders, decorations and campaign medals.

In the following listing (291A–291N) are the official Coronation Medals of James I, 1603, to Victoria, 1838. All were originally non-wearing, i.e. without suspension or ribbon, although some were later pierced or fitted with suspension for wearing. *Values of these are for silver medals only in minimum VF (Very Fine) condition.*

291A. JAMES I CORONATION MEDAL

Date: 1603.
Metal: Silver.
Size: 28mm.
Description: (Obverse) Bust of King James I facing right. Legend: IAC: I: BRIT: CAE: AVG: HAE CAESArum cae D.D. (Reverse) Lion rampant facing left. Legend: ECCE PHA(R)OS POPVLIQ(VE) SALVS (Behold a lighthouse and safety of the people)

VALUE: Silver £1200–1500

291B. CHARLES I CORONATION MEDAL

Date: 1626.
Metal: Gold, silver.
Size: 28mm.
Designer: Nicholas Briot.
Description: Bust of Charles I facing right. Legend: CAROLVS. I. DG. MAG. BRITAN. FRAN. ET. HIB. REX. (Reverse) An arm issuing from a cloud and holding a sword. Legend: DONEC. PAX. REDDITA. TERRIS. (As long as Peace returns to the lands).

VALUE: Silver £600–900

291C. CHARLES I CORONATION MEDAL

Date: 1633 (Scottish Coronation)
Metal: Gold, silver.
Size: 28mm.
Designer: Nicholas Briot.
Mintage: Gold (3), silver (Unknown)
Description: Bust of Charles I facing left. Legend: CAROLVS DG SCOTIAE. ANGLIAE. FR. ET. HIB. REX. (Reverse) A rose bush surmounted by a thistle. Legend: HINC. NOSTRAE. CREVERE. ROSAE (From this our roses abound). Exergue: CORON. 18 JVNII 1633

VALUE: Silver £450–650

291D. CHARLES II CORONATION MEDAL

Date: 1651 (Scottish Coronation).
Metal: Gold, silver.
Size: 31mm.
Designer: Sir James Balfour.
Description: Bust of Charles II facing right. Legend: CAROLVS.2. D.G. SCO. ANG. FRA. ET. HI. REX. FI. DE. cor. i. ia. scon. 1651. (Reverse) Lion rampant facing left, holding a thistle. Legend: NEMO. ME. IMPVNE. LACESSET (No one provokes me with impunity).

VALUE: Silver £2000–3000

291E. CHARLES II CORONATION MEDAL

Date: 1661 (English Coronation).
Metal: Gold, silver.
Size: 30mm.
Designer: Thomas Simon.
Description: Bust of Charles II facing right. Legend:
CAROLVS .II.DG ANG. SCO. FR. ET. HI REX. (Reverse)
Charles II, wearing royal robe, seated on throne facing
left, holding sceptre. Angel hovering over him placing
crown on his head. Legend: EVERSO. MISSVS. SVC-
CVRRERE. SECLO. XXIII APR. 1661 (the times having
been turned upside down, he has been sent to succour
us)

VALUE: Silver £350–450

291F. JAMES II CORONATION MEDAL

Date: 1685.
Metal: Gold, silver, copper (?)
Size: 34mm.
Designer: John Roettier.
Mintage: Gold (200), silver (800), copper (Unknown).
Description: Bust of James II facing right, laureate.
Legend: JACOBVS. II. D.G. ANG. SCO. FR. ET.
HI. REX. (Reverse) Hand holding the crown
above a laurel branch resting on a pillow. Legend:
A. MILITARI. AD. REGIAM. (from soldiering to
the palace). Exergue: INAVGVRAT. 23. AP. 1685.

VALUE: Silver £350–500

291G. WILLIAM AND MARY CORONATION MEDAL

Date: 1689.
Metal: Gold, silver, lead.
Size: 34mm.
Designer: John Roettier.
Mintage: Gold (515), silver (1,200), lead (Unknown).
Description: Conjoint busts of William and Mary
facing right. Legend: GVLIELMVS. ET. MARIA.
REX. ET. REGINA. (Reverse) Two-horse vehicle
lower left, Jove in cloud above right. Legend:
NE TOTVS ABSVMATVR. (let not the whole be
consumed). Exergue: INAVGVRAT. II. AP. 1689.

VALUE: Silver £350–500

291H. ANNE CORONATION MEDAL

Date: 1702.
Metal: Gold, silver, base metal.
Size: 34mm.
Designer: John Croker.
Mintage: Gold (858), silver (1,200), base metal (Unknown).
Description: Bust of Queen Anne facing left. Legend: ANNA. D:G: MAG: BR. FR. ET. HIB: REGINA. (Reverse) Pallas Athene, left, with shield and lightning bolts, attacking recumbent monster, right. Legend: VICEM GERIT. ILLA. TONANTIS. Exergue: INAVGVRAT. XXIII. AP. MDCCII. (As, making sounds, she conducts herself).

VALUE: Silver £250–300

291I. GEORGE I CORONATION MEDAL

Date: 1714.
Metal: Gold, silver, base metal.
Size: 34mm.
Designer: John Croker
Mintage: Gold (330), silver (1,200), base metal (Unknown).
Description: Bust of George I facing right. Legend: GEORGIVS. DG. MAG. BR. FR. ET. HIB. REX. (Reverse) Seated King, left, being crowned by Britannia standing right. Exergue: INAVGVRAT. XX. OCT. MDCCXIIII.

VALUE: Silver £175–250

291J. GEORGE II CORONATION MEDAL

Date: 1727.
Metal: Gold, silver, base metal.
Size: 34mm.
Designer: John Croker
Mintage: Gold (238), silver (800), base metal (Unknown)
Description: Bust of George II facing left. Legend: GEORGIVS. II. D.G. MAG. BR. FR. ET. HIB. REX. (Reverse) King seated on throne, left being crowned by Britannia, standing right. Legend: VOLENTES. PER. POVLOS (through the will of the people) Exergue: CORON. XI. OCTOB. MDCCXXVII.

VALUE: Silver £175–250

291K. GEORGE III CORONATION MEDAL

Date: 1761.
Metal: Gold, silver, bronze
Size: 34mm.
Designer: Lorenz Natter.
Mintage: Gold (858), silver (800), bronze (unknown)
Description: Bust of George III facing right. Legend: GEORGIVS. III. D.G. M. BRI. FRA. ET. HIB. REX. F.D. (Reverse) Britannia standing left, crowning King seated right. Legend: PATRIAE. OVANTI. (Crowned as the country rejoices). Exergue: CORONAT. XXII. SEPT. CI ƆI ƆCCLXI

VALUE: Silver £400–550

291L. GEORGE IV CORONATION MEDAL

Date: 1821.
Metal: Gold, silver, bronze
Size: 35mm.
Designer: Benedetto Pistrucci.
Mintage: Gold (1,060), silver (800), bronze (unknown, over 1,525)
Description: Bust of George IV, laureate, facing left. Legend: GEORGIVS IIII D.G. BRITANNIARUM REX F.D. (Reverse) Three standing ladies, left, facing seated King, right. Behind King stands angel holding crown above his head. Legend: PROPRIO JAM JURE ANIMO PATERNO (already by special right, inaugurated in the spirit of his father). Exergue: INAUGURATUS DIE JULII. XIX ANNO. MDCCXXI.
Comments: *A slightly smaller and thinner version of this medal was struck and pierced for suspension from a plain maroon ribbon. These medals are invariably named to members of the Buckinghamshire Yeomanry Cavalry Hussars who took part in lining the route of the procession. This is believed to be the first coronation medal designed to be worn.*

VALUE: Silver £200–300

291M. WILLIAM IV CORONATION MEDAL

Date: 1831.
Metal: Gold, silver, bronze
Size: 34mm.
Designer: William Wyon
Mintage: Gold (1,000), silver (2,000), bronze (1,133)
Description: Head of William IV facing right. Legend: WILLIAM THE FOURTH CROWNED SEP: 8 1831 (Reverse) Head of Queen Adelaide facing right. Legend: ADELAIDE. QUEEN CONSORT. CROWNED SEP: 8 1831.

VALUE: Silver £175–250

291N. VICTORIA CORONATION MEDAL

Date: 1838.
Metal: Gold, silver, bronze.
Size: 36mm.
Designer: Benedetto Pistrucci.
Mintage: Gold (1,369), silver (2,209), bronze (1,871)
Description: Head of Queen Victoria facing left. Legend: VICTORIA D.G. BRITANNIARUM REGINA F.D. (Reverse) Three ladies symbolic of England, Scotland and Ireland, standing left, presenting crown to Queen, seated on a dais, right. A lion lies behind her chair. Legend: ERIMUS TIBI NOBILE REGNUM (We shall be a noble Kingdom to you). Exergue: INAUGURATA DIE JUNII XXVIII MDCCCXXXVIII.

VALUE: Silver £180–220

292. EMPRESS OF INDIA MEDAL

Date: 1877.
Ribbon: 42mm crimson edged in gold.
Metal: Gold or silver.
Size: 58mm.
Description: (Obverse) a left-facing bust of Queen Victoria wearing a veil and a coronet, her name and the date of her elevation being inscribed round the circumference. (Reverse) a broad zigzag border enclosing the words EMPRESS OF INDIA and its equivalent in Urdu and Hindi across the field.
Comments: *Issued to celebrate the proclamation of Victoria as Empress of India on 1 January 1877. It was awarded in gold to Indian princes and high-ranking British officials. Indian civilians and selected officers and men of the various British and Indian regiments serving in India at the time were awarded the silver medal. It was issued unnamed but many examples were subsequently engraved or impressed privately.*

VALUE:

		Miniature
Gold	£6000–10,000	£275–360
Silver	£650–850	£100–160

292A. VISIT OF THE PRINCE OF WALES TO INDIA MEDAL 1875

(reduced)

Date: 1875–76.
Ribbon: 38mm plain white (gold), pale blue with white edges (silver).
Metal: Gold, silver or white metal with a silver crown.
Size: Oval 48mmx77mm.
Description: (Obverse) left-facing effigy of the Prince of Wales (later King Edward VII) surrounded by a laurel wreath and surmounted by a crown fitted to a suspension ring; (reverse) Prince of Wales's emblem surrounded by the chain of the GCSI.
Comments: *A large oval medal was struck to commemorate the state visit of HRH the Prince of Wales to India. Some 48 medals were struck in gold, 165 in silver and an unknown number in white metal. The gold medals are impressed on the rim with a small numeral, and engraved with the recipient's name in block capitals. The medals were numbered and named in strict order of precedence. The silver medal has a frosted relief on a mirror table. 13 small silver badges were also presented. In addition a small silver medalet was issued to the crews of HMS* Renown *and* Terrible *and the Royal Yacht* Osborne, *with the initials A and E either side of the Prince of Wales' emblem and a reverse inscribed HRH ALBERT EDWARD PRINCE OF WALES INDIA 1875–76 (similar in style to no. 308B).*

VALUE:

Gold (48)	£7000–8000
Silver (165)	£1000–1500
White metal	£200–250
Silver badge (13)	Rare
Silver medalet	£100–150

293. JUBILEE MEDAL 1887

Date: 1887.
Ribbon: Broad central blue band with wide white stripes at the edges.
Metal: Gold, silver or bronze.
Size: 30mm.
Description: (Obverse) the bust of Queen Victoria by Sir Joseph Edgar Boehm; (reverse) an elaborate wreath in which are entwined the heraldic flowers of the United Kingdom. This encloses an eight-line inscription surmounted by a crown: IN COMMEMORATION OF THE 50th YEAR OF THE REIGN OF QUEEN VICTORIA 21 JUNE 1887. The reverse was designed by Clemens Emptmayer
Comments: *Struck to celebrate the 50th anniversary of Victoria's accession to the throne. The medal in gold was given to members of the Royal Family and their personal guests. The silver medal was given to members of the Royal Household, government ministers, senior officials, distinguished foreign visitors, naval and military officers involved in the Jubilee parade on 21 June 1887 and the captains of vessels taking part in the great Naval Review at Spithead. The bronze medal was given to selected NCOs and men who took part in the parade or the Spithead Review. All medals were issued unnamed with a ring for suspension. When the Diamond Jubilee was celebrated ten years later holders of the 1887 medal were given a clasp in the form of a cable entwined around the date 1897 and surmounted by an imperial crown. Twin loops at the ends enabled the clasp to be sewn on to the ribbon. Clasp sizes: 28mm (men), 22mm (ladies).*

VALUE:

	Without clasp	With clasp 1897	*Miniature*
Gold (133)	£1350–1500	Rare	£110–160
Silver (1,012)	£160–180	£300–350	£35–40 (add £30 for clasp)
Bronze (600)	£150–175	£250–300	£35–40 (add £30 for clasp)

294. JUBILEE (POLICE) MEDAL 1887

Date: 1887.
Ribbon: Plain dark blue.
Metal: Bronze.
Size: 36mm.
Description: (Obverse) the veiled profile of Queen Victoria; (reverse) a wreath surmounted by a crown and enclosing the inscription: JUBILEE OF HER MAJESTY QUEEN VICTORIA. The year appears at the foot and the name of the force round the top.
Comments: *Issued to all ranks of the Metropolitan and City of London Police and selected civilian staff to celebrate the Jubilee on 21 June 1887. Clasps for the 1897 Jubilee q.v. were issued to recipients of this medal still serving ten years later.*

VALUE:

	Without clasp	With 1897 clasp	Miniature
Metropolitan Police (14,000)	£45–55	£55–65	£30–35
City of London Police (900)	£75–100	£100–125	£30–35
			(add £10 for clasp)

295. JUBILEE MEDAL 1897

Date: 1897.
Ribbon: Dark blue with two broad white bands and dark blue edges (as for 293).
Metal: Gold, silver or bronze.
Size: 30mm.
Description: This medal is very similar to the 1887 issue, differing solely in the date and anniversary on the reverse. Around 980 medals were awarded to army officers.

VALUE:

		Miniature
Gold (73)	£1350–1500	£90–110
Silver (3040)	£120–150	£25–35
Bronze (890)	£150–200	£20–25

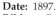

296. JUBILEE MEDAL (MAYORS AND PROVOSTS) 1897

Date: 1897.
Ribbon: White with two broad dark stripes and white edges.
Metal: Gold or silver.
Size: Height 48mm; max. width 40mm.
Description: A diamond-shaped medal with ring suspension, reminiscent of the *Klippe* coinage of central Europe. Both sides had circular centres with trefoil ornaments occupying the angles. (Obverse) the Wyon profile of the young Victoria at the time of her accession; (reverse) Sir Thomas Brock's Old Head veiled bust of the Queen.
Comments: *The gold version was presented to Lord Mayors and Lord Provosts while the silver medal was granted to Mayors and Provosts. Small silver medals of more conventional circular format were produced with these motifs and sold as souvenirs of the occasion.*

VALUE:

		Miniature
Gold (14)	£1000–1400	£820–920
Silver (512)	£350–400	£210–260

297. JUBILEE (POLICE) MEDAL 1897

Date: 1897.
Ribbon: Plain dark blue.
Metal: Bronze.
Size: 36mm.
Description: Very similar to the 1887 issue with the dates suitably amended and the name of the service round the top of the reverse.
Comments: *Separate issues were made in respect of the Police Ambulance service, St John Ambulance Brigade and the Metropolitan Fire Brigade. Holders of the previous medal merely received the 1897 clasp (Metropolitan Police 8708, City of London Police 485).*

VALUE:		Miniature
Metropolitan Police (7481)	£40–55	£55–75
City of London Police (535)	£75–85	£55–75
Police Ambulance (210)	£350–450	£55–75
St John Ambulance Brigade (910)	£65–75	£55–75
Metropolitan Fire Brigade (950)	£65–75	£55–75

298. CEYLON DIAMOND JUBILEE MEDAL 1897

Date: 1897.
Ribbon: Plain red.
Metal: Gold or silver.
Size: 35mm.
Description: (Obverse) the Boehm bust of Queen Victoria with the dates 1837-1897 at the foot. (Reverse) an elephant and a stupa (dome-shaped Buddhist shrine), with two lines of concentric inscriptions: TO COMMEMORATE SIXTY YEARS OF HER MAJESTY'S REIGN and, unusually, THE RT. HON. SIR J. WEST RIDGEWAY K.C.B., K.C.M.G., GOVERNOR. A crown above the rim was fixed to a ring for suspension.
Comments: *Awarded to local dignitaries and leading officials in the Ceylon government.*

VALUE:		Miniature
Gold	£1000–1400	£820–1020
Silver	£200–250	£160–210

299. HONG KONG DIAMOND JUBILEE MEDAL

Date: 1897.
Ribbon: Three equal stripes of dark blue, maroon and dark blue (also known with gold ribbon with two white stripes).
Metal Silver or bronze.
Size: 36mm.
Description: (Obverse) the Boehm bust of Queen Victoria with the date 1897 at the foot; (reverse) a seascape with a British three-masted sailing ship and a Chinese junk in the background and two figures shaking hands in the foreground. The name of the colony appears at the top, while two concentric inscriptions read SIR WILLIAM ROBINSON G.C.M.G. GOVERNOR and TO COMMEMORATE SIXTY YEARS OF HER MAJESTY'S REIGN 1837-1897.
Comments: *Very little is known for certainty about this medal on account of the fact that the colonial records were destroyed during the Japanese occupation.*

VALUE:	
Silver	£400–500
Bronze	£180–200

299A. LAGOS DIAMOND JUBILEE MEDAL

Date: 1897.
Ribbon: Dark blue with two broad white stripes towards the edges.
Metal Silver.
Size: 36mm.
Description: (Obverse) the veiled crowned profile of Queen Victoria (similar to the Egypt Medal 1882, No. 131) inscribed VICTORIA QUEEN AND EMPRESS with a Tudor rose at the foot; (reverse) QUEEN'S DIAMOND JUBILEE LAGOS round the circumference, with JUNE 22ND 1897 in the centre.
Comments: *Issued to civil and military personnel associated with the Diamond Jubilee celebrations in the crown colony of Lagos (1886–1906 when it was incorporated in the colony and protectorate of Southern Nigeria).*

VALUE: —

299B. INDIA DIAMOND JUBILEE MEDAL

Date: 1897.
Ribbon: White.
Metal Silver.
Size: 36mm.
Description: (Obverse) the veiled crowned profile of Queen Victoria (similar to the Egypt Medal 1882, No. 131) inscribed VICTORIA QUEEN AND EMPRESS with a Star of India at the foot; (reverse) TO COMMEMORATE THE SIXTIETH YEAR OF THE REIGN OF H.M. QUEEN VICTORIA 1897 within a laurel wreath, with royal arms above and the Star of India below.
Comments: *Issued to civil and military personnel associated with the Diamond Jubilee celebrations in India. It was also issued to Native chiefs in the colony of Natal.*

VALUE: £100–150

300. VISIT TO IRELAND MEDAL 1900

Date: 1900.
Ribbon: Plain dark blue.
Metal: Bronze.
Size: 36mm.
Description: (Obverse) a half-length version of the Boehm bust of Queen Victoria; (reverse) the female allegorical figure of Hibernia looking out over Kingstown (Dun Laoghaire) harbour in which the Royal Yacht can be seen (far left). Unusually, the medal was mounted with a suspension bar decorated with shamrocks.
Comments: *The medal designed by G. W. de Saulles commemorated Queen Victoria's visit to Ireland in 1900. It was awarded to officers of the Royal Irish Constabulary and Dublin Metropolitan Police who were involved in security and policing the various events connected with the visit. The medal was worn with the same ribbon as the Jubilee Police medals.*

VALUE:

Bronze (2285)	£120–150	*Miniature* £110–130

300A. VISIT TO THE COLONIES MEDAL 1901

Date: 1901.
Ribbon: Unknown.
Metal: Gold and Silver.
Size: Oval 20 x 24mm.
Description: (Obverse) a crowned anchor with the royal garter and rose emblem inset; (reverse) inscribed T.R.H. DUKE & DUCHESS OF CORNWALL & YORK—BRITISH COLONIES 1901 H.M.S. OPHIR.
Comments: *This small medalet was issued to commemorate the visit of the Duke and Duchess of Cornwall and York to the British Colonies aboard HMS Ophir in 1901.*

VALUE: Gold £400–500   Silver £150–200   *Miniature* £110–130

300B. TRH'S THE DUKE AND DUCHESS OF YORK MEDAL 1901

Date: 1901.
Ribbon: Dark blue with a central red stripe.
Metal: Silver.
Size: 32mm.
Description: (Obverse) the left-facing conjoined busts of the Duke and Duchess surrounded by a ribboned wreath; (reverse) a crowned anchor surmounted by the garter and rose emblem T.R.H'S THE DUKE & DUCHESS OF YORK'S VISIT TO THE COLONIES 1901 surrounded by a ribboned wreath. With ring suspension
Comments: *It is believed that this attractive medal was awarded to dignitaries on the Royal Tour of 1901.*

VALUE: £125–150   *Miniature*   —

301. CORONATION MEDAL 1902

Date: 1902.
Ribbon: Dark blue with a central red stripe and white edges.
Metal: Silver or bronze.
Size: Height 42mm; max. width 30mm.
Description: (Obverse) the left-facing conjoined busts of King Edward VII and Queen Alexandra, both crowned and wearing coronation robes. (Reverse) the crowned royal cypher above the date of the actual ceremony. The medal has an elaborate raised rim decorated with a wreath culminating in a crown through which the ring for suspension was looped.
Comments: *This medal, designed by Emil Fuchs and struck by Messrs. Elkington & Co., celebrated the coronation of King Edward VII on 9 August 1902. It was presented in silver to members of the Royal Family, foreign dignitaries, high officials of the government, senior officials and service officers involved in the celebrations. Selected NCOs and other ranks of the Army and Navy taking part in the parades were awarded the medal in bronze. Both versions were issued unnamed.*

VALUE:		*Miniature*
Silver (3493)	£150–200	£30–35
Bronze (6054)	£100–150	£30–35

302. CORONATION MEDAL (MAYORS AND PROVOSTS) 1902

Date: 1902.
Ribbon: Dark blue with a narrow white central stripe and crimson borders.
Metal: Silver.
Size: 32mm.
Description: (Obverse) conjoined right-facing busts of the King and Queen; (reverse) the crowned cypher and date. It differed from the ordinary medal by having flat, broad borders decorated with the heraldic flowers of the United Kingdom culminating at the top in a simple suspension ring.
Comments: *The medal was designed by Emil Fuchs and struck by Messrs. Elkington & Co.*

VALUE:

Silver	£140–150	*Miniature*	£110–130

303. CORONATION (POLICE) MEDAL 1902

Date: 1902.
Ribbon: Red, with a narrow dark blue central stripe.
Metal: Silver or bronze.
Size: 36mm.
Description: (Obverse) the left-facing bust of King Edward VII; (reverse) a crown above a nosegay of heraldic flowers with the words CORONATION OF HIS MAJESTY KING EDWARD VII 1902 in the upper field. The name or initials of the service appeared round the top, LCC MFB signifying London County Council Metropolitan Fire Brigade.
Comments: *Issued to all ranks of the police and associated services to celebrate the coronation, and awarded in silver or bronze to officers and other ranks respectively. 97 bronze medals were also issued to police civilian staff. The medal was designed by G. W. de Saulles.*

VALUE:	Silver	*Miniature*	Bronze	*Miniature*
Metropolitan Police	£500–600 (51)	£25–35	£25–35 (16,709)	£25–35
City of London Police	£650–850 (5)	£25–35	£65–75 (1060)	£25–35
LCC MFB	£650–850 (12)	—	£55–65 (1000)	£55–65
St John Ambulance Brigade	—	—	£55–65 (912)	£65–75
Police Ambulance Service	Unique	—	£300–350 (204)	£95–110

304. CEYLON CORONATION MEDAL 1902

Date: 1902.
Ribbon: Plain blue.
Metal: Gold.
Size: 35mm.
Description: (Obverse) a crowned left-facing bust of King Edward VII; (reverse) the elephant and stupa motif previously used (MYB298). The concentric inscription on the reverse now tactfully omitted any reference to the governor: IN COMMEMORATION OF THE CORONATION OF H.M. KING EDWARD VII 1902. The medal was fitted with a ring for suspension.
Comments: *Like its predecessor, this rare medal was struck for presentation to local dignitaries and government officials.*

VALUE:

—	*Miniature*	£260–310	

305. HONG KONG CORONATION MEDAL 1902

Date: 1902.
Ribbon: None officially designated but it is usually seen with a red, white and blue ribbon.
Metal: Silver or bronze.
Size: 36mm.
Description: (Obverse) conjoined right-facing busts of King Edward VII and Queen Alexandra with their names round the circumference; (reverse) the maritime motif of the Diamond Jubilee medal with new inscriptions in two concentric curves: SIR HENRY A. BLAKE G.C.M.G. GOVERNOR (inner) and TO COMMEMORATE THE CORONATION OF THEIR MAJESTIES THE KING & QUEEN (outer). Usually, but not always, fitted with a suspension ring.
Comments: *Issued to all British and Indian officers and other ranks serving in the colony as well as local police. Some 6,000 medals were produced by Edmonds & Son, London, and issued in cases.*

VALUE:
Bronze	£65–85
Silver	£150–250

305A. NATAL CORONATION MEDAL 1902

Date: 1902.
Ribbon: Dark blue with a central claret stripe.
Metal: Silver.
Size: 21mm, 29mm and 51mm.
Description: (Obverse) a right-facing crowned bust of King Edward VII with the inscription TO COMMEMORATE THE CORONATION OF KING EDWARD VII; (reverse) Royal coat of arms above two running wildebeests, inscribed (round top) EDWARDUS DEI GRATIA BRITANNIAR REX F:D and (round bottom) COLONY OF NATAL 26 JUNE 1902. Ring suspension.
Comments: *The small medal was distributed to schoolchildren whereas the large medal was restricted to native chiefs and is relatively scarce. It is believed that the middle-size medal was presented to local dignitaries.*

VALUE:		
	21mm	£20–30
	29mm	£85–100
	51mm	£500–600

306. DELHI DURBAR MEDAL 1903

Date: 1903.
Ribbon: Pale blue with three dark blue stripes—the colours of the Order of the Indian Empire and the Order of the Star of India..
Metal: Gold or silver.
Size: 38.5mm.
Description: (Obverse) a right-facing crowned bust of the King Emperor with DELHI DARBAR 1903 on the right side; (reverse) a three-line inscription in Farsi across the field, which translates as "By grace of the Lord of the Realm, Edward, King, Emperor of India, 1901", with an elaborate border of roses, thistles, shamrocks and Indian flowers. Ring suspension.
Comments: *Struck to celebrate the Durbar of the King Emperor at Delhi on 1 January 1903. It was awarded in gold to the rulers of the Indian princely states and in silver to lesser dignitaries, government officials, and officers and other ranks of the armed services actually involved in the celebrations.*

VALUE:		Miniature
Gold (140)	£2500–3000	—
Silver (2567)	£250–350	£35–45

307. VISIT TO SCOTLAND MEDAL 1903

Date: 1903.
Ribbon: Plain red.
Metal: Bronze.
Size: 36mm.
Description: Very similar to the Police Coronation medal but the year was changed to 1903 and the inscription SCOTTISH POLICE appeared round the top of the reverse. The medal was named to the recipient on the rim. An ornate clasp decorated with a thistle was worn above the suspension bar.
Comments: *This medal was designed by G. W. de Saulles and struck to commemorate Their Majesties' post-coronation tour of Scotland in May 1903. It was awarded to the police and troops involved in parades and escort duties, as well as the ancillary services such as the Fire Brigade and the St Andrew's Ambulance Association.*

VALUE:
Bronze (2957)	£100–150	*Miniature*	£45–55

308. VISIT TO IRELAND MEDAL 1903

Date: 1903.
Ribbon: Pale blue.
Metal: Bronze.
Size: 36mm.
Description: (Obverse) bust of King Edward VII; (reverse) as 1900 medal with the date altered at the foot. The suspension brooch is ornamented with shamrocks.
Comments: *This medal was designed by G. W. de Saulles and struck to mark the King's visit to Ireland in July 1903. It was awarded on the same terms as the Visit to Ireland Medal 1900.*

VALUE:
Bronze (7757)	£80–100	*Miniature*	£60–70

308A. VISIT OF THE PRINCE AND PRINCESS OF WALES TO INDIA

Instituted: 1905–06
Ribbon: Neck ribbon 55mm wide, maroon with wide blue stripes towards each edge.
Metal: Frosted silver.
Size: 51mm.
Description: (Obverse) conjoined busts of the Prince and Princess of Wales (later King George V and Queen Mary), facing right. ELKINGTON (manufacturers) inscribed minutely below busts. (Reverse) badge of the Prince of Wales surrounded by the chain of the GCSI, with legend T.R.H. THE PRINCE & PRINCESS OF WALES VISIT TO INDIA 1905–6 around with ELKINGTON LONDON in small letters below.
Comments: *Only 72 medals were struck, 70 of which were bestowed on British and Indian officials.*

VALUE: £600–800   *Miniature*   £55–65

308B. GEORGE PRINCE OF WALES MEDAL

Instituted: 1905-06.
Ribbon: 15mm, red, white and blue in equal parts.
Metal: Silver or gold.
Size: Oval 20 x 24mm.
Description: (Obverse) the Prince of Wales's plumes surrounded by the Garter and the chain and badge of the GCSI, flanked in the field by the letters G and M; (reverse) inscription T.R.H. GEORGE PRINCE OF WALES & VICTORIA MARY PRINCESS OF WALES with INDIA 1905-6 in the upper centre.
Comments: *The 26 gold medals were given by Their Royal Highnesses to their personal staff, while a total of 1,625 silver medals were presented to all hands aboard HMS* Renown *and* Terrible *and the Royal Yacht* Osborne.

VALUE:
Gold (26)	£1000–1500
Silver (1625)	£120–180

309. CORONATION MEDAL 1911

Date: 1911.
Ribbon: Dark blue with two thin red stripes in the centre.
Metal: Silver.
Size: 32mm.
Description: (Obverse) conjoined left-facing busts of King George V and Queen Mary in their coronation robes within a floral wreath; (reverse) the crowned royal cypher above the date of the coronation itself. Plain ring suspension.
Comments: *Designed by Sir Bertram McKennal, MVO, ARA, these medals were issued unnamed but may sometimes be found with unofficial engraving. Those who were also entitled to the Delhi Darbar Medal received a crowned clasp inscribed DELHI if they had previously been awarded the coronation medal. This was the first occasion that the medal might be awarded to those not actually present at the ceremony itself.*

VALUE:
		Miniature
Silver (15,901)	£65–75	£7–12
With Delhi clasp (134)	£600–800	£55–65

A scene at the Delhi Durbar 1903.

309A. GUILDHALL CORONATION MEDAL 1911

Date: 1911.
Ribbon: Crimson.
Metal: Silver and enamels.
Size: 37mm.
Description: (Obverse) conjoined left-facing busts of King George V and Queen Mary with their names around, surrounded by a white enamelled ring bearing the words CORONATION RECEPTION . JUNE 1911 with laurel wreath around divided by four shields, surmounted by a crown with three semi-precious stones inset; (reverse) hallmark and pin. Suspended from an ornate clasp (with additional pin) bearing a sword and sceptre.
Comments: *The reception at the Guildhall, London, was a grand affair with members of the Royal family and a number of Heads of State in attendance. The ornate medals were presented in a plush case and were designed to be worn either as a lapel badge or as a conventional medal.*

VALUE: £250–300

310. CORONATION (POLICE) MEDAL 1911

Date: 1911.
Ribbon: Red with three narrow blue stripes.
Metal: Silver.
Size: 36mm.
Description: (Obverse) a crowned left-facing bust of King George V; (reverse) an imperial crown with an ornate surround. The inscription CORONATION 1911 appears at the foot and the name of the service at the top. Ring suspension.
Comments: *By now the number of police and ancillary services had grown considerably, as witness the various reverse types which may be encountered in this medal. The medal was designed by Sir Bertram McKennal, MVO, ARA,*

VALUE:		Miniature
Metropolitan Police (19,783)	£35–45	£20–25
City of London Police (1400)	£100–150	£25–30
County and Borough Police (2565)	£90–100	£25–30
Police Ambulance Service (130)	£650–750	£95–110
London Fire Brigade (1374)	£120–150	£95–110
Royal Irish Constabulary (585)	£175–250	£160–210
Scottish Police (2800)	£80–100	£55–65
St John Ambulance Brigade (2755)	£65–85	£65–75
St Andrew's Ambulance Corps (310)	£250–300	£110–160
Royal Parks (119)	£1000–1500	£150–170

311. VISIT TO IRELAND MEDAL 1911

Date: 1911.
Ribbon: Dark green with thin red stripes towards either end.
Metal: Silver.
Size: 36mm.
Description: Very similar to the foregoing, distinguished only by the reverse which is inscribed CORONATION 1911 round the top, with the actual date of the visit round the foot.
Comments: *This medal was designed by Sir Bertram McKennal, MVO, ARA and was granted to prominent civic dignitaries and members of the Irish police forces involved in the royal visit to Ireland which took place on 7-12 July 1911.*

VALUE:
Silver (2477) £75–90 *Miniature* £75–85

311A. EAST INDIAN RAILWAY COMPANY ROYAL VISIT TO INDIA MEDAL 1911

Date: 1911.
Ribbon: Dark blue with a central maroon stripe flanked by narrow gold stripes.
Metal: Gilded bronze.
Size: 32mm.
Description: (Obverse) the arms of the East Indian Railway Company surrounded by the inscription EAST INDIAN RAILWAY COMPANY with a winged wheel at the foot; (reverse) a ten-line inscription FOR SERVICES RENDERED DURING THE RAILWAY JOURNEYS OF THEIR MAJESTIES THE KING EMPEROR AND QUEEN EMPRESS IN INDIA 1911.
Comments: *Very little is known about this rare medal, but it is believed to have been awarded to members of the Honour Guard of the East Indian Railway Volunteer Rifle Corps and employees of the company present during the tour of India undertaken in 1911 by King George V and Queen Mary. It is believed that no more than 30 medals were issued.*

VALUE: £100–£120

312. DELHI DURBAR MEDAL 1911

Date: 1911.
Ribbon: Dark blue with two narrow red stripes in the middle.
Metal: Gold or silver.
Size: 38.5mm.
Description: (Obverse) the conjoined crowned busts of King George V and Queen Mary in a floral wreath; (reverse) an elaborate Farsi text which translates as "The Durbar of George V, Emperor of India, Master of the British Lands".
Comments: *This medal marked the Delhi Durbar held in the King Emperor's honour in December 1911. Most of the gold medals went to the Indian princely rulers and top government officials, 10,000 of the 30,000 silver medals were awarded to officers and other ranks of the British and Indian Armies for exemplary service, without their necessarily being present at the Durbar itself.*

VALUE:		*Miniature*
Gold (200)	£3000–4000	£320–420
Silver (30,000)	£80–100	£25–30

312AA. DELHI DURBAR MILITARY TOURNAMENT MEDAL 1911

Date: 1911.
Ribbon: None
Metal: Gold, Silver or Bronze.
Size: 44mm.
Description: (Obverse) the left-facing crowned and robed bust of King George V; (reverse) within a wreath of laurel leaves, three tablets engraved with the words DURBAR, TOURNAMENT and the event for which the medal is awarded, e.g. HOCKEY, with the legend DELHI . CORONATION . DURBAR . 1911 around
Comments: *Minted by the Calcutta Mint, and usually named on the edge with the details of the recipient. These very rare medals were awarded for specific events at the Dehli Durbar, but they are rarely seen.*

VALUE:	Gold (6)	£1000–1500
	Silver (15–20)	£250–300
	Bronze (40–50)	£100–150

312A. VISIT OF KING GEORGE V AND QUEEN MARY TO INDIA 1911–12

Date: 1911–12.
Ribbon: None.
Metal: Silver or gold.
Size: Oval 20 x 24mm.
Description: (Obverse): GRI entwined initials as a monogram above the word INDIA; (reverse) MRI monogram and dates 1911–12, suspended from a bar by a simple ring and scroll suspender.
Comments: *Information on the issue of this medalet is sought although it is believed to have been issued to the crew of the Royal yacht.*

VALUE: Gold   £750–1000
          Silver   £60–85

312AB. QUEEN ALEXANDRA'S CHILDREN'S BANQUET MEDAL 1914

Date: 28 December 1914.
Ribbon: White, with red stripes at each edge.
Metal: Bronze.
Size: 38mm.
Description: (Obverse) bust of Queen Alexandra facing right with the inscription A GIFT FROM QUEEN ALEXANDRA; (reverse) central inscription FEAR GOD, HONOUR THE KING surrounded by the legend GUILDHALL BANQUET TO OUR SOLDIERS' & SAILORS' CHILDREN 28th DEC. 1914. The suspension is ornate and has the arms of the City of London superimposed.
Comments: *This medal, designed and manufactured by Elkington, was issued unnamed to 1,300 children and a small number of Chelsea pensioners who attended a banquet at the Guildhall on 28 December 1914. The children, between the ages of eight and thirteen, were the sons and daughters of men in the Fleet or on the Western Front. One child was chosen from each family by Sir James Gildea of the Soldiers' and Sailors' Families' Association. Relatively few medals appear to have survived.*

VALUE: £50–£70

312AC. VISIT OF THE PRINCE OF WALES TO NEW ZEALAND 1920

Date: 1920.
Ribbon: Neck ribbon 38mm maroon.
Metal: Silver, with the raised edges of the medal being milled, plain rim.
Size: 50mm.
Description: (Obverse) badge of the Prince of Wales surrounded by the chain of the GCSI; (reverse) the inscription THE VISIT OF H.R.H. THE PRINCE OF WALES TO NEW ZEALAND 1920 in seven lines, surrounded by a laurel wreath, with maker's name ELKINGTON inscribed minutely underneath the base of the wreath. Fitted with a plain suspension ring.
Comments: *This medal was awarded in connection with the visit of HRH the Prince of Wales (later King Edward VIII and Duke of Windsor) to New Zealand in the course of his tour aboard HMS Renown 1919–20.*

VALUE: £100–150

312B. VISIT OF THE PRINCE OF WALES TO INDIA 1921–22

Date: 1921–22.
Ribbon: Neck ribbon 55mm maroon with broad blue stripes towards each edge.
Metal: Frosted silver.
Size: 50mm.
Description: (Obverse) bust of Prince of Wales facing left with inscription EDWARD PRINCE OF WALES INDIA 1921–1922; (reverse) badge of the Prince of Wales surrounded by the chain of the GCSI. Fitted with a plain suspension ring.
Comments: *Only 84 medals were awarded in connection with the visit of HRH the Prince of Wales (later King Edward VIII and Duke of Windsor) to India in the course of his world tour aboard HMS Renown.*

VALUE: £700–900   *Miniature*   £85–110

312C. WELCOME HOME MEDAL FOR THE PRINCE OF WALES

Date: 1922.
Ribbon: Green with red central stripe.
Metal: Gold, silver and bronze.
Size: Oval 43mm x 34mm.
Description: An oval medal with ornate edges. (Obverse) crowned and robed bust of the Prince of Wales with the inscription EDWARD PRINCE OF WALES KG; (reverse) The Prince of Wales's feathers with the inscription WELCOME HOME 1922. With integral ornate loop for suspension.
Comments: *Struck by F. Bowcher to mark the return of the Prince of Wales to England after his world tour.*

VALUE: Gold   £500–650
            Silver   £120–150
            Bronze   £80–100

312D. VISIT OF THE PRINCE OF WALES TO BOMBAY MEDAL 1921

Date: 1921.
Ribbon: Watered blue/white with central thin white stripe.
Metal: Bronze.
Size: Oval 38mm x 30mm.
Description: An oval medal. (Obverse) bust of the Prince of Wales facing right, with the inscription EDWARD PRINCE OF WALES and surmounted by the Prince of Wales's feathers and motto ICH DIEN; (reverse) VISIT OF HIS ROYAL HIGHNESS BOMBAY NOVEMBER 1921 in six lines.
Comment: *Thought to be presented to the leading military and civil dignitaries present during the visit of the Prince of Wales. New information suggests it was also given to school children although this is unconfirmed. The number issued is not known.*

VALUE: £50–£85

312E. VISIT OF THE PRINCE OF WALES TO PATNA 1921

Date: 1921.
Ribbon: Imperial Purple.
Metal: Bronze.
Size: 40mm.
Description: (Obverse) bust of the Prince of Wales facing right with the inscription EDWARD PRINCE OF WALES, in an oval centre-piece, with an ornate floral decoration either side; (Reverse) centre blank, with the inscription VISIT OF HIS ROYAL HIGHNESS around the top half, and PATNA 22ND. DEC 1921 around the lower half of the reverse.
Comment: *Believed to have been presented to the leading military and civil dignitaries present during the visit of the Prince of Wales. The number issued is not known, but is believed to be very small.*

VALUE :   £80–£100

313. JUBILEE MEDAL 1935

Date: 1935.
Ribbon: Red with two dark blue and one white stripes at the edges.
Metal: Silver.
Size: 32mm.
Description: (Obverse) left-facing conjoined half-length busts of King George V and Queen Mary in crowns and robes of state; (reverse) a crowned GRI monogram flanked by the dates of the accession and the jubilee.
Comments: *This medal, designed by Sir William Goscombe John, RA, was issued to celebrate the Silver Jubilee of King George V and widely distributed to the great and good throughout the Empire.*

VALUE:
     Silver (85,234)   £25–30   *Miniature*   £15–20

313A. ISLE OF MAN SILVER JUBILEE MEDAL 1935

Date: 1935.
Ribbon: Three equal stripes of red, white and blue. However some medals had their ribbons substituted with black to mark the death of the King in 1936.
Metal: Nickel-plated brass or silver.
Size: 32mm.
Description: (Obverse) conjoined busts of King George V and Queen Mary in an inner circle surrounded by the legend KING GEORGE V & QUEEN MARY REIGNED 25 YEARS; (reverse) Triskelion emblem with the legend IN COMMEMORATION OF THE SILVER JUBILEE 1935. Suspended from a brooch bar of seven overlapping panels with the centre panel having the royal cypher GvR while the outer panels have two leaves in each.
Comments: *This medal was issued to celebrate the Silver Jubilee and the nickel-plated brass edition was given to all schoolchildren on the island. Just three medals are believed to have been struck in silver for presentation to civic dignitaries or officials. 8,000 medals were struck by James Fenton & Co of Birmingham.*

VALUE: Nickel-plated brass £20–30   Silver (3) £150–200

313B. GUILDHALL JUBILEE MEDAL 1935

Date: 1935.
Ribbon: None.
Metal: Enamelled silver-gilt.
Size: 38mm wide.
Description: (Obverse) Arms of the City of London within a blue enamelled garter with the date 1935 on a white panel, surmounted by the Royal cypher, crown and lion; (reverse) engraved with the date 22nd May 1935. The medal is suspended from a double scroll brooch.
Comments: *This medal was issued to selected dignitaries who attended the banquet at the Guildhall in celebration of the King's Silver Jubilee. It was made by G. Kenning & Son, London.*

VALUE: £250–300

314. CORONATION MEDAL 1937

Date: 1937.
Ribbon: Blue edged with one red and two white stripes.
Metal: Silver.
Size: 32mm.
Description: (Obverse) conjoined busts of King George VI and Queen Elizabeth in their robes of state without any inscription. The stark simplicity of this motif was matched by a reverse showing the crowned GRI over the inscription CROWNED 12 MAY 1937, with the names of the King and Queen in block capitals round the circumference.
Comments: *Issued to celebrate the coronation of King George VI on 12 May 1937.*

VALUE:	Silver (90,000)	£25–35	*Miniature*	£15–20

314A. GUILDHALL CORONATION MEDAL 1937

Date: 1937.
Ribbon: None
Metal: Silver-gilt.
Size: 34mm.
Description: A rectangular medal (obverse) conjoined busts of King George VI and Queen Elizabeth in their robes of state on a shield with palm and vine sprigs below and CORONATION in a tablet. The design struck on a rectangular base with two "steps" at each side in art deco style. Reverse blank, inscribed with the name of recipient. The medal is suspended from an ornate crowned coat of arms of the City of London with GUILDHALL above
Comments: *Issued by the City of London to selected dignitaries who attended the banquet at the Guildhall to celebrate the coronation of King George VI on 12 May 1937.*

VALUE: £150–200

314B. ROYAL VISIT TO SOUTH AFRICA 1947 CHIEFS' MEDALS

Reverse i.

Reverse ii.

Date: 1947.
Ribbon: Yellow.
Metal: Silver.
Size: Oval 25mm x 32mm or 65mm x 55mm.
Description: (Obverse) conjoined busts of King George VI and Queen Elizabeth in their robes of state without any inscription. (Reverse) (i) map of South Africa surmounted by crowned GRE cypher dividing the date 1947 with KONINKLIKE BESOEK above and ROYAL VISIT below; (ii) crowned GRE with the inscription ROYAL VISIT 1947.
Comments: *Issued to celebrate the visit of King George VI to South Africa in 1947. Two distinctly different reverses have been seen but little is known about these medals which were issued in two sizes. These medals were awarded to Native Chiefs/Indabas and worn from a red neck ribbon. It is not known who were awarded the different sizes but it is likely that the bilingual version (i) was given to South African chiefs (156 comprising King Williamstown (Ciskei) 7; Umtata (Transkei) 31; Eshowe (Zululand) 40; Pietersburg(Northern Territories) 78. The unilingual version (ii) was probably reserved for the Protectorates and possibly Rhodesias, the number awarded is unknown.*

VALUE:	Type i	£75–100
	Type ii	£75–100

314C. ROYAL VISIT TO SOUTH AFRICA 1947

Reverse i.

Reverse ii.

Date: 1947.
Ribbon: None
Metal: Silver gilt and silver.
Size: 38mm.
Description: (Obverse) conjoined busts of HM King George VI and HM Queen Elizabeth crowned and robed. Artists initials PM (Percy Metcalfe) on ribbon on King's left shoulder; (Reverse, two types) (i) map of South Africa surmounted by crowned GRE cypher dividing the date 1947 with KONINKLIKE BESOEK above and ROYAL VISIT below; (ii) crowned GRE with the inscription ROYAL VISIT 1947.
Comments: *Type i was issued to celebrate the visit of King George VI to South Africa in 1947. Only six medallions were struck in silver gilt (awarded to the Governor General of the Union of SA, the Prime Minister of SA and the Administrators of the four Provinces of the Union of SA). A total of 394 silver medals in red cases were awarded (Governor General's Staff, Cabinet Ministers in Attendance, Officers commanding Commands, miscellaneous persons, Inter-departmental Committee on Royal Tour, Royal Train, Pilot Train, Railway staff employed at Government Houses, Press, chauffeurs, National/Kruger Park officials, Native Indabas). The medals were distributed by the Prime Minister's Office. Type ii were issued for Northern and Southern Rhodesia as part of the African tour. The medallion, in a blue case, was given to "selected persons who have done special work in connection with the Royal Visit". They were presented to recipients on April 11, 1947, at the Provincial Commissioner's Office in Livingstone. The medallions seem to have been named in seriffed capitals.*

VALUE :		
Type i (in red case)		
Silver gilt (6)		£800–1000
Silver (394)		£200–250
Type ii (in blue case)		
Silver gilt (8)		£800–1000
Silver (196)		£200–250

315. CORONATION MEDAL 1953

Date: 1953.

Ribbon: Dark red with two narrow blue stripes in the centre and narrow white edges.

Metal: Silver.

Size: 32mm.

Description: (Obverse) a right-facing bust of Queen Elizabeth II in a Tudor crown and robes of state, the field being otherwise plain. (Reverse) a similar crown over the royal monogram EIIR with the legend QUEEN ELIZABETH II CROWNED 2ND JUNE 1953 round the circumference. Ring suspension.

Comments: *This medal celebrated the coronation of Queen Elizabeth II on 2 June 1953. News that Edmund Hillary and Sherpa Tenzing had successfully attained the summit of Everest reached London on the morning of the Coronation. Subsequently the members of the Hunt Expedition were invited to Buckingham Palace on 16 July 1953 where, on Her Majesty's own initiative, they were presented with coronation medals engraved MOUNT EVEREST EXPEDITION on the rim, following the precedent of the Mwele medals of 1895–96.*

VALUE:		*Miniature*
Silver (129,000)	£45–75	£12–14
Mount Everest Expedition (37)	£800–1000	

315A. ROYAL TOUR OF THE COMMONWEALTH MEDAL 1953–54

Date: 1953

Ribbon: None

Metal: Toned bronze.

Size: 38mm.

Description: (Obverse) Right facing, bare-headed, conjoined busts of HM Queen Elizabeth and Prince Philip, with the inscription "THE ROYAL VISIT" above and "MCMLIII–IV" below; (reverse) the crowned Royal coat of arms, with the Royal cypher above and the roman numerals MCMLIII–IV at the foot.

Comments: *This circular medal, designed by Mary Gillick, was struck by the Royal Mint and issued to mark the Royal Commonwealth Tour of Queen Elizabeth and Prince Philip between November 1953 and May 1954. The medal was issued to the Royal party and to local dignitaries at numerous ports of call throughout the Commonwealth. The total number of medals issued was 1,503.*

VALUE: £75–100

In addition to the official medal illustrated above (MYB 315A), all schoolchildren in New Zealand received a medal suspended from a blue ribbon, together with a folder telling the story of the Royal Family, with pictures of the Coronation regalia, royal palaces and descriptions. For the sake of completeness this medal is included below as MYB 315AA.

Date: 1953.

Ribbon: Dark blue.

Metal: Copper-coloured alloy.

Size: 38mm.

Description: (Obverse) right-facing crowned bust of Queen Elizabeth II wearing Tudor crown; (reverse) the crowned New Zealand coat of arms surrounded by sprays of flowers and the inscription ELIZABETH II ROYAL VISIT 1953–54. The copper-coloured medal is hung by a ring from a scalloped suspender as illustrated.

Comment: *Issued to all New Zealand school-children during the Royal visit, accompanied by a folder. The medals themselves are fairly common, but those with the accompanying folder are quite rare.*

VALUE: £6–10 (with accompanying folder £20–30)

315B. ROYAL VISIT TO MALTA 1954

Date: 1954.
Ribbon: None.
Metal: Gold coloured alloy.
Size: 38mm.
Description: (Obverse) right-facing crowned bust of the Queen; (reverse) shield containing the Maltese flag with the inscription TO COMMEMORATE THE ROYAL VISIT TO MALTA G.C. 1954 round the circumference.
Comments: *Issued to all Maltese schoolchildren, teachers and municipal workers in commemoration of the Royal visit to the island.*

VALUE: £5–10

315C. ROYAL VISIT TO NIGERIA MEDAL 1956

Date: 1956.
Ribbon: None.
Metal: Toned bronze.
Size: 38mm.
Description: (Obverse) Right facing, bare-headed, conjoined busts of HM Queen Elizabeth and Prince Philip, with the inscription "THE ROYAL VISIT" above and "TO NIGERIA 1956" below; (reverse) the crowned Royal coat of arms, with the Royal cypher above and the roman numerals MCMLVI at the foot.
Comments: *This circular medal was struck by the Royal Mint and issued to mark the Royal visit of Queen Elizabeth and Prince Philip to Nigeria, between 28 January and 16 February 1956. The medal was issued to the Royal party and to local dignitaries. A total of 650 medals were issued, each contained in a red leatherette box.*

VALUE: £50–75

316. JUBILEE MEDAL 1977

Date: 1977.
Ribbon: White with thin red stripes at the edges, a broad blue stripe in the centre and a thin red stripe down the middle of it.
Metal: Silver.
Size: 32mm.
Description: (Obverse) Right-facing profile of Queen Elizabeth II wearing the St Edward's crown—the first time this design was employed; (reverse) a crown and wreath enclosing the words THE 25TH YEAR OF THE REIGN OF QUEEN ELIZABETH II 6 FEBRUARY 1977. A distinctive reverse was used in Canada, showing the dates of the reign flanking the royal monogram round the foot, CANADA round the top and a large stylised maple leaf in the centre.
Comments: *The 25th anniversary of the Queen's accession was marked by the release of this unnamed medal. The total number of medals issued in the UK was relatively small at 30,000 but they were distributed to a wide range of people including members of the armed forces, crown services and a number of people engaged in important activities including industry, trade, local services, voluntary workers, the arts, entertainment and sports.*

VALUE:		Miniature
General issue (30,000)	£150–185	£8–12
Canadian issue (30,000)	£90–120	£8–12

318. GOLDEN JUBILEE MEDAL 2002

Date: February 2002.
Ribbon: Royal blue with thin red stripes at the edges, a broad white stripe in the centre and a thin red stripe down the middle.
Metal: Gold-plated cupro-nickel.
Size: 32mm.
Description: (Obverse) a right facing profile of Queen Elizabeth II wearing a crown; (reverse) the royal coat of arms flanked by the dates 1952 and 2002.
Comments: *Issued to celebrate the 50th anniversary of the Queen's accession. It was granted to all personnel of the armed forces who had completed five or more years service on February 6, 2002. Generals who have been Chief of the General Staff and Chief of the Defence Staff or equivalent RN and RAF ranks were awarded the medal even though retired. It was also issued to members of the police, ambulance, coastguard, fire services, RNLI and mountain rescue services, as well as members of the Royal Household including The Queen's Body Guard of the Yeomen of the Guard, who had completed five years service and holders of the VC or GC. One member of HM Customs & Excise was awarded the medal by the Ministry of Defence to mark his close co-operation in work and liaison between the two departments. Almost 400,000 medals were issued.*

VALUE: £75–100   *Miniature*   £10–12

318A. DIAMOND JUBILEE MEDAL 2012

Date: February 2012.
Ribbon: Dark red with royal blue edges and two narrow white stripes in the centre.
Metal: Nickel-silver.
Size: 32mm.
Description: (Obverse) right facing coinage profile of Queen Elizabeth II by Ian Rank-Broadley; (reverse) the crowned royal cypher surmounted on a faceted diamond design, with the dates 1952 – 2012 below.
Comments: *Issued to celebrate the 60th anniversary of HM the Queen's accession. Awarded to members of the armed forces (Regular and Reserve), certain emergency services and operational prison services personnel and Police Community Support Officers who have completed five years service on February 6, 2012, as well as living holders of the VC or GC and members of the Royal Household. Unusually, breaking with tradition the contract to supply the medals was awarded to Worcester Medals. An estimated 465,000 medals were issued. There are copies of this medal which at 32.4mm in diameter are slightly larger than the originals. In addition a special medal with the royal cypher reverse was struck for the Caribbean Realms.*

VALUE: *Miniature*
                        £65–75   £10–15

318A. DIAMOND JUBILEE MEDAL 2012— CARIBBEAN REALMS

Date: February 2012.

Ribbon: Dark red with royal blue edges, white stripe in the centre bisected by a thin black stripe.

Metal: Nickel-silver.

Size: 32mm.

Description: (Obverse) right facing coinage profile of Queen Elizabeth II by Ian Rank-Broadley with the legend DIAMOND JUBILEE H.M. QUEEN ELIZABETH II around; (reverse) the crowned royal cypher, with CARIBBEAN REALMS above and the dates 1952 – 2012 below.

Comments: *Issued by the Caribbean realms of Antigua and Barbuda, the Bahamas, Barbados, Grenada, Jamaica, Saint Kitts and Nevis, Saint Lucia, and Saint Vincent and the Grenadines, to celebrate the 60th anniversary of HM the Queen's accession. Similar to the British award it was awarded to members of the armed forces, certain emergency services and operational prison services personnel and Police as well as members of the public service sector for outstanding achievement.*

VALUE: *Miniature*

£100–150   £25–35

MISCELLANEOUS

Medals

Under this heading are grouped a very disparate range of medals whose only common denominator is that they do not fit conveniently into one or other of the preceding categories. They are not without considerable interest and many of them have a very keen following and a buoyant market. They are listed and added to as we have come across them, hence they are in no particular order.

319. KING'S AND QUEEN'S MESSENGER BADGE

Date: 1722.
Ribbon: Garter blue.
Metal: Silver gilt.
Size: Earliest issues variable according to monarch and jeweller; since George V—45mm x 34mm.
Description: (Issues since George V) an upright oval fitted with a plain suspension ring and having a greyhound suspended by a ring from the foot of the rim. (Obverse) the Garter inscribed HONI SOIT QUI MAL Y PENSE enclosing the royal cypher; early issues had the Royal coat of arms; (reverse) plain, engraved with an official number of issue and, on occasion, the name of the messenger.
Comments: *Messengers can be traced back to 1199, but prior to George I badges were not issued. Few of the earlier badges can be found due to a hand in and melt down order instituted by George III in 1762. During the reign of Victoria a number of different shapes and sizes were used for the badges due to a misunderstanding whereby individual messengers obtained their insignia from different jewellers instead of the Jewel Office. Since 1870 Garrards have been responsible for the design, submission and production of Messengers' badges. From 1876 to 1951 the Foreign Office, as Controllers of the Corps of Messengers, purchased and held all badges for issue to those appointed as messengers. Since 1951 messengers, on satisfactorily completing a period of probation, are given a registered number and letter of permission to purchase their badges through the Crown Jewellers. In addition to this badge, on instruction from the Home Office during World War II, a small oval badge bearing the cypher of King George VI was issued to messengers who carried sensitive material between Government departments located in various buildings within the capital city. Garrards produced only 20 of these, thus they are extremely rare.*

VALUE:		
	George III	£1500–2000
	George IV	£1200–1500
	William IV	£1200–1500
	Victoria	£1000–1500
	Edward VII	£850–1000
	George V	£650–850
	George VI	£650–850
	Elizabeth II	£800–1000

King George VI Home Service Messenger Badge.

320. ARCTIC MEDAL 1857

Instituted: 30 January 1857.
Ribbon: 38mm watered white.
Metal: Silver.
Size: Height 46mm; max. width 32mm.
Description: An octagonal medal with a beaded rim, surmounted by a nine-pointed star (representing the Pole Star) through which the suspension ring is fitted. (Obverse) an unusual profile of Queen Victoria, her hair in a loose chignon secured with a ribbon. (Reverse) a three-masted sailing vessel amid icebergs with a sledge party in the foreground and the dates 1818-1855 in the exergue. The medal was issued unnamed, but is often found privately engraved.
Comments: *Awarded retrospectively to all officers and men engaged in expeditions to the polar regions from 1818 to 1855, including those involved in the on-going search for the ill-fated Franklin Expedition of 1845-8. Thus the medal was granted to civilians, scientists, personnel of the French and US Navies and employees of the Hudson's Bay Company who took part in a number of abortive search parties for Sir John Franklin and his crew. Some 1106 medals, out of 1486 in all, were awarded to officers and ratings of the Royal Navy.*

VALUE:
Unnamed	£850–1250
Named	From £2000
Miniature	£225–350

321. ARCTIC MEDAL 1876

Instituted: 28 November 1876.
Ribbon: 32mm plain white.
Metal: Silver.
Size: 36mm
Description: A circular medal with a raised beaded rim and a straight bar suspender. (Obverse) a veiled bust of Queen Victoria wearing a small crown, dated 1876 at the foot; (reverse) a three-masted ship icebound.

Comments: *Granted to officers and men of HM ships* Alert *and* Discovery *who served in the Arctic Expedition between 17 July 1875 and 2 November 1876. The medal was later extended to include the crew on the second voyage of the private yacht* Pandora *commanded by Allen Young which cruised in Polar waters between 25 June and 19 October 1875 and from 3 June to 2 November 1876. Medals were engraved with the name, rank and ship of the recipient. Only 155 medals were awarded.*

VALUE:
Named	From £5000
Miniature	£260–310

322. POLAR MEDAL

Instituted: 1904.
Ribbon: 32mm plain white.
Metal: Silver or bronze.
Size: 33mm octagonal.
Description: (Obverse) the effigy of the reigning sovereign; (reverse) a view of the Royal Research Ship *Discovery* with a man-handling sledge party in the foreground.
Comments: *Originally issued in silver, with an appropriate clasp, to the officers and men of Captain Scott's 1902–04 Antarctic Expedition, who went out in the* Discovery *and remained throughout the stay of the ship in the Antarctic Regions, from her arrival until her departure, or to any member compulsorily invalided after 3 January 1902, or to any who joined* Discovery *during her second winter in the Antarctic. It was issued in bronze to officers and men who did not remain, for causes other than sickness, throughout the stay of the ship in Antarctic regions; and also to the officers and men of the relief ships* Morning *and* Terra Nova. *These awards continued for subsequent expeditions: the silver medal being usually awarded to officers and to men who landed or who made more than one voyage, whilst the bronze medal was awarded to those not so exposed to the dangers of the polar environment. The bronze medal ceased being awarded after those awarded for Antarctic Research Work during 1929–39. Apart from the bronze medals awarded for the British Antarctic Expedition 1902–04 and the* Aurora *Relief Expedition 1917 where the year of the expedition was on the rim of the medal, the rest all had a clasp with ANTARCTIC and the year(s) of the expedition; the exception to this being those who took part on Shackleton's expedition and who had previously been awarded the bronze medal, received a clasp to their medal. No bronze medals were awarded for the Arctic. Up to December 2005, 271 bronze awards have been made (to 259 individuals, of whom 10 received one or more additional awards); 1038 silver awards have been made (to 948 individuals, of whom 80 received one or more additional awards), 18 recipients have been awarded both the silver and bronze medals. Only six women have been awarded the medal. Names of recipients are engraved on the earlier and most recent issues, and impressed in small capitals on the earlier Elizabethan issues.*

VALUE:	Silver	Miniature	Bronze (no clasp)	Miniature (no clasp)
Edward VII	From £5000	£125–175	From £6000	£125–160
George V (B)	From £3500	£125–175	From £3000	£125–160
George V (C)	—	£125–175	From £3000	£125–160
George V (E)	From £3500	£125–175	—	£125–160
George VI	From £3000	£125–175	From £3000	£125–160
Elizabeth II	From £3000	£125–175	—	£125–160

Modern examples of miniatures £15–20

323. KING EDWARD VII MEDAL FOR SCIENCE, ART AND MUSIC

Instituted: 1904
Ribbon: 35mm scarlet with a broad central stripe of dark blue and thin white stripes towards the edges.
Metal: Silver.
Size: 32mm.
Description: The raised rim consisted of a laurel wreath and has a ring for suspension. (Obverse) the conjoined busts of King Edward VII and Queen Alexandra; (reverse) the Three Graces engaged in various cultural pursuits.
Comments: *This short-lived medal was discontinued only two years later. It was awarded in recognition of distinguished services in the arts, sciences and music. The medal was struck by Burt & Co.*

VALUE: £1250–1500

324. ORDER OF THE LEAGUE OF MERCY

Modern reverse.

Date: 1898.

Ribbon: 38mm watered white silk with a central broad stripe of black.

Metal: Originally silver, now silver-gilt.

Size: Height 51mm; max. width 39mm.

Description: Originally an enamelled red cross surmounted by the Prince of Wales's plumes enfiladed by a coronet, with a central medallion depicting the emblem of the League, a group of figures representing Charity, set within a laurel wreath. Since 1999: a silver-gilt cross with the emblem in a central medallion. Reverse: a circular plaque inscribed LEAGUE OF MERCY 1999 in four lines.

Comments: *Appointments to the Order were sanctioned and approved by the sovereign on the recommendation of the Grand President of the League of Mercy as a reward for distinguished personal service to the League in assisting the support of hospitals. Ladies and gentlemen who rendered such aid for at least five years were eligible for the award. In 1917 King George V instituted a bar to be awarded to those who gave continuing service over a period of many years after receiving the Order itself. The original Order was last awarded in 1946 and the League itself ceased to exist in 1947. However, in March 1999, 100 years after its institution, the League was re-established and today it awards silver-gilt medals for valuable service. About 150 medals have been awarded since 1999.*

VALUE:

Badge of the Order	Original £70–100	*Miniature* £55–65
	with bar £100–130	

325. QUEEN ALEXANDRA'S IMPERIAL MILITARY NURSING SERVICE CAPE BADGE

Date: 1902–49

Branch of Service: Queen Alexandra's Imperial Military Nursing Service.

Ribbon: Scarlet with two white outer stripes and two black inner stripes.

Metal: Silver.

Size: Oval 55mm by 36mm.

Description: A uniface oval ring surmounted by a Tudor crown fitted to a plain ring for suspension. The ring at the centre has the Cross of the Order of the Dannebrog, with an ornamental cypher of Queen Alexandra. The ring is inscribed in raised lettering QUEEN ALEXANDRA'S IMPERIAL MILITARY NURSING SERVICE.

Comments: *The cape badge was instituted in 1902 and was used until 1949 when the QAIMNS changed its name to the QARANC. It was worn on the right breast on ward dress for commissioned (qualified) nurses. It was issued through stores to each individual.*

VALUE: £80–100 *Miniature* £35–45

325A. QUEEN ALEXANDRA'S IMPERIAL MILITARY NURSING SERVICE RESERVE CAPE BADGE

Date: 1907–50

Branch of Service: Queen Alexandra's Imperial Military Nursing Service Reserve.

Ribbon: Black with two narrow outer white stripes and two inner scarlet stripes.

Metal: Silver.

Size: 38mm or 29mm.

Description: A uniface ring containing a prominent "R" surmounted by a Tudor crown fitted to a plain ring for suspension. The ring is inscribed in raised lettering QUEEN ALEXANDRA'S IMPERIAL MILITARY NURSING SERVICE RESERVE.

Comments: *The cape badge was instituted in 1907 and was used until 1950 when the QAIMNS(R) was incorporated into the QARTANC. It was worn on the right breast on ward dress for commissioned (qualified) nurses. It was issued through stores to each individual.*

VALUE:		*Miniature*
38mm	£40–50	£35–45
29mm	£30–40	£30–35

326. TERRITORIAL FORCE NURSING SERVICE CAPE BADGE

Date: 1907–21.

Branch of Service: Territorial Force Nursing Service.

Ribbon: Scarlet with a narrow central white stripe.

Metal: Silver.

Size: Oval 50mm by 34mm

Description: A uniface oval ring surmounted by a Tudor crown attached to a plain ring for suspension. The ring has at the centre two ornamental letters "A" interlocking and set at an angle. The ring is inscribed in raised lettering: TERRITORIAL FORCE NURSING SERVICE.

Comments: *The cape badge was instituted in 1907 and was used until 1921 when the TFNS was renamed the TANS. It was worn on the right breast on ward dress for commissioned (qualified) nurses. It was issued through stores to each individual.*

VALUE: £30–£40   *Miniature* £30–35

326A. QUEEN ALEXANDRA'S MILITARY FAMILIES NURSING SERVICE CAPE BADGE

Date: 1921–26.
Branch of Service: Queen Alexandra's Military Families Nursing Service.
Ribbon: Black with a wide central scarlet stripe.
Metal: Silver.
Size: Oval 44mm by 34mm
Description: A uniface oval ring containing an ornamental cypher of Queen Alexandra surmounted by a Tudor crown. Three plain rings are attached to the outer edge of the circle for suspension. The ring is inscribed in raised lettering: QUEEN ALEXANDRA'S MILITARY FAMILIES NURSING SERVICE.
Comments: *The cape badge was instituted in 1921 upon formation of the QAMFNS, and was used until 1926 when the QAMFNS was incorporated into the QARANC. It was worn on the right breast on ward dress for commissioned (qualified) nurses. It was issued through stores to each individual.*

VALUE: £80–£100 *Miniature* £25–35

326B. TERRITORIAL ARMY NURSING SERVICE CAPE BADGE

Date: 1921–50.
Branch of Service: Territorial Army Nursing Service.
Ribbon: Scarlet with a narrow central white stripe.
Metal: Silver.
Size: Oval 38mm by 28mm
Description: A uniface oval ring surmounted by a Tudor crown attached to a plain ring for suspension. The ring has at the centre two ornamental letters "A" interlocking and set at an angle. The ring is inscribed in raised lettering: TERRITORIAL ARMY NURSING SERVICE. Beneath, an ornate scroll bearing the Latin inscription: FORTITUDO MEA DEUS.
Comments: *The cape badge was instituted in 1921 upon the formation of the TANS and was used until 1950 when the TANS was incorporated into the QARANC. It was worn on the right breast on ward dress for commissioned (qualified) nurses. It was issued through stores to each individual.*

VALUE: £30–£40 *Miniature* £25–35

326C. QUEEN ALEXANDRA'S ROYAL ARMY NURSING CORPS CAPE BADGE

Date: 1949.
Branch of Service: Queen Alexandra's Royal Army Nursing Corps.
Ribbon: Scarlet with two white outer stripes and two black inner stripes.
Metal: Silver.
Size: Oval 46mm by 32mm.
Description: A uniface oval ring containing the Cross of the Order of the Dannebrog, with an ornamental cypher of Queen Alexandra, surmounted by a Tudor crown, fitted with a plain ring for suspension. The oval ring is inscribed in raised lettering QUEEN ALEXANDRA'S ROYAL ARMY NURSING COPRS.
Comments: *The cape badge was instituted in 1949 and continues to be issued today to all commissioned (qualified) nurses in the QARANC. It is worn on the right breast on ward dress for both female and, since 1992, male commissioned (qualified) nurses. It is issued through stores to each individual.*

VALUE: £80–100   *Miniature*   £35–45

327. INDIAN TITLE BADGE

1st Class

2nd Class

3rd Class

Instituted: 12 December 1911.
Ribbon: Light blue edged with dark blue (1st class); red edged with dark red (2nd class); or dark blue edged with light blue (3rd class).
Metal: Silver or silver-gilt.
Size: Height 58mm; max. width 45mm.
Description: A radiate star topped by an imperial crown with a curved laurel wreath below the crown and cutting across the top of a central medallion surrounded by a collar inscribed with the appropriate title. The medallion bears the crowned profile of King George V or King George VI. From the first issue of King George V's Title Badge on June 1, 1912 until 1933, his bust faced right. As from June 1, 1933 his bust faced left for the remainder of the reign. King George VI's Title Badges had his bust facing left. (Reverse) plain, but engraved with the name of the recipient.
Comments: *Introduced by King George V on the occasion of the Delhi Durbar of 1911 and awarded in three classes to civilians and Viceroy's commissioned officers of the Indian Army for faithful service or acts of public welfare. Recipients proceeded from the lowest grade to higher grades, each accompanied by a distinctive title. Each grade was issued in Hindu and Muslim versions, differing in title: Diwan Bahadur (Muslim) or Sardar Bahadur (Hindu), Khan Bahadur (Muslim) or Rai or Rao Bahadur (Hindu) and Khan Sahib (Muslim) or Rai or Rao Sahib (Hindu), in descending order of grade. These title badges took precedence after all British and Indian orders and decorations, and before campaign medals. In miniatures (at least) the George VI versions, which all have his bust facing right, are rarer than those of King George V with left-facing bust.*

VALUE:	Geo. V right	Geo. V left	Geo. VI
First class			
Diwan Bahadur	£150–200	£200–250	£350–400
Sardar Bahadur	£150–200	£200–250	£350–400
Second class			
Khan Bahadur	£100–175	£125–200	£300–350
Rao Bahadur	£100–175	£125–200	£300–350
Third class			
Khan Sahib	£100–175	£125–200	£300–350
Rao Sahib	£100–175	£125–200	£300–350

Miniatures
  George V   £75–85   George VI   £85–95

328. BADGES OF HONOUR (AFRICAN COUNTRIES)

Instituted: 1922.
Ribbon: Plain yellow, 38mm (neck) or 32mm (breast).
Metal: Bronze.
Size: 65mm x 48mm (neck); 45mm x 33mm (breast).
Description: Oval badges with a raised rim of laurel leaves terminating at the top in an imperial crown flanked by two lions. (Obverse) a crowned effigy of the reigning monarch; (reverse) the crowned cypher of the monarch or some emblem symbolic of the particular country with the country name in the exergue.
Comments: *The badge accompanied a certificate of honour awarded to chiefs and other persons of non-European descent who had rendered loyal and valuable service to the government of the territory. The original award was a neck badge suspended by a ribbon, but from 1954 onwards recipients were given the option of taking the award as a neck or breast badge. These awards were quite distinct from the decorations known as the Native Chiefs Medals (see number 70). They were first awarded to Ugandans but later extended to 14 other British territories in East and West Africa as well as the three High Commisson territories in Southern Africa. In particular the Badges issued for Nyasaland under Elizabeth II are rare, as Nyasaland became a Federation with Rhodesia in 1957. They are believed to have fallen into abeyance in the early 1980s.*

VALUE:

George V	£250–350
George VI	£175–250
Elizabeth II (neck)	£150–200
Elizabeth II (breast)	£150–200

329. BADGES OF HONOUR (NON-AFRICAN COUNTRIES)

Instituted: 1926.
Ribbon: 38mm watered silk mustard yellow.
Metal: Silver gilt.
Size: 41mm (George VI) or 32 mm (Elizabeth II).
Description: Circular with a raised rim of laurel leaves bearing a ring for suspension. (Obverse) crowned effigy of the reigning monarch; (reverse) the emblem of the country with the name round the foot.
Comments: *These medals accompanied certificates of honour awarded to indigenous persons who had rendered valuable service to the colony or protectorate. These awards appear to have been in abeyance since the early 1980s. Exceptionally, the New Hebrides badge was awarded to three British officers (Colonel (now General Lord) Guthrie (of Craigiebank), Lieutenant-Colonel C. H. C. Howgill, RM and HRH the Duke of Gloucester) in connection with the "Coconut War" in July 1980 instead of a campaign medal. The reverse types show the badges of 28 colonies or protectorates.*

VALUE:

George V	£300–400
George VI	£300–400
Elizabeth II	£350–450
Miniature	£75–100

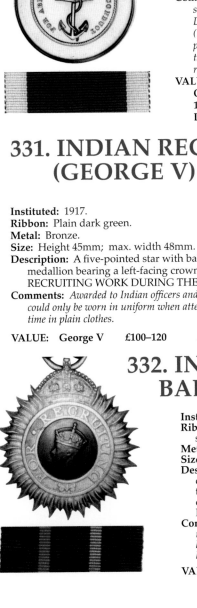

330. NAVAL ENGINEER'S GOOD CONDUCT MEDAL

Instituted: 1842.
Ribbon: Originally plain dark blue but later broad blue with white edges.
Metal: Silver.
Size: 35mm.
Description: (Obverse) a two-masted paddle steamer with a trident in the exergue; (reverse) a circular cable cartouche enclosing a crowned fouled anchor and the legend FOR ABILITY AND GOOD CONDUCT. Between the cable and the rim the details of the recipient were engraved round the circumference. Considering the rarity of the award, it is even more remarkable that the medals have several unique features. Shaw's medal, for example, had oak leaves in the exergue, flanking the trident, but this feature was omitted from later medals. Medals have been recorded with a straight bar suspender, a steel clip and ring suspender or fixed ring suspension with one or two intermediate rings.
Comments: *This medal was abolished five years after it was instituted, only seven medals being awarded in that period: to William Shaw (1842), William Dunkin (1842), William Johnstone (1843), John Langley (1843), J.P. Rundle (1845), George Roberts (1845) and Samuel B. Meredith (1846). Restrikes were produced in 1875 and at a later date. The original medals have a grooved rim, the 1875 restrikes a diagonal grained rim and the later restrikes a plain, flat rim.*
VALUE:

Original	Rare
1875 restrike	£125–150
Later restrike	£80–100

331. INDIAN RECRUITING BADGE (GEORGE V)

Instituted: 1917.
Ribbon: Plain dark green.
Metal: Bronze.
Size: Height 45mm; max. width 48mm.
Description: A five-pointed star with ball finials, surmounted by a wreathed gilt medallion bearing a left-facing crowned bust of King George V, inscribed FOR RECRUITING WORK DURING THE WAR.
Comments: *Awarded to Indian officers and NCOs engaged in recruitment of troops. It could only be worn in uniform when attending durbars or state functions, but at any time in plain clothes.*

VALUE: George V   £100–120   *Miniature*   £55–70

332. INDIAN RECRUITING BADGE (GEORGE VI)

Instituted: 1940.
Ribbon: Emerald green divided into three sections interspersed by narrow stripes of red (left) and yellow (right).
Metal: Silver and bronze.
Size: Height 42mm; max. width 39mm.
Description: A multi-rayed silver breast badge surmounted by an imperial crown with a suspension ring fitted through the top of the crown. In the centre is superimposed a bronze medallion bearing the left-facing crowned profile of King George VI, within a collar inscribed FOR RECRUITING.
Comments: *Awarded to selected civilian and military pensioners, full-time members of the Indian Recruiting Organisation, fathers and mothers having at least three children in the armed services, and wives having a husband and at least two children serving in the defence forces.*

VALUE: George VI   £70–90   *Miniature*   £65–80

333. NAVAL GOOD SHOOTING MEDAL

Subsequent award bar.

Instituted: August 1902.
Ribbon: Dark blue with a red central stripe edged in white.
Metal: Silver.
Size: 36mm.
Description: (Obverse) the effigy of the reigning monarch; (reverse) a nude figure of Neptune holding five thunderbolts in each hand. In the background can be seen the bows of a trireme and the heads of three horses, with a trident in the field. The Latin motto VICTORIA CURAM AMAT (Victory loves care) appears round the circumference. Fitted with a straight suspension bar. The recipient's name, number, rank, ship and calibre of gun are impressed round the rim.
Comments: *Instituted to promote excellent gunnery performances in the annual Fleet Competitions, it was first awarded in 1903 but was discontinued in 1914. Subsequent success was marked by the issue of a bar bearing the name of the ship and the date. A total of 974 medals and 62 bars were awarded. 53 men received one bar, three men got two bars and only one achieved three bars.*

VALUE:

		Miniature (in silver)
Edward VII	£350–450	£65–75
George V	£350–450	£65–75
With 1 bar	£600–800	£70–80

334. ARMY BEST SHOT MEDAL

Instituted: 30 April 1869.
Ribbon: Watered crimson with black, white (or buff*) and black stripes at the edges. (*The Regulations state that the stripes should be white but recent medals have been issued with buff stripes.)
Metal: Silver.
Size: 36mm.
Description: (Obverse) the veiled diademmed profile of Queen Victoria; (reverse) Victory bestowing a laurel crown on a naked warrior armed with a quiver of arrows and a bow and holding a target, impaled with arrows, in his other hand. Fitted with a straight suspension bar.
Comments: *This medal, sometimes referred to as the Queen's Medal, was awarded annually to the champion in the Army marksmanship contests held at Bisley. It was originally struck in bronze but was upgraded to silver in 1872. The award ceased in 1882 but was revived in 1923 and thereafter known as the King's Medal. The original reverse was retained, with the appropriate effigy of the reigning sovereign on the obverse. Since 1953 it has been known as the Queen's Medal again. In the post-1923 medals a bar bears the year of the award, with additional year clasps for subsequent awards. Until 1934 a single medal was awarded each year but in 1935 two medals were granted for the champion shots of the Regular and Territorial Armies respectively. Subsequently additional medals have been sanctioned for award to the military forces of India, Canada, Australia, New Zealand, Ceylon, Rhodesia, the British South Africa Police, the Union of South Africa, Pakistan, Jamaica and Ghana.*

VALUE:

		Miniature
Victoria bronze	Rare	—
Victoria silver	Rare	—
George V	£1000–1200	£40–50
George VI	£1000–1200	£40–50
Elizabeth II	£1000–1200	£25–30

335. QUEEN'S MEDAL FOR CHAMPION SHOTS OF THE ROYAL NAVY AND ROYAL MARINES

Instituted: 12 June 1953.
Ribbon: Dark blue with a broad red central stripe flanked by white
stripes.
Metal: Silver.
Size: 36mm.
Description: (Obverse) the effigy of Queen Elizabeth II; (reverse)
Neptune (as on the Naval Good Shooting Medal).
Comments: *Instituted as the naval counterpart of the Army best shot medal
with a bar which bears the year of the award.*

VALUE:

Elizabeth II	£1000–1200	*Miniature*	£20–25

336. QUEEN'S MEDAL FOR CHAMPION SHOTS OF THE ROYAL AIR FORCE

Instituted: 12 June 1953.
Ribbon: Broad crimson centre flanked by dark blue stripes bisected by
thin light blue stripes.
Metal: Silver.
Size: 36mm.
Description: (Obverse) the effigy of Queen Elizabeth II; (reverse)
Hermes kneeling on a flying hawk and holding the caduceus in one
hand and a javelin in the other. The medal is fitted with a straight
bar suspender. A date clasp is attached to the ribbon.
Comments: *Competed for at the annual RAF Small Arms Meeting at Bisley.
The medal was issued to the Champion Shot of the RNZAF under the terms
of the same Royal Warrant as the RAF.*

VALUE:

Elizabeth II	£1000–1200	*Miniature*	£25–35

337. QUEEN'S MEDAL FOR CHAMPION SHOTS OF THE NEW ZEALAND NAVAL FORCES

Instituted: 9 July 1958.
Ribbon: Crimson centre bordered with white and broad dark blue stripes at the edges.
Metal: Silver.
Size: 36mm.
Description: (Obverse) the effigy of Queen Elizabeth II; (reverse) similar to that of the Naval Good Shooting
Medal of 1903-14. Fitted with a clasp bearing the year of the award and a straight suspension bar.
Comments: *Awards were made retrospective to 1 January 1955. This medal is awarded for marksmanship in an annual
contest of the New Zealand Naval Forces. Additional clasps are granted for further success. One contestant, Lt Cdr N.
C. G. Peach, RNZN, has won this award ten times*

VALUE:

Elizabeth II	—	*Miniature*	£35–45

338. UNION OF SOUTH AFRICA COMMEMORATION MEDAL

Instituted: 1910.

Ribbon: 38mm orange-yellow with a broad central dark blue stripe.

Metal: Silver.

Size: 36mm.

Description: (Obverse) the uncrowned effigy of King George V; (reverse) Mercury as God of Commerce and Prosperity, bending over an anvil, forging the links of a chain symbolic of the uniting of the four colonies (Cape Colony, Natal, Orange Free State and the Transvaal), with the date 1910 in the exergue and the legend TO COMMEMORATE THE UNION OF SOUTH AFRICA.

Comments: *This was the first medal struck in the reign of George V and resulted from the South Africa Act of 1909. This Act proclaimed the unification on 31 May 1910, of the self-governing four colonies into a legislative Union, becoming provinces of the Union of South Africa. This medal, the obverse of which was designed by Sir Bertram MacKennal, and the reverse by Mr Sydney Marsh, was struck to mark the opening of the first Parliament of the Union by HRH the Duke of Connaught. Awarded to those who took part in the inauguration of the Parliament. Additionally it was awarded to certain officers and men of HMS* Balmoral Castle, *a Union Castle liner specially commissioned as a man-of-war to convey HRH the Duke of Connaught as the King's representative to South Africa for the celebrations. A total of 551 medals were struck by the Royal Mint, and were issued unnamed, although privately named medals are in existence.*

VALUE:	Named	£300–400
	Unnamed	£300–400
	Miniature	£25–35

339. DEKORATIE VOOR TROUWE DIENST

The other side is similar to no. 340 illustrated opposite

Instituted: 1920.

Ribbon: A broad dark blue central stripe flanked on one side by a gold stripe with a thin red stripe superimposed towards the edge, and on the other side by a yellow stripe with a thin white stripe towards the edge. Transvaal recipients wore the ribbon with the red to the centre of the chest; Orange Free State recipients wore the ribbon with the white stripe to the centre of the chest.

Metal: Silver.

Size: 36mm.

Description: (Obverse) the arms of the Transvaal; (reverse) the arms of the Orange Free State. Fitted with a fixed suspender. Recipients wore the medal with the appropriate state arms showing.

Comments: *This medal which is correctly named the Dekoratie Voor Trouwe Dienst was awarded by the Union of South Africa to officers of the two former Boer republics for distinguished service during the Second Boer War of 1899-1902. Awards to officers and men of the former Boer Republics had to be individually claimed on prescribed forms and were named with rank, initials and surname of the individual. The late Don Forsyth published a roll listing full names and commandos/units of the recipients. This clearly identifies many recipients but cannot differentiate, for example, between any of the 10 issued ABO medals that were named "Burger P. J. Botha". However, the naming style and type of suspender can help to make positive identification possible.*

Medals issued up to October 1937 had a WWI British War Medal (MYB168) suspender and typical SA Mint WWI naming. Between October 1937 and February 1942 the WWI suspender was still used, but the naming was thinner, in a slightly smaller font as on the WWII Africa Service Medal (MYB 189). All subsequent issues have the WWII style naming as well as the "thick-necked" suspender as found on the Africa Service Medal (for details and illustrations see the article by Hent Loots in the OMRS Miscellany of Honours, No. 9, 1992). By comparing the dates on the Medal Application Forms of men with the same initials and surname a particular recipient can sometimes be pinpointed. NB Please note that these medals are often found with the suspender claw flattened to varying degrees: the SA Mint, on occasion, used rather crude methods to "fix" the pin.

VALUE:	Silver (591)	£750–900		
	Paired with matching MYB340	£1100–1500	*Miniature*	£65–75

340. ANGLO-BOERE OORLOG (WAR) MEDAL

Instituted: 1920.

Ribbon: Broad green and yellow stripes with three narrow stripes of red, white and dark blue in the centre. Transvaal recipients wore the ribbon with the green to the centre of the chest, while Orange Free State recipients wore it with the yellow towards the centre.

Metal: Silver.

Size: 36mm.

Description: Both sides inscribed ANGLO-BOERE OORLOG round the top, with the dates 1899-1902 round the foot. Medallions set in a border of a square and quatrefoil show the arms of the Orange Free State on one side and the Transvaal on the other. The medal was worn with the side showing the arms of the appropriate state uppermost. Fitted with a fixed suspender.

Comments: *Correctly named the Anglo-Boere Oorlog Medal, this was awarded by the Union government to officers and men of the former Boer republics for loyal service in the war against the British. To qualify for the medal proof had to be provided that they had fought against the British without surrendering or taking parole or the oath of allegiance prior to May 31, 1902. See note on no. 339 regarding awards to men of the former Boer Republics.*

VALUE: Silver   £240–260   *Miniature*   £65–75
Lint Voor Wonden (Wound Ribbon) Certificate value: £30; if with corresponding medal: value: £50.

341. COMMONWEALTH INDEPENDENCE MEDALS

Pakistan Independence Medal

Ceylon Police Independence Medal.

Since the partition of the Indian sub-continent in 1947 and the emergence of the Dominions of India and Pakistan, it has been customary for medals to be issued to mark the attainment of independence. As these medals are invariably awarded to British service personnel taking part in the independence ceremonies, they are appended here in chronological order of institution, the date of the actual award, where later, being given in parentheses. These medals usually have symbolic motifs with the date of independence inscribed. The distinctive ribbons are noted alongside. All are 32mm wide unless otherwise stated.

	VALUE
India 1947 (1948) Three equal stripes of orange, white and green	£20–25
Ceylon Police 1948 Three equal stripes of white, red, white with narrow black edges	£50–75
Pakistan 1947 (1950) Dark green with a central thin white stripe	£15–20
Ghana 1957 Nine alternating stripes of red, yellow and green	£60–65
Nigeria 1960 (1964) Three equal stripes of green, white and green	£25–30
Sierra Leone 1961 Three equal stripes of green, white and blue	£65–75
Jamaica 1962 Black centre flanked by yellow stripes and green edges	£60–65
Uganda 1962 (1963) Six stripes of black, yellow, red, black, yellow, red	£60–65
Kenya 1963 Green with two equal red stripes towards the edges	£60–65

continued

341. COMMONWEALTH INDEPENDENCE MEDALS *continued*

Solomon Islands.

Sierra Leone.

Malawi.

For the various ribbons see ribbon charts on pp. 563 et seq.

	VALUE
Malawi 1964 Three equal stripes of black, red and green	£65–75
Guyana 1966 Red centre flanked by yellow stripes and broad green edges. The green and yellow separated (left) by a thin black stripe and (right) by a thin pale blue stripe	£60–65
Swaziland 1968 Three equal stripes of red, yellow and blue	£60–65
Fiji 1970 Grey-blue with bars half red, half white, towards each edge	£65–75
Papua New Guinea 1975 Red bordered by thin stripes of yellow and white, with black edges	£65–75
Transkei 1976	£20–25
Solomon Islands 1978 Five equal stripes of blue, yellow, white, yellow and green	£65–75
Gilbert Islands (Kiribati) 1980 Half red, half black, separated by a thin white stripe, and edged in yellow	£50–60
Ellice Islands (Tuvalu) 1980 Equal stripes of red, white and red edged yellow. the white stripe bisected by a thin blue stripe	£30–40
Zimbabwe 1980 Silver or bronze 38mm black centre flanked by red and yellow stripes with edges of green or blue	**Silver £30–45** **Bronze £20–25**
Gambia 1981	£35–45
Vanuatu 1980 (1981) 30mm stripes of red and green with central thinner stripe of yellow edged by black	£20–25
St Christopher, Nevis and Anguilla 1983 Bars of green (left) and red (right) with a black central bar having two thin white stripes, flanked by yellow stripes	£55–75

Papua New Guinea.

Nigeria.

342. MALTA GEORGE CROSS 50th ANNIVERSARY COMMEMORATIVE MEDAL

Instituted: 1992.
Ribbon: Dark blue with central stripes of white and red (the Maltese national colours).
Metal: Cupro-nickel.
Size: 36mm.
Description: (Obverse) the crowned arms of the island, which include the George Cross in the upper left corner, with the date 1992 at the foot. (Reverse) a replica of the George Cross with the eight-pointed Maltese Cross at the top and the date 1942 at the foot, with a legend BHALA SHIEDA TA'EROIZMU U DEDIKAZZJONI on one side and TO BEAR WITNESS TO HEROISM AND DEVOTION on the other. Suspension is by a fixed bar decorated with laurels, attached to a ring.
Comments: *Sanctioned by the government of Malta to celebrate the fiftieth anniversary of the award of the George Cross by King George VI to the island for its heroic resistance to prolonged Axis attack during the Second World War. The medal has been awarded to surviving veterans who served in Malta in the armed forces and auxiliary services between 10 June 1940 and 8 September 1943. Permission for British citizens to wear this medal was subsequently granted by the Queen. As a number of veterans applied for the medal after the cut-off date of 15 April 1994, the Maltese Government sanctioned a second striking—these medals carry the word COPY below the right arm of the George Cross.*

VALUE:

Cupro-nickel (original striking)	£90–120	Miniature	£20–25
Official copy	£50–60		

343. SHANGHAI VOLUNTEER CORPS MEDAL

Date: 1854.
Ribbon: Unknown—details sought.
Metal: Silver.
Size: 38mm
Description: Unknown—details sought.
Comment: *Awarded to the officers and men of the Shanghai Volunteers who took part in the battle of Soo Chow Creek (also known as the battle of Muddy Flats) which took place in April 28, 1854. Examples are of the greatest rarity and the last one to appear at auction was sold in 1991. Further details are sought.*

VALUE: —

344. SHANGHAI JUBILEE MEDAL

Instituted: 1893.
Ribbon: Watered silk half bright red, half white or red with 4mm central white stripe.
Metal: Silver or bronze.
Size: 36mm.
Description: (Obverse) triple-shield arms of the municipality surrounded by a band with thistles, shamrocks and roses round the foot and NOVEMBER 17 1843 round the top. (Reverse) a scrolled shield with the words SHANGHAI JUBILEE and NOVEMBER 17 1843 and inscribed diagonally across the centre with the recipient's name in block capitals. The shield is flanked by Chinese dragons and above is a steamship and the sun setting on the horizon. The rim is engraved "Presented by the Shanghai Municipality". Issued with a small suspension ring, but often replaced by a straight bar. This medal has also been recorded with an ornamental silver brooch bearing the dates 1843–1893.
Comments: *The British settlement in Shanghai was founded in 1843 and formed the nucleus of the International Settlement established in 1854 under the control of an autonomous Municipal Council. In effect the International Settlement functioned as an autonomous City State administered by a Municipal Committee formed from those nations comprising the Settlement. This was abolished when Shanghai was overrun by Imperial Japanese troops in 1941.*

VALUE:	Silver (625)	£500–550
	Bronze (100)	£300–400

345. SHANGHAI FIRE BRIGADE LONG SERVICE MEDAL

Instituted: Before 1904.
Ribbon: Black with broad crimson borders.
Metal: Silver.
Size: 31mm.
Description: (Obverse) an armorial device featuring a Chinese dragon standing on a symbolic high-rise building on which is displayed a flame on a pole crossed by a hook and ladder, with MIH-HO-LOONG SHANGHAI round the top and the motto "Say the word and down comes your house" round the foot; (reverse) engraved with recipient's details. It seems strange that no Chinese characters appear on the medal. Ring and double claw suspension, with a broad silver brooch bar at the top of the ribbon.
Comment: *Awarded for a minimum of twelve years regular service with the Municipal Fire Brigade. The award was presumably in abeyance following the Japanese invasion in 1937 and the wholesale destruction of the international commercial metropolis.*

VALUE: £450–500

346. SHANGHAI VOLUNTEER FIRE BRIGADE LONG SERVICE MEDAL

Instituted: 1904.
Ribbon: Red with two wide and one narrow (central) white stripes.
Metal: Gold, silver or bronze.
Size: 36mm.
Description: (Obverse) the arms and motto of the Municipality surrounded by a collar inscribed SHANGHAI VOLUNTEER FIRE BRIGADE ESTABLISHED 1866. (Reverse) originally simply engraved with name of unit, later a pair of crossed axes surmounted by a fireman's helmet under which is a horizontal tablet on which are engraved the recipient's dates of service. Round the circumference is inscribed FOR LONG SERVICE (top) and WE FIGHT THE FLAMES (foot) with quatrefoil ornaments separating the two inscriptions. Fitted with a swivelling scroll suspender.
Comments: *The medal in silver was awarded to members of the Volunteer Fire Brigade for five years service, for eight years service a clasp was added to the ribbon and for 12 years service the medal was awarded in gold. Bronze medals exist but are believed to have been specimens only.*

VALUE: £550–650

347. SHANGHAI VOLUNTEER CORPS LONG SERVICE MEDAL

Instituted: 1921.
Ribbon: Equal stripes of red, white and blue, the red bisected by a thin green stripe, the white by black and the blue by yellow.
Metal: Silver.
Size: 36mm.
Description: (Obverse) an eight-pointed radiate star bearing a scroll at the top inscribed 4th APRIL 1854. The arms of the Municipality superimposed on the star and surrounded by a collar inscribed SHANGHAI VOLUNTEER CORPS. Round the foot of the medal is a band inscribed FOR LONG SERVICE. (Reverse) plain, engraved with the name of the recipient and his period of service.
Comments: *The Volunteer Corps was raised in 1853 to protect the British and other foreign settlements. The date on the scroll alludes to the Corps' first engagement, the Battle of Muddy Flat. The Corps was cosmopolitan in structure, although the British element predominated. It was disbanded in September 1942, nine months after the Japanese overran the International Settlement. Awarded for 12 years good service. The last medal was awarded in 1941.*

VALUE: £450–500   *Miniature* £95–110

348. SHANGHAI MUNICIPAL POLICE DISTINGUISHED CONDUCT MEDAL

Instituted: 1924.
Ribbon: Red with a central blue stripe (1st class); red with a blue stripe at each edge (2nd class).
Metal: Silver or bronze.
Size: 36mm.
Description: (Obverse) arms of the Municipality and the inscription SHANGHAI MUNICIPAL POLICE; (reverse) the words FOR DISTINGUISHED CONDUCT. The recipient's name and rank were engraved around the rim.
Comments: *Awarded to officers and men of the Municipal Police in two classes, distinguished solely by their ribbons and the metal used (silver or bronze). A sliding clasp was fitted to the ribbon to denote a second award; this featured the Municipal crest and was engraved on the reverse with the details of the award. It is believed that a total of 223 medals were awarded up to 1942, including 72 to foreign members of the force.*

VALUE:	Silver	£850–1000
	Bronze	£650–750

349. SHANGHAI MUNICIPAL POLICE LONG SERVICE MEDAL

Instituted: 1925.
Ribbon: Brown with a central yellow stripe edged in white.
Metal: Silver.
Size: 36mm.
Description: (Obverse) arms of the Municipality within a collar inscribed SHANGHAI MUNICIPAL POLICE; (reverse) plain apart from the inscription FOR LONG SERVICE in two lines across the centre. The recipient's name and rank were engraved round the rim in upper and lower case lettering. Awards to Indians were named in cursive script with the Hindi equivalent alongside. Fitted with a swivelling scroll suspender.
Comments: *Awarded for 12 years good service in the Shanghai Municipal Police, an international force composed largely of Sikhs, Chinese and White Russians as well as British ex-soldiers and policemen. Dated clasps for further five year periods of service were awarded. The medal was abolished in 1942.*

VALUE:			Miniature
Without clasp	£350–400		£50–55
With clasp	£500–550		£55–65
2 clasps	£550–650		£65–75

350. SHANGHAI MUNICIPAL POLICE (SPECIALS) LONG SERVICE MEDAL

Instituted: 1929.
Ribbon: Dark brown with three white bars, each bisected by a thin yellow stripe.
Metal: Silver.
Size: 36mm.
Description: (Obverse) the arms of the Municipality with the motto OMNIA JUNCTA IN UNO (all joined in one) round the circumference. (Reverse) inscribed SHANGHAI MUNICIPAL POLICE (SPECIALS) FOR LONG SERVICE in six lines. A unique award to A.L. Anderson (1930) was inscribed on the reverse FOR DISTINGUISHED AND VALUABLE SERVICES.
Comments: *Awarded for 12 years active and efficient service in the Special Constabulary. Some 52 medals and 8 clasps for additional service are recorded in the Shanghai Gazette, but the actual number awarded was probably greater. The medal was discontinued in 1942.*

VALUE :			
Without clasp	£500–550	With clasp	Very rare
Miniature	£210–260		

351. SHANGHAI MUNICIPAL COUNCIL EMERGENCY MEDAL

Instituted: 1937.
Ribbon: 38mm bright red, having a broad white central stripe bordered black and yellow edges separated from the red by thin black stripes.
Metal: Bronze.
Size: 40mm.
Description: An eight-pointed star with ring suspension. (Obverse) a central medallion superimposed on the radiate star with the triple-shield arms of the Municipality surrounded by a collar inscribed SHANGHAI MUNICIPAL COUNCIL. (Reverse) a laurel wreath enclosing the words FOR SERVICES RENDERED - AUGUST 12 TO NOVEMBER 12 1937.
Comments: *Awarded to members of the Police, Volunteer Corps, Fire Brigade and civilians for services during the emergency of August-November 1937 when fighting between the Chinese and Japanese in and around Shanghai threatened to encroach on the International Settlement. Issued unnamed, but accompanied by a certificate bearing the name and unit of the recipient. Examples have been seen with the recipient's name engraved on the reverse.*

VALUE: £250–300   *Miniature*   £65–85

351A. CHINESE MARITIME CUSTOMS SERVICE FINANCIAL MEDAL

Instituted:
Ribbon: Green, with yellow stripes.
Metal: Gold, silver or bronze according to class.
Size:
Description: An eight-pointed radiate star suspended by a plain ring, having an oval medallion on the obverse inscribed in Chinese and depicting a Chinese junk; (reverse) a horseshoe scroll inscribed THE CHINESE MARITIME CUSTOMS MEDAL with FINANCIAL across the foot. The recipient's name was engraved in the centre.
Comments: *The Chinese Maritime Customs Service was operated and largely staffed at the higher levels by British personnel from 1854 till 1950. Medals were awarded for five years' service or shorter service of exceptional merit and were granted in three classes, each of three grades, making nine variations in all, distinguished by the respective metals, and awarded according to the rank of the recipient.*

Obverse

VALUE: **Very Rare**   *Miniature*   £100–110

351B. CHINESE MARITIME CUSTOMS SERVICE MERITORIOUS SERVICE MEDAL

Instituted:
Ribbon: Green with yellow stripes.
Metal: Gold, silver or bronze according to grade.
Size:
Description: As above, but FOR MERITORIOUS SERVICE in the tablet on the reverse.
Comments: *Awarded for 25 years continuous service, according to the rank of the recipient, but later awards in silver or gold could be made on promotion to a higher rank, or for exceptional service, notably from 1931 onwards, following the outbreak of hostilities with Japan.*

VALUE: **Very Rare**

Reverse

352. AUTOMOBILE ASSOCIATION SERVICE CROSS

Date: 1956.
Ribbon: Yellow with three narrow black stripes.
Metal: Silver.
Size: 36mm.
Description: A silver cross flory terminating in scrolls, with the AA emblem surmounted in the centre.
Comments: *Established in commemoration of the Association's Golden Jubilee, the Cross is the highest award to AA patrolmen and other uniformed members of staff for conspicuous acts of bravery involving an imminent risk of personal injury whilst on duty in uniform, or whilst engaged in an action related to duty. To date only 15 crosses have been awarded. A monetary reward accompanies the Cross.*

VALUE: £400–500

353. AUTOMOBILE ASSOCIATION SERVICE MEDAL

Date: 1956.
Ribbon: Half yellow, half black.
Metal: Silver.
Size: 36mm.
Description: A circular medal in the form of the AA badge with wings sprouting from the top and flanking a claw and ring suspension. (Obverse) AA superimposed on a wheel, with the inscription AUTOMOBILE ASSOCIATION/SERVICE MEDAL round the circumference; (reverse) details of the award.
Clasp: A silver-gilt and red enamel clasp inscribed 192064 (ie. 20 years good driving, 1964) has been reported.
Comments: *Like the Cross, the Medal of the Association was instituted in commemoration of the Association's Golden Jubilee. The medal is awarded to members of the uniformed staff for courageous or outstanding initiative and devotion to duty. To date, only 60 medals have been awarded, including four in 1997, mainly for life-saving and bravery in accidents. A monetary reward accompanies the Medal. A Service Citation is also awarded for lesser acts, a total of 63 having been bestowed so far.*

VALUE: £200–250

354. SUFFRAGETTE MEDAL

Instituted: 1909.
Campaign: Votes for women.
Ribbon: Three equal stripes of purple, silver and green.
Metal: Silver.
Size: 20mm.
Clasps: A silver dated bar, or an enamelled bar in the WSPU colours with the date on the reverse, or prison bars surmounted by a broad arrow.
Description: A small silver medal suspended by a ring from a bar with scrolled finials, engraved with the date of the award. A similarly scrolled brooch bar at the top of the ribbon is inscribed FOR VALOUR. The plain medal is engraved HUNGER STRIKE in various styles and hallmarked.
Comments: *This medal was awarded by the Women's Social and Political Union (WSPU) to those militant Suffragettes who were imprisoned for various acts of violence and who went on hunger strike while in prison. At first they were forcibly fed under the most barbaric conditions, as a result of which several died. The Government then introduced the Cat and Mouse Act, whereby hunger strikers at the point of death were released, but were then re-arrested and returned to prison when they had recovered sufficiently from their ordeal. A silver bar was awarded to those who were imprisoned and went on hunger strike whilst an enamel bar was awarded to those who were force fed in prison. The portcullis badge was given to those imprisoned in Holloway and is occasionally seen separately from the medal.*

VALUE: Boxed: From £3500
In personally inscribed case: From £6000

355. FLORENCE NIGHTINGALE MEDAL

Date: 1912.

Ribbon: White with narrow yellow and broad red stripes towards the edges.

Metal: Silver with enamels.

Size:

Description: An upright elliptical medal coming to a point at both ends, with a three-quarter length portrait of Florence Nightingale from the Crimean War period, inscribed MEMORIAM FLORENCE NIGHTINGALE 1820–1910 AD. The reverse bears the recipient's name.

Comments: *Instituted by the International Committee of the Red Cross for award to trained nurses, matrons, nursing organisers or voluntary aids for distinguished or exceptional service. Awards are made every other year on the anniversary of Miss Nightingale's birthday. This medal has been awarded very sparingly.*

VALUE: £500–700 *Miniature* £410–510

356. ANZAC COMMEMORATIVE MEDAL

Date: 1967.

Ribbon: None.

Metal: Bronze.

Size: 76mm x 50mm.

Description: (Obverse) a medallion surmounted by a Royal Crown with a laurel wreath and the word ANZAC in a scroll below. In the field is the date 1915 above a picture of John Simpson and his donkey saving a wounded soldier at Gallipoli (based on a painting by 4/26A Spr Horace Moore-Jones, NZ Engineers. (Reverse) a map of Australia and New Zealand with the Southern Cross constellation. The reverse of the scroll has New Zealand fern leaves.

Comments: *This medal was instituted jointly by the governments of Australia and New Zealand and awarded to surviving veterans of the Australian and New Zealand Army Corps who served in the Gallipoli campaign, all named on the reverse. Designed by Australian artist Raymond Ewers. There is also a half-size lapel badge bearing the obverse design and numbered on the reverse.*

VALUE: Original Medal £150–250 Lapel badge £50–60

357. NEW ZEALAND CADET DISTRICT MEDAL

Date: 1902.

Ribbon: Plain khaki or tan with a central pink flanked by dark green stripes.

Metal: Silver.

Size: 32mm.

Description: (Obverse) profile of Edward VII or George V with inscription FOR KING AND COUNTRY: PUBLIC SCHOOL CADETS, N.Z.; (reverse) DEFENCE NOT DEFIANCE round the top, with DISTRICT PRIZE (or CHALLENGE) MEDAL AWARDED TO in three lines, leaving space for the name of the recipient to be engraved below.

Comments: *These medals were instituted following the establishment of the Public School Cadets in 1902 and were awarded in two classes in Challenge competitions or as prizes in the annual examinations.*

VALUE: District Challenge £100–150
  District Prize £90–100

362. CORPS OF COMMISSIONAIRES MEDAL

Date:
Ribbon: Red, white and blue.
Metal: Silver or blackened metal.
Size: 40mm.
Description: A 16-point star bearing a central medallion with the Union Jack in the centre surrounded by the Latin mottoes: VIRTUTE ET INDUSTRIA (top) and LABOR VINCIT OMNIA (foot)—"by ability and industry" and "work conquers all" respectively. Fitted with a plain ring for suspension from the ribbon which bears an elaborate brooch consisting of crossed rifle and sabre on a fouled anchor with a cannon behind, representing the armed forces from which the Corps recruits its members.
Comments: *Awarded by the Corps of Commissionaires for long and exemplary service.*

VALUE: £30–45   *Miniature*   £25–30

363. NATIONAL EMERGENCY MEDAL

Date: 1926.
Ribbon: None.
Metal: Gold or bronze.
Size: 50mm.
Description: (Obverse) Britannia seated holding a laurel branch and resting on a shield. Above the inscription across the field FOR SERVICE IN NATIONAL EMERGENCY MAY 1926 appear the national emblems of England and Scotland with the LMS emblem between; (reverse) three female figures with arms outstretched holding locomotives dividing the inscription LARGITAS MUNERIS SALUS REIPUBLICAE (the immensity of the task, the well-being of the country).
Comments: *These medals were designed by Edward Gillick and struck by the Royal Mint on behalf of the London, Midland and Scottish Railway for presentation to those volunteers who had served the company throughout the General Strike of May 1926. The medals were struck in bronze and issued in boxes unnamed to the recipients. According to Mint records, a few medals were also struck in gold, but none has so far been recorded.*

VALUE:
Gold   —
Bronze   £45–55

364. ROYAL WARRANT HOLDERS ASSOCIATION MEDAL

Original reverse.

1977 "Jubilee" obverse.

Instituted: 1897.

Ribbon: Dark purple with a central yellow stripe.

Metal: Silver, silver-gilt or gold.

Size: 23mm.

Description: (Obverse) crowned profile of the reigning monarch; (reverse) THE ROYAL WARRANT HOLDERS ASSOCIATION round the edge with the name of the Warrant holder engraved in the centre. The medal was surmounted by an imperial crown fitted to a ring for suspension, with a brooch bar at the top of the ribbon, for issues between those of Queen Victoria and George VI. The medal fell into abeyance in 1946 due to the scarcity of silver. In 1897 the Association issued a medal in silver to commemorate the Diamond Jubilee of Queen Victoria. In 1977, for Her Majesty Queen Elizabeth's Silver Jubilee, a new medal was struck, with the dates 1952–1977 appearing below the bust. This medal is surmounted by a Tudor crown and fitted with a ring for suspension from a bar with a brooch bar at the top of the ribbon. This issue has a special reverse bearing the Royal arms—this special reverse was used again in 2002 on the occasion of the Golden Jubilee.

Comments: *This medal was originally instituted by Queen Victoria for individuals who are granted the Royal Warrant and may be worn at formal occasions of the Association. Until 1911 medals were issues in both silver and silver-gilt to members of the Association. However, from 1911 the silver-gilt and gold medals were only awarded to Council members. Miniature medals were also authorised and are believed to have been issued but they are very rare and were discontinued in 1920. Medals were struck for the reign of Edward VIII but were never issued, however unnamed examples do exist. The 1977 Silver Jubilee medal was designed by Alex Styles of Garrard the Crown jewellers. In 2002 Her Majesty the Queen gave approval for the medal to be issued in silver-gilt or gold to mark the Golden Jubilee, but it reverted to silver in 2003. The medal may be purchased by Warrant holders only.*

VALUE:

Victoria Silver-gilt	£200–250
Jubilee	£200–250
Edward VII Silver	£100–150
Silver-gilt	£200–250
George V	£150–200
Edward VIII	£200–250
George VI	£150–200
Elizabeth II	£150–200
1977 Jubilee	£200–250
2002 Jubilee	£200–250

365. ROYAL NATIONAL LIFEBOAT INSTITUTION DECORATION (see also L4)

Type I.

Type II, 2nd class in silver.

Date: 1901, 1913.
Ribbon: Blue watered silk.
Metal: Gold or silver with enamels.
Size: 27mm (type I) or 36mm (type II).
Description: Type I: a circular uniface medal depicting a lifeboat going to the assistance of a sailing ship in distress, surrounded by a white enamelled lifebelt surmounted by a gilt crown. Type II: A wavy cross in dark blue enamel, with the initials RNLI in the angles interlaced with a rope, surmounted by a Royal Crown, fitted with a ring for suspension. First Class (gold) and Second Class (silver). Type III: an oval enamelled lapel badge depicting the Institution's emblem.

Comments: *The original decoration, suspended from a bow of blue ribbon, designed by Charles Dibdin, the RNLI Secretary, was instituted as a reward for Branch Honorary Secretaries and Lady Auxiliaries for long and devoted service. 36 awards were made initially, followed by 18 other awards in 1902–9. The medal was manufactured by Alstons & Hallam of Bishopsgate. Thereafter a new decoration in the form of a cross, awarded to men and women in two classes, gold and silver, was designed by Mr Burke of the College of Heralds and manufactured by Garrards in 1912. Objections raised by King George V led to the cross being discontinued on May 14, 1914, by which time only ten gold awards had been made and no silver awards. Today long service is rewarded with an enamelled lapel badge as illustrated below.*

VALUE:	Type I	—
	Type II	—
	Type III	£20–30

Type III lapel badge.

366. MAIDSTONE TYPHOID MEDAL

Date: 1897.
Ribbon: Purple with yellow stripes at the edges.
Metal: Silver
Size: 32mm.
Description: (Obverse) the coat of arms of the town of Maidstone with MAIDSTONE KENT on a ribbon below; (reverse) an ornate panel engraved with the recipient's name in the centre and the words WITH GRATITUDE TO . . . FOR LOVING SERVICES 1897, with an olive branch below.
Comments: *A major epidemic of Typhoid fever broke out in Maidstone, Kent during late August 1897. By 9 September 117 cases had been reported, rising to 774 by the end of the month and by 9 October the number had risen to 1,200, with 42 deaths. By the end of December when the epidemic was considered to be over a total of 132 people had died. Medals were awarded to the nursing staff who served in the town during the epidemic. Many were presented by the Mayor of Maidstone at a special ceremony held at the Museum and Technical School on Wednesday 8 December 1897.*

VALUE:	Unnamed	£150–200
	Named	£350–400

367. BOYS' LIFE BRIGADE MEDAL

Date: 1905.
Ribbon: Red.
Metal: Bronze.
Size: 34mm.
Description: (Obverse) A Geneva cross within a crowned circle and a radiate background, the circle inscribed TO SAVE LIFE; a scroll round the foot inscribed THE BOYS LIFE BRIGADE; (reverse) personal details of the recipient. Fitted with a plain suspension ring. The brooch bar is the form of a scroll with a laurel wreath superimposed on the middle and a clasp bearing the date of the award.
Comments: *This medal was awarded for good attendance. The Boys' Life Brigade amalgamated with the Boys' Brigade in 1926 and the award of this medal was then abolished. The BLB Cross for Courage was also abolished at this time having been awarded only ten times in its history.*

VALUE: £20–30

367A. BOYS' BRIGADE SQUAD MEDAL

Date: 1896.
Ribbon: Originally dark blue, later maroon, suspended from an ornate brooch pin..
Metal: Bronze.
Size: 42mm.
Description: A multi-faceted, eight-pointed star surmounted by the Brigade badge: an anchor with the word SURE on the top cross-member of the anchor and STEADFAST on the lower limbs, the initials BB either side. When the Boys' Brigade amalgamated with the Boys' Life Brigade in 1926 the Geneva cross was added to the design.
Comments: *This medal is believed to have been awarded to the squad who achieved the highest average attendance over one year. The Boys' Brigade issued and continues to issue a large number of badges and medals, most of which are beyond the scope of this publication..*

VALUE: £25–35

368. GIRLS' LIFE BRIGADE MEDAL

Date: 1905.
Ribbon: Red.
Metal: Bronze.
Size: 34mm.
Description: Similar to MYB 367 above, but inscribed THE GIRLS' LIFE BRIGADE.
Comments: *This medal was awarded to members of the Brigade in similar circumstances to those for the Boys' Life Brigade.*

VALUE: £30–40

368A. RSPCA QUEEN VICTORIA MEDAL

Date: 1837.
Ribbon: White with two blue stripes towards each edge.
Metal: Silver.
Size: 34mm.
Description: (Obverse) a group of animals dominated by a standing horse with the legend ROYAL SOCIETY FOR THE PREVENTION OF CRUELTY OF ANIMALS FOUNDED 1824; (reverse) the throned effigy of Queen Victoria with the word PATRON below, surrounded by a floral wreath.
Comments: *This medal is awarded to people who have made a significant contribution to the Society. It was instituted in 1837 and the young Queen Victoria, an enthusiastic supporter of the Society, actually sketched a cat to be included in the reverse design. The name of the recipient is engraved in the exergue below the animals on the obverse.*

VALUE: £70–100

368B. RSPCA MERITORIOUS SERVICE TO ANIMALS MEDAL

Date: Unknown.
Ribbon: White with two blue stripes towards each edge (as 368A).
Size: 38mm.
Description: (Obverse)Two female figures one standing with an outstretched arm bearing a laurel wreath, the other kneeling by a horse with a small group of animals behind and the legend THE ROYAL SOCIETY FOR THE PREVENTION OF CRUELTY TO ANIMALS. (Reverse) A beribboned laurel wreath surmounted by the Royal arms surrounding the words PRESENTED TO (name) FOR MERITORIOUS SERVICE TO ANIMALS.
Comments: *It is uncertain where this medal sits in relation to 368A. It is possible this medal was awarded directly for animal welfare as opposed to contributing to the Society itself for which the RSPCA Queen Victoria Medal would be awarded. Any comments very welcome. See also Medals L31 and L38 in the Life Saving section.*

VALUE: £175–250

369. MARINE SOCIETY REWARD OF MERIT

Date: 1875.
Ribbon: Blue.
Metal: Silver.
Size: 47mm.
Description: (Obverse) a depiction of Britannia holding the hand of a young sailor with seascape behind , with MARINE SOCIETY INSTITUTED MDCCLVI around and INCORPORATED MDCCLXXII in exergue ; (reverse) a wreath of rose, thistle and shamrock enclosing inscription REWARD OF MERIT TO and with the name of the recipient engraved. Suspended from a thin straight bar swivel suspension.
Comments: *The Marine Society was instituted in 1756, at the start of the Seven Years War, by Fowler Walker, Sir John Fielding and Jonas Hanway. Its aim was to encourage poor men and boys to join the Royal and Merchant navies. In this it was successful, and by the end of the war in 1764, it had recruited 5,451 men and 5,174 boys for service at sea. Incorporated by Act of Parliament in 1772 to apprentice poor boys to the Royal and Merchant navies; it clothed them and provided them with an education suitable for their future employment. In 1783, Hanway published a paper promulgating the establishment of schools in every seaport for the training of boys for the sea. So large a concept was beyond the means of the Society but it led the way and in 1786 it commissioned the first pre-sea training ship, the* Beatty, *a sloop which housed 30 boys together with a superintendent, mate, schoolmaster, boatswain and cook. In later years, other organisations followed their example. By 1940, when the Society's training ship* Warspite *was broken up, the Society had trained and equipped some 36,000 boys for the Royal Navy and just under 35,000 for the Merchant Navy. Over the years, the Society was influential in the formation of several related organisations, including The Seamen's Hospital Society, Sail Training Association, Nautical Institute and Sea Cadet Corps. In 1976 the Marine Society merged with a number of other related charities: The Sailors' Home and Red Ensign Club (estab. 1830), The London School of Nautical Cookery (estab. 1893), The Incorporated Thames Nautical Training Trust (HMS Worcester) (estab. 1862), The Seafarers Education Service (estab. 1919), College at Sea (estab. 1938), The Merchant Navy Comforts Service Trust (estab. 1940) and the British Ship Adoption Society (estab. 1936). The Society continues to this day as a charity supporting maritime youth organisations.*

VALUE: £70–100

370. ROYAL BRISTOL VOLUNTEERS MEDAL

Date: 1875.
Ribbon: Plain crimson.
Metal: Silver.
Size: 37mm x 54 max.
Description: (Obverse) Arms of the city of Bristol within a garter bearing the words VIRTUTE ET INDUSTRIA surrounded by ROYAL BRISTOL VOLUNTEERS and IN DANGER READY in scroll below; (reverse) the Volunteers' edict: "IMBODIED FOR THE MAINTENANCE OF PUBLIC ORDER & PROTECTION OF THEIR FELLOW CITIZENS ON THE THREAT OF INVASION BY FRANCE MDCCXCVII. REVIVED AT THE RENEWAL OF HOSTILITIES MDCCCIII. DISBANDED WHEN THE DELIVERANCE OF EUROPE WAS ACCOMPLISHED BY THE PERSEVERENCE & MAGNANIMITY OF GREAT BRITAIN AND HER ALLIES MDCCCXIV" with scroll below bearing the words PRO PATRIA. Suspended from an integral wreath of laurel affixed to an ornamental scroll with the initials GR.
Comments: *This unusual medal was presumably given to all citizens who had volunteered for service when there was the real threat of invasion from France. The medal was worn from the neck on a crimson ribbon.*

VALUE: £150–175

371. GRANTON MEDAL FOR ZEAL

Date: 1915–19
Branch of Service: RN, RNR and RNVR.
Ribbon: Unknown.
Metal: Silver.
Size: 31mm.
Description: A thin medal (1mm) with a simple ring suspension. (Obverse) a raised laurel wreath with the words FOR ZEAL in the centre, in two lines; (reverse) a plain, engraved with the recipient's details.
Comments: *Instituted personally by Commodore (later Admiral and an AM recipient) Sir James Startin, SNO of Granton Naval Base, Edinburgh, and selectively awarded to naval personnel under his command who manned the trawlers, sailing ships and coastal trading boats that were involved in extensive mine clearance and Q-ship activities ranging from the North Sea to the Bay of Biscay during the First World War. This medal was awarded to both officers and men for meritorious service in circumstances that would otherwise have gone unrecognised. Although the recipients were mainly from the RNR and RNVR, these medals were awarded at special parades by visiting dignitaries to the base, including King George V, two Prime Ministers (Asquith and Lloyd George) and the Archbishop of Canterbury. Recipients also included Admiral Lord Beatty and Admiral Lord Jellicoe and a gold medal was presented to and accepted by the King. A miniature version of the medal was also available.*

VALUE: £150–200   **Miniature**   £55–80

372. SECURICOR MEDAL FOR LONG SERVICE

Date: —
Ribbon: Yellow with central dark blue stripe and blue edges.
Metal: Silver.
Size: 31mm.
Description: (Obverse) the cross keys of the company's badge with the name SECURICOR above; (reverse) a laurel wreath with centrre panel engraved with the recipient's details.
Comments: *Awarded to employees of the company who exhibit a high standard of devotion to duty over a sustained period.*

VALUE: £35–40

373. SECURICOR MEDAL FOR BRAVERY

Date: —
Ribbon: Blue with central wide yellow stripe and two thin yellow stripes.
Metal: Silver.
Size: 31mm.
Description: Similar to the above .
Comments: *Awarded to employees of the company who exhibit a particularly high standard of bravery and courage when on duty.*

VALUE: £400–500

374. ST. ANDREW'S ASSOCIATION MEDAL

Date: 1899
Ribbon: Dark red with three narrow yellow stripes.
Metal: Silver.
Size: 36mm.
Description: (Obverse) St Andrew standing before a diagonal cross with the words ST ANDREW'S AMBULANCE ASSOCIATION around the circumference; (reverse) a wreath of thistles surrounding the words FOR SERVICE IN THE ST ANDREW'S AMBULANCE CORPS.
Comments: *Given for long and faithful service in the Association. Originally the medal, in gold, silver or bronze was awarded for bravery in saving life but in 1907 the service medal was introduced for efficient completion of 15 years service. In 1954 the special medal illustrated was issued in celebration of the Association's 50th anniversary and Review by HRH the Duke of Edinburgh in Glasgow, inscribed ST ANDREW'S AMBULANCE CORPS 1904–1954, with a yellow ribbon with three narrow red stripes.*

VALUE:	1907 type	£60–75
	1954 issue	£75–100

375. SALVATION ARMY SERVICE MEDAL

Date: —
Ribbon: Maroon with two narrow blue stripes and a central thin orange stripe.
Metal: Silver.
Size: Various.
Description: An ornate cross surmounted in the centre by the Army's badge in enamels and the words LONG AND FAITHFUL SERVICE on four enamel panels around.
Comments: *Originally awarded for 25 years' service. A silver star is affixed to the ribbon for each additional 10 year period of service. This attractive medal was first instituted by General William Booth and it is believed that the higher the rank, the larger the medal awarded. It was discontinued in favour of a badge after World War II (1957 in the US). There have been other medals awarded by the SA including an extremely rare "Order of the Founder".*

VALUE: From £50

376. ROYAL NORFOLK VETERANS ASSOCIATION MEDAL

Date: 1909
Ribbon: Seven stripes consisting of a central 3mm white stripe flanked by two 3mm khaki stripes flanked by two 16mm red stripes edged by two 3mm khaki stripes.
Metal: Bronze.
Size: 31mm.
Description: (Obverse) crowned effigy of Edward VII with a laurel branch extending from the bottom of the medal around the left side and the words EDWARD VII on the right; (reverse) the words TO COMMEMORATE THE INSPECTION OF THE ROYAL NORFOLK VETERANS ASSOCIATION BY HIS MAJESTY KING EDWARD VII 25th OCTOBER 1909 in eight lines.
Comments: *This medal was issued to commemorate the inspection of the Association by King Edward VII at Crown Point, Norwich. In 1902 the King had agreed to become Patron of the Association, granting it the Royal title. The King's continued patronage resulted in the inspection of 25 members of the Association at Sandringham in 1907. In 1909 there was a further inspection by the King which resulted in the medal being struck. It is said that the King designed the ribbon for the medal but there is no documentary proof for this. Since 1902 each successive monarch has been the Patron of the Association.*

VALUE: £40–60

377. THE SHIPPING FEDERATION MEDAL FOR MERITORIOUS SERVICE

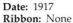

Date: 1917
Ribbon: None
Metal: Hallmarked gold or silver
Size: 28mm.
Description: (Obverse) a standing figure of Britannia holding a trident and shield, with a submarine on one side and a merchant ship on the other; (reverse) a fouled anchor above a plaque with the words "Presented by the Shipping Federation", flanked by a fish each side. The whole is surrounded by a laurel wreath with a scroll reading "1914 For services During the War 1918" beneath.
Comments: *Awarded by the Shipping Federation for meritorious service during World War I. Each medal has the recipient's name around the rim and the date of the action for which it was awarded.*

VALUE: Gold   £400–500
           Silver   £200–300

378. INNER TEMPLE SERVICE MEDAL 1914–18

Date: 1919.
Campaign: First World War.
Branch of Service: All members of the Inner Temple who participated in the First World War.
Ribbon: None.
Metal: Bronze.
Size: 50mm.
Description: (Obverse) A large Greek cross, with oak leaves in the four corners of the background. Inscription in eight lines: on the upper limb of the cross, in three lines, "The Inner Temple"; across the middle of the cross, in three lines, "To members of the Inn who fought for their country"; on the lower limb of the cross, in two lines, 1914, 1918"; (reverse) The flying figure of Pegasus, over clouds, facing left. Beneath his right front hoof, the dates in roman numerals, MCMXIV—MCMXVIII.
Comments: *Awarded to all members of the Inner Temple who participated in the First World War in any capacity. The name of the recipient is usually found round the edge of the medal, e.g. CAPT. H. F HALLIFAX, GENL. LIST CAVY. ATTD. 2/8 GURKHA RIFLES AND XX DECCAN HORSE. However, unnamed medals have been seen.*

VALUE: £65–100

379. ROYAL AGRICULTURAL SOCIETY OF ENGLAND LONG SERVICE MEDAL

Date: —
Ribbon: Plain royal blue.
Metal: Bronze.
Size: 38mm.
Description: (Obverse) An agricultural labourer wearing breeches and wielding a scythe with the words LONG SERVICE above. (Reverse) the monarch's bust with the legend ROYAL AGRICULTURAL SOCIETY OF ENGLAND . PATRON . around
Comments: *This medal is awarded to employees of Members of the Royal Agricultural Society of England for approved service of not less than 40 years with the same employer or on the same holding. Members can apply for no more than three such awards in any three year period—further awards must be purchased. An additional clasp can be awarded for 50 years service.*

VALUE: £100–150

380. CASUALTIES UNION EXEMPLARY SERVICE MEDAL

Obverse.

Date: 2012.
Ribbon: Central stripe of red (blood) flanked by broad stripes of white (training), edged with narrow stripes of blue (origin in Civil Defence), black (blackout and total war) and green (voluntary service).
Metal: Silver-coloured base metal.
Size: 36mm.
Description: (Obverse) Casualties Union Monogram; (reverse) the words FOR EXEMPLARY SERVICE within a laurel wreath with the date of the charity's formation.
Comments: *The Casualties Union was set up in 1942 in Reigate as part of the Civil Defence Training School but became a charity after the war to continue the work of making training more realistic. The medal is usually awarded for 15 years service. Clasps are awarded for 25 years and 50 years of service. When the ribbon bar alone is worn a silver rose represents the 25 year clasp and two silver roses the 50 year clasp. The award of an Exemplary service medal for less than 15 years is represented by a gilt rose on the medal bar and the medal ribbon. The recipient's name, unit and year of award are engraved on the edge.*

VALUE: —

381. CASUALTIES UNION MERITORIOUS SERVICE MEDAL

Reverse.

Date: 2012.
Ribbon: As above but the red and white stripes surmounted by thin stripes of gold (merit).
Metal: Gold-coloured base metal.
Size: 36mm.
Description: (Obverse) As above. Casualties Union Monogram; (reverse) the words FOR MERITORIOUS SERVICE within a laurel wreath with the date of the charity's formation.
Comments: *Awarded for meritorious service above the requirements for the Exemplary Service medal. Clasps are awarded for Life Member and For Merit. When the ribbon bar alone is worn a gilt rose represents the award of a Life Member or For Merit clasp. Two gilt roses represent the award of Life Member and For Merit clasps. No more than two gilt roses may be worn and multiple awards of the For Merit clasp are represented by a single gilt rose. The recipient's name, unit and year of award are engraved on the edge.*

VALUE: —

382. PRIMROSE LEAGUE MEDALS

The Primrose League was an organisation set up in 1883 by admirers of the late lamented Benjamin Disraeli, to promote the idea of Conservative principles in Great Britain. It was extremely popular for many years until its demise in the 1990s. During its existence it awarded a large number of badges, medals and pseudo orders to its members, many of which are avidly collected today. Most are very attractive and well made although regretfully there are far too many to list in this Yearbook, but information is widely available. Its insignia can easily be recognised by the appearance of the League's conjoined PL logo, as can be seen at the centre of the award illustrated here.

VALUE: Various according to age and level of award.

383. BOROUGH OF HARTLEPOOL SPECIAL CONSTABLES' MEDAL FOR SERVICE

Date: 1918.
Branch of Service: Special Constabulary.
Ribbon: Dark blue.
Metal: Silver.
Size: 35mm.
Description: (Obverse) Medieval coat of arms of the city: the legend S'COMMUNITATIS: DE: HARTLEPOL around with stag in centre, with hunting dog on its back. (Reverse) the words in reducing circles: BOROUGH OF HARTLEPOOL SPECIAL CONSTABLE / BOMBARDMENT 1914, AIR RAIDS 1915-18 / ZEPPELIN DESTROYED / 1916 in centre.
Comments: *Awarded to those special constables who served during the bombardment of the town from the sea and by Zeppelin 1914–18. Approximately 120 were issued.*

Value: £250–300

384. ARMY TEMPERANCE ASSOCIATION AWARD OF MERIT MEDAL

Instituted: 1867.

Branch of Service: Army, members of the Army Temperance Association and Royal Army Temperance Association.

Ribbon: Maroon. Suspended from a brooch fastening with palm leaves inscribed PALMAM QUI MERUIT FERAT (Let he who has deserved it bear the palm).

Metal: Silver.

Size: 50 x 29mm.

Description: (Obverse) ATA or RATA (after 1905) monogram, in centre of a beaded oval bearing the words AWARD OF MERIT and WATCH & BE SOBER, surmounted by a five pointed star. (Reverse) officially named to recipient, with rank, unit and date in 2mm block capitals.

Comments: *The Army Temperance Association was a very active organisation dedicated to the abstinence of alcohol throughout the army and, during the Victorian era especially, it issued a large number of medals as various rewards for its members. Most of these are beyond the scope of this book but information can be found in a number of publications dedicated to the subject. However, the medal illustrated here is included as it is sometimes found among veterans' groups. The design was changed from ATA to RATA in 1905. The total number awarded was 631 (257 ATA, 374 RATA) including 4 to women. None were awarded from 1915 to 1920, and only 14 from 1921 until awards ceased in 1927. A few ATA medals have been seen inscribed as REWARD OF MERIT.*

VALUE: £65–85

Above: the medal with RATA cypher. Right: the original ATA medal.

385. CATHEDRAL CONSTABLES' ASSOCIATION MEDAL

Instituted: 2011.

Ribbon: Green and blue diagonal stripes.

Metal: Gold plated base metal.

Size: 32mm.

Description: (Obverse) the association's crest consisting of an eight pointed star bearing a window with a cross surmounted by a crown, with the words "Cathedral Constables' Association" above, all surrounded by a laurel wreath with the Royal cypher at top; (Reverse) A laurel wreath enclosing the words, "For Faithful Service", surmounted by a dove carrying a laurel sprig.

Comments: *The association's medal is issued to officers who have served their respective Cathedral faithfully for 10 years. A bar is awarded for subsequent periods of 10 years. The medal is awarded jointly by the association and an officer's Cathedral trustees.*

VALUE: —

386. BRITISH RED CROSS SOCIETY MEDALS

Instituted: 1911.
Branch of Service: British Red Cross.
Ribbon: White with thin red stripes in various configurations.
Metal: Enamelled base metal.
Size: 38mm.
Description: A red enamelled cross surmounted by a red cross on a white shield surrounded by a white circle bearing the Society's title in gold lettering.
Comments: *The British Red Cross Society has issued various "medals" known as badges over the years. That illustrated is the proficiency badge with a clasp/suspender awarded for proficiency in first aid. Other clasps include Nursing, Hygiene & Sanitation, Cookery, Administration & Organisation, Tuberculosis Course and Infant & Child Welfare. The Society also has its own Gallantry Cross which is a simple red cross bearing the words "For Distinguished Services". See also MYB 165A, 171A, 266 and 355. More information on the numerous awards is available on the Society's website* www.redcross.org.uk*.*

VALUE: From £10 upwards.

387. ROYAL LIFE SAVING SOCIETY LONG SERVICE AWARD (see also L49A)

Instituted: 2002.
Ribbon: Dark blue with a narrow pale blue centre stripe suspended from a top bar enamelled with RLSS.
Metal: Enamelled base metal.
Size: 29mm.
Description: (Obverse) the emblem of the Society: crossed boathook/oar and lifebelt surmounted by the royal crown, with the words LONG SERVICE suspended below; (reverse) plain, engraved with the recipient's name and year of issue.
Comments: *Awarded by the Society for a minimum of 50 years' service.*

VALUE:

388. MEDAL FOR THE RECONSTRUCTION OF FRANCE

Instituted: 1921.

Ribbon: French Army Blue (horizon bleu) with white side stripes.

Metal: Silver.

Size: 30mm

Description: (Obverse) A shield-shaped coat of arms surmounted by a vertical sword, over an eagle with the motto "Do Right" (above) and "Fear no Man" (below). (Reverse) A left-facing wyvern with adjacent dates "1916" and "1921" and the legend "Comite Americain pour les Regions Devestees de la France".

Comments: *Issued unnamed, this silver medal was awarded to nursing and welfare staff of the "Comite Americain pour les Regions Devestees de la France" (CARD). This organisation was set up by Anne Morgan in the USA, who had previously worked in New York with the American Fund for French Wounded. She had the support of General Petain to set up an organisation to address the plight of the thousands of French families, refugees and returning forces whose homes and livelihoods had been shattered by the First World War. The headquarters of CARD was at Chateau de Blerancourt, about 75 miles north of Paris. CARD personnel operated for about two years after the Armistice. The medal was issued to all CARD members, some of whom were British, and took its design from the Blerancourt coat of arms, which showed a wyvern .*

VALUE: Rare in an attributable group.

MEDALS
For Saving Life

Medals for Saving Life fall into two categories: those awarded by the Government (official awards) and those awarded by other organisations and individuals, of which there are a large number. The first official award by the British Government was the Sea Gallantry Medal (Foreign Services) in 1841 to be followed by the Board of Trade Medal for Saving Life from Sea, then the Albert Medal and subsequently a number of others. These will be found in the main section of this Yearbook. The current section is concerned only with non-official awards for life saving.

The Royal Humane Society (1774), National Institution for the Preservation of Life from Shipwreck (later RNLI) (1824), Society for the Protection of Life from Fire (1836) and Liverpool Shipwreck and Humane Society (1839), all of which are very active to this day, were all instituted before the first official medals. They arose due to a desire to acknowledge and reward those who put the wellbeing of others before themselves. Initially, certainly as regards the RHS, the early rewards were given for the use of life saving methods to help restore the apparently dead (drowned) but the desire to reward those who braved the dangers of drowning, fires and asphyxiation was soon implemented. The RHS supported the creation of numerous humane societies in many towns and cities of Great Britain, and this was continued overseas

In addition to the principal life saving organisations indicated above, the 19th century generated an increasing number of similar but smaller organisations whose objectives were to reward life savers. These organisations were numerous and various and the following list is indicative of those that are known to us today. As will be seen, they represent philanthropic organisations and societies, social groups, commercial companies and municipal authorities. Additionally, life saving medals were issued for specific rescues by grateful survivors or their friends and family.

These awards are of considerable human interest and together with the associated citations, diplomas, parchments and other printed material are now much more appreciated for what they represent—bravery in the face of personal danger. Each life saving award is truly a gallantry award.

A number of the life saving awards from the following list (noted with an "L" number) are described in detail in this section of the **MEDAL YEARBOOK**, but many of them are as yet incompletely researched. The Life Saving Awards Research Society continues its research of these awards and as the research is completed these will be included in future editions.

LIFE SAVING SOCIETIES / FUNDS	Medal Yearbook no. (where applicable)		Medal Yearbook no. (where applicable)
		Northants Humane Society	
Bath Humane Society		Plym, Tamar, Lynher & Tavy Humane Society	L4A
Bolton & District Humane Society	L33A	Port of Plymouth Humane Society	L4B
Bristol Humane Society		Royal Humane Society	49/ L1
Carnegie Hero Fund Trust	L30	Royal National Lifeboat Institution	L4
Fleetwood Humane Society		(Royal) Society for the Protection	
Glasgow Humane Society	L2	of Life from Fire	L5
Grimsby Humane Society		Royal Life Saving Society (Mountbatten Medal)	L50
Hundred of Salford Humane Society	48/L3	Sheffield Society for the Recognition of Bravery	L27
Jersey Humane Society	L10A	Shipwrecked Fishermen & Mariners Royal Benevolent	
Lancashire Humane Society		Society	L8
Liverpool Shipwreck & Humane Society	14/15/18/L7	Shropshire Society Life Saving Medal	L13
Norfolk Humane Society			

Medal Yearbook no.
(where applicable)

Medal Yearbook no.
(where applicable)

LIFE SAVING SOCIETIES / FUNDS continued

Suffolk Humane Society	
Tayleur Fund	L9
Tynemouth Trust	L22
Windsor & Eton Humane Society	
Wisbech Humane Society	

NEWSPAPERS/MAGAZINES

Answers Medal	L16
Ally Sloper's Medal	L45A
Associated Newspapers Medal	
Daily Herald (Order of Industrial Heroism)	L36
Daily Mirror Medal	
Daily Sketch Medal	
Fleet (For Merit) Medal	
Golden Penny Medal	L00
Pluck Medal	L21
Post Office Magazine (St. Martin's Medal)	
Quiver Medal	L25
To-Day (Gallantry Fund) Medal	L19

MUNICIPAL AND OTHER AUTHORITIES

Binney Memorial Award	L:45
Birmingham Fire Medal	
Civil Aviation Authority	
Dale Award (Coventry)	L42
Dundee Corporation Medal for Bravery	
Folkestone Bravery Medal	
Corporation of Glasgow Bravery Medal	L37
Liverpool Corporation Medal for Bravery	
Metropolitan/LCC/London Fire Brigade Bravery Medal	
Plymouth City Police Bravery Medal	
Southend-on-Sea Pier Department Life Saving Medal	
Strathclyde Bravery Medal	
Tyne & Wear Fire and Civil Defence Authority Medal for Bravery	L51

YOUTH ORGANISATIONS

Boys' Brigade	L28
Boys' Life Brigade	
Church Lads' and Church Girls' Brigade	
Girl Guards (Salvation Army)	
Girl Guiding UK	
Girls' Life Brigade	
Scout Association	L32/L32A
Sea Cadet Corps	L46/L47

ANIMAL SOCIETIES

Belfast Society for the Prevention of Cruelty to Animals	
Dublin Society for the Prevention of Cruelty to Animals	
National Canine Defence League	L31A
Our Dumb Friends League	L31C
Peoples Dispensary for Sick Animals	L31B/L44A
Royal Society for the Prevention of Cruelty to Animals	L31/L38

COMMERCIAL ORGANISATIONS

Automobile Association	
Castle Mail Steam Packet Co.	
Imperial Chemical Industries	L37A
Lloyd's	L6/L17/L35/L39
Silk Cut	
Securicor	
Surrey Commercial Dock Company	

NON-COMMERCIAL ORGANISATIONS

Gallantry Medallists' League Gold Medal for Bravery	L47A
Imperial Merchant Services Guild	L30
Mercantile Marine Service Association	L11
Royal Society for the Prevention of Accidents	
St. Andrew's Ambulance Association Bravery Medal	
Order of St. John of Jerusalem Life Saving Medal	L12
Shipping Federation Medal	
Port Sunlight Order of Conspicuous Merit	L26A

SPECIFIC RESCUES

Indian Chief Medal (Ramsgate Medal)	
Carpathia and *Titanic* Medal	L34
CQD Medal	L33
SS *Drummond Castle* Medal	L23
Folkestone, Hythe & Sandgate Medal	
Gorleston i Medal	
Erinpura and *Topaz* Medal	L36A
SS *Lusitania (Wanderer)*	
Maharajah of Burdwan's Medal (HMS *Goliath*)	
Moray Floods Medal (1829)	
Osip Medal	
HMS *Niger* Medal (Deal)	
Henry Vernon Crew Fund Medal	
Wreck of the *Chusan*	
Wreck of the *Kent*	
Wreck of the *Palme*	

COLLIERY DISASTERS

Little Hulton 1866	
Hamstead Colliery 1908	L30A
Hartley Colliery 1862	L10
Hulton Colliery 1910	
Sacriston Colliery 1903	
Whitwick Colliery 1898	L25A

RAILWAYS

London, Midland & Scottish Railway	L40
London & North Eastern Railway	L44
London Passenger Transport Board	L43
Midland Railway	
Southern Railway	L41

PRIVATE AWARDS

Too numerous to mention—but each a tale of heroism in its own right!

THE
LIFE SAVING AWARDS
RESEARCH SOCIETY

The Society was formed in 1987 with the principle objective of furthering research into worldwide humanitarian awards given for saving life. This research is published in the Society's Journal which is issued three times a year.

**Appy to: The Membership Secretary Kim Claxton
Warren Cottage, 14 Bedstone,
Bucknell, Shropshire SY7 0BE
Tel: 01547 530611
e-mail: kclaxton@btinternet.com**

Subscription Rates: Annual Membership UK £24 Overseas Air Mail £33

L1. ROYAL HUMANE SOCIETY MEDALS

Date: 1774
Ribbon: None or blue (1776–1867); plain navy blue (1867); thin central yellow stripe and white edges added (silver medal, 1921). Stanhope medal: plain navy blue until 1921, when changed to blue with yellow and black edges. In 2000 the ribbon was changed to grey edges instead of black. Police medal: plain navy blue with a central yellow stripe.
Metal: Gold, silver or bronze.
Size: 51mm (1774–1867); 38mm (1867–).
Description: The first Large Medal was engraved by Lewis Pingo and is described: (obverse) a cherub, nude but for a flowing cloak, blowing on a burnt-out torch explained by the Latin legend LATEAT SCINTILLVLA FORSAN (perhaps a tiny spark may be concealed). A three-line Latin text across the exergue reads SOC. LOND. IN RESVSCITAT INTERMORTVORVM INSTIT. with the date in roman numerals. (Reverse) an oak wreath containing the engraved details of the recipient and the date of the life-saving act. Round the circumference is a Latin motto HOC PRETIVM CIVE SERVATO TVLIT (He has obtained this reward for saving the life of a citizen). Around 1826, the dies were worn out and were replaced with dies of a similar design by another engraver, Benedetto Pistrucci, the main difference being a general reworking of the cherub figure on the obverse.

In 1837 a new reverse die was produced which omitted the motto HOC PRETIUM CIVE SERVATO TULIT from the circumference. This was to be awarded in the future for "unsuccessful" rescues (note—until this date no distinction had been made between "successful" and "unsuccessful" rescues). Until this time the medal had been awarded in silver (except 13 instances of an honorary gold award), but from now onwards bronze medals were also struck.

In 1867, the "small" version (38mm diameter) of the medal was introduced. This was a wearable version having a scroll suspender fitted with a navy blue ribbon. The reverses of the smaller medals were similar to those of the larger variety except that the area inside the wreath (previously left plain for the engraved details of the rescue) were now replaced for a successful rescue with VIT.OB.SERV.D.D. SOC.REG.HVM (The Royal Humane Society presented this gift for saving life) and for an unsuccessful rescue with VIT.PERIC.EXPOS. D.D. SOC REG.HVM (The Royal Humane Society, his life having been exposed to danger). The punctuation varies on later issues. Three types of the small version are known (Type I 1867, Type II 1867–2000, Type III 2000–).

Scrolled clasps in silver and bronze were awarded from 1869 for subsequent acts of bravery deserving of a medal; the silver and bronze clasps corresponded to the previous award (i.e. a silver medal holder would only receive a silver clasp—even if the subsequent rescue was only "bronze standard"). However, a bronze medal holder would receive a silver medal if the rescue was "silver standard". The clasp continued in use (with some variations in design) up to 1950 when the last clasp (a bronze award) was issued. Since 2001 the RHS has awarded second medals for a second act of gallantry.

The Stanhope Medal in memory of Captain C. S. S. Stanhope, RN, was struck in gold and first issued in 1873. The medal was similar to the Society's silver medal but has a plaque-shaped bar fixed to the suspender embossed with the year of the award and STANHOPE MEDAL. This plaque was discontinued in 1935 or possiby earlier. The medal could be issued with either the "successful" or "unsuccessful" reverses.

Comments: *The Society was formed in 1774 for the specific purpose of diffusing knowledge about the techniques of resuscitation and saving life from drowning. Within two years of its inception, the Society's large medals were struck, chiefly in silver with 13 gold medals being honorary awards for non life saving activities. In addition monetary rewards and testimonials were granted to those who saved life, or attempted to save life from drowning, but later the Society's remit was broadened to include "all cases of exceptional bravery in rescuing or attempting to rescue persons from asphyxia in mines, wells, blasting furnaces or in sewers where foul air may endanger life". In 1837 a new medal specifically for unsuccessful rescues was introduced and at the same time medals were struck in bronze for both types of rescue. In December 1866 the Society was requested by the Duke of Cambridge, the Army's most senior officer that "some alteration might be made in the size of the Medal in question so as to admit of its being worn." The Society rapidly acceded to his request and by late 1867 the first "wearable" medals were being awarded. Details of the recipient and the act were engraved on the rim. Interestingly it wasn't until 1869 that the Army and Navy formally gave acceptance for the wearing of the Society's medals.*

The Stanhope medal (left) was first awarded in 1873 in memory of Captain C.S.S. Stanhope. This is the highest honour bestowed by the Society and is awarded annually for the most gallant rescue to have been rewarded by the Society. Since 1962, the

Second award clasp.

Liverpool Shipwreck & Humane Society, and the Humane Societies of Australasia, Canada, New Zealand and New South Wales have also participated by submitting their most gallant rescue. In January 2000, the Society introduced The Police Medal, struck in silver/gilt, to honour the police officer who has shown "courage of the highest order" during the preceding year. It is awarded to a policeman or woman who has already been awarded a Society award—usually either a Silver or a Bronze Medal.

VALUE:	Gold	Silver	Bronze
Large (Type 1, 1774–1837)	—	£850–1500	—
Large successful (Type 2, 1837)	—	£650–850	£350–550
Large unsuccessful (Type 2)	—	£450–550	£250–350
Small successful (Type I)	—	£550–850	£250–450
Small successful (Type II)	—	£500–850	£250–450
Small successful (Type III)	—	£500–750	£250–450
Small unsuccessful (Type II)	—	£400–500	£200–300
Small unsuccessful (Type III)	—	£400–500	£200–300
Stanhope Gold Medal	£4000–5000	—	—
Police Medal	—	—	—
Miniature Undated	£280–390	£60–70	£50–60
Dated	£390–500	£85–110	£55–85

L2. GLASGOW HUMANE SOCIETY MEDALS

Instituted: 1780.
Ribbon: None.
Metal: Gold or silver.
Size: 42mm.
Description: (Obverse) a naturalistic treatment of the elements of the Glasgow civic arms: the tree that never grew, the bird that never flew, the fish that never swam and the bell than never rang, with edge inscription GLASGOW HUMANE SOCIETY INSTITUTED 1780; (reverse) PRESENTED BY THE GLASGOW HUMANE SOCIETY TO above a horizontal tablet engraved with the name of the recipient; below: FOR INTREPIDITY OF COURAGE AND SUCCESS IN SAVING THE LIFE OF A FELLOW CITIZEN.
Comments: *Awarded mainly for saving people from drowning in the Clyde and Kelvin rivers but also for rescues in the Firth of Clyde.*

VALUE:
Gold: —
Silver: £600–850

L3. HUNDRED OF SALFORD HUMANE SOCIETY MEDALS

First type.

Date: 1789.
Ribbon: Plain dark blue.
Metal: Gold, silver or bronze.
Size: 32mm (circular type); height 49mm, max. width 41mm (cruciform type).
Description: Circular gold, silver or bronze medals were awarded from 1874 onwards, with the recipient's name and details engraved on the reverse, and featuring a cherub kindling a spark similar to the Royal Humane Society's medal, on the obverse. Around the time of the society's centenary in 1889, however, a more elaborate type of medal was devised, with the circular medal superimposed on a cross of distinctive shape, so that the society's name could be inscribed on the arms. Recipient's details are found on the reverse.
Comments: *This society was formed in 1789 to serve the needs of the Salford and Manchester area. After a few years it was dissolved, but was revived again in 1824. These awards ceased in 1922. The Society also awarded medals for swimming proficiency in silver and in bronze—see MYBL48.*

Second type.

VALUE:	Gold	Silver	Bronze	Miniature
Circular medal	—	£250–300	£200–250	—
Cruciform medal	£1000–1500	£185–250	—	—

L4. ROYAL NATIONAL LIFEBOAT INSTITUTION MEDALS (see also no. 365)

Date: 1824.
Ribbon: Plain blue.
Metal: Gold, silver or bronze.
Size: 36mm.
Description: The first medals bore the effigy of George IV on the obverse and it was not until 1862 that this was replaced by a garlanded profile of Victoria by Leonard C. Wyon. Medals portraying Edward VII and George V were introduced in 1902 and 1911 respectively, but when permission to portray George VI was refused in 1937 the RNLI adopted a profile of its founder, Sir William Hillary, instead. All but the Edwardian medals have a reverse showing a drowning seaman being rescued by three men in a boat with the motto LET NOT THE DEEP SWALLOW ME UP. The Edwardian medals have the seated figure of Hope adjusting the lifejacket on a lifeboatman. The earliest medals (1824) were issued without any means of suspension. Subsequent medals (1825-c. 1831) were pierced below the rim to allow a suspension ring to be fitted. Later a band of the appropriate material was added to the medal having an integral loop which allowed a larger suspension loop to be fitted. The characteristic dolphin suspension made its appearance c. 1852 and is still in use to this day. Rewards for additional rescues were initially recognised by a miniature rowing boat, gold for gold awards and silver for silver awards, suspended from short chains either being attached to the medal riband or from the medal itself. Details of the rescue were engraved on the boat. These were phased out c. 1835 and additional rewards were given by issuing additional medals. This continued until c. 1852 when second, third and subsequent rewards were recognised by the award of "service clasps" fixed to the medal suspension. Details of the rescue are engraved on the reverse of the clasp.
Comments: *The RNLI was founded, as the Royal National Institution for the Preservation of Life from Shipwreck, on 4 March 1824 and began awarding medals to "persons whose humane and intrepid exertions in saving life from shipwreck on our coasts are deemed sufficiently conspicuous to merit honourable distinction". Its title changed to the Royal National Lifeboat Institution in 1854. The medals are engraved on the edge with the recipient's name and the date, the recipient was voted the award.*

VALUE:

	Gold (150)	Silver (1,564)	*Miniature*	Bronze (793)	*Miniature*
George IV	£2000–3000	£500–675	—	—	—
Victoria	£2000–3000	£500–800	£165–220	—	—
Edward VII	£2500–3500	£850–1800	£220–280	—	—
George V	£2500–3500	£500–675	£220–280	£350–450	£165–220
Hillary	£2500–3500	£650–850	£220–280	£350–450	£165–220

L4A. PLYM, TAMAR, LYNHER AND TAVY HUMANE SOCIETY MEDALS

Date: 1836.
Ribbon: None.
Metal: Silver and bronze.
Size: 48mm.
Description: (Obverse) a winged female figure with a star on her forehead, holding the left wrist of a man who has been raised from the water and lies against a rock. Over the man's head, she is holding an oil lamp in her right hand, with the flame flickering and uncertain. Around the upper perimeter is "LATET SCINTILLULA FORSAN". In the exergue is "MDCCCXXXI"; (reverse) an oak wreath with outside the wreath "THE PLYM TAMAR LYMHER AND TAVY HUMANE SOCIETY". Within the wreath are engraved the recipient's name and details of award. The design of the medal is attributed to Lt. Col. Charles Hamilton Smith, KH, and the medallist was Benjamin Wyon.
Comments: *The Society (initially known as the Plym and Tamar Humane Society) was based on the river systems around Plymouth. The Society owed its origin and establishment to a "medical gentleman of the town" who, during the course of his practice, observed many instances of "suspended animation" where the individuals could have been revived had the necessary apparatus and knowledge been readily available. The objective of the Society was to preserve life, to bestow rewards on all who promptly risked their own lives to rescue those of their fellow creatures; to provide assistance, as far as possible, in all cases of apparent death in the town and neighbourhood; to restore the apparently drowned and dead; and to distinguish by rewards all who may be successful in such restoration. Shortly after the Society's institution in December 1831, they began to issue medals and these were struck in silver and bronze. The medals were issued without means of suspension. There are seven known examples for the period 1832–61 which have an engraved inscription in running script detailing the recipient, place of rescue and date signed by two officials (President, Hon. Secretary or Treasurer). Additionally two examples from the 1870s are recorded, with fewer details. A small number of un-named silver and bronze examples and a presentation example to Lt.-Col. H. Smith, the designer of the medal, are known. Also at least one silver-gilt presentation example is known.*

VALUE: Silver-gilt £800–1000   Silver £450–£550   Bronze £350–£400

L4B. PORT OF PLYMOUTH SWIMMING ASSOCIATION AND HUMANE SOCIETY MEDALS

Date: 1831.
Ribbon: Blue.
Metal: Silver and bronze.
Size: 36mm (40mm widest point of star).
Description: The medals were issued in silver and bronze with further acts of gallantry by medal holders being rewarded with bars to their medals. The medal has always had the basic design of a four-armed cross surmounting a wreath, with a round centre and a crown at the top (crown varied according to the reigning monarch). The centres show the swimmer diving from the left or the right to rescue a person in the water, with different scenes in the background. In others, the centres are plain, or in the case of one known award, the initials of the rescuer.
Comments: *The society was formed in 1831 as The Plym & Tamar Humane Society but in 1862/63 it amalgamated with the Port of Plymouth Swimming Association. However, for another century the Society maintained separate sections for Swimming and the Humane Society, each with its own Chairman, Secretary and Committee. The Humane Society had responsibility for investigating any acts of bravery in rescuing persons along a section of the Plymouth, Stonehouse and Devonport coastline, with the Devonport Humane Society having responsibility for the remainder of the local coastline. As a result of these investigations the Society awarded medals, certificates, watches and other pecuniary awards in those cases felt worthy of recognition. Many of the Society's records have been lost over the years but extant medals indicate that the medals were awarded from c. 1842 to the Second World War period.*

VALUE:	Silver £350–£450	Bronze £300–£350

L5. MEDALS OF THE SOCIETY FOR THE PROTECTION OF LIFE FROM FIRE

Type II.

Date: 1836.
Ribbon: Plain scarlet.
Metal: Silver or bronze.
Size: 52mm (I and II), 45mm (III), 42mm (IV &V) and 40mm (VI).
Description: The first medal (type I) had the Eye of Providence in a garter on the obverse and a reverse giving the recipient's details in an oak-leaf wreath. They were fitted with a ring suspender. The Society styled itself Royal from 1843 and a new medal (type II) was adopted the following year, with the word ROYAL added and the date at the foot of the obverse changed to 1844. In 1852 type III was introduced, with an obverse of a man carrying a woman away from a fire. This and type IV (1892) were struck in silver or bronze. As royal patronage ended with the death of Queen Victoria, a new medal (type V) was required in 1902 without the Royal title. Types IV and V show a man rescuing a woman and two children from a fire. The reverse of this medal has the words DUTY AND HONOR within a wreath, the recipient's details being placed on the rim. Type VI, awarded from 1984, has no suspension, with the recipient's details engraved on the reverse. Type VII awarded from 2013 is again suspended from a scarlet ribbon. A new design with the words FOR BRAVERY on the reverse has been introduced.

VALUE:		Silver	Bronze
I	Eye and garter (1836)	£850–950	—
II	Eye and garter (1844)	£850–950	—
III	Man and woman (1852)	£450–600	£350–450
IV	Man, woman and children (1892)	£550–650	£400–500
V	As type IV but "Royal" removed (1902)	£350–450	£300–400
VI	As type IV but details on rev.	Unique	£350–450
VII	FOR BRAVERY reverse	None yet issued	£350–450
Miniature (type IV)		£165–220	—

L6. LLOYD'S MEDALS FOR SAVING LIFE AT SEA

Date: 1836.
Ribbon: Blue, striped white, red and white in the centre.
Metal: Gold, silver or bronze.
Size: 73mm or 36mm.
Description: Both large and small medals had similar motifs. (Obverse) the rescue of Ulysses by Leucothoe; (reverse) an ornate wreath.
Comments: *The first medals, introduced in 1836, had a diameter of 73mm and were not intended for wear, but in 1896 the diameter was reduced to 36mm and a ring fitted for suspension with a ribbon.*

VALUE:

		Miniature
Large silver	£600–750	—
Large bronze	£350–450	—
Small silver	£350–500	£90–110
Small bronze	£300–400	£65–90

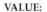

L7. LIVERPOOL SHIPWRECK AND HUMANE SOCIETY'S MARINE MEDALS

Type I.

Type II.

Date: 1839.
Ribbon: Plain dark blue.
Metal: Gold, silver or bronze.
Size: 54mm (type I), 45mm x 36mm (oval, type II) or 38mm (type III).
Description: (Obverse) a man on a spar of wreckage, taking an inert child from its drowning mother, with the stark legend LORD SAVE US, WE PERISH. This motif was retained for smaller, oval medals (type II) introduced around 1867 with the name of the Society round the edge, and a simple wreath reverse. The suspender was mounted with the Liver Bird emblem. A smaller circular version (type III) was adopted in 1874/75 and fitted with a scroll suspender. In this type the Liver Bird appeared in a wreath on the reverse. Bars engraved with the details were awarded for subsequent acts of life-saving. In addition to the general Marine medals there were distinctive awards in connection with specific marine rescues and funded separately. These had the type III obverse, but the reverse was inscribed CAMP & VILLAVERDE or BRAMLEY-MOORE. A glazed silver medal inscribed IN MEMORIAM was granted to the next of kin of those who lost their lives while attempting to save the lives of others.
Comments: *The Society was formed in 1839 to administer funds raised to help and reward those who distinguished themselves in saving life as a result of a hurricane which swept the Irish Sea in January of that year. The first medals were struck in 1844 and presented for rescues dating back to November 1839. They were large (54mm) in diameter, without suspension.*

VALUE:

	Gold	Silver	Bronze
I. Large (54mm) 1844	—	£400–550	—
II. Oval 1867	—	£500–650	—
III. Small (38mm) 1874/5	£1500–2000	£175–275	£150–200
Camp & Villaverde	—	£500–650	£450–550
Bramley-Moore	Rare	£500–650	£450–550
In Memoriam	—	£800–1200	—
Miniature (type II)	£165–220	£110–165	£110–130
(type III)	£165–220	£110–165	£110–130

L8. SHIPWRECKED FISHERMEN AND MARINERS ROYAL BENEVOLENT SOCIETY MEDALS

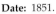

Date: 1851.
Ribbon: Navy blue.
Metal: Gold or silver.
Size: 36mm.
Description: (Obverse) the Society's arms; (reverse) inscribed PRESENTED FOR HEROIC EXERTIONS IN SAVING LIFE FROM DROWNING with a quotation from Job 29: 13 at the foot. The circumference is inscribed ENGLAND EXPECTS EVERY MAN WILL DO HIS DUTY, a quotation from Lord Nelson's signal to the fleet at Trafalgar, 1805. The first medals had a straight suspender but by 1857 a double dolphin suspender had been adopted (six variations of this suspender can be identified). Details of the recipient's name and the date of the rescue are engraved on the edge.
Comments: *The Society was founded in 1839 to raise funds for shipwrecked fishermen and mariners and the families of those lost at sea. The first medals were awarded in 1851 and the last award was made to Alexander Lamont in 1965.*

VALUE	Gold	Silver
Straight suspender	£2500–3000	£300–450
Dolphin suspender	—	£300–450
Miniature	£350–450	£165–230

L9. TAYLEUR FUND MEDALS

Date: 1854.
Ribbon: Dark blue.
Metal: Gold or silver.
Size: 45mm.
Description: (Obverse) a sinking ship with the legend TAYLEUR FUND FOR THE SUCCOUR OF SHIPWRECKED STRANGERS; (reverse) details of the award engraved.
Comments: *In January 1854 the emigrant ship* Tayleur *foundered on Lamtray Island, Dublin, Ireland. A fund was started for the relief of the survivors and the surplus used to issue silver life-saving medals. The first awards were made in 1861. Medals are known to have been awarded for ten separate rescues, the last in 1882. In December 1913 the residue of the Tayleur Fund was transferred to the RNLI and the issue of medals terminated.*

VALUE:

Gold (3)	—
Silver (46)	£450–600

L10. HARTLEY COLLIERY MEDALS

Date: 1862.
Ribbon: None.
Metal: Gold or silver.
Size: 53mm
Description: (Obverse) an angel with mine rescuers and disaster victims. Details of the award were engraved on the reverse.
Comments: *Some 204 miners perished in the disaster which overtook the Hartley Colliery, Northumberland on 10 January 1862. This medal was awarded to those involved in the rescue operations.*

VALUE:

Gold (1)	—
Silver (37)	£850–1200

L10A. JERSEY HUMANE SOCIETY MEDALS

Date: 1865.
Ribbon: Silver medal—purple 32mm wide;
　　　　Bronze medal—royal blue 32mm wide.
Metal: Gold, silver or bronze.
Size: 38mm.
Description: The medal has a plain swivel type suspension, curved, 40mm wide. (Obverse) the escutcheon of Jersey—(Three lions passant guardant heraldic "leopards"), around "HUMANE SOCIETY OF JERSEY" embossed in large capital letters: Below a naked mariner astride a ship's spar in heavy seas waving for assistance. (Reverse) a wreath around "PRESENTED TO (NAME) FOR COURAGE AND HUMANITY" embossed in capital letters.
Comments: *The first society meeting to award medals took place in June 1865 when one gold (Philip Ahier Jnr.), and two silver medals (Alex. J. Bellis and Howard Morris) were awarded. Since then, the Society has remained active with only a break during the German Occupation 1940–45, when the Military Authorities ordered the Society to cease its function and hand over all documents and medals to the Germans. These were, however, hidden by the then Secretary until the Liberation.*

VALUE:
Gold (2)	—
Silver (approx. 55)	£900–£1500
Bronze (approx. 110)	£600–£775

L11. MERCANTILE MARINE SERVICE ASSOCIATION MEDALS

Date: 1872.
Ribbon: Blue.
Metal: Gold (2) and silver (74).
Size: 38mm.
Description: (Obverse) a border with the legend "MERCANTILE MARINE SERVICE ASSOCIATION". In the centre are two seated figures of Neptune and Britannia. Neptune has a shield decorated with an anchor; Britannia a shield decorated with a sailing ship. Between the two figures are Cornucopias, Mercury's staff and a Liver bird. Beneath the two figures are the words "INCORPORATED BY SPECIAL ACT OF PARLIAMENT", and the maker's name Elkington & Co. Liverpool. The reverse bears a wreath containing the engraved details of the incident and the recipient's name.
Comments: *The medal was instituted by the MMSA in 1875 but the first awards were made retrospectively for rescues in 1872. The award was generally given to the Master and senior officers of ships engaged in life saving actions, but towards the end of its issuance some of the recipients were not officers. The medal was also awarded (in gold and in silver) to the students on the school ship* Conway *(Boy's training ship on the River Mersey) who had demonstrated "the greatest proficiency in all branches of training and education". The reverse of the medal was engraved with full details of the award. The last known award was made in 1906.*

VALUE:
Gold	—
Silver	£450–575

L11A. THE LEANDER MEDAL

London version.

Date: The Serpentine Swimming Club of London—1863 and The Birmingham Leander Swimming Club—1877.

Ribbon: No standard ribbon exists but the colours of the London Club are red and white and some combination of these colours is most common.

Metal: Silver, rarely gold.

Size: Approx 45mm.

Description: Circular, either with a ring or straight suspensory bar. (Obverse) a depiction of Leander swimming across the Hellespont (which we now know as the Dardanelles) towards the temple of Sestos where his lover, Hero, awaits. In the exergue are the words LEANDER MEDAL and sometimes, in the upper sky PERGE ITA UT FIT (continue on your present course). (Reverse) a wreath and space for engraving details. A slight difference can be seen in the illustrated London medal (upper) and the Birmingham medal (lower).

Comments: *The Leander medal was awarded many times for swimming, but only very rarely for saving life—the engraving on the reverse gives the clue.*

VALUE: (for life saving)
Gold   —
Silver   £250–350

Birmingham version.

L11B. WRECK OF THE CHUSAN

Date: 1874.

Ribbon: No ribbon but an elaborate suspension consisting of a fouled lifebelt surmounted by an anchor.

Metal: Silver.

Size: 50mm.

Description: (Obverse) within a rope and beaded circle, an engraved depiction of a vessel (the *Chusan*) in the Ardrossan harbour, a rough sea, mountains in the background, a jetty in the lower left foreground; (reverse)within the same type of border as the obverse, the engraved words: "Subscribers Medal—PRESENTED TO (NAME) FOR HEROIC EFFORTS IN SAVING LIFE AT THE WRECK OF THE CHUSAN IN ARDROSSAN HARBOUR—21ST OCT. 1874".

Comments: *This private life saving medal provided by the residents of Ardrossan, Scotland, was awarded to four seamen for life saving rescues from the paddle steamer* Chusan *wrecked in Ardrossan Harbour on October 21, 1874.*

VALUE: £450–550

L12. LIFE SAVING MEDALS OF THE ORDER OF ST JOHN

First type reverse.

Date: 1874.

Ribbon: Black, embroidered with the eight-point cross in white (1874), black watered silk (1888), white inner and red outer stripes added, separated by a black line (1950) which was subsequently removed in 1954.

Metal: Gold, silver or bronze.

Size: 36mm.

Description: The first medals (1874) had a plain eight-pointed cross of the Order on the obverse with the legend AWARDED BY THE ORDER OF ST. JOHN OF JERUSALEM IN ENGLAND; (reverse) a sprig of St John's wort bound by two ribbons, the upper bearing JERUSALEM ACRE and the lower bearing CYPRUS RHODES MALTA, within a circular border the words FOR SERVICE IN THE CAUSE OF HUMANITY. A second type of medal was adopted in 1888 and showed two tiny lions and two tiny unicorns in the interstices of the cross, with the legend FOR SERVICE IN THE CAUSE OF HUMANITY; the reverse shows sprigs of St John's wort bound with a ribbon bearing JERUSALEM ENGLAND, within a circular border AWARDED BY THE GRAND PRIORY OF THE ORDER OF THE HOSPITAL OF ST. JOHN OF JERUSALEM. A third type was adopted in 1980 in the same style as the 1888 type but with the reverse wording changed to read AWARDED BY THE MOST VENERABLE ORDER OF THE HOSPITAL OF ST. JOHN OF JERUSALEM. Bars to the medal were authorised to recognise further acts of gallantry from 1963.

Comments: *Instituted on 15 December 1874 and awarded for gallantry in saving life, these medals were originally granted in bronze or silver, but gold medals were also struck from 1907. Of the first type only 34 silver and 18 bronze were awarded. The bar to the medal has only been awarded twice in gold.*

Original ribbon.

Third type ribbon.

VALUE:

	Gold	Silver	Bronze
1st type 1874	—	£850–1200	£850–950
2nd type 1888	£1500–2000	£850–1200	£650–750
3rd type 1980	—	£750–900	£600–700
Miniature	—	£220–330	£175–250

L12A. MAHARAJAH OF BURDWAN'S MEDAL FOR GALLANT CONDUCT— BURNING OF HMS *GOLIATH* 1875

Date: 1875

Ribbon: Blue.

Metal: Silver. Bronze specimens are known

Size: 36mm.

Description: The medal has a fixed ring suspender. (Obverse) Bust of Queen Victoria wearing a coronet and veil draped behind, she wears the Order of the Star of India. Below "J. S. & A. B. Wyon". Around "VICTORIA REGINA". (Reverse) Surrounding: "THE GIFT OF THE MAHARAJAH OF BURDWAN"; within "PRESENTED BY THE LORD MAYOR OF LONDON FOR GALLANT CONDUCT AT THE BURNING OF H.M.S. GOLIATH 22nd DECr 1875",

Comment: *HMS Goliath was a training ship lent by the Royal Navy to Forest Gate School Board in 1870. Moored off Grays, Essex, it held some 450 orphan boys, mostly from the East End of London and was used for training in Naval Service. On December 22, 1875 a fire accidentally broke out in the lamp-room and the ship was completely destroyed. One officer and 19 boys are believed to have died in the disaster. Such was the conduct of the boys that the Maharajah of Burdwan wrote to The Times expressing his desire to award a medal, through the Lord Mayor of London, to those boys who had particularly distinguished themselves. The medals were presented at the Mansion House in a private ceremony by the Lord Mayor.*

VALUE: £650–875

L13. SHROPSHIRE SOCIETY LIFE SAVING MEDAL

Date: —
Ribbon: 30mm with two equal stripes of blue and yellow.
Metal: Silver.
Size: 51mm.
Description: (Obverse) a left-facing profile of Captain Matthew
    Webb whose name appears round the top, with the inscription
    •BORN IN SHROPSHIRE 1848•SWAM THE CHANNEL 1875•
    around; (reverse) two draped females holding wreath above
    panel with a swimmer in waves below, with legend •PRESENTED
    FOR BRAVERY BY THE SHROPSHIRE SOCIETY IN LONDON.
    Panel inscribed with recipient's details. Fitted with a plain ring for
    suspension and a brooch bar at the top of the ribbon.
Comment: *Struck by John Pinches and presented by the Shropshire Society in
    London (instituted in 1916) for outstanding acts of bravery in Shropshire.
    It is not known how many were awarded.*

VALUE: £450–675

L14. LIVERPOOL SHIPWRECK AND HUMANE SOCIETY'S FIRE MEDALS

Date: 1883.
Ribbon: Plain scarlet.
Metal: Gold, silver or bronze.
Size: 38mm.
Description: (Obverse) a fireman descending the stairs of a burning house
    carrying three children to their kneeling mother, her arms outstretched
    to receive them, with FOR BRAVERY IN SAVING LIFE in the exergue;
    (reverse) the wreathed Liver Bird previously noted for the third type of
    Marine medal (L7 type III). The medal is fitted with a scroll suspender.
    Clasps engraved with the details are awarded for subsequent acts.
Comments: *The first recipient was William Oversly in November 1883, for
    rescuing a child from a burning house. The first woman recipient was Miss
    Julia Keogh (12 February 1895) who saved two children in a house fire.*

VALUE:

	Gold (2)	Silver	Bronze
	Rare	£350–475	£250–300
Miniature	£280–330	£220–300	£165–220

L15. LIVERPOOL SHIPWRECK AND HUMANE SOCIETY'S SWIMMING MEDALS

Date: 1885.
Ribbon: Five equal bars, three blue and two white.
Metal: Silver or bronze.
Size: Height 44mm; max. width 30mm.
Description: This extremely ornate medal has a twin dolphin
    suspender and a free form. (Obverse) a wreath surmounted by
    crossed oars and a trident, with a lifebelt at the centre enclosing
    the Liver Bird emblem on a shield; (reverse) plain, engraved
    with the recipient's name and details.
Comments: *Not granted for life-saving as such, but for proficiency in
    swimming and life-saving techniques.*

VALUE:

Silver	£100–175	Bronze	£75–100

L15A. ALLY SLOPER'S MEDAL

Date: 1884.
Ribbon: Equal stripes of red, white and blue.
Metal: Silver.
Size: 36mm.
Description: (Obverse) Ally Sloper parodying Britannia with an umbrella converted into a trident and a barrel with the words "FOR VALOUR" in place of Britannia's shield. (Reverse) A wreath around the circumference with at the base Ally Sloper's initials intertwined. The centre is plain in which details of the recipient and details of the act which led to the award are engraved. Various suspender types to the medal are known, being either a ring and claw or a bar and claw suspender, with the bar being plain or ornate. One example of the medal with a red/white/blue ribbon is known (John Jones) but this has yet to be confirmed as the ribbon issued with the medal.
Comments: *"Ally Sloper's Half Holiday" was a comic satirical magazine published from 1884 to 1916 and was revived in three separate periods thereafter. The medal was awarded for bravery. It was awarded to the famous (i.e. the explorer H. M. Stanley and Piper Findlater, VC) and to the more humble (David Buchanan, a journeyman painter, William J. Osborn, a coastguard and John Jones, a miner). Full details of the awards can be found in copies of the magazine which are available at the British Library.*

VALUE: £350–450

L16. ANSWERS MEDAL FOR HEROISM

Date: 1892.
Ribbon: Equal stripes of blue, white, blue, white and blue.
Metal: Silver.
Size: 38mm.
Description: (Obverse) a wreath enclosing a lion crouching on a plinth with the words FOR BRAVERY, a sunburst in the background; (reverse) HONORIS CAUSA within a wreath surrounded by the legend PRESENTED BY THE PROPRIETORS OF ANSWERS. Fitted with a scroll suspender.
Comments: *This medal is typical of the many awards made by newspapers and magazines in the late 19th century. The medals were accompanied by a first class diploma. Second class diplomas were projected but never issued. It was also intended to issue a gold medal but no trace of such award has been found.*

VALUE: £400–500

L17. LLOYD'S MEDALS FOR MERITORIOUS SERVICE

Date: 1893.
Ribbon: Red with blue stripes towards the edges (1893); blue with broad white stripes towards the edges (since 1900).
Metal: Silver or bronze.
Size: 36mm x 38mm (star), 39mm x 29mm (oval), 36mm (circular).
Description: The original medal was a nine-pointed rayed star in bronze with the arms of Lloyd's on the obverse, suspended by a ring from a red ribbon with blue stripes towards the edge. A silver oval medal was introduced in 1900 with Lloyd's arms on the obverse and details of the recipient engraved on the reverse. This medal was fitted with a twin dolphin suspender and a blue ribbon with broad white stripes towards the edge. A third type, introduced in 1913, was a circular medal, struck in silver and bronze (from 1917), with Lloyd's shield on the obverse. The fourth type, still current, was introduced in 1936 and has the full arms, with crest, motto and supporters, on the obverse. The ribbon is suspended by a ring.
Comments: *These medals have been awarded to officers and men for extraordinary services in the preservation of vessels and cargoes from peril.*

2nd type.

4th type.

VALUE:

	Silver	Bronze
1st type: Star 1893	—	£150–200
2nd type: Oval 1900	£450–550	—
3rd type: Circular 1913	£350–425	£300–350
4th type: Circular 1936	£300–400	£250–350
Miniature (oval)	£275–330	—
(circular)	£220–275	—

L18. LIVERPOOL SHIPWRECK AND HUMANE SOCIETY'S GENERAL MEDALS

Date: 1894.
Ribbon: Five equal stripes, three red and two white.
Metal: Gold, silver or bronze.
Size: 38mm.
Description: (Obverse) a cross pattée with a wreathed crown at the centre and the legend FOR BRAVERY IN SAVING LIFE with the date 1894 at the foot; (reverse) the wreathed Liver Bird of the Marine medal, type III. Fitted with a scrolled or an ornate bar suspender. Bars for subsequent awards are granted.
Comments: *The first award was made on 9 June 1894 to Constables Twizell and Dean who were both injured whilst stopping runaway horses.*

VALUE:

	Gold	Silver	Bronze
General medal	—	£300–400	£250–350
Miniature	£330–385	£165–220	£110–165

L19. TODAY GALLANTRY FUND MEDALS

Date: 1894
Ribbon: Red with a central white stripe.
Metal: Silver and bronze.
Size: 38mm.
Description: (Obverse) standing figure of Britannia, lion and shield within a wreath; (reverse) the heraldic emblems of the United Kingdom with the legend ABSIT TIMOR (let fear depart) and AWARDED BY THE GALLANTRY FUND. The name of the recipient and date of the award are engraved within a wreath. The medal is fitted with a silver ornamental suspension bar for both the bronze and silver medals.
Comments: *This medal was awarded by the magazine "To-Day", published between 1893 and 1903. Its first editor was the novelist Jerome K. Jerome who enthusiastically promoted the idea of the Gallantry Fund, but when he gave up the editorship in 1897 the Fund soon fell into disuse. About 30 medals were issued.*

VALUE:
Silver	£350–450
Bronze	£275–350

L20. IMPERIAL MERCHANT SERVICE GUILD MEDALS

Date: c. 1895.
Ribbon: Blue
Metal: Silver with a silver-gilt rope and enamelled flag on a gold centre.
Size: 40mm and 63mm.
Description: A cross pattée in the centre of which, within a rope ring, is the Guild flag with the initials M.S.G. superimposed. (Reverse) plain but for the details of the recipient engraved with the formula "Presented by the Merchant Service Guild to . . . for heroism at sea (date)". The cross is suspended by a ring and hook, from a rod with a ball and point at each end. There is a brooch of similar design.
Comments: *Only three examples of this medal are known. The medal to C. Wood Robinson is 63mm and those to John H. Collin and W. Nutman are 40mm. No definite dates of issue for this award have been determined, but the rescues for which the known recipients got these awards were in 1895 and 1896.*

VALUE: —

L21. PLUCK MEDAL FOR HEROISM

Date: 1895
Ribbon: Blue
Metal: Silver (Bronze specimens are known)
Size: 32mm
Description: (Obverse) sprig of laurel and palm on left and right, with a cross pattée in the centre inscribed FOR HEROISM; (reverse) a sprig of laurel on the left of a scroll engraved with the recipient's name alongside the words PRESENTED BY PLUCK.
Comments: *"Pluck" was an adventure magazine for boys published from 1895 to 1916. Medals were issued from the inception of the periodical. In issue 8 it was announced that the award was to be known as the Answers—Pluck Award and until issue 24 the medal was similar to that given by Answers. From number 25 onwards the distinctive Pluck award was used. The last medals appear to have been issued in 1897.*

VALUE: £350–450

L22. TYNEMOUTH MEDALS

Date: 1895.
Ribbon: Dark blue, or burgundy
Metal: Gold or silver.
Size: Silver 51mm (gold smaller).
Description: Silver: (obverse) a scene viewed from the north of King Edward's Bay at Tynemouth, with Pen Bal Crag surmounted by a lighthouse. In the left foreground is a ship, sinking by the stern and a lifeboat putting off into stormy seas to the rescue. Around the top is the inscription PALAM QUI MERUIT and around the bottom TYNEMOUTH MEDAL; (reverse) recipient's engraved name surrounded by a laurel wreath. The medal is suspended by a scroll suspender with an ornate bar. **Gold:.** The obverse is similar to the silver medal but has no motto and there are numerous changes to the scene. The reverse carries the motto on a large lifebuoy within which are the details of the recipient.
Comments: *The Tynemouth Medal Trust was formed in response to a request from Mr E. B. Convers, a New York lawyer, who witnessed a rescue in the Tynemouth area. He was so impressed that he had a medal designed and produced and sent 100 silver medals to the Trustees to be awarded for acts of heroism to Tynesiders worldwide, or for acts of heroism in the Tyne and the surrounding area. A variant to the silver medal exists in which the reverse of the medal is not inverted in relation to the suspender—this is known as the Tynemouth Extension Medal. The original medal has the reverse inverted.*

VALUE:	Gold	£1000–1500
	Silver (approx. 100)	£450–575

L23. *DRUMMOND CASTLE* MEDAL

Date: 1896.
Ribbon: Plain crimson.
Metal: Silver.
Size: 38mm.
Description: (Obverse) the veiled profile of Queen Victoria; (reverse) a wreath enclosing the name of the ship and the date of its sinking with the legend FROM QUEEN VICTORIA A TOKEN OF GRATITUDE. Fitted with a scrolled suspender.
Comments: *Presented on behalf of Queen Victoria by officials from the British Embassy in Paris to inhabitants of Brest, Ushant and Molene for their generosity and humanity in rescuing and succouring the survivors of the SS* Drummond Castle *which struck a reef off Ushant on 16 June 1896. Of the 143 passengers and 104 crew, all but three perished. 282 medals were struck and 271 of these were awarded to those who helped save the living and assisted in the recovery and burial of the victims.*

VALUE:	£350–450

L24. NEWFOUNDLAND SILVER STAR FOR BRAVERY

Date: 1897.
Ribbon: Two equal stripes of dark blue and crimson.
Metal: Silver.
Size: 36mm max.
Description: A six-pointed radiate star with ball ornaments in the interstices, surmounted by a circular medallion showing a ship in distress and having the inscription FOR BRAVERY AT SEA in a collar. Fitted with a plain ring for suspension.
Comment: *Originally instigated by the Governor of Newfoundland, Sir Terence O'Brien, in 1893, as a bravery award. A total of 27 were made. In 1897 three were awarded to those who assisted in putting out a fire on the SS* Aurora *which, loaded with dynamite, was docked in St John's Harbour, Newfoundland. These three were altered to have the name of SS* Aurora *added to the legend.*

VALUE: £850–1250

L25. QUIVER MEDALS

Date: c.1897.
Ribbon: Dark blue for water rescues, red for land, both with a broad diagonal white stripe from lower left to upper right.
Metal: Silver (29) or bronze (29).
Size: 38mm.
Description: A thick medal weighing two ounces. (Obverse) a naked figure holding a rescued child, with the winged skeletal figure of Death hovering over a stormy sea in the background; (reverse) a laureated tablet bearing the name of the recipient and the date of the act. The circumference is inscribed round the top: FOR HEROIC CONDUCT IN THE SAVING OF LIFE and THE QUIVER MEDAL round the foot. The very elaborate suspension ring is in the form of a laurel wreath and is fitted to the suspender bar by means of a scroll inscribed THE QUIVER MEDAL. Brooch mounting at top of ribbon.
Comments: *The popular Victorian magazine "Quiver" took a keen interest in rewarding heroic deeds and encouraged its readers to submit details of such bravery "to include rescues by land and water, and in any part of the world". "Quiver" also took a particular interest in promoting safety at sea and organised a Lifeboat Fund which provided not only a number of lifeboats named "Quiver" but also this gallantry award. At least 58 silver and bronze medals were awarded of which four were presented to the survivors of the Margate surf boat disaster on December 2, 1897. A specially struck medal (of a different design) was awarded by "Quiver" to Captain Inch of "Volturno" fame.*

VALUE:		
	Silver	£450–575
	Bronze	£350–450

If you know of a British Life Saving medal that is not included in the MEDAL YEARBOOK we would be delighted to hear from you.

Or if you can supply us with a photograph of any of the medals not illustrated in this publication we would be pleased to include it next year.

If you can help, please contact the Managing Editor,
John Mussell, telephone 01404 46972 or at the address on page 1. Thank you!

L25A. WHITWICK COLLIERY DISASTER MEDAL

Date: 1898.
Ribbon: No ribbon—medal suspended by a pin through top loop.
Metal: Bronze 26mm x 26mm
Description: A bronze cross pattée bearing a chased likeness of the Whitwick pit with WHITWICK COLLIERY DISASTER 1898 on the four arms of the cross. The reverse is plain with the inscription PRESENTED TO [space for recipient's name] FOR BRAVERY APRIL 22 1898. The recipient's first name and surname are engraved in capitals.
Comments: Instituted following the underground fire at the Whitwick pit on 19/20 April 1898, to reward the 119 men who entered the mine in dangerous conditions to initially rescue the survivors but latterly to recover the dead. Of the 42 miners in the mine only seven survived.

VALUE: £150–200

L26. HUMANE SOCIETY OF NEW ZEALAND MEDALS

Second type.

Date: 1898.
Ribbon: Scarlet edged with broad beige stripes on which was embroidered gold fern leaves (1898–1914) or 32mm plain royal blue (from, 1915).
Metal: Gold, silver and bronze versions.
Size: 38mm.
Description: Originally an eight-pointed cross with ball points, with a circular medallion at the centre showing two figures surrounded by an inscription ROYAL HUMANE SOCIETY at the top and NEW ZEALAND round the foot, the cross mounted on an oak wreath surmounted by a Royal Crown fitted with a plain ring for suspension. The reverse was engraved with the recipient's name, date and details of the award. The second type consists of a circular medal with (obverse) an allegorical life-saving scene, name of the Society round the top and FOR LIFE SAVING in two lines in the field; (reverse) a laurel wreath with the recipient's name and details engraved in the centre. Early versions of this medal had a scrolled swivel suspension bar but later versions had a plain suspension bar. The top of the ribbon is fitted with a plain brooch.
Comments: *Presented by the Governor General as Patron of the Royal Humane Society of New Zealand. Only one or two awards are made each year. The medal is worn on the right breast. Until 1913 the Society also awarded a special gold medal, known as the Stead Medal, for acts of outstanding bravery. It was similar to the gold medal but had a suspension bar inscribed STEAD MEDAL. It was revived in 1963 for award to unsuccessful nominees for the Stanhope Gold Medal.*

VALUE:	Gold	Silver	Bronze
Type I	£2500–3750 (6)	£1250 –1800 (73)	£650–£800 (89)
Type II	£2000–2500 (10)	£650–800 (82)	£450 –550 (449)
Stead Medal	—		

L26A. PORT SUNLIGHT ORDER OF CONSPICUOUS MERIT

Date: 1901.
Ribbon: None.
Metal: Gold (15 carat).
Size: 45mm high x 42mm wide.
Description: The medals were only issued in 15 carat gold (Birmingham hallmarks). The medal is in the form of a cross pattée with a ring suspender (to allow attachment of a chain or similar for suspension). The obverse has a central legend "PORT SUNLIGHT ORDER OF CONSPICUOUS MERIT". The reverse is plain upon which the details of the recipient, the act of bravery and the date and time of the incident are engraved. The hallmark is also impressed on the reverse.
Comments: *In 1887, William Hesketh Lever (later Lord Leverhulme) began looking for a new site on which he could expand his soap-making business, at that time based in Warrington. He purchased 56 acres of unused marshy land at the site which became Port Sunlight (after his best-selling brand of soap), which was relatively flat, allowed space for expansion, and had a prime location between the River Mersey and a railway line. The garden village was founded to house his factory workers. Lever personally helped to plan the village, and employed nearly 30 different architects. He introduced schemes for welfare, education and the entertainment of his workers, and encouraged recreation and organisations which promoted art, literature, science or music. His stated aims were "to socialise and Christianise business relations and he also decided to instigate a form of recognition for the various acts of bravery that they had shown in rescuing those in distress. To this end he founded the Port Sunlight Order of Conspicuous Merit. The first medals were presented at a meeting held in the Hume Hall, Port Sunlight on 26 August 1901, where five awards were made for acts of bravery during that year. The final award was made in 1923—a total of only 19 awards having been made.*

VALUE: —

L27. THE SHEFFIELD SOCIETY FOR THE RECOGNITION OF BRAVERY MEDAL

Date: c. 1903.
Ribbon: Blue.
Metal: Gold, silver and bronze.
Size: 38 mm.
Description: (Obverse) a laurel branch and an oak leaf branch, tied to form a wreath, surmounted by a crown with inside the wreath an array of arrows above three sheaves of corn; (reverse) a laurel wreath upon which is a shield on which are inscribed details of the recipient and the act of bravery, with SHEFFIELD SOCIETY FOR RECOGNISING BRAVERY around.
Comments: *The Society owes its inception to Colonel Sir John E. Bingham, Bt. The rewards were intended to be given to any person residing in the city of Sheffield or within a radius of six miles from the Sheffield Parish Church, including the borough of Rotherham, for a conspicuous act of bravery, but not for rescues or attempted rescues from drowning and rescue or attempted rescues from asphyxia in mines, wells, sewers, and the like, or for any act of bravery that received an award from the Royal Humane Society.*

VALUE:		
Gold	—	
Silver	£400–525	
Bronze	£300–400	

L28. BOYS' BRIGADE CROSS FOR HEROISM

Date: September 1902.

Ribbon: Originally royal blue with two equal white stripes, but changed to plain royal blue in 1941.

Metal: Bronze.

Description: A cross pattée formed of four V-shaped finials linked to a circular disc inscribed the BOYS' BRIGADE CROSS FOR HEROISM and enclosing the emblem of the Boys' Brigade. The cross has a suspension ring and a plain brooch bar at the top of ribbon. There are two types, with or without a Geneva cross behind the anchor in the emblem (added in 1926 when the Boys' Life Brigade amalgamated with the Boys' Brigade).

Comments: *First awards were made in 1904, the cross was awarded only 194 times up to the end of 1985, including five posthumous awards. Simon Herriott, aged 8, became the youngest holder in 1980.*

VALUE: First type (without central cross) £750–1000
Second type (with central cross) £500–600

L29. GOLDEN PENNY MEDAL

Date: 1901

Ribbon: None

Metal: Bronze

Size: 36mm

Description: (Obverse) Britannia as found on pre-decimal Bitish currency, with the legend THE GOLDEN PENNY but without a date in the exergue; (reverse) THE GOLDEN PENNY above AWARDED TO . . . FOR BRAVERY, with the recipient's name engraved or impressed .

Comments: *The medal appears to have been issued at irregular intervals between November 1901 and June 1904. It is estimated that approximately 33 medals were issued during this period. A variant of this medal is known where the reverse legend "THE GOLDEN PENNY" is replaced by "HOUR GLASS". An example of this medal is known in its John Pinches case of issue. This corresponds with the fact that the "Golden Penny" magazine changed its name to "Hour Glass" for a short period in 1904 then reverted back to "Golden Penny".*

VALUE: £450–550

L30. CARNEGIE HERO FUND MEDAL

Date: 1908.
Ribbon: None.
Metal: Bronze.
Size: 90mm.
Description: UK version: (Obverse) an angel and a nude male figure surrounded by an inscription "HE SERVES GOD BEST WHO MOST NOBLY SERVES HUMANITY"; (reverse) two wreaths surrounding a central tablet inscribed "FOR HEROIC ENDEAVOUR TO SAVE HUMAN LIFE…" surrounding a further inscription "PRESENTED BY THE TRUSTEES OF THE CARNEGIE HERO FUND". Details of the recipient are engraved on the rim.
Comments: *The Carnegie Hero Fund Trust was established by Andrew Carnegie, first in the USA and Canada in 1904 and in Scotland in 1908 followed by eight other countries. The first UK medallion was awarded posthumously on 26 November 1909 to Thomas Wright for a life saving act on 23 September 1908. To date fewer than 200 medallions have been awarded in the UK. The design above is that of the UK medal but there are other designs for each of the 11 countries who administer the funds.*

VALUE:

UK		USA & Canada	
Bronze	£1000–2000	Gold	£5000–10,000
		Silver	£1000–2000
		Bronze	£750–1000

Details of recipient are embossed here

Design of the US & Canadian version

L30A. HAMSTEAD COLLIERY MEDAL 1908

Date: 1908.

Ribbon: Pale blue (30mm).)

Metal: Gold (24) and Silver (16).

Size: 38mm.

Description: A circular medal suspended from an ornamental bar joined to the medal by a ring. The ribbon has a top suspender bar with a pin back of the same ornamental design as the lower bar. (Obverse) within a wreath a heroic figure effecting the rescue of a miner, rubble and mining implements are in the background. To the sides a wreath partially surrounding. (Reverse) on a surrounding band the words: HAMSTEAD COLLIERY DISASTER . MARCH 1908., whilst within the band are the words: PRESENTED TO (name engraved) FOR CONSPICUOUS BRAVERY IN ATTEMPTING TO RESCUE THE ENTOMBED MINERS.

Comments: *The Hamstead Colliery, near Birmingham, suffered a disastrous fire on 4 March 1908, whereby 24 miners were entombed. Rescue attempts by the Hamstead men were augmented by the efforts of the Tankersley (Barnsley) and Altofts (Normanton) mine rescue brigades. One of them, a Yorkshireman named John Welsby, lost his life in the subsequent rescue attempts, and in spite of their valorous efforts all 24 trapped miners died. The Committee charged with the administration of the Hamstead Colliery Disaster Relief Fund decided that 25 gold medals would be awarded to the Hamstead miners who attempted to reach their trapped colleagues before the arrival of the Yorkshire rescue parties. Silver medals plus £10 would be presented to each of the local miners who assisted in the later exploration work. The Government Inspectors and higher mining officials who directed underground operations at great personal risk would each receive gold medals. In addition to the above, five Edward Medals (Mines) in silver and two in bronze were also awarded. John Welsby's widow received £262 from a special fund and his Edward Medal (posthumous award).*

VALUE: Gold   £2000–3000   Silver   £1500–1800

L31. RSPCA LIFE-SAVING MEDALS

Date: 1909.
Ribbon: Blue with three white stripes in the centre, the central stripe being narrower than the others (silver); blue with a central white stripe flanked by narrow red and white stripes (bronze).
Metal: Silver or bronze.
Size: 36mm.
Description: (Obverse) a seated female figure surrounded by a cow, sheep, cat, dog, goat and horse; (reverse) plain, with an inscription. The recipient's name usually appears on the rim. Both medals have a brooch bar inscribed FOR HUMANITY.
Comments: *Instituted in 1909 by the Royal Society for the Prevention of Cruelty to Animals, this medal is awarded in silver or bronze for acts of gallantry in saving the lives of animals, the early bronze awards are gilt. See also L38.*

VALUE:		Miniature
Silver	£300–365	£150–200
Bronze	£175–250	£100–150

L31A. NATIONAL CANINE DEFENCE LEAGUE MEDAL

Date: c. 1900.
Ribbon: Red.
Metal: Silver or bronze.
Size: 30mm.
Description: (Obverse) Victory standing with sword in hand over vanquished dragon, her right hand resting on a dog; NATIONAL CANINE DEFENCE LEAGUE inscribed round the top; (reverse) spray of oak leaves with a placard engraved with the name of the recipient and date of the award. Fitted with a plain ring for suspension
Comments: *Awarded for acts of bravery or exceptional humanity in the rescue of dogs from dangerous situations. Medals in bronze were intended for award to dogs for brave acts.*

VALUE:	Silver (early issue)	£1000–1600
	Silver (late issue)	£300–375
	Bronze	£250–300

L31B. THE PEOPLE'S DISPENSARY FOR SICK ANIMALS CROSS

Date: —
Ribbon: Broad red band with a narrow blue central stripe and broad white edges.
Metal: Silver.
Size: 32mm.
Description: A plain cross pattée with the initials PDSA on the arms. At the centre is a medallion bearing the figure of St Giles. The reverse is plain except for the name of the recipient and date of the award.
Comments: *Awarded to people who have performed acts of bravery involving animals. The PDSA also award medals to animals, the Dickin Medal (no. 358) being the most important.*

VALUE: £150–275

L31C. OUR DUMB FRIENDS LEAGUE MEDAL

Date: —
Ribbon: Plain red.
Metal: Silver or bronze.
Size: Heart-shaped, 45mm x 50mm.
Description: (Obverse) Figures of a horse, dog, cat and donkey within a heart-shaped ribbon inscribed OUR DUMB FRIENDS LEAGUE A SOCIETY FOR THE ENCOURAGEMENT OF KINDNESS TO ANIMALS; (reverse) engraved with the name of the recipient and date of the award.
Comments: *Awarded by the League for acts of bravery involving the rescue of animals. Also awarded as prizes at annual shows.*

VALUE:
Silver	£400–475
Bronze	£350–400

L32. SCOUT ASSOCIATION GALLANTRY MEDALS

Bronze award ribbon.

Silver award ribbon.

Gilt award ribbon.

Date: 1909.
Ribbon: Red (bronze), blue (silver) or half red, half blue (gilt).
Metal: Bronze, silver and gilt.
Size: 33mm.
Description: The medal is in the form of a cross pattée with the fleur-de-lys emblem at the centre. *Type 1* 1909–19 (obverse) FOR SAVING LIFE and the motto BE PREPARED; (reverse) (i) indent of Scout emblem and motto with ridge underneath; (ii) plain. *Type 2* 1920–66 (obverse) FOR GALLANTRY with motto BE PREPARED, (reverse) plain with maker's name "Collins, London". *Type 3* 1966– date (obverse) FOR GALLANTRY with the new Scout emblem with inverted "V", no emblem; (reverse) plain. The Type 1 medal is suspended from a ring suspender and Types 2 and 3 have a fixed bar suspender.
Comments: *The Scout movement began informally in 1907 and the Boy Scouts Association was founded a year later. The Scout Association's highest award is the Cornwell Scout badge, named after "Boy" Cornwell of Jutland fame. However, gallantry awards were instituted in 1908 and 1909. The bronze cross is the highest award of the Association for gallantry, granted for special heroism or action in the face of extraordinary risk. The silver cross is awarded for gallantry in circumstances of considerable risk. The gilt cross is awarded for gallantry in circumstances of moderate risk. In Canada, the order is reversed, with gilt (with red ribbon) being the highest and bronze (with red/blue ribbon) being the lowest. A clasp may be awarded to the holder of any gallantry award for further acts of gallantry in circumstances of similar risk. Collective awards may also be made to Troops, Groups or other Units within the Scout Movement and in 1943 the Boy Scouts of Malta & Gozo received the unique distinction of being awarded the Bronze Cross.*

VALUE: (British)
Bronze (148)	£1000–1500
Silver (1343)	£650–900
Gilt	£450–650

L32A. CORNWELL SCOUT BADGE

Date: 1916.
Ribbon: None.
Metal: Bronze.
Size: 30 x 25mm.
Description: The fleur de lys of the Scout Association surrounded by a large stylised capital C, suspended by a brooch pin with attached safety chain.
Comments: This award was named after John Travers Cornwell who won a posthumous Victoria Cross at the Battle of Jutland. At the age of 16 Jack Cornwell was one of the youngest winners of the VC and had been a Scout before entering the Navy. It was originally awarded "in respect of pre-eminently high character and devotion to duty, together with great courage and endurance" but is now reserved exclusively to members of a training section of the Scout Association under 25 years of age (until 2002, under 20 years of age) who have an outstanding record of service and efficiency. It is very rarely awarded, the last occasion being in 1998. To date a total of 634 badges have been awarded.

VALUE: £350–525

L33. C.Q.D. MEDALS

Date: 1909.
Ribbon: Plain dark blue or crimson (*).
Metal: Silver-gilt, silver, bronze.
Size: 45mm.
Description: (Obverse) the SS *Republic* with the initials C.Q.D. at the top; (reverse) the words FOR GALLANTRY across the middle, with a very verbose inscription round the circumference and continued in eight lines across the field. Ring suspension. Issued unnamed, but examples are known with the recipient's name and ship privately engraved.
Comments: *This medal takes its curious name from the CQD signal (All Stations Distress) sent out by the stricken White Star steamship* Republic *after it collided with the Italian steamer* Florida *on January 21, 1909. The liner* Baltic *responded to the call. The* Republic *was the more severely damaged vessel, but all of her passengers and crew were transferred, first to the* Florida *and then to the* Baltic, *before she sank. The saloon passengers of the* Baltic *and* Republic *subscribed to a fund to provide medals to the crews of all three ships in saving more than 1700 lives. Silver-gilt examples without suspender were presented to senior officers of the three ships involved and to Jack Binns, the Marconi operator aboard the* Republic *who sent out the CQD radio signal. Silver medals with ring suspenders were presented to the officers and crews. Binns became a hero when the survivors reached New York and was given a welcome parade. This was the first time that radio was used to effect a rescue at sea and indirectly sealed the fate of the* Titanic *three years later, as the White Star Line wrongly assumed that any larger liner would take several hours to sink and radio would obtain help quickly within well-used shipping lanes and lifeboats would only be required to effect the transfer of passengers and crew. As a result the number of lifeboats on the* Titanic *was severely reduced. Coincidentally, Jack Binns was offered the post of wireless officer on board the new* Titanic *but declined. It is believed that bronze examples exist but the Editor would be pleased to learn of any definite sightings of these.*
 * Originally it was believed this medal was awarded with a dark blue ribbon. However, many examples have appeared on the market with a plain crimson ribbon. The Times of February 8, 1909 carried a report that described the medal as being "fitted with a ring for suspension, from a crimson ribbon 1½" wide."

VALUE:
Silver-gilt	£1000–1500
Silver	£450–550

L33A. BOLTON & DISTRICT HUMANE SOCIETY MEDAL

Date: 1895.
Ribbon: Plain dark blue.
Metal: Silver and bronze.
Size: 51.3mm (general medal) or 35mm (Hulton Colliery medal).
Description: The Society's general medal is described thus: (Obverse) a vertical figure of flying angel holding a wreath in her left hand, with "VIRTUTE ET PATIENTIA" around the border. There is a small flower at the six o'clock position, beneath which is the maker's name "JENKINS . BIRMM". (Reverse) around the border is "BOLTON AND DISTRICT HUMANE SOCIETY". The centre is blank for the recipient's name and the date of the act. In 1911 the Society additionally issued the Hulton Colliery variety medal, which is a smaller medal in bronze, with the same obverse and reverse design, albeit with the legend "HULTON COLLIERY DISASTER DECEMBER 21ST 1910" in the reverse centre. The latter variety medal was issued unnamed. The suspender consists of ornamental laurel leaves, very similar to that on the Crimea Medal.
Comments: *Established in Bolton in 1895, the Society issued its own silver and bronze medals and testimonials for acts of lifesaving in Bolton and neighbouring areas. Between 1895 and 1911 the Society awarded approximately 19 silver and 48 bronze medals. The Hulton Colliery variety of the Society's medal was created following the explosion of 21 December 1910 at Hulton Colliery (Pretoria Pit), which killed at least 344 miners. Large numbers of their colleagues were involved in rescue efforts and the grim and dangerous work of recovering the bodies. Rescuers efforts were recognized by awards of the Edward Medal (Mines) 2nd class, the Order of St John Life Saving Medal, Royal Humane Society medals, the Lancashire and Cheshire Coal Owners Rescue Station Medal with "Hulton 1911" clasp, and the Bolton Society's own special medal, the latter going to approximately 165 recipients.*

VALUE: General medal in silver: Rare
General medal in bronze: Rare
Hulton Colliery variety medal in bronze: £300–375

L34. *CARPATHIA* AND *TITANIC* MEDALS

Date: 1912.
Ribbon: Maroon.
Metal: Gold, silver or bronze.
Size: Height 40mm; max. width 35mm.
Description: The ornately shaped medal, in the best Art Nouveau style, has the suspension ring threaded through the head of Neptune whose long beard flows into two dolphins terminating in a fouled anchor and ship's spars. (Obverse) the *Carpathia* steaming between icebergs; (reverse) a twelve-line inscription, with the name of the recipient and the name of the manufacturer at the foot. The ribbon hangs from a straight bar suspender.
Comments: *This medal recalls one of the greatest tragedies at sea, when the White Star liner* Titanic *struck an iceberg on her maiden voyage and sank with the loss of 1490 lives. The 711 survivors were picked up by the* Carpathia *whose officers and men were subsequently awarded this medal in gold, silver or bronze according to the rank of the recipient.*

VALUE:		
Gold (14)		£30,000–40,000
Silver (110)		£12,000–15,000
Bronze (180)		£6000–8000

L35. LLOYD'S MEDALS FOR SERVICES TO LLOYD'S

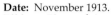

Date: November 1913.
Ribbon: Blue with broad white stripes towards the edge.
Metal: Gold or silver.
Size: 36mm.
Description: (Obverse) Neptune in a chariot drawn by four horses; (reverse) an oak-leaf wreath enclosing a scroll inscribed FOR SERVICES TO LLOYD'S. Fitted with ring suspension.
Comments: *Instituted by Lloyd's Committee, this medal was intended to reward services of a general nature.*

VALUE:		Miniature
Gold (14)	£2000–4750	—
Silver (10)	£1000–1250	£200–250

L35A. *ERINPURA* AND *TOPAZE* MEDAL

Date: June 1919.
Ribbon: None.
Metal: Silver or bronze.
Size: 32mm.
Description: (Obverse) simple inscription . 526 . MEN, WOMEN AND CHILDREN . TAKEN OFF . S.S. BRINPURA . AGROUND ON . MUSHEGERA REEF BY H.M.S.TOPAZE . 15.6.19; (reverse) an oak-leaf wreath with A MEMENTO PRESENTED BY THE PASSENGERS within.
Comments: *In a severe dust storm on 15 June 1919 the SS* Erinpura *went aground at full speed on the Mushegera Reef in the Red Sea. HMS* Topaze, *a Gem Class scout cruiser, came to her aid and took off the passengers and most of the crew, leaving a few men on board to maintain the engines. Attempts to refloat her were unsuccessful as the bow section was stuck fast and eventually had to be cut away and completely replaced. The medals were struck on behalf of the grateful passengers and presented to the officers and crew of HMS* Topaze. *The medals are known in bronze although there are unconfirmed reports of examples in silver—perhaps presented to the officers (?). The obverse is incorrectly inscribed* <u>BRINPURA</u> *as the ship has been confirmed as the* Erinpura, *built for the British India Steam Navigation Co. Ltd in 1910 and sunk by German bombers en route to Malta in World War II.*

VALUE:	Bronze	£100–150	Silver	—

L36. ORDER OF INDUSTRIAL HEROISM

Date: 1923.
Ribbon: Bright watered red.
Metal: Bronze.
Size: 28mm.
Description: (Obverse) a modern interpretation of St Christopher carrying Christ (by Eric Gill); (reverse) inscription ORDER OF INDUSTRIAL HEROISM around the perimeter and in the upper half AWARDED BY THE DAILY HERALD above the recipient's name and date of award.
Comments: *Created by the "Daily Herald" and first issued in 1923. It was given as a reward to the "workers" who demonstrated bravery in the workplace and was initially only to be awarded to members of a Trade Union. However, there are numerous examples of the awards being given to non Union members and the definition of "workplace" was wide. The award was intimately associated with the "Daily Herald" throughout the lifetime of the newspaper and when it ceased publication in 1963 the award was discontinued. The medal was always awarded with a certificate and a monetary award. 440 were awarded.*

VALUE:	£650–850

L36A. COLONEL WOODCOCK'S SWIMMING PRIZES TRUST MEDAL

Date: Approx. 1925.
Ribbon: Seen as dark blue—25mm.
Metal: Silver.
Size: 28mm.
Description: Circular with a ring suspension. (Obverse) a swimmer in the centre with the words COLONEL WOODCOCK'S SWIMMING MEDAL around; (reverse) a wreath, open at the top, with space for engraving details in the centre.
Comments: *The Bristol City and County Council, on the recommendation of the Baths and Education Committees, award twelve medals each year—eight for swimming and four for life saving. About 1950 the medals were discontinued and lapel badges instituted instead.*

VALUE: (for life saving)   £150–250

L37. CORPORATION OF GLASGOW BRAVERY MEDALS

Type I obverse.

Date: 1924
Ribbon: Green with red edges.
Metal: Gold, silver or bronze.
Size: 38mm (type I), 33mm (type II), 30mm (type III).
Description: Type I: (obverse) Fame blowing a trumpet and holding a laurel wreath in front of a circular scrolled cartouche inscribed FOR BRAVERY; (reverse) plain, engraved with the name and details of the recipient. Type II: (obverse) wreath enclosing the words FOR BRAVERY; (reverse) Arms of the Corporation of Glasgow and details of the recipient. Type III: (obverse) Arms of the Corporation of Glasgow with FOR BRAVERY above and two sprigs of laurel below; (reverse) plain for details of the recipient. Fitted with a ring suspension and an ornate thistle brooch inscribed GALLANTRY in a scroll.
Comments: *Following the reorganisation of local government in Scotland in 1975, the award ceased and was replaced by the Strathclyde Regional Council Medal for Bravery.*

VALUE:	Type I	Type II	Type III
Gold	—	—	£350–450
Silver	£300–400	£300–400	—
Bronze	—	—	—

L37A. IMPERIAL CHEMICAL INDUSTRIES BRAVERY AWARD

Date: 1930.
Ribbon: Dark blue suspended from a brooch bar bearing the word "Fortis".
Metal: Gold (9ct) (pre-war), later bronze.
Size: 38mm x 26mm
Description: (Obverse) "Awarded for Bravery" with a lion rampant bearing the letters "I.C.I."; (reverse) inscription in raised letters (name, location and date of incident).
Comments: *A meeting of the ICI Central Council in 1929 proposed an award to be given for outstanding acts of bravery by ICI workers whilst at work. Originally awarded in 9ct gold but after World War II issued in bronze. The first award was made to Harry Smithies in 1929 and the last to James Nicol in 1975. ICI were taken over in 2008.*

VALUE:		
	Gold	£1000–1500
	Bronze	£800–1000

L38. RSPCA MARGARET WHEATLEY CROSS

Date: 1936.

Ribbon: 32mm blue with a white stripe towards each edge.

Metal: Bronze.

Size: 33mm square.

Description: Cross pattée with a central circular cross with rounded ends superimposed. R.S.P.C.A. across the top arm of the outer cross and INSTD. 1936 across the lower arm. THE MARGARET WHEATLEY CROSS inscribed in four lines across the centre. (Reverse) central circle inscribed FOR BRAVING DEATH ON BEHALF OF ANIMALS, above and below a raised horizontal panel engraved with the details of the award. Fixed ring for suspension.

Comments: *The RSPCA's highest award, it was named in memory of 16 year-old Margaret Wheatley who was killed by a train at Grange-over-Sands on June 4, 1936 while saving her dog that had got trapped on the railway line. She was posthumously awarded the RSPCA's Silver Medal and was also the first recipient of the cross named in her honour. To date, a total of 70 crosses have been awarded, at least 32 of them posthumously.*

VALUE: —

L38A. DUNDEE CORPORATION MEDAL FOR GALLANTRY

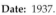

Date: 1937.

Ribbon: Blue with silver top bar bearing the word GALLANTRY.

Metal: Silver.

Size: 38mm.

Description: A circular medal with plain ring suspension bearing (obverse) the coat of arms of the City and Corporation of Dundee. (Reverse) a thistle flower and leaves with the words AWARDED TO . . . FOR BRAVERY above.

Comments: *Awarded for acts of gallantry within the city of Dundee irrespective of whether or not the person was a citizen of Dundee. Manufactured and supplied by the local firm of Laurence W. Strachan. Only 41 medals were awarded between its institution in 1937 and 29 September 1951.*

VALUE: £550–650

L39. LLOYD'S MEDAL FOR BRAVERY AT SEA

Date: 1940.

Ribbon: White with broad blue stripes at the sides.

Metal: Silver.

Size: 36mm.

Description: (Obverse) a seated nude male figure holding a laurel wreath, extending his hand towards a ship on the horizon; (reverse) a trident surmounted by a scroll inscribed BRAVERY, enclosed in a wreath of oak leaves. It has a ring suspender.

Comments: *Instituted by Lloyd's Committee, it was awarded to officers and men of the Merchant Navy and fishing fleets for exceptional bravery at sea in time of war. A total of 523 medals was awarded up to December 1947 when it was discontinued.*

VALUE:
Silver   £550–850   *Miniature*   £200–250

L40. LONDON, MIDLAND AND SCOTTISH RAILWAY MEDAL

Date: 1940.
Ribbon: Dark blue.
Metal: Silver.
Size: 38mm.
Description: (Obverse) Three different steam locomotive chimneys with a radiant sun in the right background with the inscription LONDON, MIDLAND AND SCOTTISH RAILWAY round the circumference; (reverse) a locomotive driving wheel on which is superimposed at the left a sprig of laurel, with the inscription FOR COURAGE or FOR MERIT round the top of the circumference. The date 1940 appears in the exergue. Fitted with a plain ring for suspension.
Comments: *Instituted by the Chairman of the LMS Company for acts of gallantry or meritorious service, hence the two different reverse types. The Chairman, Lord Stamp, was killed in an air raid in 1941 and it is believed that many of the records relating to this medal perished with him. Although the exact number of awards is not known, it is believed that about 20 awards were made.*

VALUE: —

L41. SOUTHERN RAILWAY MERITORIOUS SERVICE MEDAL

Date: 1940.
Ribbon: Green with railway track and sleepers in gold.
Metal: Silver gilt.
Size: 32mm.
Description: (Obverse) a cross formy with SR in a circle at the centre, superimposed on a laurel wreath surrounded by a locomotive driving wheel; (reverse) FOR MERIT in seriffed capitals over a space for the recipient's name and SOUTHERN RAILWAY across the foot. The ornamental suspension bar is in the form of a vehicle spring. This medal was designed by Kruger Gray and struck at the Royal Mint.
Comments: *Instituted by the Directors of the Company for award to those employees considered to have performed outstanding deeds in the performance of their duties. 18 medals were awarded at a ceremony on August 16, 1940, and a further six medals were subsequently awarded.*

VALUE: —

L42. THE DALE AWARD

Instituted: November 1940.
Ribbon: White with broad blue and narrow black stripes towards the edges.
Metal: Silver.
Size: 33mm.
Description: (Obverse) a central medallion enamelled in white bearing the spires of Coventry Cathedral, surrounded by an inscription: THE DALE AWARD/COVENTRY.NOV.14.1940; (reverse) a laurel wreath enclosing a ten-line inscription across the middle: AWARDED BY THE COVENTRY HOSPITAL FUND FOR DEVOTION TO HOSPITAL & AMBULANCE DUTY DURING THE COVENTRY AIR RAID NOVEMBER 14th 1940. The medal bears the Birmingham assay marks and maker's mark of Thomas Fattorini. The medal was not named.
Comments: *This medal was awarded by the Coventry and Warwickshire Hospital Saturday Fund to ambulance drivers and others for devotion to duty during the air raid of 14 November 1940. It is believed that 32 awards were made. A fascinating recollection by a recipient can be found on the website www. coventrymemories.co.uk.*

VALUE: £450–550

L43. LONDON PASSENGER TRANSPORT BOARD MEDAL FOR BRAVERY

Instituted: 1940.

Ribbon: Red with green central stripe and four narrow white stripes on either side.

Metal: Cupro-nickel.

Size: 38mm.

Description: (Obverse) a naked man kneeling and turning a large wheel; (reverse) the words LONDON TRANSPORT above a sprig of laurel, with a space for the recipient's name and a three-line inscription across the foot: FOR BRAVERY AND DEVOTION TO DUTY. Plain suspension bar and an ornamental brooch fitment at the top of the ribbon.

Comments: *This medal was instituted by Lord Ashfield, Chairman of the LPTB, to reward "special deeds of bravery" undertaken by LPTB staff during the Blitz. Only nine medals were awarded (all presented on February 21, 1941) before the medal was discontinued, after some government pressure, to encourage nominations for the official civilian bravery awards of the George Cross and George Medal. A few unnamed specimens are known, possibly reaching the market from the stock of John Pinches when they ceased business.*

VALUE:
Named (9)	£750–850
Unnamed	£250–300

L44. LONDON AND NORTH EASTERN RAILWAY GALLANTRY MEDAL

Date: 1941.

Ribbon: Dark blue with a central white stripe flanked by narrow white stripes.

Metal: Silver with a matt finish.

Size: 38mm.

Description: (Obverse) a shield containing the arms of the company, superimposed on a laurel wreath surrounded by the inscription LONDON AND NORTH EASTERN RAILWAY on a raised band; (reverse) a scroll for the recipient's name superimposed on a laurel wreath with the rising sun in the background. The raised band is inscribed FOR COURAGE AND RESOURCE. Fitted with a plain suspension bar and an ornamental brooch bar at the top of the ribbon.

Comments: *Awarded "for outstanding acts of gallantry and resource which are not connected with enemy action, but which are of such a standard as would warrant recommendations for Government recognition had the acts been connected with enemy action". As some of the medals were awarded for actions resulting from enemy air raids the phrase "not connected with enemy action" was very liberally interpreted. A total of 22 medals were awarded, the last in 1947.*

VALUE: —

L44A. DICKIN MEDAL

Date: 1943.
Ribbon: Three equal bands of green, dark brown and pale blue.
Metal: Bronze.
Size: 36mm.
Description: (Obverse) a laurel wreath enclosing the inscription "For Gallantry" in raised cursive script over the motto WE ALSO SERVE in block capitals; the initials PDSA in a tablet at the top of the wreath; (reverse) the date, name of recipient and details of the award. Fitted with a plain ring for suspension.
Comments: *Awarded by the People's Dispensary for Sick Animals to recognise acts of bravery by birds and animals in wartime, and consequently popularly known as the Animals' VC. Originally, Maria Dickin, founder of the PDSA, also instituted a lesser award for acts of bravery by animals, known as the PDSA Silver Medal. The Dickin Medal is very rarely awarded but in recent years two were awarded to guide dogs that assisted their blind handlers to safety. The 29th canine recipient was "Sasha", a labrador, killed by an explosive device in Afghanistan in 2008. To mark the centenary of WWI in 2014, an Honorary Dickin Medal was bestowed to WWI war horse "Warrior". Two awards were presented to dogs in 2015/16; one to "Diesel", a Belgian Malinois, awarded posthumously in December 2015 after he was killed during the Paris terror attacks of that year; a second in April 2016 was awarded to "Lucca" a German Shepherd serving in the US Marine Corps. Also in 2016, awarded posthumously to Sergeant Reckless, a US Marine Corp horse who served during the Korean War. During the Battle of Outpost Vegas in 1953, despite being wounded twice, Reckless made 51 trips from the ammunition supply point to the firing sites. She then carried wounded soldiers down the mountain before heading back into the fierce battle. Medals to famous animals tend to sell for far higher figures.*

VALUE: £10,000–20,000
(Spink sold the medal to Rip a mongrel dog for £24,000+, including the buyer's premium, in April 2009)

L45. BINNEY MEMORIAL MEDAL

Date: 1947.
Ribbon: None.
Metal: Bronze.
Size: 48mm.
Description: (Obverse) a bust of Captain R.D. Binney, CBE, RN; (reverse) inscription FOR COURAGE IN SUPPORT OF LAW AND ORDER and AWARDED TO above the recipient's name on a raised tablet.
Comments: *Instituted in memory of Captain Ralph Douglas Binney who was killed on 8 December 1944 in the City of London while attempting to apprehend two armed robbers single-handedly. It is awarded annually to the British citizen who displays the greatest courage in support of law and order within the areas under the jurisdiction of the Metropolitan Police and the City of London Police. The medal is not intended for wear. See MEDAL NEWS, August 1998 for a detailed article on the medal by Victor Knight.*

VALUE: £750–1000

Sergeant Reckless was nominated for the PDSA Dickin Medal by her biographer Robin Hutton, supported by the US Marine Corps. Hutton commented: "Her heroics embody the word Marine and those who served alongside Reckless truly loved her. She was loved by the marines; they took care of her better than they took care of themselves—throwing their flak jackets over her to protect her when incoming fire was heavy, risking their own safety. (Image courtesy of www.pdsa.org).

L46. SEA CADET GALLANTRY CROSS

Date:
Ribbon: Red with a central white stripe and blue stripes towards the edges.
Metal: Silver.
Size: 36mm.
Description: (Obverse) a fouled anchor within a wreath superimposed on a cross pattée inscribed FOR GALLANTRY with initials N and L on the left and right arms of the cross to signify the Navy League; (reverse) blank.
Comments: *Awarded by the Sea Cadet Association, originally the Navy League, for gallantry in saving or attempting to save life under circumstances of exceptional danger and personal risk to the saver. It has been very rarely awarded.*

VALUE: £800–1000

L47. SEA CADET GALLANTRY MEDAL

Date:
Ribbon: Red with a central white stripe and blue stripes towards the edges.
Metal: Bronze.
Size: 36mm.
Description: A circular medal with a plain ring suspension. (Obverse) an image of the cross as above but without the initials on the arms; (reverse) blank.
Comments: *Awarded for gallantry in saving or attempting to save life under circumstances of considerable danger and personal risk to the saver. Both the cross and the medal are manufactured by Spink & Son. Gallantry certificates and commendations are also awarded for life saving in lesser circumstances.*

VALUE: —

L47A. GALLANTRY MEDALLISTS' LEAGUE GOLD MEDAL FOR COURAGE

Date: 2006
Ribbon: Red with a dark blue stripe towards the right and light blue towards the left, representing the colours of the Gallantry Medallists League.
Metal: 9ct white gold and gilded.
Size: 36mm.
Description: The medal is made in two pieces. (Obverse) a six-pointed star with a central disc hand painted in enamels surrounded by a red enamel ring bearing the words "FOR COURAGE". The central disc depicts a hand at the top pulling up another hand, symbolising rescue, the upper hand has wings symbolising the innocence of youth. These wings are carried over into the design of the suspension. (Reverse) inscribed with the name of the medal, the recipient and details of the act for which the award is made.
Comments: *The medal is to be presented each year to the most deserving recipient of the* Woman's Own *"Children of Courage" award—a ceremony which was instituted in 1973 to honour ten of the UK's most deserving children who have acted heroically over the previous year. The heroism can take many forms from courage in the face of disability or steadfast devotion to bravery in saving life. The first award was made in December 2006 to nine-year-old Lewis Woodruffe who calmly led his young brothers and sisters to safety during a disastrous fire at the family home.*

VALUE: —

L48. HUNDRED OF SALFORD HUMANE SOCIETY SWIMMING PROFICIENCY MEDALS

Date: 1889.

Ribbon: Special Proficiency Medal and Proficiency Medal issued without a ribbon, although often seen with a blue ribbon.

Metal: Both silver.

Size: Special Proficiency Medal—irregular shape with small ring suspender. Proficiency Medal—circular 26mm with a small ring suspender.

Description: Special Proficiency Medal: (obverse) an ornamental pattern of three shields, bearing the arms of Salford backed by crossed tridents. An intertwined blue enamel band around the medal carries the legend HUMANE SOCIETY FOR THE HUNDRED OF SALFORD; (reverse) plain. Proficiency Medal: (obverse) a single shield carrying the arms of Salford surrounded by a blue enamel band that carries the words HUMANE SOCIETY FOR THE HUNDRED OF SALFORD, the whole is encircled by a wreath and is surmounted by a crown; (reverse) plain.

Comments: *Following the discontinuing of awards for life saving in 1921, the Society began to run competitions for children with the object of encouraging swimming proficiency with a view to life saving. Two medals were awarded, the Special Proficiency Medal and the Proficiency Medal. Each year there are a number of winners of the Proficiency Medal and the best boy and girl are selected to receive the Special Proficiency Medal.*

VALUE:

Special Proficiency Medal	£75–125
Proficiency Medal	£50–80

L49. ROYAL HUMANE SOCIETY SWIMMING PROFICIENCY MEDAL

Date: 1882.

Ribbon: None.

Metal: Silver.

Size: 51mm.

Description: (Obverse) a life saving scene, circumscribed by the motto NARE EST ALIENAM NOSSE SALUTEM in sans serif capitals and by a heavily beaded border. The exergue is blank to allow the engraved details of the school and the date of award to be entered; (reverse) "Awarded FOR PROFICIENCY IN SWIMMING EXERCISE with reference to saving life from DROWNING". Above this "ROYAL HUMANE SOCIETY", and below "INST: 1774" and again circumscribed by heavy beading.

Comments: *In February 1882, the RHS received a letter from Dr Dukes, the physician at Rugby School, relating to the establishment of a prize "for swimming and for a knowledge of the treatment of the apparently drowned". The Society saw merit in this and by the end of the year the medal was awarded to seven winners of competitions held at seven public schools. The competition grew in popularity and for many years 20 to 30 medals per year were awarded. However, with increasing competition from the Royal Life Saving Society the RHS award declined in popularity and the last awards were made in 1948. The medal was awarded only in silver, although a bronze specimen is known.*

VALUE: £75–125

L49A. ROYAL LIFE SAVING SOCIETY PROFICIENCY MEDALS (see also no. 387)

Diploma with Honours.

First type Award of Merit.

Date: Bronze Medallion—1892.
    Award of Merit (silver)—1908.
    Diploma (gold)—1896.

Ribbon: 33mm—light blue with centre white stripe and two intermediate dark blue stripes.

Metal: Bronze; Silver; Gold.

Size: Differing designs: 25–32mm.

Description: First type (1891–1904) (obverse) a water rescue with THE LIFE SAVING SOCIETY ESTABLISHED 1891 around; (reverse) the name of the recipient in the centre with QUEMCUNQUE MISERUM VIDERIS HOMINEM SCIAS (WHOMSOEVER YOU SEE IN DISTRESS, RECOGNIZE IN HIM A FELLOW MAN), the motto of the Society, around. Second type (1905–37) (obverse) the name of the Society with added ROYAL. Third type (1938–54) (obverse) the name of the Society within a circle with a boathook and an oar crossed and tied with a bow. Fourth type (1955–80) same as third type but reduced in size from 32mm to 25mm. Fifth type (1981 to date) reinstated to 32mm size. (Reverse) plain, engraved with the name of the recipient. The Award of Merit comes in three types: type I silver, depicting a rescue, type II the same but with a wreath around and type III the Lifebelt and crossed boathook/oar design—since 1952 this has been awarded in gilt metal with blue and white enamelled centre. The Diploma medal is a gold coloured medal bearing a blue enamelled shield.

Comments: *The awards of this society are very complex, for example silver awards of merit fall into at least five classes, which are outside the scope of this Yearbook. These medals were awarded for various stages of proficiency in swimming and lifesaving. In 1945 a further exam medal, the Bronze Cross in two sizes to go between the Bronze Medallion and Award of Merit, was established. From 1955 to about 1990 the medals were reduced to 25mm diameter.*

VALUE:

Bronze Medal	£5–10
Bronze Cross	£10–15
Award of Merit	£20–35
Diploma	£80–100

Second type Bronze Medallion.

Second type Award of Merit.

Bronze Cross.

L50. THE ROYAL LIFE SAVING SOCIETY MOUNTBATTEN MEDAL

Date: 1951.
Ribbon: None.
Metal: Silver.
Size: 51mm.
Description: A circular medal without suspender. The medal is cased. The obverse has the family crest of the Mountbatten family and on the reverse is "The Mountbatten Medal of the Royal Life Saving Society for the award holder who makes the best rescue of the year—Presented by the President RLSS The Earl Mountbatten of Burma". The name of the recipient and the year of the award is engraved on the lower rim of the medal.
Comments: *Earl Mountbatten instituted the medal in 1951 and it was to be awarded annually for a rescue adjudged by RLSS Commonwealth Council to be the bravest performed in that year by an award holder of the RLSS who, in the opinion of the Commonwealth president, makes the best rescue of the year. Originally, the conditions of the award required that the potential recipient should, "not have been otherwise signally honoured". This effectively disqualified many worthy recipients for consideration of the award, so, in 1965 this condition was removed. Since its inception the medal has generally been awarded annually, but occasionally no award was made, as the rescues in those years were adjudged not to have met the high standard necessary to qualify for the medal. Exceptionally, in 1955, 2004 and 2006 there were two recipients. To date 36 awards have been made.*

Value: £500–600

L51. TYNE & WEAR FIRE AND CIVIL DEFENCE AUTHORITY MEDAL FOR BRAVERY

Date: 1986
Ribbon: Three blue and two white stripes.
Metal: Base metal with colouring according to class.
Size: 35mm.
Description: (Obverse) The medal took the form of a five winged star representative of the Tyne & Wear Fire Service badge with a central device consisting of an outer collar bearing the words "Tyne and Wear Fire and Civil Defence Authority", the inner circle having stylised flames with "Award for Bravery" incorporated above and below the flames; (reverse) a plain back on which were engraved the recipient's name and the date of act that the medal was awarded for. Details of the act of bravery were not included but were recorded in a Roll of Honour book.
Comments: *The medal was awarded in three classes: Gold, Silver and Bronze to recognise acts of bravery by members of the public in emergency situations in Tyne & Wear. It was also awarded to members of the Fire Service for acts of bravery outside their normal firefighting duties. In 1992 the award was replaced by a scroll.*

VALUE:

Gold (21)	£200–250
Silver (45)	£100–150
Bronze (84)	£75–100

In June 2014, the French Government announced that all those who took part in Operations in France from June 1944 until May 1945, who were still alive, would receive the award of the Legion d'Honneur. Pictured above are a number of Normandy Veterans who were presented with the Legion d'Honneur by the Mayor of Arromanches, M. Jardin, at a special ceremony on June 5, 2016. The two year wait was down to the fact that the French Government hadn't considered the sheer number of surviving veterans. Thankfully the administrative problems were finally ironed out and more of the medals have been presented since the above ceremony.

FOREIGN MEDALS
Found in British Groups

In this section we have included a selection of the most common "foreign" medals found in British Groups, i.e. those medals issued by a foreign authority to British or Commonwealth personnel which they in turn have sought permission to wear alongside those medals awarded by their own government. Quite often these medals, when found, were awarded for gallantry where the recipient was directly involved in action with allies from the country who conferred the medal, either fighting alongside them or in an act of heroism involving one of their countrymen.

We are deeply indebted to readers, and especially those members of the British Medal Forum, who have forwarded suggestions for which medals to include within this section to allow it to expand, we do hope that more will be forthcoming in the future. We are particularly interested in any information on numbers of these medals and decorations awarded to British personnel as this will undoubtedly affect value considerably.

It must be stressed that included here are only the most common medals found in British and Commonwealth groups and the list is by no means exhaustive. It has always been common practice amongst high ranking officers of all countries to, in effect, "swap" orders and decorations with allies, some of which would never be received by the ordinary fighting soldier, sailor or airman. Because of the rarity of these awards within British groups it has been decided to exclude them at this stage, although we are grateful for all examples of "one-offs" that have been sent in.

As always it must be stressed that the prices given here are for single examples as found in dealers' lists and websites, when found in an attributable group their value dramatically increases.

Apart from medals given by "foreign" governments in wartime, various awards are also given by overseas authorities for attendance on particular occasions or for valuable service rendered, these are far too diverse and numerous to include in this publication, although many do recieve restricted permission to wear. A good example is the medal illustrated left, awarded by the Sultan of Johore in 1955 on the occasion of his Diamond Jubilee: this medal is typical of the type of medal awarded to British citizens by overseas authorities and given restricted permission to wear by Her Majesty the Queen. In this instance permission was granted to wear: *a.* In the presence of the Sultan; *b.* In the presence of any member of the Ruling House; *c.* On all official occasions whilst in Johore.

This and other medals awarded by "foreign" governments are detailed in the book *Honour the Recipients of Foreign Awards* which lists every gazetted British and Dominion recipient of such an honour from 1914 until 1968. This is another title in the "Honour" series by Michael Maton published in 2013 by Token Publishing Ltd (see advertisement on page 126).

BELGIUM

As with most orders, these are awarded in various classes. In this section we have concentrated on those most commonly encountered.

Order of Leopold II, Officer's breast badge.

Order of the Crown, Commander's badge.

ORDER OF LEOPOLD II

Commander's neck badge	£200–350
Knight's badge	£55–75
Officer's badge	£50–65
Miniature	£30–40

ORDER OF THE CROWN

Commander's badge	£250–350
Officer's badge	£40–55
Knight's badge	£30–45
Miniature	£30–40

CROIX DE GUERRE

WWI	£30–45
WWII	£35–50
Miniature	£14–17

DECORATION MILITAIRE

DECORATION MILITAIRE	£30–45
Miniature	£12–16

FRANCE

LEGION d'HONNEUR 1870–1951

Commander's neck badge	£350–450
Officer's badge	£125–175
Knight's badge	£75–100
Miniature	£30–45

LEGION d'HONNEUR 1951 to date

As awarded to British veterans	£100–150

MÉDAILLE MILITAIRE 1870 £35–45

Miniature £30–40

CROIX DE GUERRE

1914–15 reverse	£30–45
1914–16 reverse	£30–45
1914–17 reverse	£30–45
1914–18 reverse	£25–35
WWII	£45–55
for each star or palm add £5	
Miniature	£14–17

MEDAILLE d'HONNEUR DES AFFAIRE ETRANGERE

	Military with swords	Civil
First class "en vermeil"	£250–300	£150–200
2nd class "en argent"	£100–150	£50–75
3rd class "en bronze"	£50–75	£30–45
Miniature	£20–25	£15–20

GREECE

ORDER OF THE REDEEMER
    Commander's badge   £400–650
    Knight's badge   £250–350
    Officer's badge   £150–200

    Miniature   £50–60

GREEK WAR CROSS   £50–100

    Miniature   £15-20

ITALY

ORDER OF THE CROWN
    Commander's badge   £150–250
    Officer's badge   £75–100
    Knight's badge   £55–75

    Miniature   £45–65

AL VALORE (unnamed)
    Bronze   £30–45
    Silver   £45–55
    Silver-gilt   £55–65

    Miniature   *bronze* £20–25
                         silver £30–35
                         gilt £30–35

Restrikes are also known. They can be distinguished from the originals by the omission of the initials FG at the bottom on the obverse.

ITALY *continued*

In addition to the above medals, the Messina Earth-quake Medal, awarded by the King of Italy in 1908 to British personnel who went to the aid of victims of the tragic earthquake at Messina, can be found under Medal No. 163A

WAR MERIT CROSS   £20–30

Miniature   £15-20

JAPAN

ORDER OF THE RISING SUN

3rd Class	£550–650
4th Class	£400–500
5th Class	£250–300
6th Class	£200–250
7th Class	£55–75
8th Class	£35–55
Miniature	£40-60

ORDER OF THE SACRED TREASURE

3rd Class	£475–600
4th Class	£250–350
5th Class	£150–250
6th Class	£100–175
7th Class	£40–50
8th Class	£35–45
Miniature	£45-65

LUXEMBOURG

**CROIX DE GUERRE
WWII**   £60–80

Miniature   £20–25

NORWAY

**KING HAAKON VII
FREEDOM CROSS**   £175–250

Miniature   £20–25

**KING HAAKON VII
FREEDOM MEDAL**   £120–180

Miniature   £20–25

OMAN

SULTAN'S COMMENDATION MEDAL   £20–40
   Miniature   £20–25

GENERAL SERVICE MEDAL   £20–35
   Miniature   £20–25

AS SUMMOOD MEDAL   £25–45
   Miniature   £20–25

OMAN PEACE MEDAL   £20–35
   Miniature   £20–25

These and other Omani medals were awarded to British personnel seconded to the Sultanate following periods of unrest in that country. For more information on them and on the role of British Forces see *Awards of the Sultanate of Oman* by Lt-Col Ashley Tinson.

POLAND

CROSS OF VALOUR
WWII	£65–85
Miniature	£15–20

ORDER OF POLONIA RESTITUTA
WWI	From £100
WWII	£75–100
Miniature	£15–20

ROMANIA

ORDER OF THE STAR OF ROMANIA
WITH SWORDS (1864–1931) £75–150

Miniature £40–55

ORDER OF THE CROWN (1881–1932) £75–150

Miniature £30–40

RUSSIA

ORDER OF ST STANISLAUS
Gold — From £5000+
Silver-gilt — £1500–2000

Miniature — £170–290

ORDER OF ST ANNE

Gold — From £6000+
Miniature — £170–290

CROSS OF ST GEORGE
3rd Class — £350–525
4th Class — £250–400

Miniature — £85–110

MEDAL OF ST GEORGE
3rd Class — £150–265
4th Class — £100–210

Miniature — £35–55

MEDAL FOR ZEAL
Silver — £225–325

Miniature — £35–55

See also MYB 203A and 203AA.

SOVIET UNION

The Soviet Union awarded some 160 orders and medals to British Servicemen either during or immediately after World War II. The most numerous of these being the Order of the Patriotic War (1st and 2nd class), the Medal for Valour, the Medal for Meritorious Service in Battle and the Order of the Red Star. However, the numbers of these awarded to British personnel were still less than 30 in each case and as such documented examples come on the market very rarely making it extremely difficult to give accurate valuations. For more information see MEDAL NEWS June/July 2001.

SERBIA

ORDER OF KARAGEORGE (1904–15)
  4th Class   £450–575

  Miniature   £60–75

ORDER OF THE WHITE EAGLE (1882–1915)
  Knight's badge   £350–475

  Miniature   £90–110

TURKEY

ORDER OF THE OSMANIEH
  1st Class   £550–675
  2nd Class   £450–550
  3rd Class   £250–350
  4th Class   £95–150
  5th Class   £65–85

  Miniature   £35–60

ORDER OF THE MEDJIDIEH
  Commander's badge   £550–750
  Knight's badge   £250–300

  Miniature   £45–65

UNITED STATES

DISTINGUISHED SERVICE CROSS   from £75
(Army)

US NAVY CROSS   from £75

US AIR FORCE CROSS   from £75

DISTINGUISHED SERVICE MEDAL   from £75
(Army)

Miniatures of US medals are available, prices range from £5–10 for "plain" examples to £10–20 for more sophisticated "fancy" pieces.

375

UNITED STATES *continued*

US DISTINGUISHED SERVICE MEDAL　£25–35
(Navy-Marine Corps)

US DISTINGUISHED FLYING CROSS　£25–35

Legionnaire

LEGION OF MERIT
　Commander　　　　£150–250
　Officer　　　　　　£120–175
　Legionnaire　　　　£75–100

US SILVER STAR　　£35–50

US BRONZE STAR　　£25–35

US AIR MEDAL　　£25–35

MEDALS
Of the Irish Republic (Eire)

Since 1921 Ireland has been divided into two distinct countries: the Irish Free State in the south and Ulster in the north, both as separate countries within the British Empire. However, in 1949 the Irish Free State proclaimed itself a republic and became known as Eire. Since that time it has issued its own medals and honours, including a number of retrospective awards for the troubled times prior to independence and for the period before it became a republic. Irish men and women served with the British armed forces at home and overseas and many Irish regiments famously took part in many of the fiercest actions of World War I. Medals and awards for these actions will be found in the main section of this book. During World War II the Irish Defence Forces remained neutral although the Dublin Goverrnment assisted the British war effort in many ways. Today Irish troops regularly serve with the United Nations and have been in action on a number of occasions. Interestingly in the 1950s the Irish Government decided to standardise the Irish language and introduced An Caighdean Ofigiuil, which was a change in the Irish alphabet. The earlier Irish medals carry inscriptions in the old Irish alphabet but to simplify matters we have given the modern Irish equivalent in these listings where possible.

E1. 1916 MEDAL

Instituted: January 1941.
Ribbon: Two equal stripes of green (left) and orange, suspended from an ornate clasp of Celtic design.
Metal: Bronze.
Size: 38mm, max.
Description: (Obverse) based on the cap badge of the Irish Republican Army, viz. an eight-pointed star with "flames" between the points, surmounted by a double circle on which is a depiction of "Cuchulainn", the memorial erected at the General Post Office, Dublin, to commemorate the 1916 uprising; (reverse) central medallion inscribed SEACTMAIN NA CASGA (Easter Week) curved above 1916. With plain ring suspension.
Comments: *The medal, which takes precedence over all other Irish medals, was instituted by the Irish Republican Government to commemorate the Easter Uprising in Dublin, April 1916. Recipients, who were mostly members of the Dublin Brigade of the Irish Republican Army, also received a pension in respect of this medal. Of the 2,000 medals originally struck some 1,906 were issued. Of these 266 were named and presented to the next of kin of those who had died before the date of issue, including the 88 who were killed in the rebellion and 16 executed afterwards; the remainder were issued unnamed. Another 450 medals were struck and issued later.*

VALUE:		
	Original named 1916 casualty (88)	From £55,000
	1941 issue named medal	From £12,000
	Post 1941 named late issue medal	From £6000
	Unnamed	£2000–3000
	Miniature	£150–200

E2. MILITARY MEDAL FOR GALLANTRY

Instituted: 4 December 1944.

Ribbon: Dark green with a central stripe of crimson (1st Class), dark green with crimson edges (2nd Class), dark green with crimson edges and central crimson stripe (3rd Class).

Metal: Silver (1st Class), light bronze (2nd Class), dark bronze (3rd Class).

Size: 36mm.

Description: (Obverse) a Celtic cross with a longer lower limb, surrounded by a laurel wreath with the words DE BARR CALMACTA (For Gallantry) in the centre; (reverse) inscribed AN BONN MILEATA CALMACTA (The Military Gallantry Medal) above a scroll bearing the recipient's name.

Comments: *The medal is intended to be awarded in three different classes to members of the Defence Forces who have performed actions of outstanding gallantry in the course of their military duty whilst not on war service. Only seven medals have so far been awarded in 2nd or 3rd Class. The 1st Class has never been awarded, making this probably one of the rarest gallantry awards.*

VALUE: —

1st class. *2nd class.*   *3rd class.*

E3. DISTINGUISHED SERVICE MEDAL

Instituted: February 1964.

Ribbon: Dark green with 6mm black centre stripe (1st Class), 5mm black edges (2nd Class) or 3mm black edges and black centre stripe (3rd Class), suspended from a clasp with a stylised Celtic design.

Metal: Silver (1st Class) or bronze (2nd and 3rd Class).

Size: 36mm.

Description: (Obverse) a figure of Cuchulainn driving a two-horse chariot; (reverse) legend AN BONN SEIRBISE DEARSCNA (The Distinguished Service Medal) around. With simple ring suspension.

Comments: *Awarded in three classes for acts of bravery or special devotion to duty which do not merit the award of the Military Medal for Gallantry (MYBE2).*

VALUE:	
1st class	—
2nd class	£500–750
3rd class	£400–600

E4. CIVIL MEDAL FOR BRAVERY

Instituted: —.

Ribbon: Crimson with two narrow white stripes 3mm apart at centre (gold) or dark blue with two narrow white stripes 3mm apart at centre.

Metal: gold (1st Class), silver (2nd Class) and bronze (3rd Class).

Size: 36mm.

Description: (Obverse) a winged figure brandishing a flaming sword standing over another winged figure representing death and the inscription MIR GAILE GNIOM TARRTALA (The Council for Deeds of Bravery) below; (reverse) the words ARNA BRONNAD AG COMAIRLE NA MIR GAILE AR (Awarded by the Council for Deeds of Bravery to) in the top half with the recipient's name engraved to the right of an olive branch below.

Comments: *Awarded by the Department of Justice. The gold and silver medals are awarded for an individual act of bravery in saving life; the bronze is awarded to civilians for brave deeds which do not merit the other awards.*

VALUE:	1st class	2nd class	3rd class
	—	£1000–1500	£500–750

E5. GENERAL SERVICE MEDAL 1917–21

Instituted: January 1941.
Ribbon: Two equal stripes of black (left) and orange, suspended from an ornate clasp of Celtic design.
Metal: Bronze.
Size: 38mm.
Clasp: COMRAC (this word has two meanings, combat or action).
Description: (Obverse) a standing figure of a soldier holding a rifle surrounded by the crests of the four provinces of Ireland and bisecting the word "EIRE", at the foot COGAD NA SAOIRSE (War of Independence); (reverse) plain except for a laurel wreath around.
Comments: *Awarded to those who took part in the struggle for independence between the Easter Uprising of 1916 to ratification of the treaty which ensured independence from Britain and the establishment of the Irish Free State in 1921. The COMRAC clasp was awarded to those who took an active part in the military operations. When this clasp is worn the simple ring suspender is exchanged for one of an ornate triangular design. Approximately 15,000 medals were issued with a clasp, and 40,000 without, of these 1,080 Comrac medals and 1,360 no clasp medals were issued named.*

VALUE:	Unnamed	Named	*Miniature*
With clasp	£450–650	From £1,000	£55–75
Without clasp	£250–450	£350–550	£35–55

E6. THE EMERGENCY SERVICE MEDAL 1939–46

Instituted: 6 October 1944.
Ribbon: Orange-red with two white 4.5mm stripes 1.5mm apart at centre or with one central 10mm stripe, suspended from a bar bearing the words SEIRBHIS NAISIUNTA (National Service).
Metal: Bronze.
Size: 38mm.
Clasp: Laurel spray between the dates 1939 and 1946 for each two years extra service.
Description: (Obverse) a female figure of Ireland holding a sword, with Irish wolf hound on a leash at her side and the legend RE NA PRAINNE (Emergency Period) above and around; (reverse) a branch of laurel and the dates 1939 and 1946, with the recipient's unit above.
Comments: *The medal was instituted to reward Defence Service personnel who served between September 3, 1939 and March 31, 1946. A total of 11 different units were recorded and medals are inscribed on the reverse with the unit in which each recipient served. The most popular unit for collectors is the 26th Battalion which was comprised of veterans from the 1916 Uprising. The qualifying period was one year's service with the Defence Forces, the Chaplaincy Service, the Army Nursing Service or the Local Defence Forces (the ribbons for which have two stripes) or two years with the Air Raid Precautions Service, the Irish Red Cross Society or the Local Security Force (the ribbons for which have one stripe). A clasp was awarded for each extra two years service, with a maximum of two being available.*

VALUE:	
Army, Air Corps, Navy (Na Forsai Cosanta)	£75–100
Naval Reserve (An Sluag Muiri)	£300–350
26th Battalion IRA (An 26u Cathlan)	£350–450
Chaplaincy Service (An Seirbhis Seiplineachta)	£850–1250
Local Defence Force (An Forsa Cosanta Aitiuil)	£75–100
Volunteer Reserve (Forsa na n-Oclac, 2u Line)	£100–150
Army Nursing Service (Seirbis Altranais an Airm)	£550–850
Volunteer Aid (Red Cross) (Ranna Cabair Deontaca Cumann Croise Deirge na h-Eireann)	£100–150
First Aid (Red Cross) (Ranna Cead-Cabair Cumann Croise Deirge na h-Eireann)	£100–150
Air Raid Precautions (Na Seirbisi Reamcuraim In Agaidh Aer-Ruatar)	£75–150
Local Security Force (Na Caomnoiri Aitiula)	£50–75
Miniature	£25–35

E7. MERCHANT SERVICE MEDAL 1939–46

Instituted: 6 October 1944.

Ribbon: Blue with central white stripe, suspended from a clasp bearing the words SEIRBHIS NAISIUNTA (National Service).

Metal: Bronze.

Size: 38mm.

Clasp: Laurel spray between the dates 1939 and 1946 for each two years extra service.

Description: (Obverse) as MYB E6 above,—a female figure holding a sword, with Irish wolf hound at her side and RE NA PRAINNE (Emergency Period) above; (reverse) a steamship sailing left and a sailing ship in the background with the words AN TSEIRBHIS MUIR-TRACTALA (The Merchant Marine Service) above and the dates 1939–1946 over a laurel branch below.

Comments: *Awarded for six months' continuous service on Irish registered merchant ships between September 1939 and March 1946. A total of just over 500 of these medals were issued, including 127 with single extra service bars, 37 with two bars and a further 57 with three bars.*

VALUE:

Without bar	£700–850
One bar	£800–1000
Two bars	£1000–1500
Three bars	£1000–1750

E8. PERMANENT DEFENCE FORCES SERVICE MEDAL

Instituted: 13 September 1944.

Ribbon: There are two types of ribbon for this medal: plain blue for NCOs and other ranks but with a central gold stripe when a bar is awarded; officers, members of the Chaplaincy Service and the Army Nursing Service also have the ribbon with gold stripe. Both types are suspended from a bar bearing the word SEIRBIS.

Metal: Bronze.

Size: 38mm.

Clasps: Bronze bar with a cross and laurel design for extra service.

Description: (Obverse) Eire, represented as a female figure, placing a wreath on a kneeling soldier and AN BONN SEIRBISE (For good service) to left; (reverse) the words THE SERVICE MEDAL (in English) around with the recipient's details inscribed in the centre.

Comments: *Awarded to members of the Chaplaincy Service and the Army Nursing Service and to officers of the Permanent Defence Forces for a minimum of 15 years satisfactory and continuous service with a bar awarded for additional 5 years service. Officers can only qualify for one bar. The qualifying period for NCOs and other ranks is 10 years with a bar awarded for further 6 years service. Second award bars bear the inscription "21".*

VALUE:

Without bar	£75–£120
With bar	£125–£150

E9. PERMANENT DEFENCE FORCES SERVICE FOR GOOD CONDUCT

This medal, instituted in 1987 is exactly the same as E8 but inscribed AN BONN BEA IOMPAIR (For good conduct) and is suspended from a ribbon of diagonal green and orange stripes.

E10. ST JOHN AMBULANCE BRIGADE OF IRELAND SERVICE MEDAL

Instituted: September 1945.

Ribbon: Watered white with a single black centre stripe with two thinner black stripes each side and green edges.

Metal: Silver or silver-gilt.

Size: 38mm.

Description: (Obverse) the Maltese Cross emblem of the Brigade with sprigs of shamrock in the angles, surrounded by the legend THE ST JOHN AMBULANCE BRIGADE OF IRELAND; (reverse) the words FOR SERVICE inside a wreath of St John's wort leaves and flowers.

Comments: *Awarded in silver to members of the Brigade in Ireland for 15 years service and in silver-gilt for 50 years service.*

VALUE:	Silver	£35–55
	Silver-gilt	£100–125

E11. THE UNITED NATIONS PEACEKEEPERS MEDAL

Instituted: 3 October 1989

Ribbon: 32mm wide with central vertical stripe of United Nations blue, 3mm wide, flanked by orange vertical stripes, 4.5mm wide, flanked by white vertical stripes, 5mm wide, with vertical green stripe, 5mm wide each side.

Metal: Nickel-plated brass (silver appearance).

Size: 35mm.

Description: (Obverse) female figure of Eireann standing on a shoreline releasing a dove of peace into the sky with an olive branch in its beak and three wild geese flying into the distance; (reverse) NÁ NÁISIUN AONTAITE DON TSÍOCÁIN—FOR PEACE UNITED NATIONS.

Comments: *The official name of this medal is An Bonn Chosantoiri Síochána na Naisiun Aontaithe (The United Nations Peacekeeper's Medal). Any member of the Irish Defence Forces who is entitled to a United Nations Service medal, is entitled to this medal. Only one United Nations Peacekeeper's Medal is awarded irrespective of how many peacekeeping tours the recipient has taken part in and there are no bars or other indicators to show how many tours the recipient has been on.*

VALUE: £100–175

E12. 1916-1966 "SURVIVORS" MEDAL

Instituted: 1966.

Ribbon: Green with 5mm orange edges and a white 1mm central stripe.

Metal: Hallmarked silver (gilded).

Size: 38mm max.

Description: The same type of ring suspender as the 1916 medal, MYB E1 (qv), with a similar wearing brooch, which has the maker's name stamped on the reverse. (Obverse) as 1916 medal; (reverse) plain circular back with 1916/Ca'isc/1966 (1916 Easter 1966) in three lines.

Comments: *Issued to the recipients of the 1916 medal who were still alive in 1966 on the 50th Anniversary of the Easter Rising. 964 medals were issued. None of these medals were officially named.*

VALUE: £3000–4500

E13. 1921-71 "SURVIVORS" MEDAL

Instituted: 1971.
Ribbon: Orange with green edges and a black central stripe.
Metal: Gilt bronze.
Size: Significantly smaller than the 1917–21 medal.
Description: A circular medal with the same type of ring suspender as the 1917–21 medal (MYB E5) and with a similar wearing brooch. (Obverse) same as 1917–21 medal; (reverse) as the 1917-21 medal except with "1921–71" in the area where the blank space is on the 1917-21 medal.
Comments: *Issued to the recipients of the 1917-21 medal who were still alive in 1971 on the 50th Anniversary of the Truce. There is no difference between the medals issued to combatants and non-combatants. None of these medals were officially named.*

VALUE: £300–350

E14. RESERVE DEFENCE FORCES LONG SERVICE MEDAL

Instituted:
Ribbon: Blue ribbon with yellow edges (7 years), and blue ribbon with yellow edges and a central yellow stripe (12 and 21 years).
Metal: A golden coloured medal.
Size: 38mm.
Description: Circular medal with suspender similar to the Irish UN Service Medal. (Obverse) a Celtic warrior with shield and spear surrounded by the words Cus Na Saoirse / Faire Biodgac; (reverse) plain circle with around the edges An Bonn Seirbise / F.C.A. 7 S.M.
Comments: *Awarded to members of An Forsa Cosanta Aitiuil (Local Defence Force) and An Slua Muiri (Naval Reserve) after 7 years service. A bar is awarded after 12 years service and a further bar is awarded after 21 years service. This medal is no longer issued as it is to be replaced by a new medal to reflect the fact that following the reorganisation of the reserve forces the FCA has been replaced by the RDF and the Slua Muiri by the NSR. The reverse of the new medal will read An Bonn Seirbhise - na hOglaig Cultaca (The Service Medal Reserve Forces).*

VALUE:	7 years	12 years	21 years
	£100–150	£120–180	£200–275

MEDALS OF AN GARDA SÍOCHÁNA

E15. SCOTT MEDAL FOR VALOR

Instituted: 1923.
Ribbon: 34mm wide. Three equal stripes of green, white and orange.
Metal: Gold (first class), Silver (second class) and Bronze (third class).
Size: 44mm.
Description: The medal is in the form of a Celtic cross. (Obverse) the entwined GS of the Garda crest in the centre with "Walter Scott Medal" on the top arm of the cross and "For Valor" on the bottom arm; the left arm carries the shield and eagle crest of the United States and the right arm the harp and sunburst of Ireland; (reverse) New York City coat of arms surrounded by the coats of arms of each of the four Irish provinces (Leinster, Munster, Connacht, Ulster), one in each of the arms of the cross with the words "Garda Síochána na h-Éireann". The medals are suspended from a pin brooch, on which is engraved the name of the recipient.
Comments: *In 1923, the then Commissioner of the Garda Síochána, General Eoin O'Duffy met Colonel Walter Scott, an Honorary Commissioner of the New York City Police and a well known philanthropist. Colonel Scott expressed the wish to assist in some way with what was, at the time, the world's youngest Police Force, namely the Garda Síochána. He presented to An Garda Síochána a $1,000 gold bond, the interest from which would pay, in perpetuity, for a gold medal. The one condition attached to the award of the Scott Medal was: "No action, however heroic, will merit the award of the Scott medal unless it takes the shape of an act of personal bravery, performed intelligently in the execution of duty at imminent risk to the life of the doer, and armed with full previous knowledge of the risk involved". In 1925, Colonel Scott presented a further $500 bond to provide silver and bronze medals to members who, during the year performed similar acts in the execution of duty but with less risk to their lives and who are next in order of merit. A Scott medal ceremony is held annually when recipients are formally presented with their medals by the Minister for Justice, Equality and Law Reform. The ceremony usually takes place at the Garda College.*

VALUE: **From £3000**

E16. GARDA SÍOCHÁNA LONG SERVICE MEDAL

Instituted: 1972.
Ribbon: Green ribbon with two white central stripes.
Metal: Silver coloured.
Size: 34mm.
Description: (Obverse) The scales of justice surrounded by the words "Garda Síochána" which are at the centre of a star with 22 points (one for each year of service); (reverse) the words "Seirbhís Fhada" (Long Service) with a Celtic design.
Comments: *Awarded to members of An Garda Síochána after 22 years service. Issued unnamed.*

VALUE: **£100–150**

E17. GARDA SÍOCHÁNA GOLDEN JUBILEE MEDAL

Instituted: 1972.
Ribbon: Three equal stripes of yellow, blue, yellow.
Metal: Gold coloured.
Size: 34mm.
Description: (Obverse) The entwined GS of the Garda Síochána crest surrounded by a pentagon with 10 stars; (reverse) a pillar of justice with a scroll going through and around it with the words "Jubaile Orga 1922-1972" (Golden Jubilee 1922-1972).
Comments: *Struck to commemorate the 50th Anniversary of the founding of the force in 1972. The medal was given to anyone serving in the police that year (approx 9,000) and was issued unnamed.*

VALUE: £65–85

E18. GARDA SÍOCHÁNA MILLENNIUM MEDAL

Instituted: 2000.
Ribbon: Pale blue with a broad central yellow stripe edged with white stripes with red edges.
Metal: Gold coloured.
Size: 34mm.
Description: (obverse) Scales suspended from the Garda crest with MM in the left pan and a dove in the right with the inscription "Garda Siochana" and the date "2000" below.
Comments: *Issued unnamed to all serving officers in commemoration of the Millennium.*

VALUE: £75–100

E19. GARDA UNITED NATIONS SERVICE MEDAL

Instituted:
Ribbon: Dark blue central stripe with equal white stripes each side and narrow light blue edges.
Metal: A gold coloured medal
Size: 34mm.
Description: (Obverse) The entwined GS of the Garda Síochána crest in a circle below a dove of peace with an olive branch in its beak and the words "Seirbhis Thar Lear" (Overseas Service); (reverse) plain back with the words "Garda Siochana – don tSiochain – Na Naisiuin Aontaithe" (Garda Siochana – for Peace – United Nations).
Comments: *The medal was given to a very few members of the force who served with the United Nations overseas. Issued unnamed*

VALUE: £200–275

E20. CIVIL DEFENCE LONG SERVICE MEDAL

Instituted: 1961.

Ribbon: Pale blue with a single red stripe in the centre for ten years service or two red stripes for twenty years service.

Metal: Gold coloured.

Size: 36mm.

Description: (Obverse) The Celtic Cross with the words "Seirbhis Fada—Long Service" inscribed between the arms of the cross. The centre of the Cross has the International CD badge of a blue triangle on an orange background inset in coloured enamel; (reverse) is concave and blank for recipient's details.

Comments: *The medal is issued by the Minister of Defence and was first awarded in 1997. Suspension is from a straight bar.*

VALUE: £100–150

E21. CIVIL DEFENCE MILLENNIUM MEDAL

Instituted: 2000

Ribbon: Orange with two pale blue stripes separated by a central green stripe with clasp "1950–2000".

Metal: Gold coloured

Size: 36mm

Description: (Obverse) An Irish harp in the centre surrounded by the words "Cosaint Sibhalta—Civil Defence"; (reverse) blank space for recipient's details surrounded by a rope pattern around the edge.

Comments: *The medal was issued by the Civil Defence Officers Association initially in the year 2000 to mark the 50th anniversary of the Civil Defence. Suspension is from a straight bar.*

VALUE: £75–100

Do you know about the Commemorative Medals available?

UNOFFICIAL
Medals

Interest has been steadily growing in recent years in unofficial medals, a subject on the fringes of medal collecting. The term is deliberately vague and encompasses a very wide range of medals, medalets and medallions of a commercial, private or local nature. Such a generic term would, for example, include regimental medals awarded for marksmanship or good conduct, often associated with official medal groups of the 19th century. This is a very esoteric group, often consisting of medals which were specially engraved for the occasion and therefore exceedingly difficult to quantify.

On the other hand, many of the earlier medals, now highly regarded as forerunners of the general campaign series, were unofficial in origin, and relied upon the enterprise of public-spirited individuals and prize agents such as Alexander Davison (MYB 78 and 85) or Matthew Boulton (MYB 84), generals such as Elliot (MYB 74), Earl St Vincent (MYB 80) or Gordon of Khartoum (MYB 133) or even private bodies such as the Highland Society (MYB 83).

Then there is the large and fascinating group of civic or institutional medals which were presented to volunteers returning from the Boer War of 1899–1902. M. G. Hibbard, in his splendid monograph Boer War Tribute Medals (1982), recorded no fewer than 78 such medals, 40 from towns and cities in England, 25 from other parts of the United Kingdom and 13 from Commonwealth countries. Some of these were fitted with ribbons and were obviously intended for wear alongside the official medals of the war; others were 'danglers' intended to be fitted to watch-chains; and others still were not fitted with any form of suspension and were thus in the nature of commemorative medals intended purely as a memento of volunteer service.

So far as can be ascertained, such tribute medals were not produced in previous conflicts, which were predominantly fought by regular troops; and such was the scale of the involvement of volunteers and later conscripts in the First World War that the cost of providing civic medals of this nature would have been prohibitive. Instead, returning soldiers had to be content with some form of paper testimonial, at best. A notable exception was the gold medal presented by the Lord Mayor of London to the members of the anti-aircraft gun crews which shot down the first Zeppelin (listed below).

Apart from that, the Boer War group therefore constitutes a unique, but clearly defined group. They are, however, generally outside the scope of this YEARBOOK, although it should be noted that several medals in this category have long been accepted in the regular canon: the Kimberley Star (no. 154), the Kimberley Medals (MYB 155), the Yorkshire Imperial Yeomanry Medal (MYB 156) and the Medal for the Defence of Ookiep (MYB 157). The reason for their acceptance is quite arbitrary, and just why the Yorkshire Imperial Yeomanry medal should be so highly regarded while others are not seems to rest on the fact that this medal is more commonly met with than the others— which is hardly a valid criterion.

For the sake of completing the record we have endeavoured to introduce a number of unofficial medals, particularly as groups including certain of these medals are coming onto the market and inevitably some purchasers are curious to know their origins.

In addition there are a number of other unofficial medals available to veterans such as the "Battle for Britain" medal with its various clasps but it is not the intention to make this a definitive guide, so we have decided to limit this section to those medals that were initially commissioned or supported by the relevant veterans associations and mainly produced in recent years in order to fill the gap left in the official series*.

Credit for reviving such medals must go to the Mayor of Dunkirk on whose initiative the medal awarded to survivors of the 1940 evacuation was instituted in 1965. Subsequently distribution of this medal was taken over by the Dunkirk Veterans' Association, applications being strictly limited to those who could prove that they had taken part in that historic event. This practice continued with the commissioning of the Bomber Command Medal by their Association (following a design competition in MEDAL NEWS) in response to the long-standing grievance of veterans of the Second World War who felt that their contribution to the ultimate victory had been deliberately ignored for political reasons. The success of this medal encouraged the production of similar awards for other categories of servicemen, or for campaigns which many felt should have had a distinctive campaign medal. However, it must be stressed that most of these modern medals are available for purchase only by bona-fide veterans or their proven next of kin with sales also benefitting related charities. The wearing of these medals has always been a contentious issue, with many veterans choosing to wear them below but never alongside their official decorations.

*As many of the modern medals are still being struck, it has been decided not to give valuations for these.

U1. CHERRY MEDAL

Date: 1904.
Campaign: China, 1900–4
Branch of Service: Royal Navy.
Ribbon: Cherry red.
Metal: Silver.
Size: 38mm.
Description: (Obverse) a bare cherry tree with five naval officers in the foreground and a large number of other officers, all in frock coats, moving up in single file, with a scroll across the foot inscribed in Latin SUB HOC CERESO MANEMUS (under this cherry tree we remain); (reverse) a fouled anchor flanked by the Golden Fleece and a Chinese Dragon with the legend ARGONAUT CHINA 1900–1904 round the circumference. The medal is fitted with a plain suspension ring.
Comments: *The name of the medal and the colour of ribbon allude to Captain George Henry Cherry RN, commander of HMS* Argonaut *which served on the China Station in 1900-4. The five officers on one side of the tree represent the only ones remaining of the original number when the ship was paid off: Lieutenant Arthur Vernon Ross, Captain T. H. Hawkins RM, Chief Engineer A. W. Turner, Senior Engineer T. W. Cleave and Chaplain T. A. Dexter. The other line represents those officers who left the ship during the commission. The obverse motto contains a spelling error: CERESO instead of CERASO. This medal started off as a joke. Captain Cherry was a terrible martinet and his disgruntled officers felt that they deserved a medal for having to put up with him. It was designed by Miss Ross, sister of the senior watchkeeper, and struck by Gamage's of London. Only 100 medals were struck. Originally it was intended to be given only to the five officers who had stuck it out to the bitter end, but others complained and thus were awarded the medal with a bar indicating each year of service. Many years later, Admiral Cherry was offered one of the medals and graciously received it.*

VALUE: £250–350

U1A. EMIN RELIEF EXPEDITION STAR

Date: 1889.
Campaign: Sudan.
Ribbon:
Metal: Sterling silver.
Size: 50mm.
Description: A five-pointed star with a plain reverse and a central medallion bearing the monogram of the Royal Geographical Society, surrounded by an incuse inscription EMIN RELIEF EXPEDITION / 1887-9.
Comments: *This medal was awarded mainly to the Zanzibaris forming the bulk of the expedition organised in 1889 to discover the whereabouts of Emin Pasha, Governor of Equatoria, who had retreated south with Egyptian troops, officials and their families in the aftermath of the Mahdist revolt and the fall of Khartoum. The expedition, led by H. M. Stanley, located Emin and his followers in April 1888. Emin, in fact, refused to be relieved and the expedition not only failed in its primary objective but was a disaster, most Europeans and many Zanzibaris perishing before they returned empty-handed. The Royal Geographical Society commissioned the medals from Carrington. Some 200 were produced and of these 178 were issued to surviving members of the expedition. Of these, only nine were named to the recipients.*

VALUE: £450–550

U2. SECOND CRUISER SQUADRON MEDAL

Date: 1908.
Campaign: Goodwill tour of South America and South Africa.
Branch of Service: Royal Navy.
Ribbon: Pale blue.
Metal: Bronze.
Size: 36mm.
Description: (Obverse) a right-facing lady in Edwardian dress waving to distant ships, with the words SOUTH AFRICA and SOUTH AMERICA round the edge on either side of the suspender; (reverse) a seven-line inscription: 2ND CRUISER SQUADRON—GOOD HOPE, DEVONSHIRE, ANTRIM, CARNARVON—1908. The words CLOSER UNION appear at the sides.
Clasps: 14—Buenos Aires, Monte Video, Rio de Janerio, St Helena, Capetown, Simonstown, Port Elizabeth, East London, Ladysmith, Bloemfontein, Johannesburg, Pretoria, Pietermaritzburg, Durban.
Comments: *Privately issued and named to members of the goodwill cruise. It is uncertain how many medals were issued but they can be encountered with various combinations of clasps or none at all. It appears that there were two distinct strikings, the named examples being on a slightly thicker flan. The thinner, unnamed versions are believed to have been restrikes for specimen purposes. It is not known who funded or manufactured these medals.*

VALUE: **£150–350 dependent on number of clasps**

U2A. NATIONAL SERVICE LEAGUE MEDAL

Date: 1912.
Ribbon: White with a narrow central red stripe and narrow blue edges.
Metal: Bronze, silver or gold.
Size: 32mm (bronze) or 26mm (others).
Description: (Obverse) Standing figure of Britannia, helmeted and cloaked, her hands resting on the pommel of an unsheathed broadsword, with the inscription FOR KING AND COUNTRY round the upper part of the circumference. Fitted with a plain ring for suspension, with a brooch bar at the top of the ribbon inscribed NATIONAL SERVICE LEAGUE; (reverse) THE PATH OF DUTY IS THE PATH OF SAFETY and wreath.
Comments: *The National Service League was founded by Field Marshal Lord Roberts in the aftermath of the Boer war. The aim of the League was to warn Britain of the German menace and encourage young men to become proficient marksmen. Its wider aims were "to secure the legislative adoption of universal naval and military training for national defence". Ironically, Lord Roberts was proved right all too soon, and the League was dissolved in 1921.*

VALUE: **Gold £450–600   Silver £250–350   Bronze £50–75**

U2B. EMDEN MEDAL

Date: 1915.
Campaign: First World War.
Branch of Service: Royal Australian Navy.
Ribbon:
Metal: Silver.
Size: 60mm x 36mm.
Description: Mexican silver dollar surmounted by a crown and two concentric scrolls at the top inscribed NOV. 9. 1914 and HMAS SYDNEY / SMS EMDEN.
Comments: *Shortly after the outbreak of the War the Australian cruiser* Sydney *located the German light cruiser* Emden *in the Cocos Islands. After a brief engagement the* Emden *was boarded and captured. A quantity of Mexican silver dollars were found on board and these were subsequently mounted by the firm of W. Kerr of Sydney and presented to the crew of the* Sydney *as a memento of the action.*

VALUE: **£1000–1500**

U3. LORD MAYOR OF LONDON'S MEDAL FOR THE DESTRUCTION OF ZEPPELIN L15

Date: 1916.
Campaign: First World War.
Branch of Service: Royal Artillery.
Ribbon:
Metal: 9 carat gold.
Size: 29mm.
Description: (Obverse) the arms of Sir Charles Wakefield within a double ring inscribed PRESENTED BY THE LORD MAYOR round the top and COLONEL SIR CHARLES WAKEFIELD round the foot; (reverse) An anti-aircraft gun and two scrolls inscribed WELL HIT and MARCH 31st and number L15. It is engraved near the top with the rank and name of the recipient. It was issued unmounted but various ornamental suspensions loops were later fitted privately.
Comments: *The Lord Mayor of London offered a reward of £500 to the first gun crew to shoot down a Zeppelin. On 3 April 1916 Capt. J. Harris submitted a claim on behalf of the Purfleet gun crew that they were responsible for the bringing down of the airship L15, but it later transpired that gun crews from Abbey Wood, Dartford, Erith, North Woolwich, Plumstead and the Royal Arsenal, among others, were also involved. It was decided to use the prize money in procuring these medals, a total of 353 being awarded.*

VALUE: £1000–1500

U3A. HMAS *SYDNEY* MEDAL

Date: 1941.
Campaign: World War II.
Branch of Service: Royal Australian Navy.
Ribbon: none.
Metal: Oxidised silver.
Size: 57mm.
Description: (Obverse) HMAS *Sydney* in action; (reverse) 13-line inscription surmounted by a crowned anchor and flanked by laurel leaves at top and bottom.
Comments: *This medal, struck by Amor of Sydney, was presented by the citizens of Sydney to the officers and crew of HMAS* Sydney *which resulted in the sinking of the Italian cruiser* Bartolomeo Colleoni *on July 19, 1940. Some 640 medals were issued but most of them were lost when the* Sydney *sank in 1941.*

VALUE: £450–500

U4. DUNKIRK MEDAL

Date: 1960.
Campaign: Dunkirk evacuation, 1940
Branch of Service: All British and Allied forces.
Ribbon: Chrome yellow with one thin and one wide red stripe each side with two very thin black lines bisecting both sides.
Metal: Bronze.
Size: 36mm wide.
Description: (Obverse) a shield bearing the arms of Dunkirk (a lion passant above a heraldic dolphin) mounted on an anchor; (reverse) a circle bearing a burning lamp with DUNKERQUE 1940 beneath, surrounded by a laurel wreath and surmounted by crossed swords; the whole mounted on and surrounded by a laurel wreath.
Comments: *This medal was first made available to veterans of the Dunkirk evacuation and later administered by the now disbanded Dunkirk Veterans Association. It was created by the French National Association of Veterans of the Fortified Sector of Flanders and of Dunkirk and awarded in recognition of the sacrifice of 30,000 combatants between 29 May and 3 June 1940.*

VALUE: £60–70   *Miniature*   £15–20

U5. BOMBER COMMAND MEDAL

Date: 1985.
Campaign: Second World War.
Branch of Service: RAF Bomber Command.
Ribbon: Midnight blue with a central flame stripe and blue-grey edges.
Metal: Cupro-nickel.
Size: 36mm.
Description: (Obverse) A Tudor crown surmounting a laurel wreath containing the letters RAF, flanked by smaller wreaths containing the brevet letters of the aircrew signifying courage, team spirit and leadership; (reverse) a Lancaster bomber flanked by the dates 1939 and 1945 with inscription A TRIBUTE TO THE AIRCREW OF BOMBER COMMAND round the circumference.
Comments: *Produced at the behest of Air Vice Marshal Donald Bennett following a design competition in MEDAL NEWS. The competition was the brainchild of author Alan Cooper campaigning on behalf of Bomber Command veterans. The first medal was struck by Lady Harris (widow of the wartime commander of Bomber Command). Now available from Award Productions Ltd.*

U5A. ARMY CADET FORCE ANNIVERSARY MEDAL

Instituted: 1985.
Branch of Service: Army Cadet Force.
Ribbon: Red and blue separated by a thin yellow stripe.
Metal: Enamelled white metal.
Size: 55 x 85mm.
Description: (Obverse) the insignia of the ACF superimposed by figures of an officer and cadet shaking hands, the dates 1860 and 1985 flanking the motto at the foot. Fitted with a ring above the crown for suspension. (Reverse) plain, apart from the manufacturer's mark of Reu & Company of Heubach, Wurttemberg, Germany. A brooch bar in the form of a scroll 20mm deep is fitted to the top of the ribbon and bears a three-line inscription: ARMY CADET FORCE 125H ANNIVERSARY ONE DAY MARCH 26TH OCTOBER 1985.
Comments: *The medal was awarded to all members of the ACF who took part in the one-day march to celebrate the 125th anniversary of the Force.*

U6. NORMANDY CAMPAIGN MEDAL

Date: 1987.
Campaign: Service in the Normandy campaign between June 6 and August 20, 1944.
Branch of Service: All British and Allied forces.
Ribbon: Dark red with deep navy blue stripes towards the edges and light blue edges, symbolising the three services.
Metal: Cupro-nickel.
Size: 36mm.
Description: (Obverse) insignia of the combined services surrounded by 13 stars (representing the USA) and the inscription BLESSENT MON COEUR D'UNE LANGUEUR MONOTONE ("wounds my heart with monotonous languor"), a quotation from Verlaine broadcast by the BBC at 21.15 on June 5, 1944 to signal the start of the D-Day operations. (Reverse) a tank landing craft with its ramp on the beaches of France symbolised by fleurs-de lys; NORMANDY CAMPAIGN round the top and the date of the campaign inscribed on the ramp. The medal is fitted with a plain suspension bar while the ribbon bears a clasp inscribed NORMANDY between oak leaves.
Comments: *Commissioned by the Normandy Veterans Association whose Welfare and Benevolent Fund benefits from the proceeds of sales.*

U7. ARCTIC CAMPAIGN MEDAL

Date: 1991.
Campaign: Second World War.
Branch of Service: Personnel of the Russian convoys.
Ribbon: 32mm watered weave in equal stripes of blue and white representing ice and sea.
Metal: Cupro-nickel.
Size: 36mm.
Description: (Obverse) a liberty ship framed in the cross-hair of a U-boat periscope, with the inscription FOR SERVICE IN THE ARCTIC ZONE 1939-45 round the top; (reverse) four figures representing merchant seamen, Royal Naval, Army and RAF personnel, with the inscription THE ARCTIC CAMPAIGN round the top.
Comments: *This award was proposed by the Russian Convoy Club in conjunction with the North Russia Club who are the beneficiaries of the project.*

U8. MERCHANT NAVAL SERVICE MEDAL

Date: 1998.
Campaign: —
Branch of Service: Merchant Navy and DEMS Gunners.
Ribbon: Dark blue with a central narrow white stripe flanked by broader green and red stripes, representing the navigation lights of an approaching ship.
Metal: Cupro-nickel.
Size: 36mm.
Description: (Obverse) a stockless anchor encompassed by its heavy cable, surmounted by the initials MN; (reverse) a capstan surmounted by a naval crown and flanked by grotesque sea monsters, the whole encircled by a rope tied at the foot in a reef knot. The outer circumference is inscribed FOR MERCHANT NAVAL SERVICE. The medal is fitted to a plain suspension bar by an ornamental scroll.
Comments: *Veterans were eligible for this medal in respect of at least two years' service in the Merchant Navy. The award was inspired by the fact that although service in the mercantile marine was recognised after World War I and during World War II, it was ignored after World War II. King George's Fund for Sailors' benefits from the sale of this medal.*

U9. ALLIED EX-PRISONERS OF WAR MEDAL

Date: 1991.
Campaign: All wars of the 20th century.
Branch of Service: Prisoners of war.
Ribbon: Green with red edges. The centre has a broad black stripe edged in white, having a white strand of barbed wire running down the middle.
Metal: Cupro-nickel.
Size: 36mm.
Description: (Obverse) a young bird trapped by barbed wire, against a globe of the world, with the inscription INTERNATIONAL PRISONERS OF WAR; (reverse) a twisted barb of wire whose four strands divide the inscription INTREPID AGAINST ALL ADVERSITY. Fitted with a plain suspension bar.
Comments: *This award proposed by the National Ex Prisoners of War Association is applicable to any former PoWs whose countries were allies of Britain at the time of their capture irrespective of whether the United Kingdom was itself involved in the conflict.*

U10. RESTORATION OF PEACE MEDAL

Date: 1995.
Campaign: Second World War.
Branch of Service: Armed forces and civilians involved in the war effort.
Ribbon: Rich claret with a central broad gold stripe.
Metal: High-security HS1 gold-coloured alloy.
Size: 36mm.
Description: (Obverse) the letter V enclosing the date 1945, superimposed on a globe with the inscription A TIME FOR PEACE round the circumference; (reverse) a simple wreath enclosing the inscription FOR ALL WHO STRIVED FOR PEACE. The plain suspension bar is fitted to the medal by a peace dove on both sides.
Comments: *Produced at the behest of the British Red Cross Society to mark the 50th anniversary of the cessation of hostilities in the Second World War.*

U11. SUEZ CANAL ZONE MEDAL

Date: 1995.
Campaign: Suez Canal Zone, 1945-57.
Branch of Service: British and French forces.
Ribbon: Sand-coloured edged with narrow stripes of red, white and blue. A broad central crimson stripe has a light blue stripe down the middle.
Metal: High-security HS1 gold-coloured alloy.
Size: 36mm.
Description: (Obverse) the Sphinx and Pyramid flanked by the dates 1951-54 and 1956-57, representing the two most recent periods of conflict; (reverse) stylised papyrus grass with the words TO MARK SERVICE IN THE CANAL ZONE at left. Fitted with an ornamental suspension bar in the form of Pharaonic wings.
Comments: *The Ex-Services Mental Welfare Society (Combat Stress) is the beneficiary of this project.*

U12. NATIONAL SERVICE MEDAL

Date: 1991.
Campaign: Period of conscription, 1939-60.
Branch of Service: National Service, both military and civilian.
Ribbon: Dark blue with a narrow central gold stripe and narrow white and red stripes at the edges representing the involvement of the Royal British Legion.
Metal: Cupro-nickel.
Size: 36mm.
Description: (Obverse) the seated figure of Britannia supported by a lion, with the inscription NATIONAL SERVICE 1939-1960; (reverse) a wreath enclosing the inscription FOR CROWN AND COUNTRY. Fitted with scrolled suspension.
Comments: *Between January 1939 when the National Service Act was passed, and December 1960 when it was repealed, some 5,300,000 young people were conscripted into the armed services. The medal was proposed by the Royal British Legion and almost 110,000 have been issued to date.*

U13. JORDAN SERVICE MEDAL

Instituted: April 1997.
Branch of Service: British ex-service personnel who served in the Hashemite Kingdom of Jordan between 1948 and 1957 and again during the 1958 emergency, i.e. the 16th Independent Parachute Brigade and attached units.
Ribbon: Golden sand, edged on both sides with four thin stripes of the Jordanian national colours (black, white, green and red).
Metal: Gilt brass.
Size: 36mm.
Description: (Obverse) Effigy of King Hussein; (reverse) inscription in raised lettering: FOR SERVICE IN THE HASHEMITE KINGDOM OF JORDAN, with or without the date 1958 below.
Comments: *This medal was produced on the initiative of G. E. Harris of Haverfordwest with the approval of the late King Hussein. Sales of the medal benefit the SSAFA Forces Help charity. It was manufactured by the Bigbury Mint, Ermington, Devon. To date nearly 2,000 veterans have applied for the medal (either version), including two of the four female nurses who served in Jordan.*

U14. HONG KONG SERVICE MEDAL

Instituted: 1999.
Branch of Service: All former civil and military personnel who served for a minimum of six months in the Crown Colony of Hong Kong, or their next of kin.
Ribbon: Pale blue with a central yellow stripe.
Metal: Gilt metal.
Size: 36mm.
Description: (Obverse) Bird of Paradise surounded by the words HONG KONG SERVICE MEDAL 1841–1997; (reverse) HONG KONG in Cantonese characters surrounded by a circular wreath. The medal is suspended from a unique suspender depicting two mythical Chinese dragons.
Comments: *SSAFA Forces Help, the ex-servicemen's charity, benefits from the sales of this medal.*

U15. BRITISH FORCES GERMANY MEDAL

Instituted: 1999.
Branch of Service: All British service personnel in Germany, 1945–89.
Ribbon: 32mm NATO blue with central narrow stripes of black, red and gold (the German national colours).
Metal: Rhodium-plated cupro-nickel.
Size: 36mm.
Description: (Obverse) Standing figures of a soldier and airman holding the Union Jack, BRITISH FORCES GERMANY round the top with ARMY 1945–1989 RAF round the foot; (reverse) a laurel wreath incorporating the recipient's name, rank and service number over the years of service. Plain suspension bar.
Comments: *All men and women who served with the British Forces in Germany from the end of World War II until 1989 are eligible for this medal designed by Martin Duchemin and available from Royal British Legion Industries and Award Productions Ltd.*

U16. ROYAL NAVAL PATROL SERVICE MEDAL

Instituted: 1989.
Branch of Service: Royal Naval Patrol Service of World War II.
Ribbon: Watered dark and light green with a central orange stripe edged with black.
Metal: Cupro-nickel.
Size: 36mm.
Description: (Obverse) The badge of the RNPS with a shark swimming around it.
Comments: *Commissioned by the Royal Naval Patrol Service Association to commemorate service. Available only to veterans or their next of kin.*

U17. HORS DE COMBAT MEDAL

Instituted: 2001.
Branch of Service: All uniformed British service personnel.
Ribbon: Rich red bordered by narrow bands of blue with wider outer edges of white. A poppy is attached to the ribbon if the medal is issued to next of kin to those killed in action.
Metal: Cupro-nickel.
Size: 36mm.
Description: (Obverse) A gladiator kneeling before a female figure with the legend IN THE LINE OF DUTY; (reverse) a stylised rendering of the surgeon's knot with the same legend.
Comments: *For all those who sustained wounds or injury in the line of duty. Also available to next of kin. The Ex-Services Mental Welfare Society (Combat Stress) benefits from the sale of this medal.*

U18. INTERNATIONAL SUBMARINE SERVICE MEDAL

Instituted: 2002.

Branch of Service: Submariners of all nations.

Ribbon: Navy blue with a thin red stripe flanked by thin black and white stripes.

Metal: Cupro-nickel

Size: 36mm.

Description: (Obverse) a modern submarine viewed from the bow, with inscription INTERNATIONAL SUBMARINE SERVICE; (reverse) a depth gauge with the inscription BY SKILL AND STEALTH WE COME UNSEEN.

Comments: *Commissioned by London Submariners and the International Submarine Association in recognition of the men who have served, and continue to serve, beneath the world's oceans.*

U19. QUEEN'S GOLDEN JUBILEE COMMEMORATIVE MEDAL

Instituted: 2002.

Branch of Service: All service personnel, past or present, including police, coastguard, ambulance and other services.

Ribbon: Broad gold bands at the edges, with thin white, purple and white stripes in the centre.

Metal: Gilt brass.

Size: 36mm.

Description: (Obverse) left-facing robed bust of the Queen inscribed QUEEN ELIZABETH II GOLDEN JUBILEE 2002; (reverse) royal arms.

Comments: *This attractive medal was produced for the benefit of the SSAFA (Soldiers, Sailors and Air Forces Association) on the initiative of G. E. Harris who also instigated the Jordan Service Medal (no. U13) and is manufactured by the Bigbury Mint. It provides a need for those who were not entitled to the official medal.*

U20. NORTH AFRICA SERVICE MEDAL

Instituted: 1999.

Branch of Service: Veterans of the North African campaigns of World War II.

Ribbon: Yellow and sky-blue stripes at the edges, with navy blue, red and air force blue in the centre representing the armed services.

Metal: Bronze.

Size: 36mm.

Description: (Obverse) a camel standing beside a desert rat, with the inscription FOR SERVICE IN NORTH AFRICA, M.E.L.F.; (reverse) ornamental edge with centre blank for engraving with the name of the recipient.

Comments: *Designed and manufactured by the Bigbury Mint on the initiative of Ron Skeates of Aveton Gifford.*

U21. CAMERONIANS (SCOTTISH RIFLES) MEDAL

Instituted: 1999.

Branch of Service: Those who served in the regiment either as regulars or on National Service, including wives.

Ribbon: Three stripes of blue, black and dark green taken from the regimental tartan.

Metal: Silver-plated brass.

Size: 36mm.

Description: (Obverse) regimental badge of the Cameronians; (reverse) FOR SERVICE IN THE CAMERONIANS SCOTTISH RIFLES.

Comments: *The regiment was named in memory of the Covenanting leader Richard Cameron and was raised at Douglas, Lanarkshire in 1689. It later merged with the 90th (Perthshire) Regiment, at which point it adopted the Government tartan. However, in 1891 they were authorised to use the Douglas tartan.*

U22. BRITISH NUCLEAR WEAPONS TEST MEDAL

Instituted: October 3, 2004.

Branch of Service: Australian and British personnel involved in the testing of nuclear weapons in Australia from 1952 onwards.

Ribbon: White with a narrow central black stripe flanked by two shades of red.

Metal: Cupro-nickel.

Size: 36mm.

Description: (Obverse) depicts the nuclear symbol surrounded by the words "British Nuclear Weapons Test in Australia & Pacific". Fitted with a straight bar for suspension.

Comments: *The medal was produced by Award Productions in conjunction with the Australian and British Nuclear Tests Veterans' Associations.*

U23. ARABIAN SERVICE MEDAL

Instituted: 2005.

Branch of Service: Civil and Military personnel who served in Aden and other parts of Arabia.

Ribbon: Three equal stripes of blue, yellow and green.

Metal: Cupro-nickel.

Size: 36mm.

Description: Crossed daggers within a Saracenic arch border inscribed ARABIAN SERVICE / 1839-1967. A crescent and star attaches the medal to the bar suspension.

Comments: *Instituted by the Aden Veterans Association it commemorates British involvement in South Arabia from 1839 till the withdrawal of British forces in 1967.*

U24. BATTLE FOR MALTA MEDAL

Instituted: September 2005.
Branch of Service: Veterans who served in Malta or supplied the island between 1940 and 1943.
Ribbon: Two equal stripes of white and red.
Metal: Cupro-nickel.
Size: 36mm.
Description: The George Cross with inscription REUNION 7 60TH COMMEMORATION OF VICTORY IN MALTA IN WORLD WAR II.
Comments: *Commissioned by the Battle of Malta International Veterans Committee.*

U25. VIETNAM VETERANS MEDAL

Instituted: 2005.
Branch of Service: Commonwealth forces who served in Vietnam between 1960 and 1972.
Ribbon: Broad central yellow stripe with three thin red stripes superimposed, and green and dark blue stripes at the edges.
Metal: Gold-coloured alloy.
Size: 36mm.
Description: Dragon and soldier in combat gear, with VIETNAM VETERANS MEDAL round the circumference.
Comments: *Produced by Award Productions for the Vietnam Veterans of Australia.*

U26. ACTIVE SERVICE MEDAL

Instituted: 2003.
Branch of Service: British and Commonwealth Forces.
Ribbon: Central white stripe, with red edges surrounded by yellow.
Metal: Gold plated bronze.
Size: 36mm.
Description: (Obverse) A serviceman draws his sword ready for action. Alongside him is the dove of peace. A number of clasps are available for this medal, stating where the recipient has seen his/her active service.
Comments: *This medal is produced for the benefit of SSAFA Forces Help on the initiative of G. E. Harris. It is manufactured by Bigbury Mint Ltd.*

U27. GENERAL SERVICE CROSS

Instituted: 1992.
Branch of Service: British and Commonwealth Forces who have served. in peacetime or during hostilities.
Ribbon: Equal bands of blue, white and red.
Metal: Hallmarked silver.
Size: 36mm.
Description: A Winged Lion carrying a trident is surrounded by the words "For General Service".
Comments: *The War Widows have benefited from the sale of this medal. The medal is manufactured by Bigbury Mint Ltd.*

U28. RAF BOY ENTRANTS COMMEMORATIVE MEDAL

Instituted: 2004.
Branch of Service: Royal Air Force.
Ribbon: Maroon.
Metal: Hallmarked sterling silver.
Size: 36mm.
Description: (Obverse) badge of the Royal Air Force Boy Entrants Association with 1994 10TH ANNIVERSARY RAFBEA 2004 round the circumference; (reverse) a four-bladed propeller with 1934-2004 70th ANNIVERSARY OF FOUNDATION OF BOY ENTRANT SCHEME round the circumference.
Comments: *Medal struck on behalf of the Boy Entrants Association by the Pobjoy Mint.*

U29. BORDER SERVICE MEDAL

Instituted: August 2006.
Branch of Service: British and Commonwealth forces on frontier duty throughout the world (Germany, Hong Kong, Cyprus, Northern Ireland, Malaysia, Borneo, Gibraltar, Belize, etc).
Ribbon: Green with a central red band.
Metal: Antique bronze.
Size: 36mm.
Description: (Obverse) a watch tower with a fortified border in the background; (reverse) the recipient's number, rank and name and place of service. .
Comments: *Produced by Martin Duchemin on behalf of Royal British Legion Industries.*

U30. OPERATION VIBRATTO COMMEMORATIVE MEDAL

Instituted: June 21, 1981.
Branch of Service: Military personnel of Allied Forces Southern Europe who came to the aid of victims of the earthquake of November 23, 1980 in Campania and Baslilicata, Italy.
Ribbon: A narrow blue central stripe, flanked by white stripes, with red, yellow and red, stripes on either side.
Metal: Bronze.
Size: 36mm.
Description: (Obverse) a female, fireman and soldier with arms raised in a supportive gesture towards the earthquake region; (reverse) equestrian statue and public building in Naples with the word BENEMERONZA (Merit) above and COMMISSARIATO STRAORDINARIO DELLA CAMPANIA E DELLA BASILICATA (Office of the Special Commissioner of Campania and Basilicata) round the circumference.
Comments: *About 100 medals were awarded to members of the Tri-Service British contingent based at Naples. Although accepted by the Ministry of Defence it may not be worn on the uniform of serving personnel.*

U31. BLACK WATCH MEDAL

Instituted: 2006.
Branch of Service: Service in the Black Watch (Royal Highland Regiment).
Ribbon: Dark blue, red and green.
Metal: Cupro-nickel.
Size: 37mm.
Description: (Obverse) the regimental badge with inscription THE BLACK WATCH / ROYAL HIGHLAND REGIMENT round the circumference; (reverse) FOR SERVICE TO THE BLACK WATCH x ROYAL HIGHLAND REGIMENT, 1739-2006. The ribbon is fitted with a brooch bar and suspended by a ring attached to the medal.
Comments: *The medal was struck by the Bigbury Mint.*

U32. ROYAL HIGHLAND FUSILIERS MEDAL

Instituted: 2009.
Branch of Service: Service in the Royal Highland Fusiliers.
Ribbon: Dark green and blue bisected by a thin yellow line.
Metal: "Golden" alloy.
Size: 36mm.
Description: (Obverse) the Royal Highland Fusiliers badge with the date 1959; (reverse) the new regimental badge of the Royal Regiment of Scotland with inscription ROYAL HIGHLAND FUSILIERS 50th ANNIVERSARY 1959–2009 round the circumference. The ribbon is fitted with a brooch bar.
Comments: *The medal was produced by ScotMint of Ayr to celebrate the 50th anniversary of the formation of the Royal Highland Fusiliers (after the amalgamation of the Highland Light Infantry and the Royal Scots Fusiliers).*

U33. LOWER SAXONY FIREFIGHTING MEDAL 1975

Instituted: 2009.
Branch of Service: Royal Engineers.
Ribbon: Red with a white stripe at centre.
Metal: Bronze coloured base metal.
Size: 30mm.
Description: (Obverse) a depiction of flames roaring through a forest; (reverse) the words WALDBRAND KATASTROPHE IN NIEDERSACHSEN AUGUST 1975. With ring suspension.
Comments: *This medal was officially presented by the Lower Saxony Land Ministry to members of the team of Royal Engineers who, with their Centurion tanks and bulldozers, helped dig fire breaks to stop a forest fire from spreading on Luneburg Heath in August 1975.*

U34. ROYAL GREEN JACKETS COMMEMORATIVE MEDAL

Date: 2007.
Branch of Service: Royal Green Jackets.
Ribbon: Green with one red and one black stripe.
Metal: Silver.
Size: 36mm.
Description: (Obverse) Insignia of the Royal Green Jackets; (reverse) RGJ emblem with inscription and date of "coming out of the line" when the new regiment The Rifles were formed.
Comments: *Struck by the Bigbury Mint as an initiative with the RGJRA and available to all past members of the RGJ, RGJ-TA. Eligibility extends to members of the past regiments which made up the RGJ (43 & 52 The Ox & Bucks LI, KRRC and RB).*

U35. RHODESIAN INDEPENDENCE COMMEMORATIVE MEDAL

Date: 2009.
Branch of Service: Available to all those who lived in Rhodesia during its independence from November 11, 1965 until December 11, 1979.
Ribbon: Dark green with a central, wide white stripe.
Metal: Silver.
Size: 36mm.
Description: Roaring lion's head with inscription over.
Comments: *This unofficial medal was commissioned on behalf of the joint committee of the Rhodesian Army, Rhodesian Air Force and British South Africa Police Associations.*

U36. AFPS MEDAL

Date: 2009.
Branch of Service: Members of Parliament.
Ribbon: One stripe of crimson and one of green separated by a thinner yellow stripe, representing the House of Commons, the House of Lords and the Monarch.
Metal: Silver.
Size: 36mm.
Description: The Combined Services emblem surmounted by the Parliamentary portcullis badge.
Comments: *This unofficial medal was instituted by the Armed Forces Parliamentary Scheme to reward MPs who have carried out at least four annual 22-day commitments with the armed forces over a period of ten or more years.*

U37. CADET FORCES COMMEMORATIVE MEDAL

Date: 2010.

Branch of Service: Available to all those who served in the Cadet Forces, their next of kin or direct descendants.

Ribbon: Outer stripes of red, dark blue and light blue representing the Army, Air Force and Navy bounded by equal bands of yellow with a central green stripe.

Metal: Silver.

Size: 36mm.

Description: (Obverse) A fouled anchor, the L98-A1 Cadet GP Rifle and propellor with year dates; (reverse) mottoes of the various Cadet Forces.

Comments: *Produced by Award Productions Ltd to mark the 150th anniversary since the first Cadet Corps formed at Rossall School in 1860 as an army contingent to help the country's defence numbers following heavy losses in the Crimean War.*

U38. COLD WAR COMMEMORATIVE MEDAL

Date: 2010.

Branch of Service: For those who served in the Armed Forces of any country opposing the totalitarian regimes of the Communist Pact between 1945 and 1991 (next of kin or direct descendants also eligible).

Ribbon: Red, white and blue strip on the left representing the Allies and the bright red of the Soviet flag on the right.

Metal: Silver.

Size: 36mm.

Description: (Obverse) Rolled up flags of the three main players in the Cold War—the Soviet Union contained by the UK and US and dates 1945–91; (reverse) The Russian Bear on a wall clutching a missile with the Lion of the UK and the Eagle of the US repelling.

Comments: *Produced by Award Productions Ltd to pay tribute to those who served during this tense period of history. Ten per cent of the net cost of each medal sold will be donated to the National Cold War Exhibition at the RAF Museum Cosford.*

U39. BEVIN BOYS MEDAL

Date: 2009.

Branch of Service: The Bevin Boys Medal was commissioned by the Bevin Boys Association and as such is their official medal.

Ribbon: Black edged on both sides by a pale blue and green stripe.

Metal: Silver.

Size: 36mm.

Description: Colliery gantry with inscription over.

Comments: *The Bevin Boys medal is available to ballotees, optants, volunteers or next of kin called up between 1942 and 1948. There is no minimum length of service to be eligible for this medal but details of the training colliery and name of colliery worked, if known has to be provided. Struck by Bigbury Mint, a donation is made to the Bevin Boys Association from the sale of each medal.*

U40. THE TERRITORIAL ARMY CENTENNIAL MEDAL

Date: April 2008

Campaign: Available to all those who served or are currently serving in the TA or TAVR, their next of kin or direct descendants

Branch of Service: Territorial Army.

Ribbon: Diagonal green and yellow stripes representing the TA and the blue stripe the period 1967-1979 when the TAVR (Territorial Army and Volunteer Reserve) units were formed.

Metal: Gilt nickel.

Size: 36mm.

Description: An antique bronzed oval medal: (obverse) the monogram TA with the year dates 1908 and 2008 in an oak wreath; (reverse) the Army crossed swords symbol with the inscription TERRITORIAL ARMY CENTENNIAL MEDAL.

Comments: *Struck in association with The Resolution Project which is the beneficiary of this project.*

U41. THE COMMEMORATIVE SERVICE MEDAL

Date: September 2008

Campaign: Available to all those who served or are currently serving in any of the 19 Regiments and Services detailed below, their next of kin or direct descendants.

Branch of Service: Royal Navy, Army, Royal Air Force, Royal Marines, Royal Artillery, Royal Army Service Corps, Royal Engineers, REME, Royal Signals, Army Catering Corps, Light Infantry, Parachute Regiment, Royal Army Medical Corps, Royal Army Ordnance Corps, Royal Army Pay Corps, Royal Corps of Transport, Royal Military Police, Royal Tank Regiment and RAF Regiment.

Ribbon: Red for Army and Regiments, Navy Blue for Royal Navy, Green for Royal Marines and Air Force Blue for the RAF and RAF Regiment.

Metal: Silver-plated nickel.

Size: 36mm.

Description: (Obverse) Each medal bears the appropriate Regimental or Service emblem in the nickel silver plated centre framed by a 24 ct gold plated border; (gold plated reverse) a laurel wreath encasing the words FOR CROWN AND COUNTRY.

Comments: *The association of each Service or Regiment is the beneficiary of this project.*

Bevin Boys workiing with an older, experienced miner at Ollerton Colliery, Nottinghamshire, February 1945 (image Wikipedia public domain)

U42. THE CADET FORCES FIRST AID MEDAL

Date: 2010.
Branch of Service: Cadet Forces.
Ribbon: Three stripes of dark blue (RN), red (Army) and light blue (ATC). The central red stripe edged with thin yellow stripes.
Metal: Nickel silver or gilt.
Size: 32mm.
Description: (Obverse) a Maltese cross surrounded by a laurel wreath and an outer legend; (reverse) blank but named to the qualifying participant.
Comments: *The gilt medal was awarded to winning teams in the ACF, ATC, CCF and SCC Cadet 150 2010 national first aid competitions. Nickel silver medals were awarded to qualifying participants in Cadet 150 Festival of First Aid 2010, or trained or supported teams for Cadet 150 Festival of First Aid 2010. Cadet 150 Festival of First Aid signifies any of the events held over the period October 16–17, 2010 including the national first aid competitions of each of the ACF, ATC, CCF and SCC, the Inter Services and St John Ambulance Young Grand Prior events. Nickel silver medals without Cadet 150 reverse engraving may also be issued for qualifying events in 2011 or later years. The medal is unofficial and may not be worn in uniform.*

U43. ALLIED SPECIAL FORCES MEDAL

Date: 2011.
Branch of Service: Available to any member of an elite or special force of Britain or ally of Britain, their next of kin or direct descendants.
Ribbon: The green, sky blue and sea blue stripes represent involvement.
Metal: Silver.
Size: 36mm.
Description: (Obverse) A dagger and wings surmount a globe of the world. The words ALLIED SPECIAL FORCES surround the globe; (reverse) a globe with lightning bolts and mottoes of the various branches of service.
Comments: *Produced by Award productions Ltd to pay tribute to all of the Special and Elite forces of the United Kingdom and those of their allies around the world.*

U44. COMMEMORATIVE QUEEN'S DIAMOND JUBILEE MEDAL

Date: 2012.
Branch of Service: Available to all those who have served Queen Elizabeth II from 6 February 1952 including current serving members of the Armed Forces, Emergency Services, Prison Service, Police Community Support Officers, holders of the Victoria Cross and George Cross and members of the Royal Household. Next of kin and direct descendants may also apply.
Ribbon: Rich purple broad stripes, central white "diamond" white, bordered with red, white and blue narrow stripes.
Metal: Silver.
Size: 36mm.
Description: (Obverse) Multi layered textured diamond, central crown and traditional surround; (reverse) English Rose, Scottish Thistle, Irish Shamrock and Welsh Leek framed with a traditional laurel.
Comments: *Produced by Award Productions Limited to commemorate the 60th anniversary of the reign of Queen Elizabeth II.*

U45. BRITISH FORCES CAMPAIGN SERVICE MEDAL

Date: 2013.
Branch of Service: British Forces.
Ribbon: Central red stripe flanked by narrow white and wide blue stripes.
Metal: Silver.
Size: 36mm.
Description: (Obverse) a compass-like design representing the global dominance of the British Forces, surmounted by a crown representing the monarch's place as the head of the armed forces and framed with BRITISH FORCES FOR CROWN & COUNTRY around. (Reverse) laurel wreath surrounding the crowned words FOR BRITISH FORCES CAMPAIGN SERVICE.
Comments: *Produced by Award Productions Ltd to pay tribute to and to recognise the contributions of British Forces involved in campaigns and operations otherwise unrecognised. Qualifying criteria for this medal is one or more days service or posting in one or more of the qualifying regions or operations in FALKLANDS, NORTHERN IRELAND, GERMANY, GIBRALTAR, SINGAPORE; service alongside NATO forces or as part of a NATO-led initiative, protection of a BORDER and/or COASTAL PATROL for which relevant clasps are available.*

U46. HOME SERVICES MEDAL

Date: 2013.
Branch of Service: Civil.
Ribbon: Black with a central yellow stripe.
Metal: Silver coloured
Size: 36mm.
Description: (Obverse) The points of the compass surmounted by clasped hands with HOME SERVICES MEDAL around; (reverse) Laurel wreath enclosing a crown and the words FOR SERVICES TO HUMANITY.
Comments: *This medal, marketed by Medals of Distinction, is intended as a reward for any civilian who served in Northern Ireland during the "Toubles". A donation to the charities SANDS and Pilgrim Bandits is made for each purchase.*

U47. ARMED FORCES VETERAN MEDAL

Date: 2013.
Branch of Service: British Armed Forces.
Ribbon: Green with three equal stripes of dark blue, red and light blue. stripe.
Metal: Silver coloured.
Size: 36mm.
Description: (Obverse) A globe surrounded by emblems of the armed forces with ARMED FORCES VETERAN around; (reverse) Laurel wreath enclosing the words FOR SERVICES RENDERED.
Comments: *This medal, marketed by Medals of Distinction, is intended as a reward for any person who served in the British armed forces in any capacity. A number of different clasps are available to denote the area of involvement. A donation to the charities SANDS and Pilgrim Bandits is made for each purchase.*

U48. THE VETERANS STAR

Date: 2014.
Branch of Service: British and Commonwealth Forces.
Ribbon: Army red, Navy blue and Air Force blue framed between red, white and blue stripes representing Great Britain and The Commonwealth.
Metal: Silver.
Size: 36mm.
Description: The obverse of the medal comprises the flag of Great Britain surrounded by the words "For Crown and Country". The distinctive star formation has been inspired by the First and Second World War Stars. Unlike other UK medals it has a highly polished nickel-plated finish. The reverse of the star has a sandblasted finish.
Comments: *Produced by Award Productions Ltd, the Veterans Star is available to veterans who served in any of our Great British and Commonwealth Forces for a minimum period of two years. Next of kin or direct descendants may also apply.*

U49. THE UNIFORM SERVICE MEDAL

Date: 2016.
Branch of Service: All uniformed services.
Ribbon: Pale blue with a central darker blue stripe..
Metal: Silver.
Size: 33mm octagonal.
Description: The obverse of the medal is inspired by the shape of the Union flag represented by members of the uniformed services coming together to the same centre point, united in their services. The reverse of the medal has a satin finish suitable for naming with the service details of the recipient. Fitted with a suspension bar featuring a crown.
Comments: *Produced by Award Productions Ltd, the Uniform Service medal is available to those who have served or are currently serving for a minimum period of two years in any of the uniformed services: Armed Forces, Border Control, Coast Guard, Fire and Rescue, Nursing, Police, Ambulance and Prison services, etc. Next of kin and direct descendants may also apply. St John Ambulance is the beneficiary of this medal.*

U50. COMMEMORATIVE QUEEN'S SAPPHIRE JUBILEE MEDAL

Date: 2017.
Branch of Service: Available to all those who have served Queen Elizabeth II from 6 February 1952 including current serving members of the Armed Forces, Emergency Services, Prison Service, Police Community Support Officers, holders of the Victoria Cross and George Cross and members of the Royal Household. Next of kin and direct descendants may also apply.
Ribbon: A central stripe in sapphire blue with light blue and silver white stripes highlighting the reflective facets of the gem and medal.
Medal: Silver.
Size: 36mm.
Description: (Obverse) A multi-faceted design to reflect the sapphire cut gemstone with an English rose, Scottish thistle, Irish clover and Welsh leek, representing the plants of the United Kingdom; (reverse) a regal crown sits at the top of the medal with wording ELIZABETH II SAPPHIRE JUBILEE and 1952-65-2017, encircling the bottom.
Comments: *Produced by Award Productions Ltd to commemorate the 65th anniversary of the reign of Queen Elizabeth II. St John Ambulance is the beneficiary of this medal.*

ABBREVIATIONS

and initials

The medal collector is constantly coming across initials and abbreviations on medals and in documents—many of which are commonplace and easily decipherable. However, there are many more which can cause problems when trying to identify a medal recipient. The following list represents only a small selection of the inexhaustible number of abbreviations encountered, but hopefully it will be of some assistance to the collector. The "Token Book of Militarisms" contains literally hundreds more if you cannot find the abbreviation you are looking for here.

1 E Ang	1st East Anglian Regiment
1 R Dgns	1st Royal Dragoons
1 QDG	1st Queen's Dragoon Guards
11H	11th Royal Hussars
12L	12th Royal Lancers
13/18H	13th/18th Royal Hussars
14/20H	14th/20th Royal Hussars
15/19H	15th/19th Royal Hussars
3 E Ang	3rd East Anglian Regiment
4 QOH	4th Queen's Own Hussars
4H	4th Royal Hussars
5 DGds	5th Royal Inniskilling Dragoon Guards
7QOH	7th Queen's Own Hussars
7GR	7th Gurkha Rifles
A/	Acting
A Avn	Army Aviation
Abn Inf	Airborne Infantry
A/CWEM	Acting Chief Weapons Engineering Mechanic
A/LMEM	Acting Leading Marine Engineering Mechanic
A/LRO(G)	Acting Leading Radio Operator (General)
A/PO	Acting Petty Officer, Acting Pilot Officer
A&SH	The Argyll and Sutherland Highlanders
AAC	Army Air Corps
AAF	Auxiliary Air Force
AAU	Air Ambulance Unit
AB	Able Seaman; Airborne
ABDS	Army Bomb Disposal Squad
AC1	Aircraftman 1st Class
ACC	Army Catering Corps, Armoured Car Company
ACF	Army Cadet Force
ADALS	Assistant Director, Army Legal Service
ADC	Aide de Camp
AE	Army Education Officer, Air Efficiency Award
AER	Army Emergency Reserve
AFC	Air Force Cross
AFM	Air Force Medal
AGS	Africa General Service Medal
AIF	Australian Imperial Force
AIY	Ayrshire Imperial Yeomanry
ALO	Air Liaison Officer
ALS	Army Legal Services
AM	Albert Medal
AM1	Air Mechanic 1st Class
AMA	Acting Master at Arms
AMS	Assistant Military Secretary; Army Medical Staff
AOC	Army Ordnance Corps

APC	Army Pay Corps
APL	Aden Protectorate Levies
APTC	Army Physical Training Corps
AQ	Assistant Quartermaster; Administrative
Armd	Armoured
ASC	Army Service Corps; Air Service Command
ATO	Ammunition Technical Officer
Aux AF	Auxiliary Air Force
B&H	The Bedfordshire & Hertfordshire Regiment
BAAT	British Army Advisory Team
BATT	British Army Training Team
BAO	British Army of Occupation
Bdr	Bombadier
BDU	Bomb Disposal Unit
BEM	British Empire Medal
BF	British Forces
BGS	Brigadier, General Staff
BIY	Bedford Imperial Yeomanry
BM	Brigade Major
BORD.R	Border Regiment
BR	British
Brig	Brigadier
Br Coy	Bearer Company
BSA Police	British South Africa Police
Buffs	The Buffs (Royal East Kent Regiment)
BW	Black Watch (Royal Highland Regiment)
BWM	British War Medal
C&TC	Commissariat and Transport Corps
C/Sgt	Colour Sergeant
C&S	Command & Staff
CAC	Canadian Armoured Corps
CADC	Canadian Army Dental Corps
CAEA	Chief Air Engineering Artificer
CAHTC	Cape Auxiliary Horse Transport Corps
CAMN HIGH	Cameron Highlanders
Capt	Captain
CAR	Central African Rifles
CASC	Canadian Army Service Corps
CATO	Commander Ammunition Technical Officers
CB	Companion of the Order of the Bath
CBE	Commander of the Order of the British Empire
CBF	Commander British Forces
CC	Cadet Corps; Coastal Command; Combat
CCAEA	Charge Chief Air Engineering Artificer
CCCC	Cape Colony Cyclist Corps
CCF	Combined Cadet Force
CCMEA	Charge Chief Marine Engineering Artificer
CCS	Casualty Clearing Station
C de G	Croix de Guerre
Cdr	Commander

CE	Canadian Engineers
CEO	Chief Executive Officer; Chief Education Officer
CG	Coast Guard; Commanding General; Chaplain
CGC	Conspicuous Gallantry Cross
CGM	Conspicuous Gallantry Medal
Cheshire	The Cheshire Regiment
CI	Crown of India, Imperial Order; Counter Intelligence
CIV	City Imperial Volunteers
CIE	Companion of the Order of the Indian Empre
CLY	County of London Yeomanry
CMEM	Chief Marine Engineering Mechanic
CMFR	Commonwealth Monitoring Force Rhodesia
CMG	Companion of the Order of St Michael and St George
CMM	Commander of the Order of Military Merit
CMO	Chief Medical Officer
CMMP	Corps of Military Mounted Police
CMP	Corps of Military Police
CMSC	Cape Medical Staff Corps
CMR	Cape Mounted Riflemen
CMT	Corps of Mechanical Transport
CO	Commanding Officer
Col	Colonel
Coldm Gds	Coldstream Guards
Comd	Commander
COS	Chief of Staff
CP	Cape Police
Cpl	Corporal
CPO	Chief Petty Officer
CPOAEA	Chief Petty Officer Air Engineering Artificer
CPOWEA	Chief Petty Officer Weapons Engineering Artificer
CQMS	Company Quartermaster Sergeant
CSI	Companion of the Order of the Star of India
CSM	Company Sergeant Major; Campaign Service Medal
CT, C/T, Ch Tech	Chief Technician
CVO	Commander of the Royal Victorian Order
D	Diver
D Comd	Deputy Commander
D&D	The Devon and Dorset Regiment
DAD	Deputy Assistant Director
DADOS	Deputy Assistant Director of Ordnance Services
DADVRS	Deputy Assistant Director Veterinary & Remount Services
DANS	Director of Army Nursing Services
DAPM	Deputy Assistant Provost Marshal
DAT	Director of Army Training
DBE	Dame Commander, Order of the British Empire
DCLI	The Duke of Cornwall's Light Infantry
DCM	Distinguished Conduct Medal
DCMG	Dame Commander of the Order of St Michael and St George
DCO	Duke of Cambridge's Own; Duke of Connaught's Own
DCOS	Deputy Chief of Staff
DCVO	Dame Commander of the Royal Victorian Order
DDSD	Deputy Director Staff Duties
DEO	Duke of Edinburgh's Own
DERR	The Duke of Edinburgh's Royal Regiment (Berkshire & Wiltshire)
Det	Detached; Detachment
Devon	The Devonshire Regiment
DFC	Distinguished Flying Cross
DFM	Distinguished Flying Medal
DG	Dragoon Guards

DI	Defence Intelligence
DLI	The Durham Light Infantry
DMT	District Mounted Troops
Dorset	The Dorset Regiment
DOS	Director of Ordnance Services
DS	Defence Secretary; Deputy Secretary; Defensive Section
DSC	Distinguished Service Cross
DSM	Distinguished Service Medal
DSO	Distinguished Service Order
DWR	The Duke of Wellington's Regiment
EAR	East African Rifles
ED	Efficiency Decoration
EF	Expeditionary Force
EGM	Empire Gallantry Medal
EM	Edward Medal; Efficiency Medal
EOD	Explosive Ordnance Disposal
ERA	Engine Room Artificer
ERD	Emergency Reserve Decoration
ERE	Extra Regimentally Employed
FA	Field Ambulance
FANYC	First Aid Nursing Yeomanry Corps
FBRA	Field Battery Royal Artillery
FC	Fighter Command
Fd	Field
FARELF	Far East Land Forces
FF	Field Force
FFL	French Foreign Legion
FFR	Frontier Force Rifles
FL, F/L, Flt Lt	Flight Lieutenant
FM	Field Marshal
FMR	Frontier Mounted Rifles
FO, F/O, Fg Off	Flying Officer
FS	Fighter Squadron; Field Security
FS, F/S, Flt/Sgt	Flight Sergeant
Fus	Fusilier
G Howards	Green Howards (Alexandra, Princess of Wales's Own Yorkshire Regiment)
G(OR)	General Staff Operational Requirements
GBE	Grand Cross, Order of the British Empire
GC	George Cross
GC, G/C, GpCapt	Group Captain
GCB	Knight Grand Cross Order of the Bath
GCH	Knight Grand Cross Hanoverian Order
GCIE	Knight Grand Commander Order of the Indian Empire
GCLH	Grand Cross Legion of Honour
GCM	Good Conduct Medal
GCMG	Knight Grand Cross Order of St Michael and St George
GCSI	Knight Grand Commander Order of the Star of India
GCVO	Knight Grand Cross Royal Victorian Order
Gdsmn	Guardsman
GLI	Guernsey Light Infantry
Glosters	The Gloucestershire Regiment (28th/61st Foot)
GM	George Medal
Gnr	Gunner
GOC	General Officer Commanding
Gordons	The Gordon Highlanders (75th/92nd Regiment)
GPR	Glider Pilot Regiment
GR	Gurkha Rifles
GS	General Service
GSC	General Service Corps
GSM	General Service Medal
GSO	General Staff Officer
HA	Horse Artillery
HAC	Honourable Artillery Company
HBM	Her Britannic Majesty

HCR	Household Cavalry Regiment
HG	Home Guard; Horse Guards
HLI	The Highland Light Infantry
HQ	Headquarters
IAOC	Indian Army Ordnance Corps
IASC	Indian Army Service Corps
IC	In Charge
IDSM	Indian Distinguished Service Medal
IE	Order of the Indian Empire
IG	Irish Guards
Int	Intelligence
Int Corps	Intelligence Corps
Int & Sy Coy	Intelligence and Security Company
IO	Intelligence Officer
IOM	Indian Order of Merit
IRC	Infantry Reserve Corps
ISM	Imperial Service Medal
ISO	Imperial Service Order
IY	Imperial Yeomanry
JSSC	Joint Services Staff College
KAR	King's African Rifles
KB	Knight Bachelor
KBE	Knight Commander, Order of the British
KC	Knight Commander
KCB	Knight Commander Order of the Bath
KCH	Knight Commander of the Royal Hanoverian Guelphic Order
KCIE	Knight Commander Order of the Indian Empire
KCIO	King's Commissioned Indian Officer
KCMG	Knight Commander Order of St Michael and St George
KCSI	Knight Commander Order of the Star of India
KCVO	Knight Commander Royal Victorian Order
KDG	King's Dragoon Guards
KG	Knight of the Order of the Garter
KGL	King's German Legion
Kings	The King's Regiment (Liverpool)
KLH	Knight of the Legion of Honour
KM	King's Medal
KOM	Knight of the Order of Malta
KORB	The King's Own Royal Border Regiment
KOSB	The King's Own Scottish Borderers
KOYLI	The King's Own Yorkshire Light Infantry
KPM	King's Police Medal
KRRC	The King's Royal Rifle Corps
KSG	Knight of the Order of St George
KSLI	The King's Shropshire Light Infantry
KT	Knight of the Order of the Thistle
L/Cpl	Lance Corporal
L/Sgt	Lance Sergeant
LAC	Leading Aircraftman
Lanc Fusiliers	The Lancashire Fusiliers
Lanc R	The Queen's Lancashire Regiment
LC	Labour Corps
Leic	The Royal Leicestershire Regiment
LG	Life Guards; London Gazette
LI	Light Infantry
Linc	The Royal Lincolnshire Regiment
LM	Legion of Merit
LMA	Leading Medical Assistant
LS	Leading Seaman
LS&GC	Long Service and Good Conduct (medal)
Lt	Lieutenant
Lt-Cdr	Lieutenant Commander
Lt-Col	Lieutenant-Colonel
LVO	Lieutenant of the Royal Victorian Order
MA	Military Attache
Maint	Maintenance

Maj	Major
Maj-Gen	Major-General
Mal.LBC	Maltese Labour Corps
MBE	Member of the Order of the British Empire
MC	Military Cross
MEM	Marine Engineering Mechanic
MFA	Mercantile Fleet Auxiliary
MFS	Medical Field Service
MGC	Machine Gun Corps
MGS	Military General Service (medal)
MH	Medal of Honour
MI	Mounted Infantry
MID	Mentioned in Despatches
MKW	Military Knights of Windsor
MM	Military Medal; Medal of Merit
MMGS	Motor Machine Gun Service
MMWM	Mercantile Marine War Medal
Mne	Marine
MMR	Mercantile Marine Reserve
MR	Middlesex Regiment
MRCVS	Member Royal College of Veterinary Surgeons
MSC	Medical Staff Corps
MSM	Meritorious Service Medal
MTO	Mechanical Transport Officer
MVO	Member of the Royal Victorian Order
NACS	Naval Air Commando Squadron
NAS	Naval Air Squadron
NCO	Non-Commissioned Officer
NFA	Natal Field Artillery
NGS	Naval General Service (Medal)
NZEF	New Zealand Expeditionary Force
OBE	Officer of the Order of the British Empire
OBLI	Ox and Bucks Light Infantry
OC	Officer Commanding
OCS	Officer Cadet School
OEO	Ordnance Executive Officer
OHBMS	On Her Britannic Majesty's Service
OM	Order of Merit
OR	Operational Requirements; Other Ranks; Organised Reserve
Ord	Ordnance
OS	Ordinary Seaman; Ordnance Survey
PAOCVA	Prince Albert's Own Cape Volunteer Rifles
PAVG	Prince Albert's Volunteer Guard
Para	The Parachute Regiment
PO	Petty Officer
PO, P/O, Plt Off	Pilot Officer
PO/AC	Petty Officer Aircrewman
POMA	Petty Officer Medical Assistant
POMEM	Petty Officer Marine Engineering Mechanic
PR	Public Relations
PSO	Personal Staff Officer
Pte	Private
PVCP	Permanent Vehicle Check Point
PWO	The Prince of Wales's Own Regiment of Yorkshire
Q Ops	Quartermaster General Branch Operations
QARANC	Queen Alexandra's Royal Army Nursing Corps
QCBA	Queen's Commendation for Bravery in the Air
QCBC	Queen's Commendation for Brave Conduct
QCVS	Queen's Commendation for Valuable Service
QCVSA	Queen's Commendation for Valuable Service in the Air
QFSM	Queen's Fire Service Medal
QDG	The Queen's Dragoon Guards
QGM	Queen's Gallantry Medal
QLR	The Queen's Lancashire Regiment
QM	Quartermaster

QMAAC	Queen Mary's Army Auxiliary Corps	**RRW**	Royal Regiment of Wales
QMS	Quartermaster Sergeant	**RS**	The Royal Scots (The Royal Regiment)
QPM	Queen's Police Medal	**RSDG**	Royal Scots Dragoon Guards
QRIH	Queen's Royal Irish Hussars	**RSF**	Royal Scots Fusiliers
QSA	Queen's South Africa (Medal)	**R Sig**	Royal Signals
Queens	The Queen's Regiment—Queen's Division	**RSM**	Regimental Sergeant Major
QVRM	Queen's Volunteer Reserves Medal	**RSO**	Regimental Supply Officer
R Anglian	Royal Anglian Regiment	**RTR**	Royal Tank Regiment, Royal Armoured
R Fus	Royal Fusiliers (City of London Regiment)		Corps
R Innis	Royal Inniskilling	**RUC**	Royal Ulster Constabulary
R Signals	Royal Corps of Signals	**RUR**	The Royal Ulster Rifles
RA	Royal Artillery	**RVM**	Royal Victorian Medal
RAAF	Royal Australian Air Force	**RVO**	Royal Victorian Order
RAC	Royal Armoured Corps	**RWF**	The Royal Welsh Fusiliers
RAChD	Royal Army Chaplains Department	**RWK**	The Queen's Own Royal West Kent
RAEC	Royal Army Educational Corps		Regiment
RAF	Royal Air Force	**RW Kent R**	Royal West Kent Regiment
RAFVR	Royal Air Force Volunteer Reserve	**S/L, S/Ldr, Sqn Ldr**	Squadron Leader
RAMC	Royal Army Medical Corps	**S/Sgt**	Staff Sergeant
RAOC	Royal Army Ordnance Corps	**SAAF**	South African Air Force
RAPC	Royal Army Pay Corps	**SAC**	Senior Aircraftman
RARO	Regular Army Reserve of Officers	**SAS**	Special Air Service Regiment
RASC	Royal Army Service Corps	**SC**	Staff College; Staff Captain; Signal Corps
RAVC	Royal Army Veterinary Corps	**SF**	Special Forces
R Aux AF	Royal Auxiliary Air Force	**SG**	Scots Guards
RB	The Rifle Brigade	**SGM**	Sea Gallantry Medal
RCAF	Royal Canadian Air Force	**Sgmn**	Signalman
RCT	Royal Corps of Transport	**Sgt**	Sergeant
RE	Corps of Royal Engineers	**SI**	Star of India (Order)
RECC	Reconnaissance Corps	**SJAB**	St John Ambulance Brigade
REME	Corps of Royal Electrical and Mechanical	**SMIO**	Special Military Intelligence Officer
	Engineers	**SMIU**	Special Military Intelligence Unit
RF	Royal Fusiliers	**Smn**	Seaman
RFA	Royal Field Artillery	**SO1**	Staff Officer, Grade 1
RFC	Royal Flying Corps	**Som LI**	Somerset Light Infantry
Rfmn	Rifleman	**SWB**	The South Wales Borderers
RFR	Royal Fleet Reserve	**TA**	Territorial Army
RGJ	Royal Greenjackets	**T&AVR**	Territorial and Army Volunteer Reserve
RHA	Royal Horse Artillery	**TD**	Territorial Decoration
RHF	The Royal Highland Fusiliers	**TEM**	Territorial Efficiency Medal
RHG	Royal Horse Guards	**TF**	Territorial Force
RHG/D	The Blues and Royals	**TFEM**	Territorial Force Efficiency Medal
RHIGHRS	Royal Highlanders	**TFWM**	Territorial Force War Medal
RI	Royal Irish Rangers (27th (Inniskilling),	**TG**	Town Guard
	83rd and 87th)	**Trg Gp**	Training Group
RI Regt	Royal Irish Regiment	**UKLF**	United Kingdom Land Forces
RIC	Royal Irish Constabulary	**UNM**	United Nations Medal
RIF	The Royal Irish Fusiliers	**UNSM**	United Nations Service Medal
RM	Royal Marines	**VA**	Victoria and Albert (Order)
RMA	Royal Military Academy; Royal Malta	**VC**	Victoria Cross
RMC	Royal Military College	**VM**	Victory Medal
RMLI	Royal Marine Light Infantry	**VR**	Volunteer Reserve
RMP	Corps of Royal Military Police	**WAAF**	Women's Auxiliary Air Force
RN	Royal Navy	**WAFF**	West African Frontier Force
RNAS	Royal Naval Air Services	**W/C, W/Cdr, Wg Cdr**	Wing Commander
RNASBR	Royal Naval Auxiliary Sick Berth Reserve	**W&S**	Worcestershire & Sherwood Foresters
RNF	The Royal Northumberland Fusiliers	**WEA**	Weapons Engineering Artificer
RNR	Royal Naval Reserve	**WG**	Welsh Guards
RNVR	Royal Naval Volunteer Reserve	**Wilts**	Wiltshire Regiment
RNZAF	Royal New Zealand Air Force	**WO**	Warrant Officer
RNWAR	Royal Naval Wireless Auxiliary Reserve	**WOI**	Warrant Officer Class I
RO	Radio Operator	**WOII**	Warrant Officer Class II
RPC	Royal Pioneer Corps	**WRAC**	Women's Royal Army Corps
RRC	Royal Red Cross (Medal)	**WRAF**	Women's Royal Air Force
RRF	Royal Regiment of Fusiliers	**WRNS**	Women's Royal Naval Service

CURRENT
Regiments

As many British medals carry the names of regiments that no longer exist, we list here all of the regiments of the British Army as published in the current Army List, together with their predecessors, and the dates of amalgamations and redesignations The current regiment title is indicated in bold type with former names underneath in normal type. Old regimental numbers are included in brackets.

HOUSEHOLD CAVALRY REGIMENT

Life Guards

1st Life Guards
2nd Life Guards
The Life Guards (1st & 2nd)

Blues and Royals
(Royal Horse Guards and 1st Dragoons)

Royal Horse Guards (The Blues)
Royal Dragoons (1st Dragoons)

1st The Queen's Dragoon Guards

1st The King's Dragoon Guards
Queen's Bays (2nd Dragoon Guards)

Royal Scots Dragoon Guards
(Carabiniers and Greys)

3rd Dragoon Guards (Prince of Wales's)
Carabiniers (6th Dragoons)
3rd/6th Dragoon Guards
3rd Carabiniers (Prince of Wales's Dragoon Guards)
Royal Scots Greys (2nd Dragoons)

Royal Dragoon Guards

4th Royal Irish Dragoon Guards
7th Dragoon Guards (Princess Royal's)
4th/7th Dragoon Guards
4th/7th Royal Dragoon Guards
5th Dragoon Guards (Princess Charlotte of Wales's)
Inniskillings (6th Dragoon Guards)
5th/6th Dragoons
5th Inniskilling Dragoon Guards
5th Royal Inniskilling Dragoon Guards

Queen's Royal Hussars
(The Queen's Own & Royal Irish)

3rd The King's Own Hussars
7th The Queen's Own Hussars
Queen's Own Hussars
4th The Queen's Own Hussars
8th The King's Royal Irish Hussars
Queen's Royal Irish Hussars

King's Royal Hussars

10th Royal Hussars (Prince of Wales's Own)
11th Hussars (Prince Albert's Own)
Royal Hussars (Prince of Wales's Own)
14th King's Hussars
20th Hussars
14th/20th Hussars
14th/20th King's Hussars

Light Dragoons

13th Hussars
18th Royal Hussars (Queen Mary's Own)
13th/18th Hussars
13th/18th Royal Hussars (Queen Mary's Own)
15th The King's Hussars
19th Royal Hussars (Queen Alexandra's Own)
15th/19th Hussars
15th The King's Royal Hussars
15th/19th The King's Royal Hussars

Royal Lancers (Queen Elizabeth's Own)

9th/12th Royal Lancers (Prince of Wales's)
9th Queen's Royal Lancers
12th Royal Lancers (Prince of Wales's)
Queen's Royal Lancers
16th The Queen's Lancers
5th Royal Irish Lancers
16th/5th Lancers
16th/5th The Queen's Royal Lancers
17th (Duke of Cambridge's Own Lancers)
21st Lancers (Empress of India's)
17th/21st Lancers

Royal Tank Regiment

Heavy Branch Machine Gun Corps
Tank Corps
Royal Tank Corps

Royal Horse Artillery

Royal Regiment of Artillery

Royal Field Artillery
Royal Garrison Artillery
Royal Malta Artillery

Corps of Royal Engineers

Royal Corps of Signals

Grenadier Guards

Coldstream Guards

Scots Guards

Irish Guards

Welsh Guards

Royal Regiment of Scotland / 7 battalions

Royal Scots (The Royal Regiment)(1)
Royal Highland Fusiliers (Princess Margaret's Own Glasgow and Ayrshire Regiment)(21, 71 & 74)
Royal Scots Fusiliers (21)
Highland Light Infantry (City of Glasgow Regiment) (71 & 74)
King's Own Scottish Borderers (25)
Black Watch (Royal Highland Regiment)(42 & 73)
Highlanders (Seaforth, Gordons and Camerons) (72, 75, 78, 79 & 92)
Seaforth Highlanders (Ross-shire Buffs, Duke of Albany's)(72 & 78)
Queen's Own Cameron Highlanders (79)
Queen's Own Highlanders (Seaforth & Camerons) (72, 78 & 79)
Gordon Highlanders
Argyll & Sutherland Highlanders (Princess Louise's) (91 & 93)
52nd Lowland Regiment
51st Highland Regiment

Princess of Wales's Royal Regiment (Queen's & Royal Hampshire) (2, 3, 31, 35, 37, 50, 67, 70, 97 & 107)

Queen's Royal Regiment (West Surrey)(2)
East Surrey Regiment (31 & 70)
Queen's Royal Surrey Regiment
Buffs (Royal East Kent Regiment)(3)
Queen's Own Royal West Kent Regiment (50 & 97)
Queen's Own Buffs (The Royal Kent Regiment)
Royal Sussex Regiment (35 & 107)
Middlesex Regiment (Duke of Cambridge's Own) (57 & 77)
Queen's Regiment
Royal Hampshire Regiment (37 & 67)

Duke of Lancaster's Regiment (King's, Lancashire and Border) 3 battalions

King's Own Royal Border Regiment (4, 34 & 55)
King's Own Royal Regiment (Lancaster)(4)
Queen's Lancashire Regiment (30, 40, 47, 59 81 & 82)
East Lancashire Regiment (30 & 59)
South Lancashire Regiment (The Prince of Wales's Volunteers)(40 & 82)
Lancashire Regiment (Prince of Wales's Volunteers)
Loyal Regiment (North Lancashire)(47 & 48)
Border Regiment (34 & 55)
King's Regiment (8, 63 & 96)

King's Regiment (Liverpool)(8)
Manchester Regiment (63 & 96)
King's Regiment (Manchester & Liverpool)(8, 63 & 96)

Royal Regiment of Fusiliers (5, 6, 7 & 20)

Royal Northumberland Fusiliers (5)
Royal Warwickshire Regiment (6)
Royal Warwickshire Fusiliers (6)
Royal Fusiliers (City of London Regiment) (7)
Lancashire Fusiliers (20)

Royal Anglian Regiment (9, 10, 12, 16, 17, 44, 48, 56 & 58)

Bedfordshire & Hertfordshire Regiment (16)
Essex Regiment (44 & 56)
3rd East Anglian Regiment (16th/44th Foot)
Royal Norfolk Regiment (9)
Suffolk Regiment (12)
1st East Anglian Regiment (Royal Norfolk & Suffolk)
Royal Lincolnshire Regiment (10)
Northamptonshire Regiment (48 & 58)
2nd East Anglian Regiment (Duchess of Gloucester's Own Royal Lincolnshire & Northamptonshire)
Royal Leicestershire Regiment (17)

Yorkshire Regiment / 4 battalions

Prince of Wales's Own Regiment of Yorkshire (14 & 15)
West Yorkshire (Prince of Wales's Own) (14)
East Yorkshire Regiment (Duke of York's Own) (15)
Green Howards (Alexandra, Princess of Wales's Own Yorkshire Regiment) (19)
Duke of Wellington's Regiment (West Riding) (33 & 76)
Duke of Wellington's Regiment (33)
76th Regiment of Foot
Halifax Regiment

Mercian Regiment / 4 Battalions

Cheshire Regiment (22)
Worcestershire & Sherwood Foresters Regiment (29, 36, 45 & 95)
Worcester Regiment (29 & 36)
Sherwood Foresters (Nottingham & Derbyshire Regiment)(45 & 95)
Staffordshire Regiment (Prince of Wales's) (38, 64, 80 & 98)
South Staffordshire Regiment (38 & 80)
North Staffordshire Regiment (Prince of Wales's) (64 & 98)
The Mercian Regiment (Volunteers)

Royal Welsh / 2 battalions

Royal Welch Fusiliers (23)
Royal Regiment of Wales (24th/41st Foot)
South Wales Borderers (24)
Welch Regiment (41 & 69)
Monmouthshire Regiment TA
Royal Welsh Regiment TA

Royal Irish Regiment (27th (Inniskilling), 83rd, 87th, and Ulster Defence Regiment)

Royal Inniskilling Fusiliers (27 & 108)

Royal Ulster Rifles (83 & 86)
Royal Irish Rifles (83 & 86)
Royal Irish Fusiliers (Princess Victoria's) (87 & 89)
Ulster Defence Regiment
Royal Irish Rangers
4th/5th Battalion The Royal Irish Rangers
(Volunteers)

Parachute Regiment / 3 battalions

The Gurkha Brigade

The Royal Gurkha Rifles / 2 battalions

2nd King Edward VII's Own Gurkha Rifles (The
Sirmoor Rifles)
6th Queen Elizabeth's Own Gurkha Rifles
7th Duke of Edinburgh's Own Gurkha Rifles
10th Princess Mary's Own Gurkha Rifle

Queen's Gurkha Engineers

Queen's Gurkha Signals

Queen's Own Gurkha Logistic Regiment

22nd Special Air Service Regiment

The Rifles / 8 battalions

Devonshire & Dorset Light Infantry (11, 39, & 54)
Devonshire & Dorset Regiment (11, 39, & 54)
Devonshire Regiment (11)
Dorset Regiment (39 & 54)
Royal Gloucestershire, Wiltshire & Berkshire Light
Infantry (28, 49, 61, 62, 66 & 99)
Royal Gloucestershire, Wiltshire & Berkshire
Regiment (28, 49, 61, 62, 66 & 99)
Wiltshire Regiment (Duke of Edinburgh's) (62 & 99)
Royal Berkshire Regiment (Princess Charlotte of
Wales's) (49 & 66)
Duke of Edinburgh's Royal Regiment (Berkshire
and Wiltshire)
Gloucestershire Regiment (28 & 61)
Light Infantry (13, 32, 46, 51, 53, 68, 85, 105 & 106)
Somerset Light Infantry (Prince Albert's) (13)
Duke of Cornwall's Light Infantry (32 & 46)
Somerset & Cornwall Light Infantry (13, 32, & 46)
King's Own Yorkshire Light Infantry (51 & 105)
King's Shropshire Light Infantry (53 & 85)
Durham Light Infantry (68 & 106)
Royal Green Jackets (43rd & 52nd, King's Royal
Rifle Corps, Rifle Brigade)
Oxfordshire & Buckinghamshire Light Infantry (43
& 52)
1st Green Jackets (43 & 52)
King's Royal Rifle Corps (60)
2nd Green Jackets (The King's Royal Rifle
Corps) (60)
Rifle Brigade (Prince Consort's Own)
3rd Green Jackets (The Rifle Brigade)
Royal Rifle Volunteers
Rifle Volunteers
2nd (Volunteer) Battalion The Royal
Gloucestershire, Berkshire and Wiltshire Regiment
1st Battalion The Wessex Regiment (Rifle
Volunteers)
2nd Battalion The Wessex Regiment (Volunteers)

Army Air Corps

Glider Pilot Regiment
Air Observer Corps
Air Observation Post Squadrons, Royal Artillery

Special Reconnaissance Regiment

Royal Army Chaplains' Department

Royal Logistic Corps

Royal Army Service Corps
Royal Corps of Transport
Royal Army Ordnance Corps
Royal Pioneer Corps
Army Catering Corps
Royal Engineers—Postal and Courier Service

Royal Army Medical Corps

Corps of Royal Electrical & Mechanical Engineers

Adjutant General's Corps

Adjutant General's Corps
(Staff and Personnel Support Branch)

Royal Army Pay Corps
Women's Royal Army Corps (less those to
Regiments)
Royal Army Ordnance Corps Staff Clerks
Regimental Clerks

Adjutant General's Corps (Provost Branch)

Royal Military Police
Military Provost Staff Corps
Military Provost Guard Service

Adjutant General's Corps
(Education & Training Service Branch)

Royal Army Educational Corps

Adjutant General's Corps (Army Legal Branch)

Royal Army Veterinary Corps

Small Arms School Corps

Royal Army Dental Corps

Intelligence Corps

Royal Army Physical Training Corps

Army Gymnastic Staff
Army Physical Training Corps
Army Physical Traing Corps

Queen Alexandra's Royal Army Nursing Corps

Queen Alexandra's Imperial Military Nursing
Service
Queen Alexandra's Military Families Nursing
Service

Corps of Army Music

Royal Military Academy Band Corps

ARMY RERSERVE (formerly TERRITORIAL ARMY)

Royal Monmouth Royal Engineers (Militia)

Honourable Artillery Company

Royal Yeomanry

Westminster Dragoons
Sherwood Rangers Yeomanry
Staffordshire, Warwickshire, Worcestershire
Yeomanry
Kent and Sharpshooters Yeomanry
Shropshire Yeomanry
Leicestershire and Derbyshire Yeomanry

Queen's Own Yeomanry

Yorkshire Yeomanry
Duke of Lancaster's Own Yeomanry
Cheshire Yeomanry
Northumberland Hussars

Scottish and North Irish Yeomanry

Lothian and Border Yeomanry
Ayrshire (Earl of Carrick's Own) Yeomanry
Fife and Forfar Yeomanry (Scottish Horse)
North Irish Horse

Royal Wessex Yeomanry

Royal Wiltshire Yeomanry (Prince of Wales's Own)
Royal Gloucestershire Hussars.
Royal Devon Yeomanry
Dorset Yeomanry

Royal Regiment of Artillery (Volunteers)

Corps of Royal Engineers (Volunteers)

Royal Corps of Signals (Volunteers)

Royal Regiment of Scotland

6th Battalion 52nd Lowland
7th Battalion 51st Highland

The London Regiment

3rd (Volunteer) Battalion The Princess of Wales's Royal Regiment (Queen's & Royal Hampshire)

4th Battalion the Duke of Lancaster's Regiment (King's, Lancashire and Border)

5th Battalion The Royal Regiment of Fusiliers

4th Battalion The Yorkshire Regiment

14/15, 19, 33/76 Foot)

4th Battalion The Mercian Regiment

3rd Battalion The Royal Welsh

The Welsh Volunteers
3rd Battalion Royal Welch Fusiliers
3rd Battalion Royal Regiment of Wales (24th/41st Foot)

4th Battalion Royal Regiment of Wales (24th/41st Foot)
The Royal Welsh Regiment

2nd Battalion The Royal Irish Regiment (27th Inniskilling), 83rd, 87th and Ulster Defence Regiment

4th Battalion The Parachute Regiment

6th Battalion The Rifles

7th Battalion The Rifles

21st Special Air Service (Artists)

23rd Special Air Service

7th (Training) Regiment Army Air Corps

Various Services/Corps as for the Regular Army with (Volunteers) in their titles)

Officer Training Corps

COLONIAL UNITS

Royal Gibraltar Regiment

The Bermuda Regiment

SOME FORMER TA INFANTRY REGIMENTS

East of England Regiment
Lancastrian and Cumberland Volunteers
Tyne-Tees Regiment
East & West Riding Reiment
West Midlands Regiment
King's and Cheshire Regiment

SOME DISBANDED REGIMENTS WITH NO LOGICAL SUCCESSOR

22nd Dragoons	25th Dragoons
23rd Hussars	26th Hussars
24th Lancers	27th Lancers

Reconnaissance Regiment
Highland Regiment
Lowland Regiment
Royal Irish Regiment (18)
Cameronians (Scottish Rifles)(26 & 90)
York and Lancaster Regiment (65)
Connaught Rangers (88 & 94)
Prince of Wales's Leinster Regiment (Royal Canadians) (100 & 109)
Royal Munster Fusiliers (101 & 104)
Royal Dublin Fusiliers (102 & 103)
Royal Guernsey Light Infantry
Royal Militia of the Island of Jersey
King's Own Malta Regiment of Militia
West India Regiment
Army Cyclist Corps
Machine Gun Corps
Army Remount Service
Cyprus Regiment
Royal Flying Corps
Royal Defence Corps
Queen' Mary's Army Auxiliary Corps
Auxiliary Territorial Service
Women's Royal Army Corps

RESEARCHING
Your Medals

The fact that many British medals are named enables the serious collector to engage in researching both the life and service history of the recipient as well as being able to learn about the history of the regiment/ship/unit or whatever with which he served. There is no easy or definitive guide to the range of research materials that are available, nor to the range of information likely to be found. The sort of information available varies greatly depending on whether the recipient was an officer or other rank, the service and unit with which he served, and the period during which he served. The experience and perseverance of the researcher can also affect the outcome. For those who are new to research, or who live a long way from the original sources, it may be wise to employ a professional researcher, at least initially. The National Archives keep a list of independent researchers who undertake this kind of work.

When researching a medal and its recipient, experienced collectors regularly refer to a mixture of manuscript and printed sources:

Manuscript Sources
The National Archives, previously the Public Record Office (Ruskin Avenue, Kew, Surrey TW9 4DU) and the Oriental & India Office Collections (OIOC, British Library, 96 Euston Road, London NW1 2DB) are the two major depositories of official records of interest to the medal collector. Generally speaking the collector of medals to the British Armed Services will find the National Archive records essential to their enquiries, whilst anyone interest in the Indian Army and Navy (formerly the armed services of the Honourable East India Company), also the participation of British Forces in Indian campaigns, will find the OIOC to be an essential source of information. County Record Offices, Libraries and Museums, and also Regimental Museums can also have important holdings of manuscript records.

A first visit to the National Archive and the OIOC can be daunting. The range of records held by both Record Offices is also awe-inspiring once research has gone beyond consulting medal rolls and service papers.

Whilst there is no substitute for experience in learning successfully to branch out from the main stream of records, it is essential to be well prepared. It is important to have some idea of where to start looking and to realise the scope and limitations of the documents—it should be noted that the National Archive is subject to the standard 30 year closure rule for records, with many personal records being closed for longer periods. A great deal of time can be spent in simply locating the relevant references. To help you be more informed and to help eliminate time-wasting there are a number of important guides available that will aid in the location of the most relevant documents.

In addition it is worth noting that:

1. The National Archives produces a range of leaflets which provide useful information about particular classes of records—records relating to military, naval and air services are particularly well-covered. The leaflets are free to visitors.
2. The Mormons have published a wide range of guides to genealogical research which cover subjects of interest to medal/military researchers.
3. The National Army Museum occasionally holds a study day on the subject of military research.
4. New information is becoming available all the time and in new forms.

Additionally, it is important to be aware that new documents are released periodically to public access. Probably the most important in recent years are those at the National Archives relating to World War I. \
Also there are a growing number of important websites of immense help to the researcher. Among these are:

www.westernfront.co.uk (Western Front Association),
www.crimeanwar.org (Crimean War Research Society),
www.cwgc.org (Commonwealth War Graves Commission),
www.nationalarchives.gov.uk (National Archives (Downloadable MICs)),
www.anglozuluwar.com (Anglo Zulu War Society),
www.britishmedalforum.com (Medal Forum),
www.bl.uk/collections/orientaloffice.html (India Office), and many more.

Medal Entitlement/Verification
Most collectors start their research by checking with the campaign medal roll (if available) that the recipient

is indeed entitled to the medal and any clasps. It is a logical point at which to begin. This is often regarded as a simple, routine procedure, but for the unwary there are pitfalls and complications. The following points should always be borne in mind:

1. Printed medal rolls will always contain errors in transcription, thus any discrepancies between a medal and the roll should, whenever possible, be checked back with the original manuscript roll. The more complex the original roll, the more transcription errors are likely to occur (for example, the claimaints' lists for the Naval General Service Medal 1793-1840 and even the Military General Service Medal 1793-1814 are good examples of rolls where difficulties are likely to arise).
2. Some rolls have not survived—for example that for the Gwalior Campaign 1843. In such instances prize or bhatta rolls may exist at either the Public Record Office or the India Office. The inclusion of a recipient's name will at least indicate that he was most likely "entitled" to a medal and/or clasp (prize rolls indicate the share of money—realised from the loot captured in an action and then sold—allocated to each participant; bhatta is an extra allowance of pay made for field service).
3. Some medal rolls are incomplete, as with some of the regimental rolls for the Crimea Medal 1854–56.
4. With some campaign medal rolls, supplementary lists and late claimants' documentation have not survived.
5. Some medal rolls are difficult to search and therefore one has to take time in understanding the background to the documents one is looking at—the various lists of recipients for the Military General Service Medal 1794–1814 is a case in point.

It is important to note that the establishment of a recipient's entitlement is not the same thing as verifying a medal. Verification also requires the numismatic knowledge to know that the medal and clasps appear genuine. Where entitlement cannot be confirmed from the medal rolls, some collectors may be happy to rely on their numismatic knowledge to assure themselves that a medal is "genuine".

Published Sources

The published literature on medals is far-reaching and diverse, ranging from simply-produced booklets to detailed studies published in several volumes. A full bibliography of medallic and related works would in itself fill several volumes, particularly if fully cross-referenced.

Most collectors seek to build up a solid library which reflects their main interests, but inevitably there are always books that have to be consulted elsewhere. Major libraries and national museums, such as the British Museum Library, the National Army Museum, the Imperial War Museum, the Hendon Royal Air Force Museum, the Greenwich Maritime Museum, and the Portsmouth Naval Musuem have extensive holdings of relevant material which can be consulted on the premises. City and County Reference Libraries are important for collectors who rarely visit London. Some Regimental Museums have libraries attached. Most libraries of any size will have a subject index to their collection of books (and sometimes manuscripts and photographs). In addition *Medal News* magazine reviews most new books that are of interest to the collector, many of which Token Publishing Ltd stock. Visit ww.tokenpublishing.com for more details.

Documents often found with medals can sometimes provide important research information.

SOCIETIES
For Medal Collectors

Listed here are some of the many societies around the world that cater for the medal collector or those interested in military history. The details given are mostly the private addresses or telephone numbers of the membership secretaries to whom all correspondence should be sent. We would appreciate any information from other Societies who would like their details included in the next YEARBOOK.

Aldershot Militaria Society Galpin Hall, Windsor Way, Aldershot, Hants. Tel: 01753 654763.

Association de Collectionneurs de Décorations et Médailles (MEDEC) Paasbloemstraat 81, B-2170 Merksem, Belgium.

Austrian Orders Research Society Salesianergasse 9, A-1037 Wien, Postfach 20, Austria.

Birmingham Medal Society Martin Harrison, Tel: 07971 457179, www.birminghammedalsociety.com.

The Crimean War Research Society 4 Castle Estate, Ripponden, West Yorkshire HX6 4JY.

Crown Imperial B. Sutton, The Old Smithy, 35 Liverpool Rd, Buckley, Flintshire CH7 3LH.

Deutsche Gesellschaft fur Ordenskunde Juergen Lindner, Wuerttemberger Hof 3, 71126 Gaeufelden., email: geschaeftsfuehrer@dgo-ev.de

Indian Military Historical Society A. N. McLenaghan, 33 High Street, Tilbrook, Huntingdon, Cambs PE28 0JP, email: membership@imhs.org.uk.

Life Saving Awards Research Society Kim Claxton, Waren Cottage, 14 Bedstone, Bucknell, Shropshire SY7 0BE. tel: 01547 530611. email:kclaxton@btinternet.com.

London Medal Club Jim Lees, 020 8560 7648.

Medal Society of Ireland 1 The Hill, Stillorgan, Co. Dublin, Ireland, email: sales@msoi.eu.

Mid-Western Orders & Medals Society (MIDOMS) 5847 Gilbert Avenue, La Grange, IL 60525, USA.

Military Collector's Club of Canada (MCCofC) PO Box 64009, RPO Morse Place, Winnipeg, MB, R2K 4K2, Canada, www.canadianmilitariaclub.org.

Military Medal Society of South Africa 27 Balvicar Road, Blairgowrie, Johannesburg, SA 2194.

Naval Historical Collectors and Research Association Hickory Hollow, Old Coach Road, Cross, Axbridge Somerset BS26 2EQ. www.nhcra-online.org.

Northumbrian Medal Society Tel: 0191 4217175.

Orders & Medals Society of America (OMSA) PO Box 540, Claymont, DE 19703-0 540, USA. www.omsa.org.

Orders & Medals Research Society (OMRS) PO Box 6195, Royal Leamington Spa, CV31 9JU. membershipsecretary@omrs.org.

ditto, Australia Branch (Sydney) Graeme Marfleet. Email: graemem@attachesoftware.com

ditto, Canada Branch (Ottawa) Nelson Mercier, email: omrs.ottawa@gmail.com.

ditto, Canada Branch (Toronto) David Harris, tel: 001 905 294 5138, email: daharris@yahoo.ca.

ditto, Cotswold Branch (Cheltenham) John Wright. Tel: 01242 519815, email: qcmilitaria@btconnect.com.

ditto, East Anglian Branch Nick Tucker. Tel: 01842 879426.

ditto, Hong Kong Branch Steve Verralls. Tel: 852 9465 1496, email: secretary@omrs-hk.org.

ditto, Kent Branch Glen Jones. Tel: 01634 851912, email: glenwardjones@yahoo.co.uk.

ditto, London Branch Bob Barltrop. Tel: 01582 715472, email: robert.barltrop@btinternet.com.

ditto, Medal Ribbon Branch Graham Carter. Tel: 01202 304043, email: graham_carter@live.co.uk.

ditto, Miniature Medals Branch Steven Fullman. email: stevenfullman@hotmail.co.uk

ditto, New Zealand Branch (Wellington) Howard Chamberlain. Tel: 64 4 293 3504, email: clas.chamberlain@xtra.co.nz.

ditto, Northern Branch (Manchester) Martyn Lovell. Tel/Fax: 01925 753039, email: martynlovell@btinternet.com.

ditto, Northumbrian Branch 41 Ashdown Avenue, Durham DH1 1DB.

ditto, Wessex (formerly Salisbury) Branch Paul Capon. Tel: 01980 673757, email: p_m_capon@yahoo.co.uk.

ditto, Scottish Branch Gordon Taylor. Email: gort@btinternet.com

ditto, Sussex Branch Paul Turner. Email: paulturner@17northmeads.freeserve.co.uk.

ditto, Surrey Branch Graham Grist. Tel: 01932 229281, email: grahamila@googlemail.com.

ditto, Thames Valley Branch Peter Weedon. Email: peterweedon@btconnect.com.

ditto, Ottawa Branch Mark Reid. Email: tapir@rogers.com.

Ordenshistorik Selskab Falkoneralle 79, DK 2000 Frederiksberg, Denmark.

Société Suisse de Phaleristique Case postale 5616, 1211 Geneva 11, Switzerland.

Stockport Militaria Collectors Society 10 Bradgate Place, Bradgate, Rotherham, South Yorkshire, S61 1LB. Tel: 01709 557622.

Studiekring Faleristiek Straatakker 2, 8700 Tielt, Belgium. www.skf-vzw.org.

Studiekring Ridderorden en Ondenscheidingen Bert Keers, Zamenhoflaan 23, 3706 VA, Zeist, Netherlands. www.vereniging-sro-nl.

Victorian Military Society 20 Priory Road, Newbury, Berks RG14 7QN. www.victorianmilitarysociety.org.uk.

West of England Medal Club (Exeter) Otterburn Farm, Halwill, Beaworthy, Devon EX21 5UG. Tel: 01395 264939.

Zimbabwe Medal Society (Harare) 14 Straker Ave, Gunhill, Harare, Zimbabwe, email: rgill@zol.co.zw.

PROFESSIONAL

Directory

On the following pages are the names and addresses of auctioneers, dealers, booksellers and fair organisers, all of whom will be of assistance to the medal collector. Most are full time and many have retail shops and the collector is usually welcome during normal business hours. Some have extensive stocks of medals whilst others include medals in a more diverse inventory. A number of dealers are part time or work from small premises or from home and appointments are necessary as many keep their stock in the bank for security. Telephone numbers and email addresses have been included where known and it is always sensible to make contact before travelling any distance.

AUCTIONEERS

The following hold regular medal auctions or feature medals in general numismatic or militaria sales.

Baldwin's of St James's
10 Charles II Street, London, SW1Y 4AA. Tel: 020 7930 7888, fax: 020 7930 824, email: info@ bsjauctions.com, www.bsjauctions.com. Specialist auctioneers of coins and medals.

Biddle & Webb
Icknield Square, Ladywood, Middleway, Birmingham. Tel: 0121 455 8042, www. biddleandwebb.com. Antiques and militaria.

Blythe & Co
Arkenstall Center, Station Road, Haddenham, CB6 3XD.Tel: 01353 930094, www.blyths.com. Sales of militaria, coins and artefacts.

Bonhams (Glendining's)
Montpelier Street, London, SW7 1HH & 101 New Bond Street, London, W1S 1SR. Tel: 020 7393 3914, fax: 020 7393 3905, www.bonhams.com. Auctioneers and valuers of medals.

Bosleys
Remnantz (The Old Military College), Marlow, Buckinghamshire, SL7 2BS. Tel: 01628 488188, fax: 01628 488111, www.bosleys.co.uk. Specialist auctioneers of medals and militaria

Brightwells
Antiques and Fine Art Department, Easters Court, Leominster, Herefordshire, HR6 0DE. Tel: 01568 611122, www.brightwells.com. Occasional auctions of medals and militaria.

C&T Auctions
Unit 4, High House Business Park, Kenardington, Nr Ashford, Kent, TN26 2LF. Tel: 01233 510050, www.candtauctions.co.uk. Auctions of medals, badges, insignia, headdress & militaria items.

Charterhouse
The Long Street Salerooms, Sherbourne, Dorset, DT9 3BS. Tel: 01935 812277, www.charterhouse-auctions.co.uk. Medal auctions.

City Coins
Tulbagh Square, Cape Town, South Africa. Tel: 0027 21 425 2639, fax: 0027 21 425 3939, email: auctions@citycoins.co.za, www.citycoins.com. Postal medal auctions.

Colonial Coins and Medals
218 Adelaide Street, Brisbane, Australia. Tel: + 61 7 3221 8460, www.coinmedalshop.com.au. Auctions of medals and coins.

Corbitts
5 Mosley Street, Newcastle Upon Tyne, NE1 1YE. Tel: 0191 2327268, fax: 0191 2614130. Coins, medals, stamps and collectables.

Cotswold Auction Co.
Chapel Walk, Cheltenham, GL50 3DS. Tel: 01242 256363, www.cotswoldauction.co.uk. Auctioneers and valuers.

Diss Auction Rooms (Twgaze)
Roydon Road, Diss, Norfok, IP22 4LN. Tel: 01379 650306, www.twgaze.com. Occasional auctions of medals and militaria.

Dix Noonan Webb
16 Bolton Street, Piccadilly, London, W1J 8BQ. Tel: 020 7016 1700, fax: 020 7016 1799, email: medals@dnw.co.uk, www.dnw.co.uk. Auctioneers and valuers. Regular auctions of medals. Also coin and banknote auctions.

Dominic Winter Auctions
Mallard House, Broadway Lane, South Cerney, Nr Cirencester, GL7 5UQ. Tel: 01285 860006, fax: 01285 862461, email: henry@dominicwinter.co.uk, www.dominicwinter.co.uk. Medal and militaria auctioneers and valuers.

Downie's
3 Redland Drive, Mitcham, Melbourne, Vic 3132, Australia. Tel:+61 (0)3 8456 8456, fax: +61 (0) 3 8456 8456), www.downies.com. Sales with emphasis on Australian and UK medals.

Dukes
Brewery Square, Dorchester, Dorset, DT1 1GA. Tel: 01305 265080, www.dukes-auctions.com. Regular auctions of coins, medals, militaria and ephemera.

Fellows
Augusta House, 19 Augusta Street, Birmingham, B18 6JA. Tel: 0121 212 2131, fax: 0121 212 1249, email: info@fellows.co.uk, www.fellows.co.uk. Medals and coins.

Gorringes
15 North Street, Lewes, East Sussex, BN7 2PD. Tel: 01273 472503, www.gorringes.co.uk. Sales of medals, militaria and fine art.

Heritage Auctions
3500 Maple Avenue, 17th Floor, Dallas, Texas 75219, USA (www.ha.com). Auctioneers of orders, decorations and medals. USA and world coins.

Hermann Historica
Linprunstr, 16, D–80335, Munich. Tel: +49 89 547 26490, email: contact@hermann-historica.com. Auctions of medals and militaria.

Jeffrey Hoare Auctions Inc.
319 Springbank Drive, London, Ontario, Canada, N6J 1G6. Tel: (519) 473 7491 fax: (519) 473 1541, www.jeffreyhoare.on.ca. Regular sales of medals and militaria.

Alec Kaplan
115 Dunottar Street, Sydenham, Johannesburg, South Africa. Tel: 011 485 2195, email: medals@wirelessza.co.za. Regular sales of medals and militaria.

George Kidner
The Lymington Saleroom, Emsworth Road, Lymington, Hampshire, SO41 9BL. Tel: 01590 670070, www.georgekidner.co.uk. Auctions of Arms and militaria.

Künker
Nobbenburger Strasse 4a, 49076 Osnabrueck. Tel: 0049-541-962020, email: service@kuenker.de, www.kuenker.de. Coins and medals

Lockdales
52 Barrack Square, Martlesham Heath, Ipswich, Suffolk, IP5 3RF. Tel: 01473 627110, www.lockdales.com. Medals, coins, collectables.

Mellors & Kirk
Gregory Street, Nottingham, NG7 2NL. Tel: 0115 979 0000, email: enquiries@mellorsandkirk.com, www.mellorsandkirk.com. Medals and collectables.

Morton & Eden
Nash House St George Street, London, W1S 2FQ. Tel: 020 7493 5344, fax: 020 7495 6325, www.mortonandeden.com. Advisory service and auctioneers of medals. Also coins, banknotes and medallions.

Mowbray Collectables
247-253 Main Highway 1, Otaki 5581, New Zealand. Tel: +64 6 3648270, www.mowbraycollectables.co.nz. Auctioneers of Coins, medals and banknotes.

Noble Numismatics Pty Ltd
169 Macquarie Street, Sydney, 2000, Australia. Tel: +61 2 9223 45478, fax: +61 2 9233 6009, email: info@noble.net.au. Regular sales of British and Commonwealth medals.

Reeman Dansie
8 Wyncolls Road, Severalls Business Park, Colchester, Essex ,CO4 9HU. Tel: 01206 754754, fax: 01206 754750, www.reemandansie.com. Medals, militaria, coins and medallions.

Sincona AG
Limmatquai 112, CH-8001, Zurich, CH-8001, Switzerland. Tel: + 41 44 215 10 90, fax: +41 44 215 10 99, www.sincona.com. Specialist auctioneers of medals and coins.

Smiths of Newant
The Old Chapel, Culver Street, Newent, GL18 1DB. Tel: 01531 821 776, www.smithsnewentauctions.co.uk. Coins and collectables.

Spink & Son Ltd
69 Southampton Row, Bloomsbury, London, WC1B 4ET. Tel: 020 7563 4000, fax: 020 7563 4085, email: info@spink.com, www.spink.com. Auctioneers and valuers. Regular sales of medals.

Stacey's
Essex Auction Rooms, 37 Websters Way, Rayleigh, Essex, SS6 8JQ. Tel: 01268 777122, www.staceyauction.com. Militaria and medals

Stacks
123, West 57th Street, New York, NY 10019, USA. info@stacksBowers.com, www.stacksbowers.com. Auctioneers of world orders, decorations and medals. Also USA and world coins.

Tennants
The Auction Centre, Leyburn, North Yorkshire, DL8 5SG. Tel: 01969 623780, www.tennants.co.uk. Auctions of medals and coins.

Thomas Del Mar
25 Blythe Road, London, W14 0PD. Tel: 020 7602 4805, www.thomasdelmar.com. Antique arms, armour and militaria.

Thomson Roddick Auctioneers
The Auction Centre, Marconi Road, Carlisle, CA2 7NA. Tel: 01228 528 939, email: carlisle@thomsonroddick.com. Also at The auction Centre, 118 Carnethie Street, Rosewell, Edinburgh, EH24 9AL. Tel: 0131 440 2448, Auctions of orders, medals, militaria and coins.

Trevanion and Dean
The Joyce Building, Station Road, Whitchurch, Shropshire, SY13 1RD. Tel: 01948 800 202, info@trevanionanddean.co.uk, www.trevanionanddean.com. Auctioneers and valuers.

Wallis & Wallis
West Street Auction Galleries, Lewes, Sussex BN7 2NJ. Tel: 01273 480208, fax: 01273 476562, email: auctions@wallisandwallis.org, www.wallisandwallis.org. Regular sales of militaria, arms, armour and medals.

Warwick & Warwick
Chalon House, Scar Bank, Millers Road, Warwick CV34 5DB. Tel: 01926 499031 fax: 01926 491906, email: richard.beale@warwickandwarwick.com, www.warwickandwarwick.com. Regular sales of orders, decorations and other collectables.

Wellington Auctions
37 Rookery Lane, Great Totham, Maldon, Essex, CM9 8DF. Tel: 07976 266293, email: mail@wellingtonauctions.com, www.wellingtonauctions.com. On-line auctions of orders, decorations and medals.

Whytes
38 Molesworth Street, Dublin 2, Ireland. Tel: +353 (0)1 676 2888 www.whytes.com. Irish Collectables. Bi-annual sales.

Woolley & Wallis
51-61 Castle Street, Salisbury, SP1 3SU. Tel: +44 (0)1722 424500 fax: 01722 424508. Medals, coins, collectables and specialist silver sales.

DEALERS

Aberdeen Medals
PO Box 10524, Aberdeen, AB12 9DU. Tel: 07748 040021, www.aberdeenmedals.com. Specialists in medals to Scottish Regts, Indian Army & Colonial.

Ackley Unlimited
PO Box 82144, Portland, Oregon, USA, 97282-0144. Tel: 001 503 659 4681, email: ackleyunlimited@comcast.net. Orders, medals and decorations. Free quarterly lists on request.

Arctic Medals & Militaria
www.arcticmedals.com. Medals, Military badges and Insignia.

Aussie Fire Shed
101 Numurkah Road, Shepparton, Victoria 3630, Australia. Tel: 0061 418 135 875, www.aussiefireshed.com.au. Medals and framing.

Michael Autengruber
Orders of the World, Schulthaissstrasse 10, D-78462 Konstanz, Germany. Tel: 0049 7531 284469, email: michael.autengruber@orden-der-welt.de. Orders, decorations & medals.

Award Productions Ltd
PO Box 300, Shrewsbury, Shropshire, SY5 6WP. Tel: 01952 510053, fax: 01952 510765, www.awardmedals.com. Suppliers unofficial medals for veterans. Medallists to the Royal British Legion.

Louis Bannon
21 Royal Arcade, Cardiff, CF10 1AE. Tel: 02920 221528, www.bannon.co.uk. Medals and military antiques, medals to Welsh Regiments

Bigbury Mint
Bigbury Mint, River Park, Ermington, Ivybridge, Devon, PL21 9NT. Tel: 01548 830717, email: info@bigburymint.com, www.bigburymint.com. Makers of fine medals, commemorative and historical products.

Bill Friar Medals
44 Knowsley Drive, Leigh, Lancs, WN7 3LY. Tel: 01942 671 980, email: sales@billfriarmedals.co.uk, www.billfriarmedals.co.uk. British medals and decorations.

Bostock Medals
"Pinewoods", 15 Waller Close, Leek Wootton, Nr Warwick, CV35 7QG. Tel: 01926 856381, fax: 01926 856 381, email: bostockmilitaria@aol.com, www.bostockmedals.co.uk. British orders, medals and decorations. Callers welcome by appointment.

British Medals (Rennie Alcock)
PO Box 14, Castletown, Isle of Man, IM99 5YY. Tel: 01624 827664, www.british-medals.co.uk. British orders, medals and decorations.

Gary Brown
PO Box 334, Gorleston-on-Sea, Great Yarmouth, Norfolk, NR30 9FF. Tel: 01493 651577, www.garybrownmedals.com. British orders, medals and decorations.

Jim Bullock Militaria
PO Box 217, Romsey, SO51 5XL. Tel/fax: 01794 516455, email: jimbullockmilitaria.com, www.jimbullockmilitaria.com. Quality medals and militaria, medal framing and mounting service.

Mark Carter
PO Box 470, Slough, Berkshire, SL3 6RR. Tel: 01753 534777, email: markgcarter@bulldoghome.com. Medal dealer and organiser of the Mark Carter Militaria & Medal Fairs in Aldershot, Stratford Upon Avon, Yate and Woking. Also the Britannia Medal Fair.

Cambridge Medal Mounting Services
3 Pepys Road, St Neots, PE19 2EN. Tel: 01480 395827, email: shelton946@aol.com.

John Cannon
2 Crees Meadow, Windlesham, Surrey, GU20 6QA. Tel: 01276 451126. Medals and militaria.

Castle Galleries
81 Castle Street, Salisbury, Wilts, SP1 3SP. Tel: 01722 333734, email: johnlodge1236@btinternet.com. Medals, militaria and books.

Cathedral Court Medals
First Floor Office, 30A Market Place, West Ripon, North Yorkshire, HG4 1BN. Tel: 01765 601 400. Coin and medal sales. Medal mounting and framing.

Chester Militaria
Shop B9, Chester Market, 6 Princess Street, Chester, CH1 2HH. Tel: 01244 376140, www.chestermedals.com. Medals, militaria and mounting service.

Chieftain Medals
Tel: 07882 003678, email: info@chieftainmedals.com, www.chieftainmedals.com.

City Coins
Tulbagh Center, 9 Hans Strijdom Ave Lane, Cape Town. Tel 0027 21 425 2639, www.citycoins.com. Coins, banknotes, medals and accessories.

Coinote
74 Elwick Road, Hartlepool TS26 9AP. Tel: 01429 890894, www.coinote.co.uk. Medals, coins, banknotes and accessories. Regular stall holders at Stockton-on-Tees and Scorton (Nr Catrick) indoor market.

Norman W. Collett
56 Grierson Road, Honor Dale Park, London, SE23 1PE. Tel/fax: 020 8291 1435, www.medalsonline.co.uk. British medals and decorations, mainly groups.

Collectors World
188 Wollaton Road, Wollaton, Nottingham, NG8 1HJ. Tel: 01159 280347. Medals, coins, tokens, banknotes and accessories.

J. Collins Medals Limited
Navarino, St. Boniface Rd, Ventnor, IOW, PO38 1PN. Tel/fax: 01983 853473, email: jonathan@jcollinsmedals.co.uk, www.jcollinsmedals.co.uk. Naval, Military, and Airforce Research Service.

Colonial Coins and Medals
Shop 1/218 Adelaide Street, Brisbane, QLD 4000, Australia. Tel: 61 7 3229 3949, email: coinshop@bigpond.net.au, www.coinmedalshop.com.au. British, Commonwealth orders and medals.

Command Post of Militaria
1306 Government Street, Victoria, British Columbia, Canada V8W 1Y8. Tel: (250) 383 4421. Medals, badges and uniforms.

Conglomerate Coins & Medals

GPO Box 2831, Brisbane, Queensland, Australia 4001. Retail: Level 3, 276 Edward Street, Brisbane, QLD. Tel: (07) 3221 1217, email: alforgan@ powerup.com.au. Medals

Constantius

Visit our website: www.constantius.co.uk for quality British Victorian campaign medals, WWI groups and plaques. Tel: 015395 32452 or email: constantius@talktalk.net.

Peter R. Cotrel

7 Stanton Road, Bournemouth, Dorset BH10 5DS. Mail order only—callers by appointment. Tel: 01202 388367. British, American, general foreign medals and decorations. Medal albums. Regular email lists issued.

Cultman Collectables

27 Bowers Fold, Doncaster, South Yorkshire DN1 1HF. Tel: 07772 966375, or email: info@cultmancollectables.com, www. cultmancollectables.com. Militaria, medals, badges and police memorabilia.

DCM Medals

21 The Parade, St. Mary's, Shrewsbury SY1 1DL Tel: 01743 600951, www.dcmmedals.com. British /Imperial orders, decorations & medals.

C. J. & A. J. Dixon Ltd

1st Floor, 23 Prospect Street, Bridlington, East Yorkshire, YO15 2AE. Tel: 01262 603348, email: chris@dixonsmedals.co.uk, www.dixonsmedals. co.uk. British & world orders, medals and decorations. 4 lists a year £20 (UK), £25 USA, £30 (ROW) for 4 issues.

De Winters Medals

Tel: 07584 895918, email: dewintersmedals@ hotmail.com, www.dewintersmedals.co.uk. Gurkha, Guards and RM campaign medals.

D.M.D. Services

P O Box 356, Reigate, Surrey, RH2 2AQ. Tel: 01737 216 246. Victorian campaign medals and decorations.

Frank Draskovic

PO Box 803, Monterey Park, CA 91754, USA. Tel: 001 626 281 9281, email: fdraskovic@hotmail. com. UK and worldwide orders and medals.

Elite-Collections.Com

PO Box 56, Pontypridd CF37 2YL, South Wales. www.elite-collections.com. 30 page catalogue of British medals.

E. L. M.

57 Medal House, Yishun Industrial Estate, Park A, Singapore 768730. Tel: 0065 6487 7777. www.elm. com.sg. Manufacturer of medals. Medal mounting and restoration.

Fraser Medals

Telephone: Canada 001 905 982 0387. www.frasermedals.com. British and commonwealth medals.

Frontier Medals

8 Tai Hang Chung Sum Wai, Tai Hang, Tai Po, New Territories, Hong Kong. Tel: 00 852 94651496, www.frontiermedals.com. Medals

Andy Garrett

Unit 9, Brackley Antique Cellar, Draymans Walk, Brackley, Northants NN13 6BE. British and foreign medals, groups, badges and militaria.

G. A. Medal Services

P.O. Box 374, Winchester, SO23 7XQ. Email: peter@gamedals.co.uk. Repairs and restoration.

Gladman & Norman

51–53 Tenby St North, Birmingham B1 3EG. Tel: 0121 236 5752, www.gladman-norman.co.uk. Manufacturer of orders and medals.

Glance Back

17 Upper Church Street, Chepstow, Gwent NP6 5EX. Tel: 01291 626562. Large stock of books.

Louis E. Grimshaw

612 Fay Street, R.R. 1 Kingston, Ontario, Canada, K7L 4VI. Tel: 001 613 549 2500. Military antiques and collectables, including medals. .

Gradia Militaria

Woodpeckers, How Green Lane, Hever, Kent, TN8 7PS. Tel: 01732 700103, email: caroline@ gradiamilitaria.com, www.gradiamilitaria.com. Specialising in British, Commonwealth, Allied, and Polish cap badges, medals and patches.

Great War Medals

PO Box 1914, London N14 7XS. Tel: 020 8482 1918, email: info@greatwarmedals.co.uk, www.greatwarmedals.com. Established 1985. Specialising in WW1 British & Allied medals, plus badges, books, maps, photos & ephemera.

A. D. Hamilton & Co

7 St. Vincent Place, Glasgow, G1 2DW. Tel: 0141 2215423, email: jefffineman@hotmail.com, www. adhamilton.co.uk. Medals, militaria, coins and banknotes. Retail shop open Monday–Friday, 10am until 4.30pm (Saturday 10am until 2pm).

Harland Military Antiques

Tel: 01429 232782/07904 349727. www. harlandmilitaryantiques.com. British Medals.

Intramark Limited

Windsor Lodge, 56 Windsor Street, Burbage, Leic, LE10 2EF. Tel: 01455 612400, fax: 01455 612483, email: intramark@btclick.com. Manufacturers of medals, miniatures, etc.

Jacks Medals and Militaria

7 Lawndale Avenue, North Rocks, New South Wales, Australia, 2151. Tel: 0061 2 9871 8015, email: jacksmedals@bigpond.com. Medals

Jager Medals & Militaria

Tel: 0141 840 2622, email: enquiries@ jagermedals.com, www.jagermedals.com. British campaign medals bought and sold.

Alec Kaplan

115 Dunottar Street, Sydenham, 2192, Johannesburg, South Africa. Tel: 0027 11 485 2195, fax: 0027 11 640 3427, email: medals@ wirelessza.co.za, www.aleckaplan.co.za. Contact for free catalogue.

Ian Laidler

No-Where, 17 Wavell Grove, Wakefield, WF2 6JW. Tel: 0781 548 4641, email: ian@ianlaidler. orangehome.co.uk. Medals and militaria.

Liverpool Medals

1 The Causeway, Altrincham, Cheshire, WA14 1DE, Tel: 0161 928 3272, email: sales@ liverpoolmedals.com, www.liverpoolmedals.com. British & world orders, medals, decorations.

John Manning

18 Fengate, Heacham, nr. Kings Lynn, Norfolk, PE31 7BG. Tel: 01485 570153.

Medal Masters
PO Box 7204, Bundaberg North, Queensland, Australia, 4670. Tel: 0061 403 250170, email: info@medalmasters.com.au, www.medalmasters.com.au. Replica medals and specialist framers.

Medals, Mementos & More
3 Acacia Court, Strathalbyn, South Australia, 5255. Tel/fax: 0061 08 8536 8089. www.medalsmementos.com. Medal mounting/framing, replicas and miniatures, by appointment only.

Medals of England
PO Box 258, Lingfield, Surrey, RH7 9AH. Tel: 01342 870926. www.medalsofengland.com. Medals and military items.

Military Memorabilia
PO Box 21-022, Henderson, Auckland, 0650, New Zealand. Tel: 0064 9 837 6150, +64 21 271 5141. email: medals@ihug.co.nz. Medal mounting & researcher.

Peter Morris
1 Station Concourse, Bromley North BR Station, Kent / PO Box 223, Bromley, Kent BR1 4EQ. . Tel: 020 8313 3410, email: info@petermorris.co.uk, www.petermorris.co.uk. Medals, decorations, militaria, coins & banknotes.

MSM Awards
8 Price Tce, Matamata, 3400, New Zealand. Tel: (NZ) 0064 7 888 9064, email: mikes@kol.co.nz, www.honours.homestead.com/home.html. Medal remounter for the serving military or Veteran.

Nordheide-Versand
Nordheid-Versand Kai Winkler, Schulstrasse 11a, 21220 Seevetal (Maschen). Tel: +0049 4105 665 832, www.nordheideversand.de. Medals, awards, award-documents, miniatures, pins, uniforms etc.

North West Medal
PO Box 21070, 640 River Street, Thunder Bay, ON, P7A 8A7 Canada. Email: nwmedal@shaw.ca, www.northwestmedal.com. Medals and decorations.

Personalia
Email: enquiries@personalia.co.uk, www.personalia.co.uk. Dealers in historical manuscripts, letters and medals.

Poppy Militaria
4 Beatrice Street, Oswestry. Tel: 01691 670 079, www.poppymilitaria.co.uk, www.poppymedalframing.co.uk. Medal framing, medals and militaria for sale.

Q & C Militaria
22 Suffolk Road, Cheltenham, Gloucestershire, GL50 2AQ. Tel/fax: 01242 519815, www.qcmilitaria.com. British and Commonwealth orders, medals, decorations and miltaria. Retail shop.

R & L Medals
Tel: 00 35 339835933, email: richard@rlmedals.com. www.rlmedals.com. Specialists in Gallantry and non-Gallantry Groups to Army, Navy and non-Combatants.

R & M International
PO Box 6278, Bellevue, Washington, USA. 98008-0278 email: surlamer86@prodigy.net. www.randminternational.com. British, Canadian. U.S. and Russian orders, medals.

RBJ Militaria
Parade Antiques Market, 27b New Street, Barbican, Plymouth, Devon, PL1 2NB. Tel: 07714 544777, www.rbjmilitaria.com.

Barbara Radman
Westfield House, 2G Westfield Road, Witney, Oxon, OX28 1JG. Tel: 01993 772705. British and Foreign orders, medals & decorations especially Russian.

RS Medal Mounting Service
PO Box 760, Taunton, TA1 9BA. Tel: 01823 259675, email: colin.hole@virgin.net. Medal mounting and framing.

ScotMint
68, Sandgate, Ayr, Scotland, KA7 1BX. Tel: 01292 268244 or 07939 345407, www.scotmint.com. British & worldwide medals groups, badges and militaria. Also coins and banknotes. Retail premises.

S. E. Sewell
Cronin, Westhorpe Road, Finningham, Stowmarket, IP14 4TN. Tel: 01449 782185 or 07739 071822, email: sewellmedals@hotmail.com, www.sewellmedals.co.uk. Wholesalers to the Medal Trade.

Murray Shaw Medals
The Old Dairy, Home Farm, Meriden Road, Berkswell, Coventry, CV7 7BG. Tel: 01676 525840, fax: 016766 523511. Military medals.

South African Militaria
Email: andrew@rolynengineering.co.za. www.southafricanmilitaria.com. Medals etc.

Specialist Medals.com
P.O Box 278, Wallingford, Oxon, OX10 1AU. Tel: 01491 825974, email: roger@willoughby.ie, www.specialistmedals.com. LS medals and civil awards.

Spink & Son Ltd
69 Southampton Row, Bloomsbury, London WC1B 4ET. Tel: 020 7563 4000, fax: 020 7563 4085, email: info@spink.com, www.spink.com. Tel: 01904 654769. Medal dealers and auctioneers.

Strachan Militaria
Tel : 0044 1543 490932, www.ismilitaria.co.uk. 20th Century German, British, US and militaria.

Sunset Militaria
Castle End Cottage, Lea, Ross on Wye, Herefordshire, HR9 7JY. Tel: 01989 750470, mobile: 07583 669571. Medals, Ribbons, Badges, Buttons, Militaria, Brooch Bars & Mini Medals.

Jeremy Tenniswood
2 Temple Road, Colchester, Essex, CO2 9JN. Tel: 01206 368787, fax: 01206 367836, www.militaria.co.uk. Medals, decorations, militaria and books.

The London Medal Company
13 Cecil Court, London, WC2N 4AN. Tel: 020 7836 8877, email: shop@london-medals.co.uk, www.london-medals.co.uk.

The Medal Centre
10B Hencotes, Hexham, Northumberland, NE46 2EJ. Tel: 01434 609794 or 07950421704 www.themedalcentre.co.uk.

The Mess Dress Ltd
88 Stewart Road, Bournemouth, BH8 8NU. Tel: 01202 302846. www.messdress.com.

Toye, Kenning & Spencer Ltd
Regalia House, Newtown Road, Bedworth, Warks. CV12 8QR. Tel: 024 7684 8800. Manufacturers of medals, badges, etc.

Treasure Bunker Militaria Shop
21 King Street, Merchant City, Glasgow, G1 5QZ. Tel/fax: 0141 552 8164, www.treasurebunker.com. Medals, badges, uniforms etc.

Matthew Tredwen
PO Box 318, Bromley, Kent, BR1 2UX. Tel: 07939 252206, email: info@falleneagle.com, www.falleneagle.com. Specialists in Militaria.

Ulric of England
PO Box 55, Church Stretton, Shropshire, SY6 6WR. Tel: 01694 781354, fax: 01694 781372, www.britishmilitarymedals.com. All British military medals, particularly Waterloo medals.

Tanya Ursual
PO Box 788, Kemptville, Ontario, Canada, KOG 1JO. Tel: 001 613 258 5999, fax: 001 613 258 9118, email: tanya@medalsofwar.com, www.medalsofwar.com. Medals, orders, decorations, miniatures and militaria.

V. F. M. R. Orders & Medals
Email: victor@vfme-ordersandmedals.com, www.vfmr-ordersandmedals.com Medals and militaria

V. J. C. Collectables
Email: valbaz@hobs20.fsnet.co.uk. Medals and militaria.

Stephen Wheeler
20 Cecil Court, Leicester Square, London, WC2N 4HE. Covent Garden Market, Stand 111, (Mondays). Tel: 02072406827 or 07778 848555. www.buymilitarymedals.com. British & Foreign medals.

War & Son
14, Drapers Lane, Leominster, Herefordshire, HR6 8ND. Tel: 01568 616 414, or 07714 631313. www.warandson.co.uk. Specialists in British and world medals. Military Antiques.

Wolf Pack Militaria
Tel 07941 602639, email: rustycant@gmail.com. www.wolfpackmilitaria.com.

Worcestershire Medal Service Ltd
56 Broad Street, Sidemoor, Bromsgrove, B61 8LL. Tel: 01527 835375, fax: 01527 576798. email: wms@worcmedals.com, www.worcmedals.com. Medals and medal mounting, storage and display cases, miniature medals, blazer badges and replacement medals.

Worldwide Militaria
Jeffery Stone, 2000 Bloomingdale Road, Suite 200, Glendale Heights, IL 60139, USA. Tel 001 630 571 8340.

I. S. Wright
262 Castlereagh Street, Sydney, NSW, Australia. Tel: 0061 02 9264 7555, email: sydney@iswright.com.au. A wide range of military collectables.

York Coin & Stamp Centre,
Cavendish Antique & Collectors Centre, 44 Stonegate, York, YO1 8AS. Tel: 01904 611653. Medals and decorations.

Carsten Zeige
Eilenau 2, 22089, Hamburg, Germany. Tel:0049 40 3571 3636, email: info@zeige.com. www.zeige.com. German and Foreign medals.

BOOKSELLERS/DEALERS

In addition to the names listed below, it should be noted that a number of the medal dealers listed above regularly or occasionally include books on their medal lists.

Ian Allan

12 Ethel Street, Birmingham, B2 4BG. Tel: 01932 266600. www.ianallanpublishing.com. Military Titles.

Peter Barnes

www.barnesbooks.co.uk. Pre-owned, out-of-print, rare, old and collectors editions of military, naval and aviation book.

Buffo Books

32 Tadfield Road, Romsey, Hants, SO51 5AJ. Tel: 01794 517149. Military and aviation only.

Andrew Burroughs

34 High Street, St Martins, Stamford, Lincs, PE90 2LJ. Tel: 01780 765140. Military and naval.

Chelifer Books

Todd Close, Curthwaite, Wigton, Cumbria, CA7 8BE. Military history, including units. Lists available.

Q. M. Dabney & Company

PO Box 849, Princetown Junction, NJ 08550, USA. www.qmdabneycom. Military books of all periods. Lists available.

Peter de Lotz

20 Downside Crescent, Hampstead, London, NW3 2AP. Tel: 020 7794 5709, fax: 020 7284 3058. Military, naval and aviation history.

Francis Edwards

72 Charing Cross Road, London, WC2H 0BE. Tel: 020 7379 7669, www.francisedwards.com. All aspects of military history. Lists.

Empire Books

61 Broad Lane, Rochdale, Lancs, OL16 4PL. Tel: 01706 666678. Military, naval and aviation. Special interest Australian forces, Vietnam and Colonial wars.

Falconwood Transport and Military Bookshop.

5 Falconwood Parade, The Green, Welling, Kent, DA16 2PL. Tel: 020 8303 8291. Military, naval and aviation history.

G. L. Green.

18 Aldenham Avenue, Radlett, Herts, WD7 8HX. Tel: 01923 857077. www.glbreen.co.uk. Naval and maritime history.

Hersant's Military Books

17 The Drive, High Barnet, Herts, EN5 4JG. Tel/fax: 020 8440 6816. General military history. Lists available by period.

Steven J. Hopkins

Court Farm, Kington, Flyford Flavell, Worcs, WR7 4DQ. Tel: 01386 793427, email: tokyngton@aol.com. Military books and prints.

John Lewcock

6 Chewells Lane, Haddenham, Ely, Cambs, CB6 3SS. Tel: 01353 741152. Naval history.

Liverpool Medal Company Ltd

1 The Causeway, Altrincham, Cheshire, WA14 1DE. Tel: 0161 9283272, fax: 0161 8202522. www.liverpoolmedals.com. Medal dealers, also an occasional separate book catalogue.

Ian Lynn

258 Upper Fant Road, Maidstone, Kent, ME16 8BX. Tel: 01622 728525. Military history.

McLaren Books

22 John Street, Helensburgh, Dunbartonshire, G84 8BA. Tel: 01436 676453, wwwmclarensbooks.com. Naval history.

Military Bookman at Chartwell Booksellers

55 East 52nd Street, New York, NY 10055, USA. www.militarybookman.com. Large stock of military history relating to all services worldwide and all periods.

Military History Bookshop

PO Box 590, Folkestone, Kent, CT20 2WX. Tel: 01303 246500. www.militaryhistorybooks.com. Military book specialists.

Military Parade Bookshop

The Parade, Marlborough, Wilts, SN8 1NE. Tel: 01672 515470, fax: 01980 630 150. New and secondhand books. Lists available.

Pen & Sword Books Ltd.

47 Church Street, Barnsley, S. Yorks, S70 2AS. Tel: 01226 734222, fax: 01226 734438, www.pen-and-sword.co.uk. Military titles.

Anthony J. Simmonds

66 Royal Hill, Greenwich, London, SE10 8RT. Tel: 020 8692 1794, www.navalandmaritimebooks.com. Naval and maritime history. Occasional catalogues.

Spink & Son Ltd

69 Southampton Row, Bloomsbury, London, WC1B 4ET. Tel: 020 7563 4000, fax: 020 7563 4066, www.spink.com. Specialist Book Department.

Token Publishing Ltd.

40 Southernhay East, Exeter, Devon, EX1 1PE. Tel: 01404 46972, email: info@tokenpublishing.com, www.tokenpublishing.com. Publishers of MEDAL NEWS and COIN NEWS. Extensive range of medal, coin and banknote titles.

Turner Donovan Military Books

Flat 1, 22 Florence Road, Brighton, BN1 6DJ. www.turnerdonovan.com. Printed works and manuscript material relating to the British Military Services.

The information included in this Directory is correct at the time of going to press.
For an extensive range of medal and military titles log onto
www.tokenpublishing.com

FAIRS

Many fairs are held regularly and organised by professionals and societies (Victorian Military Society, Aldershot Militaria Society, etc.). The dates are usually well advertised in MEDAL NEWS and other publications, however, times and venues are liable to change so it is advisable to telephone the organisers beforehand. Listed below are the major fair organisers and the events known to us.

Abergavenny Militaria and Medal Fair
Market Hall, Cross Street, Abergavenny. Tel: 01873 735811.

Bromley Medal and Militaria Fair
Civic Centre, Kentish Way, Bromley, Kent. Ray Brough. Tel: 07714 094009.

Cardiff Fair
City Hall, Cardiff. M. J. Promotions. Tel: 01792 415293.

Mark Carter Militaria & Medal Fairs
Aldershot—The Princess Hall, Princes Way, GU11 1NX

Britannia—Carisbrooke Hall, Victory Services Club, 63-79 Seymour Street, Marble Arch, London, W2 2HF.

Stratford upon Avon—Stratford Leisure Center, Bridgefoot, CV37 6YY.

Yate (Bristol)—Yate Leisure Centre, Kennedy Way, BS37 4DQ.

Mark Carter Tel: 01753 534777

Cheltenham Fairs
The Cheltenham Regency Hotel, Gloucester Road, Cheltenham, GL51 0ST

St Andrews United Reform Church, Montpellier, Cheltenham, GL50 1SP

Mark Grimsley Tel: 0117 962 3203.

Dublin Coin & Medal Fair
Serpentine Hall, RDS, Ballsbridge, Dublin 4, Ireland. Mike Kelly Tel: 00353 8687 14 880)

Northern Arms Fairs
Darlington—Scotch Corner Holiday Inn, DL10 6NR

Leeds—Pudsey Civic Hall, Dawsons Corner, Stanningley, Pudsey, LS28 5TA

Liverpool—The Village Hotel, Whiston, L35 1RZ.

Newark—Cedric Ford Pavillion, Showground, Winthorpe Road, NG24 2NY.

Tel: 01423 780759.

OMRS Annual Convention
Crowne Plaza Stratford upon Avon, CV37 6YR. Contact: OMRS Membership Secretary, PO Box 248, Snettisham, King's Lynn, Norfolk PE31 7TA.

Preston Arms and Militaria Fair
Lancastrian Suite, Park Hall Hotel, Charnock Richard, (Via Charnock Richard Services M6) Chorley, Lancashire, PR7 5LP. Tel: 01254 263260

Stockport Antique Arms, Medals & Militaria Fair
Britannia Hotel, Dialstone Lane, Offerton. Tel: 0161 624 6211.

The Medal Center Medal and Militaria Fairs
Bowburn—Community Centre, Bowburn Village, County Durham, DH6 5AT.

Wakefield—Outwood Memorial Hall, Outwood, W. Yorks WF1 2NE.

Andrew Dukes Tel: 01434 609794

Wakefield Coin & Medal Fair
Cedar Court Hotel, Denby Dale Road, Calder Grove, Wakefield, WF4 3QZ.

Eddie Smith Tel: 01522 684681.

York Coin & Medal Fair
The Grandstand, York Racecourse, York, YO23 1EX. Tel: 01793 513431 or 020 8946 4489.

The information included in this Directory is correct at the time of going to press. Please check with fair organisers before setting off on a long journey as venues may possibly have changed.
Fair organisers, please advise us on 01404 469721 or email: info@tokenpublishing.com if the entry for your event is incorrect.
Thank you!

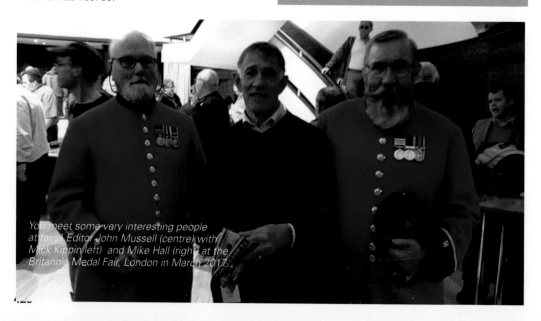

You meet some very interesting people at fairs! Editor John Mussell (centre) with Mick Kippin (left) and Mike Hall (right) at the Britannia Medal Fair, London in March 2017.

MUSEUMS

And Collections

The majority of the museums listed below are the regimental museums of the British Army, Militia, Yeomanry and Territorials, but we have included other museums pertaining to the Royal Navy, the Royal Marines and the Royal Air Force where medals form a significant part of the collections. So, too, the museums of the police forces, fire brigades, Red Cross, Royal National Lifeboat Institution and similar bodies have been included where relevant. Readers should also bear in mind that many general museums in our towns and cities boast fine collections of military medals pertaining to their local regiments. We have included those of which we are aware. The date of foundation is shown in brackets after the name.

Some service museums have been undergoing refits, relocations and amalgamations. We would welcome further information from readers about these changes and about other general museums in their areas with a good coverage of medals to local regiments.

Space prevents us from going into details regarding the scope of individual museum holdings. We give the postal address, telephone number wherever possible. Please contact the museums directly for opening times and admission prices. It is always sensible, particularly before travelling long distances to visit a museum or collection, to telephone and check that the published details are still correct.

Some museums may have libraries holding archival material; this should be checked out and the conditions for use ascertained as such holdings will not have the resources to answer detailed research enquiries.

Where museums are devoted to one particular regimental/service/unit or whatever, they are listed by title in alphabetical order. This may not always accord with the exact official name of the museum which is given on the address line. The well-known national museums are listed alphabetically by name. More general museums which include medal collections are listed by the name of the town. If you cannot see the name of the museum you require at first glance, it may be worth searching through the full list, as some museums escape neat classification and would require extensive cross-referencing to do them full justice.

Aberdeen Maritime Museum (1984)
Shiprow, Aberdeen, AB11 5BY. Tel: 01224 337700, www.aagm.co.uk/Venues/AberdeenMaritimeMuseum

Airborne Assault, Museum of the Parachute Regiment and Airborne Forces
Building 213, North Base, Imperial War Museum, Duxford, Cambridge, CB22 4QR. Tel: 01223 839 909, email: curator@paradata.org.uk www.paradata.org.uk.

Aldershot Military Museum
Queen's Avenue, Aldershot, Hants, GU11 2LG. Tel: 01252 314598, www.hants.gov.uk/museums/aldershot-museum.

Argyll and Sutherland Highlanders Regimental Museum
The Castle, Stirling, FK8 1EH. Tel: 01786 475165, www.argylls.co.uk/museum.

Army Medical Services Museum
Keogh Barracks, Ash Vale, Aldershot, GU12 5RQ. Tel: 01252 868612, email: armymedicalmuseum@btinternet.com. www.ams-museum.org.uk.

Army Physical Training Corps Museum (1949)
Fox Lines, Queen's Avenue, Aldershot, Hampshire, GU11 2LB. Tel: 01252 547542,

Arundel Toy and Military Museum (1978)
Dolls House, 23 High Street, Arundel, West Sussex. Tel: 01903 507446/882908.

Aylmer Military Collection
Nunwell House, Brading, Isle of Wight, PO36 0JQ. Tel: 01983 407240.

Ayrshire Yeomanry Museum
Rozelle House, Monument Road, Alloway by Ayr, KA7 4NQ. Tel: 01292 445447.

Bedfordshire and Hertfordshire Regimental Museum
Wardown Park Museum, Old Bedford Road, Luton, LU2 7HA. Tel: 01582 546725, www.wardownparkmuseum.com

Black Watch Museum (1924)
Balhousie Castle, Perth, PH1 5HR. Tel: 01738 638152, www.theblackwatch.co.uk.

100th Bomb Group Memorial Museum (1978)
Common Road, Dickleburgh, near Diss, Norfolk, IP21 4PH. Tel: 01379 740708, www.100bgmm@tiscali.co.uk. Medals and memorabilia.

Border Regiment and King's Own Royal Border Regiment Museum (1932)
Cumbria's Museum of Military Life, Alma Block, The Castle, Cumbria, CA3 8UR. Tel: 01228 532774, www.cumbriamuseumofmilitarylife.org.

British in India Museum (1972)
Hendon Mill, Hallam Road, Nelson, BB9 8AD. Tel: 01282 613129.

British Red Cross Museum and Archives (1984)
UK Office, 44 Moorefields, London, EC2Y 9AL. Tel: 0344 871 11 11, email: enquiry@redcross.org.uk, www.medicalmuseums.org.

Bygones
Fore Street, St Marychurch, Torquay, Devon, TQ1 4PR. Tel: 01803 326108, email: info@bygones.co.uk www.bygones.co.uk

Caernarfon Airworld Aviation Museum
Caernarfon Airport, Dinas Dinlle, Caernarfon, Gwynedd, LL54 5TP. Tel: 01286 832154, email: info @ airworldmuseum.co.uk. www.airworldmuseum.com.

Castle and Regimental Museum, Monmouth
The Castle, Monmouth, NP25 3BS. Tel: 01600 772175, email: curator@monmouthcastlemuseum. org.uk, www.monmouthcastlemuseum.org.uk.

Cheshire Military Museum (1972)
The Castle, Chester, CH1 2DN. Tel: 01244 327617, www.cheshiremilitarymuseum.co.uk.

Churchill Museum and Cabinet War Rooms (1984)
Clive Steps, King Charles Street, London, SW1A 2AQ. 020 7416 5000, www.iwm.org.uk/visits/churchill-war-rooms.

City of London Police Museum (1964)
Access though - Guildhall Library, Aldermanbury, London, EC2V 7HH. Tel: 020 7332 1868, www. cityoflondon.police.uk/about-us/history/museum.

Coldstream Museum
12 Market Square, Coldstream, TD12 4BD. Tel: 01890 882630, www.holy-island.info/coldstream-museum.

Dingwall Museum Trust (1975)
Town House, High Street, Dingwall, Ross-shire, IV15 9RY. Tel: 01349 865366, www.dingwallmuseum.co.uk. Medals and militaria of the Seaforth Highlanders, and items pertaining to Major General Sir Hector Macdonald .

Duke of Cornwall's Light Infantry Regimental Museum (1925)
The Keep, Victoria Barracks, Bodmin, PL31 1EG. www.cornwall.com/attractions/dcli-museum.

Duke of Wellington's Regiment Museum (1960)
Regimental Museum, Bankfield Museum, Boothtown Road, Park, Halifax, HX3 6HG. Tel: 01422 354823, email: museums@calderdale.gov.uk, www.museums. calderdale.gov.uk.

Durham Light Infantry Museum (1969)
Palace Green Library, Palace Green, Durham DH1 3RN. Tel: 0191 334 2932, email: pg.library.ac.uk, www.dur.ac.uk/palace green.

Essex Regiment Museum (1938)
Oaklands Park, Moulsham Street, Chelmsford, Essex, CM2 9AQ. Tel: 01245 605700, www.chelmsford.gov.uk/museums.

Firing Line, Cardiff Museum of the Welsh
The Interpretation Centre, Cardiff Castle, Cardiff, CF10 2RB. Tel: 02920 873623, www.cardiffcastlemuseum.org.uk.

Fleet Air Arm Museum (1964)
RNAS Yeovilton, Somerset, BA22 8HT. Tel: 01935 840565, www.fleetairarm.com.

Fusiliers Museum of Northumberland
The Abbot's Tower, Alnwick Castle, Alnwick, NE66 1NG. Tel: 01665 602152, www.northumberlandfusiliers.org.uk.

Glasgow Art Gallery and Museum (1854)
Argyle Street, Glasgow, G3 8AG. Tel: 0141 276 9599. www.glasgowlife.org.uk. Medals of the Glasgow Yeomanry, Highland Light Infantry and regiments associated with the city.

Gordon Highlanders' Museum (1961)
St Lukes, Viewfield Road, Aberdeen, AB15 7XH. Tel: 01224 311200. www.gordonhighlanders.com

Green Howards Regimental Museum
Trinity Church Square, Richmond, Yorkshire, DL10 4QN. Tel: 01748 826561. www.greenhowards.org.uk

Guards Museum (1988)
Wellington Barracks, Birdcage Walk, London, SW1E 6HQ. Tel: 0207 414 3271, www.theguardsmuseum. com.

Gurkha Museum (1974)
Peninsular Barracks, Romsey Road, Winchester, Hants, SO23 8TS. Tel: 01962 842832, www.thegurkhamuseum.co.uk.

Gwynedd Museum & Art Gallery, Bangor
Ffordd Gwynedd, Bangor, Gwynedd, LL57 1DT. Tel: 01248 353368.Medals, militaria of Welsh regiments.

Hawkinge, Kent, Battle of Britain Museum (1969)
Aerodrome Road, Hawkinge, Nr Folkestone, Kent, CT18 7AG. Tel: 0130 389 3140, www.kbobm.org.

Herefordshire Light Infantry Museum (1967)
Suvla Barracks, Harold Street, Hereford, HR1 2QX. Tel: 01432 359917, www. herefordshirelightinfantrymuseum.com. By appointment

Hertford Regiment Museum
At the Hertford Museum at 18 Bull Plain, Hertford, SG14 1DT. Tel: 01992 582 686. www.hertfordshireregimentmuseum.org.

Honourable Artillery Company Museum
Armoury House, City Road, London, EC1Y 2BQ. Apply in writing for a visit. www.hac.org.uk.

Hornsea Folk Museum (1978)
11-17 Newbegin, Hornsea, East Riding of Yorkshire, HU18 1AB. Tel: 01964 533443, email: hornseamuseum@tiscali.co.uk, www.hornseamuseum.com.

Household Cavalry Museum
Household Cavalry Museum, Horse Guards, Whitehall, London, SW1A 2AX. Tel: 020 7930 3070, email: museum@householdcavalry.co.uk. www.householdcavalrymuseum.co.uk.

Household Cavalry Museum
Combermere Barracks, Windsor, Berkshire, SL4 3DN. Tel: 01753 755112.

HMS Belfast(1978)
The Queen's Walk, London, SE1 2JH. Tel: 020 7940 6300, www.iwm.org.uk/visits/hms-belfast.

Imperial War Museum (1917)
Lambeth Road, London, SE1 6HZ. Tel: 020 7416 5000, www.iwm.org.uk.

Imperial War Museum Duxford (1976)
Duxford, Cambridge, CB22 4QR. Tel: 01223 835000

Imperial War Museum North (2002)
The Quays, Trafford Wharf Road, Trafford Park, Manchester M17 1TZ. Tel: 0161 836 4000, www.iwm.org.uk.

Inns of Court and City Yeomanry Museum (1947)
10 Stone Buildings, Lincoln's Inn, London, WC2A 3TG. Tel: 020 7405 8112.

Jersey Militia Museum
Elizabeth Castle,St Aubin's Bay, St Helier, JE3 3NU. Tel: 01534 833135.

The Keep Military Museum
Barrack Road, Dorchester, DT1 1RN. Tel: 01305 264066, email: info@keepmilitarymuseum.org, www.keepmilitarymuseum.org.

Kent and Sharpshooters Yeomanry Museum (1966(
Hever Castle, Tonbridge, Kent, TN8 7NG. www.ksymuseum.org.uk.

King's Own Royal Regiment Museum (Lancaster)
Lancaster City Museum, Market Square, Lancaster LA1 1HT. Tel: 01524 64637, www.kingsownmuseum.com.

King's Own Scottish Borderers Regimental Museum (1954)
Berwick Barracks, The Parade, Berwick-upon-Tweed, TD15 1DG. Tel: 01289 307426. www.kosb.co.uk.

King's Own Yorkshire Light Infantry Regimental Museum (1932)
Museum and Art Gallery, Chequer Road, Doncaster, South Yorks, DN1 2AE. Tel: 01302 734293.

King's Regiment Museum (1930)
Museum of Liverpool, Pier Head, Liverpool L3 1DG. Tel: 0151 478 4545, www.liverpoolmuseums.org.uk/mol/visit/galleries/soldiers.

15th/19th King's Royal Hussars (Light Dragoons)
Discovery Museum, Blandford Square, Newcastle-upon-Tyne, NE1 4JA. Tel : 0191 232 6789, www.lightdragoons.org.uk.

Kohima Museum (1991)
Imphal Barracks, Fulford Road, York, YO10 4HD. 01904 665 806, www.kohimamuseum.co.uk.

HorsePower: The Museum of The King's Royal Hussars Museum in Winchester (1980)
Home Headquarters (South): Peninsula Barracks, Romsey Road, Winchester, SO23 8TS. Tel: 01962 828539, www.horsepowermuseum.co.uk.

Light Infantry Museum (1990)
Peninsular Barracks, Romsey Road, Winchester, SO23 8TS. Tel: 01962 828530, www.winchestermilitarymuseum.co.uk.

Liverpool Scottish Regimental Museum
Archive Office: Artists Club, 5 Eberle Street, Liverpool L2 2AG. Appointment only. Tel: 0151 645 5717.

London Fire Brigade Museum (1967)
Pop up Museum: The Workshop, Lambeth High Street, London, SE1 7JS.

The London Scottish Regimental Museum
Regimental Headquarters, 95 Horseferry Road, London, SW1P 2DX. Tel: 020 7630 1639.

Military Intelligence Museum
Defence Intelligence and Security Centre, JITG Chicksands, Shefford, Beds, SG17 5PR. Tel: 01462 752342, email: intcorpshq-museum-mailbox@mod.uk, www.intelligencemuseum.org.

National Army Museum (1960)
Royal Hospital Road, Chelsea, London, SW3 4HT. 020 7730 0717, email: info@nam.ac.uk. www.nam.ac.uk.

National Maritime Museum (1934)
Romney Road, Greenwich, London, SE10 9NF. Tel: 020 8858 4422, email: RMGenquiries@rmg.co.uk, www.rmg.co.uk.

National Museum of Ireland (1877)
Collins Barracks, Benburb Street, Dublin 7. Tel +00353 16777 444, www.museum.ie.

National War Museum
The Castle, Edinburgh, EH1 2NG. Tel: 0300 123 6789, email: s.allen@nms.ac.uk enquiries, www.nms.ac.uk.

Newark (Notts & Lincs) Air Museum Ltd (1968)
Drove Lane, Newark,Nottinghamshire, NG24 2NY. Tel: 01636 707170, www.newarkairmuseum.org.

Northamptonshire Regimental Museum
Abington Park Museum, Park Avenue South, Northampton, NN1 5LW. Tel: 01604 838110, www.northampton.gov.uk./museums.

Order of St. John of Jerusalem Museum
St. John's Gate, St. John's Lane, Clerkenwell, London, EC1M 4DA. Tel: 020 7324 4005.

Oxfordshire & Bucks Light Infantry Museum
Park Street, Woodstock , OX20 1SN. Tel 01993 810210, www.sofo.org.uk.

Polish Institute and Sikorski Museum
20 Princes Gate, London, SW7 1PT. Tel: 020 7589 9249, www.pism.co.uk.

Prince of Wales's Own 9th /12th Lancers Regimental Museum (1972)
Derby Museum and Art Gallery, The Strand, Derby, DE1 1BS. Tel: 01322 641901, www.derbymuseums.org/locations/museum-art-gallery.

Prince of Wales's Own Regiment of Yorkshire Museum
3 Tower Street, York YO1 9SB. Tel: 01904 731532, www.yorkarmymuseum.co.uk.

Princess of Wales's Royal Regiment and Queen's Regiment Museum (1987)
Dover Castle, Kent, CT16 1HU. Tel: 01304 240121, www.english-heritage.org.uk.

1st The Queen's Dragoon Guards Regimental Museum
Cardiff Castle, Cardiff, South Glamorgan, CF10 2RB. Tel: 029 20229367, www.qdg.org.uk

Queen's Lancashire Regiment (1929)
Incorporating East Lancashire Regiment, South Lancashire Regiment (Prince of Wales's Volunteers), Loyal Reg.(North Lancashire) Lancashire Regiment. Fulwood Barracks, Watling Street Road, Preston, Lancs, PR2 8AA. Tel: 01772 260584.

Queen's Own Royal West Kent Regimental Museum (1961)
Maidstone Museum & Bentlif Art Gallery, St Faith's Street, Maidstone, Kent, ME14 1LH. Tel: 01622 602838, www.museum.maidstone.gov.uk/our-museums/queens-own.

Queen's Royal Lancers and Nottingham Yeomanry Museum
Thoresby Courtyard, Thoresby Park, Nr Perlethorpe, Nottinghamshire, NG22 9EP. Tel 01623 824222.

Redoubt Fortress and Military Museum
Royal Parade, Eastbourne, East Sussex, BN22 7AQ. Tel: 01323 410300, www.eastbournemuseums.co.uk.

The Rifles (Berkshire and Wiltshire) Museum
The Wardrobe, 58 The Close, Salisbury, SP1 2EX. Tel 01722 419419, Royal Berkshire, www.thewardrobe.org.uk.

Royal Air Force Museum (1963)
Grahame Park Way, London, NW9 5LL. Tel: 020 8205 2266, email: london@rafmuseum.org, www.rafmuseum.org.uk/london.

Royal Armoured Corps Museum (1939), The Tank Museum (1923)
Bovington, Wareham, Dorset, BH20 6JG. Tel: 01929 405096, www.tankmuseum.org.

Royal Armouries Museum (1996)
Armouries Drive, Leeds, LS10 1LT. Tel : 0113 220 1999, www.royalarmouries.org/leeds.

Royal Devon Yeomanry (1845)
Museum of North Devon, The Square, Barnstaple, Devon, EX32 8LN. Tel 01271 346747, www.devonmuseums.net/barnstaple.

Royal Dragoon Guards Museum
The Regimental Museum of the Royal Dragoon Guards, 3 Tower Street, York, YO1 9SB. Tel: 01904 642036, email: hhq@rdgmuseum.org.uk, www.rdgmuseum.org.uk.

Royal East Kent Regiment, Third Foot (The Buffs) Museum
National Army Museum, Royal Hospital Road, London, SW3 4HT. Tel: 0207 730 0717, www.nam.ac.uk.

Royal Electrical and Mechanical Engineers Museum of Technology. (1958)
Prince Phillip Barracks, Lyneham, Chippenham, SN15 4XX. Tel: 01249 894 869, email: enquiries@rememuseum.org.uk, www.rememuseum.org.uk.

Royal Engineers Museum
Prince Arthur Road, Gillingham, Kent, ME4 4UG. Tel: 01634 822839, www.re-museum.co.uk.

Royal Fusiliers Museum (1962)
HM Tower of London, EC3N 4AB. Tel: 0203 166 6912, www.fusiliermuseumlondon.org.

Royal Green Jackets Museum
Peninsula Barracks, Romsey Road, Winchester, SO23 8TS. Tel: 01962 828549. www.rgjmuseum.co.uk

Royal Hampshire Regimental Museum (1933)
Serle's House, Southgate Street, Winchester, Hants SO23 9EG. Tel: 01962 863658, www.royalhampshireregiment.org.

Royal Highland Fusiliers Regimental Museum (1960)
518 Sauchiehall Street, Glasgow, G2 3LW. Tel: 0141 332 5639, www.rhf.org.uk

Royal Hospital Chelsea
Royal Hospital Road, Chelsea, London, SW3 4SR. Tel: 020 7881 5200, www.chelsea-pensioners.co.uk.

13th/18th Royal Hussars (Queen Mary's Own) Regiment (1957) and The Light Dragoons
Cannon Hall Museum, Cawthorne, Barnsley, South Yorkshire, S75 4AT. Tel: 01226 790270, www.lightdragoons.org.uk.

Royal Inniskilling Fusiliers Regimental Musuem
The Castle, Enniskillen, Co. Fermanagh, N. Ireland, BT74 7HL. Tel: 028 6632 3142, email: info@inniskillingsmuseum.com, www.inniskillingsmuseum.com.

Royal Irish Fusiliers
Sovereign's House, The Mall, Armagh, BT61 9DL. Tel: 028 37 522911, www.royal-irish.com.

Royal Irish Regiment Museum (1993)
Currently closed pending relocation. www.royal-irish.com/museums/royal-irish-regiment-museum

Royal Leicestershire Regiment Museum (1969)
Newarke Houses Museum, Leicester, LE2 7BY. Tel: 0116 225 4980, www.royalleicestershireregiment.org.uk/the-regimental-museum.

Royal Lincolnshire Regimental Museum (1985)
The Old Barracks, Burton Road, Lincoln, LN1 3LY. Tel: 01522 782040, www.thelincolnshireregiment.org/museum.shtml.

Royal Logistic Corps Museum (1995)
The Princess Royal Barracks, Deepcut, near Camberley, Surrey, GU16 6RW. Tel: 01252 833371, www.royallogisticcorps.co.uk/heritage/museum

Royal Marines Museum
Eastney Esplanade, Southsea, Hants PO4 9PX. Tel: 023 9281 9385, www.royalmarinesmuseum.co.uk.

Royal Military Police Museum (1979)
Southwick Park (Postal Point 38), Nr. Fareham, Hampshire, PO17 6EJ. Tel: 023 9228 4372, email: museum_rhqrmp@btconnect.com, www.rhqrmp.org. Visits by appointment only.

Royal National Lifeboat Institution Museums (1937)
Bamburgh NE69 7AE. Tel: 01668 214910
Cromer NR27 9ET. Tel 01263 511294
Chatham ME4 4TZ. Tel: 01634 823800
Eastbourne, BN21 4BY. Tel: 01323 730717
Salcombe TQ8 8BZ. Tel: 01548 844386
Whitby YO21 3PU. Tel 01947 602001
www.rnli.org/find-my-nearest-museums

Royal Naval Museum (1911)
HM Naval Base, Portsmouth PO1 3NH. Tel 02392 891370, www.nmrn-portsmouth.org.uk. Combined ticket for all attractions at the Historic Dockyard.

Royal Navy Submarine Museum
Haslar Jetty Road, Gosport, Hampshire, PO12 2AS. Tel: 023 9251 0354, www.submarine-museum.co.uk.

Royal Norfolk Regimental Museum (1945)
Shirehall, Market Avenue, Norwich, NR1 3JQ. Tel: 01603 493650, www.rnrm.org.uk.

Royal Observer Corps' Museum
Newhaven Fort, Fort Road, Newhaven, East Sussex, BN9 9DS. Tel: 01273 517622, www.newhavenfort.org.uk.

The Royal Regiment of Fusiliers Museum (Royal Warwickshire)
St John's House, Warwick, CV34 4NF. Tel: 01926 491653, www.warwickfusiliers.co.uk.

The Royal Regiment of Wales (Brecon) Museum (1934)
The Barracks, Brecon, Powys, LD3 7EB. Tel: 01874 613310, email: info@royalwelsh.org.uk, www.royalwelsh.org.uk/museum.

Royal Scots Regimental Museum (1951)
Edinburgh Castle, Edinburgh, EH1 2YT. Tel: 0131 310 5015, email: museum@theroyalscots.co.uk, www.theroyalscots.co.uk.

Royal Signals Museum
Blandford Camp, Blandford, Dorset DT11 8RH. Tel: 01258 482248, email: info@royalsignalsmuseum.com, www.royalsignalsmuseum.co.uk.

Royal Sussex Regimental Museum (1930) also the Queen's Royal Irish Hussars and Sussex Combined Forces
Redoubt Fortress, Royal Parade, Eastbourne, East Sussex, BN22 7AQ. Tel: 01323 410300, www.eastbournemuseums.co.uk/collections.

Royal Ulster Constabulary Museum (1983)
Brooklyn, Knock Road, Belfast, BT5 6LE. Tel: 028 9070 0116, www.rucgcfoundation.org/policing-museum.

Royal Ulster Rifles Museum (1963)
5 Waring Street, Belfast, BT1 2EW. Tel: 028 9023 2086, www.royal-irish.com/museums/royal-ulster-rifle-museum.

Royal Welch Fusiliers Museum (1955)
Caernarfon Castle, Gwynedd, LL55 2AY. 01286 673362, fax: 01286 677042, www.rwfmuseum.org.uk.

The Sandhurst Collection, RMAS
Royal Military Academy, Sandhurst, Camberley, Surrey, GU15 4PQ. www.sandhurstcollection.co.uk.

School of Infantry and Small Arms School Corps Weapons Collection (1953)
HQ SASC, HQ Infantry, Land Warfare Centre, Warminster BA12 0DJ. Tel: 01985 222487, www.infantry-weapons.org.

Scott Polar Research Institute Museum
University of Cambridge, Lensfield Road, Cambridge, CB2 1ER. Tel: 01223 336540, www.spri.cam.ac.uk/museum.

Sherwood Foresters Regimental Museum (1923)
The Castle, Nottingham, NG1 6EL. Tel: 0115 8761 400.

Shropshire Regimental Museum (1985)
The Castle, Shrewsbury, SY1 2AT. Tel: 01743 358516, www.shropshireregimentalmuseum.co.uk.

Soldiers of Gloucestershire Museum
Custom House, Gloucester Docks, Gloucester, GL1 2HE. Tel: 01452 522682, www.soldiersofglos.com. Medals of the Gloucestershire Regiment Royal Gloucestershire Hussars.

Somerset Military Museum (1974)
Somerset County Museum, Taunton Castle, Taunton, Somerset, TA1 4AA. Tel: 01823 255088, www.somerset.gov.uk/museums.

South Nottinghamshire Hussars Museum (1974)
Thoresby Courtyard, Thoresby Park, Nr Perlethorpe, Nottinghamshire, NG22 9EP. Tel 01623 824222.

Staffordshire Regiment Museum (1962)
Whittington Barracks, Lichfield, Staffs WS14 9PY. Tel: 01534 434394, www.staffordshireregimentmuseum.com.

Suffolk Regiment Museum (1967)
The Keep, Gibraltar Barracks, Newmarket Road, Bury St Edmunds, Suffolk IP33 3RN. Tel: 01284 752394, www.suffolkregiment.org/museum.html.

Surrey Infantry Museum (1979)
Closed due to fire. The Surrey History Centre will now be dealing with research enquiries relating to The Queen's Royal, East Surrey and Queen's Royal Surrey Regiments (2nd, 31st and 70th Foot). Contact: Surrey History Centre, 130 Goldsworth Road, Woking, Surrey GU21 6ND. Tel: 01483 518737.

Sussex & Surrey Yeomanry Museum (1993)
Newhaven Fort, Fort Road, Newhaven, East Sussex, BN9 9DS. Tel: 01273 517622.

Tangmere, Military Aviation Museum (1992)
Tangmere, near Chichester, West Sussex, PO20 2ES. Tel: 01243 790090, www.tangmere-museum.org.uk.

The 11 (Fighter) Group Operations Room
RAF Uxbridge, Middlesex, UB10 0RZ. Tel: 01895 238154, www.raf.mod.uk/battleofbritainbunker.

The Fusilier Museum (1933)
Moss Street, Bury, Lancs, BL9 0DF. Tel: 0161 763 8950, www.fusiliermuseum.com.

The Highlanders Museum
Fort George, Ardersier, Inverness, IV2 7TD. Tel: 0131 310 8702, www.thehighlandersmuseum.com.

The Tank Museum (1923), Royal Armoured Corps Museum (1939)
Bovington, Wareham, Dorset, BH20 6JG. Tel: 01929 405096, email: info@tankmuseum.org, www.tankmuseum.org.

Towneley Hall Art Gallery and Museum (1902)
Towneley Park, Burnley, Lancs, BB11 3RQ. Tel: 01282 477130, www.townley.org.uk. Small collection including two VCs.

Warwickshire Yeomanry Museum (1981)
The Court House, Jury Street, Warwick, CV34 4EW. Tel: 01926 492212, www.warwickshire-yeomanry-museum.co.uk.

Wellington Museum
Apsley House, 149 Piccadilly, Hyde Park Corner, London, W1J 7NT. Tel: 0207 499 5676, www.english-heritage.org.uk/visit/places/apsley-house.

West Midlands Police Museum (1991)
Sparkhill Police Station, 639 Stratford Road, Birmingham, B11 4EA. Tel: 0845 1135000, www.westmidlandspolicemuseum.co.uk.

Woodbridge, 390th Bomb Group Memorial Air Museum (1981)
Parham Airfield Museum, Parham, Framlingham, Suffolk IP13 9AF. Tel: 01728 621373, www.parhamairfieldmuseum.co.uk.

Worcestershire Regiment Museum (1925)
City Museum and Art Gallery, Foregate Street, Worcester. WR1 1DT. Tel: 01905 25371, Archives: 01905 354359, www.worcestershire.gov.uk/museums/info/2/city_art_gallery_and_museum.

York and Lancaster Regimental Museum (1947)
Clifton Park and Museum, Clifton Lane, Rotherham, S65 2AA. Tel: 01709 336633.

Yorkshire Air Museum and Allied Air Forces Memorial
Halifax Way, Elvington, York, YO41 4AU. Tel: 01904 608595, www.yorkshireairmuseum.org.

The information included in this Directory is correct at the time of going to press. Please advise us on 01404 469721 or email: info@tokenpublishing.com should any of the above details be incorrect. Thank you!

www.medaltracker.com
The UK's leading medal tracking website

MEDALTRACKER.COM has proved incredibly successful in recent months—mainly due to a number of improvements that now make it far easier to use. To have a medal listed on MEDALTRACKER.COM you no longer need to fill in the form found in MEDAL NEWS magazine (although you can if you want to!) as you can now add your medals yourself on-line! As always the magazine version is FREE to subscribers but the on-line version carries a small £5 fee per entry (an "entry" is the recipient and not the medal—you can search for as many medals to one recipient as you like) but remember that the website entry stays until the medal is found, your medals will stay listed until you tell us to remove them.

To check to see which medals have been added recently—who knows you may well have one or more of them in your collection—simply visit www.medaltracker. com and click on browse—then simply select whether you want to see medals entered in the last week, month, three months etc! If you have any information on the whereabouts of any of the medals listed on the site, do please get in touch - simply click the "Report" button to the right of any listing. And remember it's all done in confidence—if you don't want your details revealed to the person looking for the medals they won't be, after all not everyone is seeking to retrieve medals for their collections, sometimes they just want to know the medals are still around.

So whether you are looking for your Grandfather's medals, hoping to reunite a broken group, complete a collection or are simply just curious as to a medal's whereabouts then the MEDALTRACKER.COM may be the way to go—and as the service is advertised in military journals and family history magazines worldwide there is a constant influx of new medals being sought—so make sure you check the listings regularly!

MEDAL RIBBONS

In this section we feature the majority of the ribbons for the medals included in the main sections of the book. Where the same ribbon is used for more than one medal, only one is illustrated here.
(Not all shown to scale, see reference number for actual sizes)

ORDERS OF KNIGHTHOOD MEDAL RIBBONS
(Not all shown to scale, see reference number for actual sizes)

1. The Most Noble Order of the Garter

2. The Most Ancient and Most Noble Order of the Thistle

3. The Most Illustrious Order of St Patrick

4. The Most Honourable Order of the Bath

5. The Royal Guelphic Order

6. The Most Distinguished Order of St Michael & St George

7. The Most Exalted Order of the Star of India

8. The Most Eminent Order (George V)

9. The Royal Family Order (George IV)

9. The Royal Family Order (Edward VII)

9. The Royal Family Order (George V)

9. The Royal Family Order (George VI)

9. The Royal Family Order (Elizabeth II)

11. The Imperial Order of the Crown of India

12. The Royal Victorian Order

13. The Royal Victorian Medal

13. The Royal Victorian Medal (foreign Associates)

15. Order of Merit

16. The Most Excellent Order of the British Empire (Civil 1st type)

16. The Most Excellent Order of the British Empire (Civil 2nd type)

16. The Most Excellent Order of the British Empire (Military 1st type)

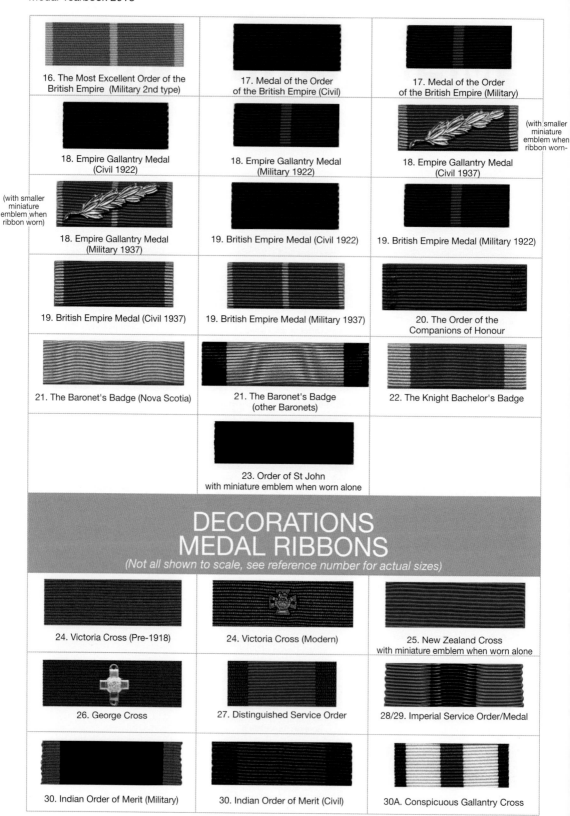

16. The Most Excellent Order of the British Empire (Military 2nd type)

17. Medal of the Order of the British Empire (Civil)

17. Medal of the Order of the British Empire (Military)

18. Empire Gallantry Medal (Civil 1922)

18. Empire Gallantry Medal (Military 1922)

18. Empire Gallantry Medal (Civil 1937)

(with smaller miniature emblem when ribbon worn-

(with smaller miniature emblem when ribbon worn)

18. Empire Gallantry Medal (Military 1937)

19. British Empire Medal (Civil 1922)

19. British Empire Medal (Military 1922)

19. British Empire Medal (Civil 1937)

19. British Empire Medal (Military 1937)

20. The Order of the Companions of Honour

21. The Baronet's Badge (Nova Scotia)

21. The Baronet's Badge (other Baronets)

22. The Knight Bachelor's Badge

23. Order of St John with miniature emblem when worn alone

DECORATIONS
MEDAL RIBBONS
(Not all shown to scale, see reference number for actual sizes)

24. Victoria Cross (Pre-1918)

24. Victoria Cross (Modern)

25. New Zealand Cross with miniature emblem when worn alone

26. George Cross

27. Distinguished Service Order

28/29. Imperial Service Order/Medal

30. Indian Order of Merit (Military)

30. Indian Order of Merit (Civil)

30A. Conspicuous Gallantry Cross

31. Royal Red Cross

32. Distinguished Service Cross

33. Military Cross

34. Distinguished Flying Cross pre-1919

34. Distinguished Flying Cross post-1919

35. Air Force Cross pre-1919

35. Air Force Cross post-1919

36. Order of British India (Original)

36. Order of British India (1st Class, ii)

36. Order of British India (2nd Class, ii)

36. Order of British India (1st Class, post-1939)

36. Order of British India (2nd class, post-1939)

37. Order of Burma

38. Kaisar-i-Hind

39. Albert Medal, original (1866) and 2nd Class, Sea, 1867-1904

39. Albert Medal, 1st Class, Sea, 1867-1949

39. Albert Medal, 2nd Class, Sea, 1904-71

39. Albert Medal, 1st Class, Land, 1877-1949

39. Albert Medal, 2nd Class, Land, 1877-1904

39. Albert Medal, 2nd Class, Land, 1904-71

40. SA Queen's Medal for Bravery

41. Distinguished Conduct Medal

42. Distinguished Conduct Medal (Dominion & Colonial)

43. DCM (KAR and WAFF)

44. Conspicuous Gallantry, 1st ribbon

44. Conspicuous Gallantry

44. Conspicuous Gallantry, (Flying)

45. George Medal

46. King's Police Medal 1916

46. King's Police Medal (Gallantry)

47. Queen's Police Medal

47. Queen's Police Medal Gallantry

48. Queen's Fire Service Medal

48. Queen's Fire Service Medal (Gallantry)

48A. Queen's Volunteer Reserves Medal

48B. Queen's Ambulance Service Medal for Distinguished Service

49. King's Police Medal (South Africa)

50/51. Edward Medal

52. Indian Distinguished Service Medal

53. Burma Gallantry Medal

54. Distinguished Service Medal

55. Military Medal

56. Distinguished Flying Medal pre-1919

56. Distinguished Flying Medal post-1919

57. Air Force Medal pre-1919

57. Air Force Medal post-1919

58. Constabulary Medal Ireland 1842

58. Constabulary Medal Ireland 1872

59. Indian Police Medal (Meritorious Service)

59. Indian Police Medal (From 1942)

60. Burma Police Medal

61. Colonial Police Medal (Gallantry)
62. Colonial Fire Brigade Medal (Gallantry)

61. Colonial Police Medal (Meritorious Service)
62. Colonial Fire Brigade (Meritorious Service)

63. Queen's Gallantry Medal

64. Allied Subjects Medal

65. King's Medal for Courage in the Cause of Freedom

66. King's Medal for Service in the Cause of Freedom

67/68. Sea Gallantry Medal

68. Sea Gallantry Medal till 1922

69. British North Borneo Company's Bravery Cross

70. Native Chief's Medal (i)

70. Native Chief's Medal (ii)

CAMPAIGN MEDAL RIBBONS
(Not all shown to scale, see reference number for actual sizes)

71. Louisburg Medal

79. Seringapatam

82. Sultan's Medal for Egypt

87. Bagur and Palamos Medal

91. Burma Medal

93. Naval Gold Medal

94. Naval General Service Medal

95. Army Gold Cross/96. Maida Gold
97. Army Gold Medal

98. Military General Service Medal

99. Waterloo Medal

100. Brunswick Medal for Waterloo

101. Hanoverian Medal for Waterloo

102. Nassau Medal for Waterloo

103. Saxe-Gotha-Altenburg Medal

104. Army of India Medal

105. Ghuznee Medal (original type)

105. Ghuznee Medal

105A. British Legion Medal

106. St Jean D'Acre Medal

107. Candahar, Ghuznee, Cabul
Medal/109. Kelat-I-Ghilzie

108. Jellalabad

110. China War Medal

111. Scinde Medal

112. Gwalior Star

113. Sutlej Medal

114. Punjab Medal

115. South Africa Medal

116. Sir Harry Smith's Medal

117. India General Service 1854–95

118. Baltic Medal

119. Crimea Medal

120. Turkish Crimea Medal

121. Indian Mutiny Medal

122. Second China War (original type)

122. Second China War (second type)

123. New Zealand Medals

124. Abyssinia 1867–68

125. Canada General Service

126. Ashantee/ 137. E&W Africa

127. South Africa Medal

128. Afghanistan 1878–80

129. Kabul to Kandahar Star

130. Cape of Good Hope GSM

131. Egypt Medal

132. Khedive's Star
133. Gordon's Khartoum Star

134. North West Canada Medal

135. Royal Niger Company's Medal

136. Imperial BEA Co.s Medal

137. East and West Africa Medal

138. BSA Co.s Medal

139. Hunza Nagar badge

140. Central Africa Medal

141. Hong Kong Plague Medal

142. India Medal 1895–1902

143. Jummoo and Kashmir

144. Ashanti Star

145. Queen's Sudan Medal

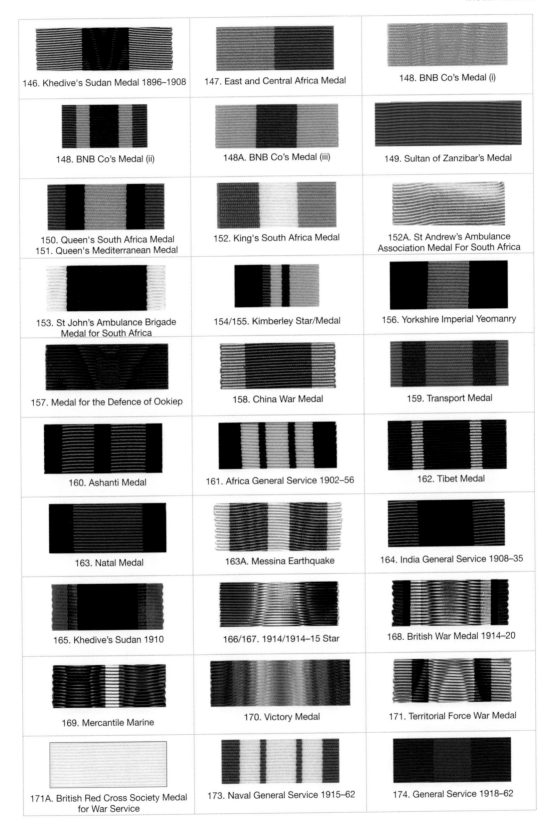

146. Khedive's Sudan Medal 1896–1908

147. East and Central Africa Medal

148. BNB Co's Medal (i)

148. BNB Co's Medal (ii)

148A. BNB Co's Medal (iii)

149. Sultan of Zanzibar's Medal

150. Queen's South Africa Medal
151. Queen's Mediterranean Medal

152. King's South Africa Medal

152A. St Andrew's Ambulance
Association Medal For South Africa

153. St John's Ambulance Brigade
Medal for South Africa

154/155. Kimberley Star/Medal

156. Yorkshire Imperial Yeomanry

157. Medal for the Defence of Ookiep

158. China War Medal

159. Transport Medal

160. Ashanti Medal

161. Africa General Service 1902–56

162. Tibet Medal

163. Natal Medal

163A. Messina Earthquake

164. India General Service 1908–35

165. Khedive's Sudan 1910

166/167. 1914/1914–15 Star

168. British War Medal 1914–20

169. Mercantile Marine

170. Victory Medal

171. Territorial Force War Medal

171A. British Red Cross Society Medal
for War Service

173. Naval General Service 1915–62

174. General Service 1918–62

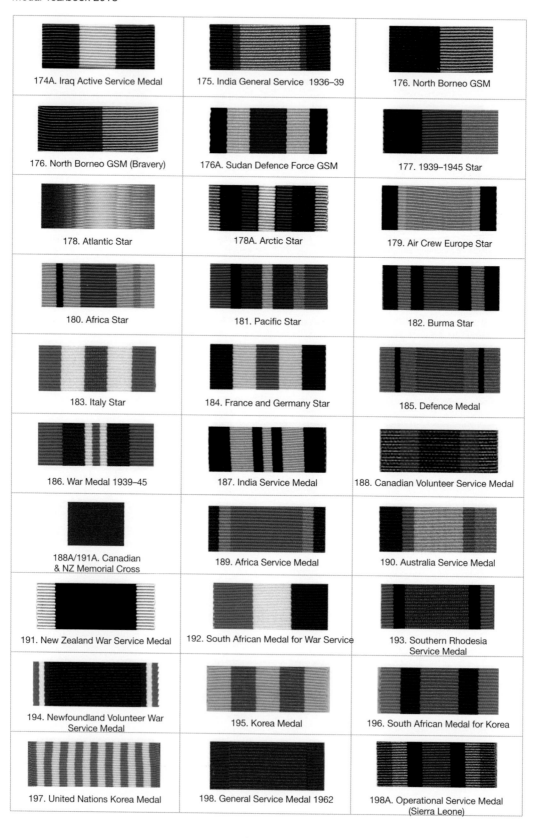

174A. Iraq Active Service Medal

175. India General Service 1936–39

176. North Borneo GSM

176. North Borneo GSM (Bravery)

176A. Sudan Defence Force GSM

177. 1939–1945 Star

178. Atlantic Star

178A. Arctic Star

179. Air Crew Europe Star

180. Africa Star

181. Pacific Star

182. Burma Star

183. Italy Star

184. France and Germany Star

185. Defence Medal

186. War Medal 1939–45

187. India Service Medal

188. Canadian Volunteer Service Medal

188A/191A. Canadian & NZ Memorial Cross

189. Africa Service Medal

190. Australia Service Medal

191. New Zealand War Service Medal

192. South African Medal for War Service

193. Southern Rhodesia Service Medal

194. Newfoundland Volunteer War Service Medal

195. Korea Medal

196. South African Medal for Korea

197. United Nations Korea Medal

198. General Service Medal 1962

198A. Operational Service Medal (Sierra Leone)

198A. Operational Service Medal (Congo)	198A. Operational Service Medal (Afghanistan)	198B. Accumulated Campaign Service
198C. Accumulated Campaign Service Medal 2011	198D. General Service Medal 2008	199. UN Emergency Force Medal
200. Vietnam Medal	200A. Vietnam Logistic and Support Medal	201. South Vietnam Campaign Medal
202. Rhodesia Medal	203. South Atlantic Medal	203A. Soviet 40th Anniversary Medal
203B. Pingat Jasa Malaysia Medal	203C. King Hussein Medal	204. Gulf Medal
204A. Brunei General Service Medal	204AA. Sierra Leone General Service Medal	204B. Iraq Medal
204C. IRAQ Reconstruction Service Medal	204D. The Civilian Service Medal (Afghanistan)	205. Saudi Medal for Liberation of Kuwait
205A. Multinational Force and Observers Medal	205A. Multinational Force and Observers Medal (Civilian)	206. Kuwait Liberation Medals
206A. NATO Former Yugoslavia	206A. NATO Kosovo	206A. NATO Macedonia
206A. NATO Service Medal Eagle Assist	206A. NATO Service Medal Active Endeavour	206A. NATO (i) Non Article 5

206A. NATO Non Article 5 (revised) (Iraq)	206B. European Community Monitoring Mission Medal	206C. Western European Union Mission Service Medal
206D. European Security and Defence Policy Service Medal	207. United Nations Medal UNTSO & UNOGIL	**UN Ribbons change for each operation— see MYB 207 for the full list.**
207. United Nations Medal ONUC	207. United Nations Medal UNTEA	207. United Nations Medal UNMOGIP & UNIPOM
207. United Nations Medal UNYOM	207. United Nations Medal UNFICYP	207. United Nations Medal UNEF 2
207. United Nations Medal UNDOF	207. United Nations Medal UNIFIL	207. United Nations Medal UNIIMOG
207. United Nations Medal UNAVEM	207. United Nations Medal ONUCA	207. United Nations Medal UNTAG
207. United Nations Medal ONUSAL	207. United Nations Medal UNIKOM	207. United Nations Medal MINURSO
207. United Nations Medal UNAMIC	207. United Nations Medal UNTAC	207. United Nations Medal UNOSOM
207. United Nations Medal UNMIH & UNSMIH	207. United Nations Medal UNIMOZ & ONUMOZ	207. United Nations Medal UNPROFOR & UNCRO
207. United Nations Medal UNOMIL	207. United Nations Medal UNOMUR	207. United Nations Medal UNOMIG

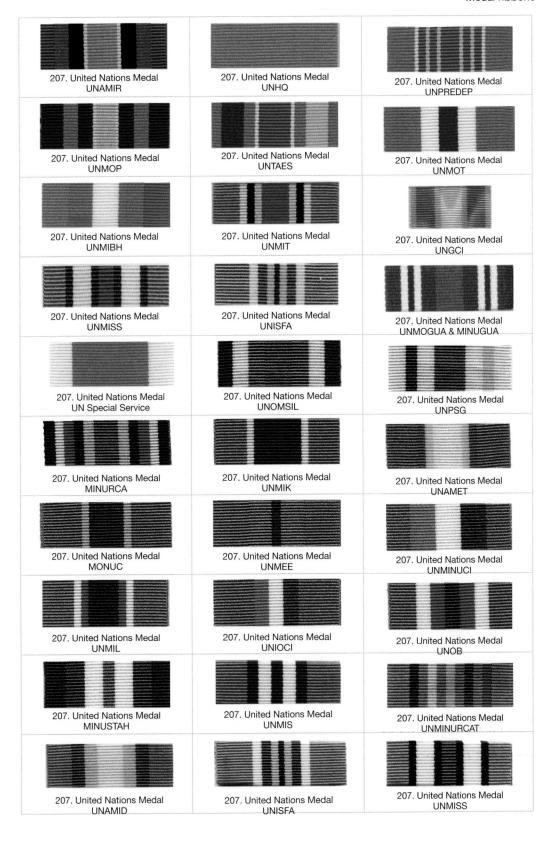

207. United Nations Medal
UNAMIR

207. United Nations Medal
UNHQ

207. United Nations Medal
UNPREDEP

207. United Nations Medal
UNMOP

207. United Nations Medal
UNTAES

207. United Nations Medal
UNMOT

207. United Nations Medal
UNMIBH

207. United Nations Medal
UNMIT

207. United Nations Medal
UNGCI

207. United Nations Medal
UNMISS

207. United Nations Medal
UNISFA

207. United Nations Medal
UNMOGUA & MINUGUA

207. United Nations Medal
UN Special Service

207. United Nations Medal
UNOMSIL

207. United Nations Medal
UNPSG

207. United Nations Medal
MINURCA

207. United Nations Medal
UNMIK

207. United Nations Medal
UNAMET

207. United Nations Medal
MONUC

207. United Nations Medal
UNMEE

207. United Nations Medal
UNMINUCI

207. United Nations Medal
UNMIL

207. United Nations Medal
UNIOCI

207. United Nations Medal
UNOB

207. United Nations Medal
MINUSTAH

207. United Nations Medal
UNMIS

207. United Nations Medal
UNMINURCAT

207. United Nations Medal
UNAMID

207. United Nations Medal
UNISFA

207. United Nations Medal
UNMISS

207. United Nations Medal UNAMID (alternative)

207A. International Conference on the Former Yugoslavia

207B. Interfet Medal

207C. Unitas Medal

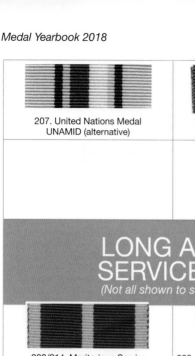

LONG AND MERITORIOUS SERVICE MEDAL RIBBONS
(Not all shown to scale, see reference number for actual sizes)

208/214. Meritorious Service Medals/212. Colonial MSM (Canada)

209. Royal Marines Meritorious Service Medal (first type)

209. Royal Marines Meritorious Service Medal (second type)

210. Army Meritorious Service Medal (first type)

210. Army Meritorious Service Medal (second type)

210. Army Meritorious Service Medal (third type)

211. RAF Meritorious Service Medal (original)

212. Colonial MSM (Cape of Good Hope)

212. Colonial MSM (Natal)

212. Colonial MSM (Commonwealth of Australia)

212. Colonial MSM (New South Wales)

212. Colonial MSM (Queensland)

212. Colonial MSM (South Australia)

212. Colonial MSM (Tasmania)

212. Colonial MSM (New Zealand)

213/214. Indian Army MSM 1848/88

215. African Police Medal for Meritorious Service

216. Union of South Africa MSM

217. Royal Household FS QV

217. Royal Household FS GVIR

217. Royal Household FS EIIR

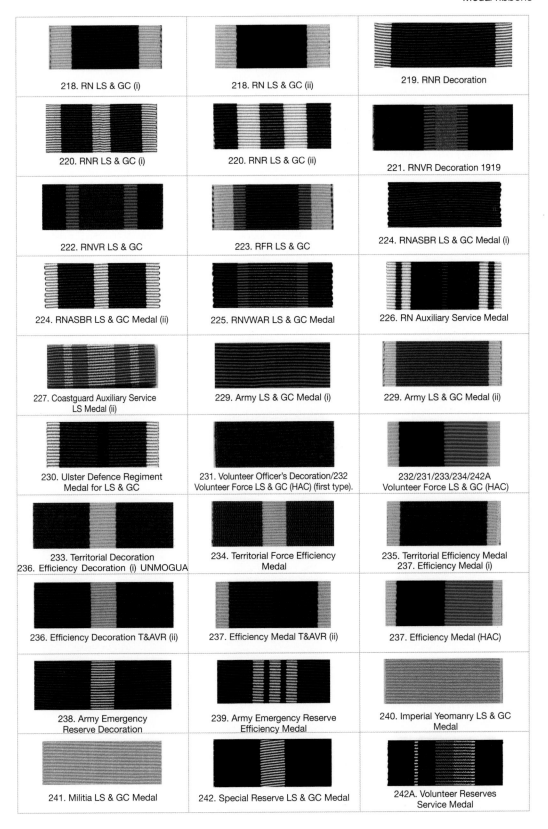

218. RN LS & GC (i)

218. RN LS & GC (ii)

219. RNR Decoration

220. RNR LS & GC (i)

220. RNR LS & GC (ii)

221. RNVR Decoration 1919

222. RNVR LS & GC

223. RFR LS & GC

224. RNASBR LS & GC Medal (i)

224. RNASBR LS & GC Medal (ii)

225. RNVWAR LS & GC Medal

226. RN Auxiliary Service Medal

227. Coastguard Auxiliary Service LS Medal (ii)

229. Army LS & GC Medal (i)

229. Army LS & GC Medal (ii)

230. Ulster Defence Regiment Medal for LS & GC

231. Volunteer Officer's Decoration/232 Volunteer Force LS & GC (HAC) (first type).

232/231/233/234/242A Volunteer Force LS & GC (HAC)

233. Territorial Decoration
236. Efficiency Decoration (i) UNMOGUA

234. Territorial Force Efficiency Medal

235. Territorial Efficiency Medal
237. Efficiency Medal (i)

236. Efficiency Decoration T&AVR (ii)

237. Efficiency Medal T&AVR (ii)

237. Efficiency Medal (HAC)

238. Army Emergency Reserve Decoration

239. Army Emergency Reserve Efficiency Medal

240. Imperial Yeomanry LS & GC Medal

241. Militia LS & GC Medal

242. Special Reserve LS & GC Medal

242A. Volunteer Reserves Service Medal

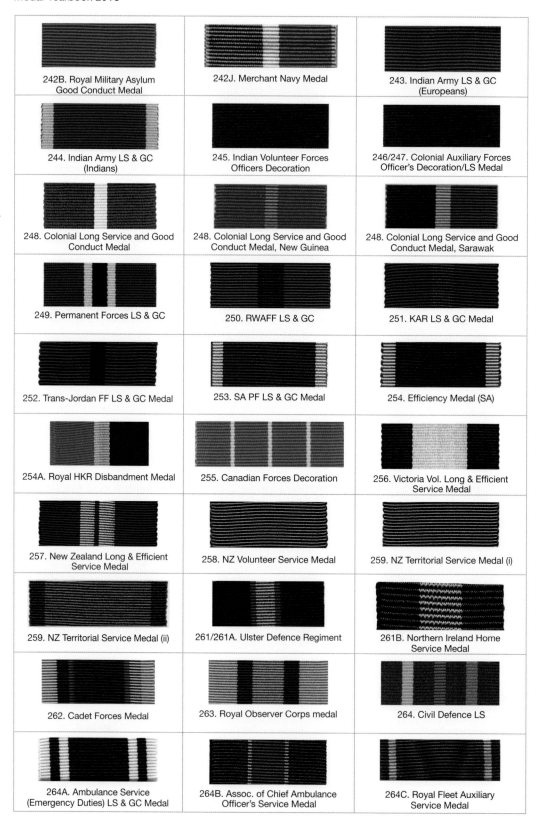

242B. Royal Military Asylum Good Conduct Medal

242J. Merchant Navy Medal

243. Indian Army LS & GC (Europeans)

244. Indian Army LS & GC (Indians)

245. Indian Volunteer Forces Officers Decoration

246/247. Colonial Auxiliary Forces Officer's Decoration/LS Medal

248. Colonial Long Service and Good Conduct Medal

248. Colonial Long Service and Good Conduct Medal, New Guinea

248. Colonial Long Service and Good Conduct Medal, Sarawak

249. Permanent Forces LS & GC

250. RWAFF LS & GC

251. KAR LS & GC Medal

252. Trans-Jordan FF LS & GC Medal

253. SA PF LS & GC Medal

254. Efficiency Medal (SA)

254A. Royal HKR Disbandment Medal

255. Canadian Forces Decoration

256. Victoria Vol. Long & Efficient Service Medal

257. New Zealand Long & Efficient Service Medal

258. NZ Volunteer Service Medal

259. NZ Territorial Service Medal (i)

259. NZ Territorial Service Medal (ii)

261/261A. Ulster Defence Regiment

261B. Northern Ireland Home Service Medal

262. Cadet Forces Medal

263. Royal Observer Corps medal

264. Civil Defence LS

264A. Ambulance Service (Emergency Duties) LS & GC Medal

264B. Assoc. of Chief Ambulance Officer's Service Medal

264C. Royal Fleet Auxiliary Service Medal

265. WVS Long Service Medal

266. Voluntary Medical Service Medal

267. Service Medal of the
Order of St John of Jerusalem

268/269. RAF LS & GC Medal

270. Air Efficiency Award

271. Police LS & GC

272. Special Constabulary LS

273. RUC Service Medal (original type)

273. RUC Service Medal (post-2001)

274. Colonial Police LS

275. Colonial Special Constabulary LS

276. Ceylon Police LS & GC Medal (I)

277. Ceylon Police LS & GC Medal (II)

278. Ceylon Police Medal for Merit

278a. Ceylon Police Medal
for Gallantry

279. Cyprus MP LS & GC Medal

280. HK Police Medal for Merit
(1st Class)

280. HK Police Medal for Merit
(2nd Class)

280. HK Police Medal for Merit
(3rd Class)

280. HK Police Medal for Merit
(4th Class)

280B. Royal Hong Kong Police

280C. Royal HK Aux. Police
Commemoration Medal

281. HK Royal Naval Dockyard Police
Long Service Medal

281A. HK Disciplined Service Medal

281B. Tientsin British Emergency
Corps Medal

282. Malta Police LS & GC Medal

282A. Mauritius Police LS & GC

282A. Mauritius Police LS & GC
Medal (I) (first type)

282B. Mauritius Police LS & GC
Medal (II)

283. NZ Police LS & GC Medal
(Second type)

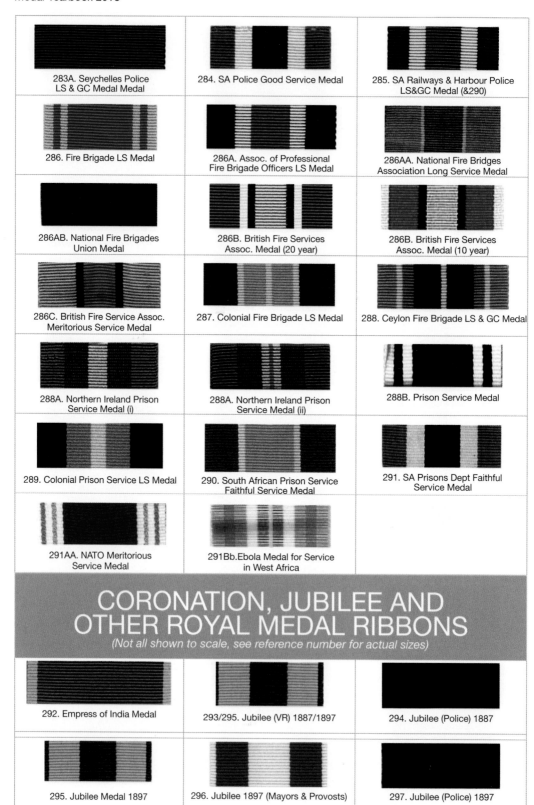

283A. Seychelles Police
LS & GC Medal Medal

284. SA Police Good Service Medal

285. SA Railways & Harbour Police
LS&GC Medal (&290)

286. Fire Brigade LS Medal

286A. Assoc. of Professional
Fire Brigade Officers LS Medal

286AA. National Fire Bridges
Association Long Service Medal

286AB. National Fire Brigades
Union Medal

286B. British Fire Services
Assoc. Medal (20 year)

286B. British Fire Services
Assoc. Medal (10 year)

286C. British Fire Service Assoc.
Meritorious Service Medal

287. Colonial Fire Brigade LS Medal

288. Ceylon Fire Brigade LS & GC Medal

288A. Northern Ireland Prison
Service Medal (i)

288A. Northern Ireland Prison
Service Medal (ii)

288B. Prison Service Medal

289. Colonial Prison Service LS Medal

290. South African Prison Service
Faithful Service Medal

291. SA Prisons Dept Faithful
Service Medal

291AA. NATO Meritorious
Service Medal

291Bb.Ebola Medal for Service
in West Africa

CORONATION, JUBILEE AND OTHER ROYAL MEDAL RIBBONS
(Not all shown to scale, see reference number for actual sizes)

292. Empress of India Medal

293/295. Jubilee (VR) 1887/1897

294. Jubilee (Police) 1887

295. Jubilee Medal 1897

296. Jubilee 1897 (Mayors & Provosts)

297. Jubilee (Police) 1897

298. Ceylon Diamond Jubilee 1897	299. HK Diamond Jubilee Medal	299A. Lagos Diamond Jubilee Medal
299B. India Diamond Jubilee Medal	300. Visit to Ireland 1900	301. Coronation 1902
302. Coronation 1902 (Mayors & Provosts)	303. Coronation 1902 (Police)	304. Ceylon Coronation 1902
305. HK Coronation 1902	306. Delhi Durbar 1903	307. Visit to Scotland 1903
308. Visit to Ireland 1903	308A. Visit of the Prince and Princess of Wales to India	308B. George Prince of Wales Medal
309. Coronation 1911 / 312. Delhi Durbar 1911	309A. Guildhall Coronation Medal 1911	310. Coronation 1911 (Police)
311. Visit to Ireland 1911	312AB. Queen Alex. Children's Banquet Medal 1914	313. Jubilee 1935
313A. Isle of Man Silver Jubilee 1935	314. Coronation 1937	315. Coronation 1953
315A. Royal Visit to New Zealand Medal 1953–54	316. Jubilee 1977	318. Golden Jubilee 2002
	318A. Diamond Jubilee	

MISCELLANEOUS MEDAL RIBBONS
(Not all shown to scale, see reference number for actual sizes)

319. King's and Queen's Messenger Badge

320. Arctic Medal (1857)

321. Arctic Medal (1876)

322. Polar Medal

323. EVII Medal for Science, Art & Music

324. Order of the League of Mercy

325. Queen Alex. Imperial Military Nursing Service Cape Badge

325A. Queen Alex. Imperial Military Nursing Service Reserve Cape Badge

326. Territorial Force Nursing Service Cape Badge

326A. Queen Alex. Military Families Nursing Service Cape Badge

326B. Territorial Army Nursing Service Cape Badge

326C. Queen Alex. Royal Army Nursing Corps Cape Badge

327. Indian Title Badge (1st Class)

327. Indian Title Badge (2nd Class)

327. Indian Title Badge (3rd Class)

328. Badge of the Cert. of Honour

329. Badge of Honour (non-African countries)

330. Naval Engineers GC Medal

331. Indian Recruiting Badge (GV)

332. Indian Recruiting Badge (GVI)

333. Naval Good Shooting

334. Army Best Shot Medal

335. Queen's Medal for Champion Shot (RN/RM)

336. Queen's Medal for Champion Shot (RAF)

337. Queen's Medal for Champion Shot NZ Naval Force

338. Union of South Africa Commemoration Medal

339. Loyal Service Decoration (SA)

340. Anglo-Boer War Medal	The various Commonwealth Independence Medals are all included as MYB 341	341. India Independence Medal
341. Pakistan Independence Medal	341. Nigeria Independence Medal	341. Sierra Leone Independence Medal
341. Jamaica Independence Medal	341. Uganda Independence Medal	341. Malawi Independence Medal
341. Guyana Independence Medal	341. Fiji Independence Medal	341. Papua Independence Medal
341. Solomon Islands Independence Medal	341. Gilbert Islands Independence Medal	341. Ellice Islands Independence Medal
341. Zimbabwe Independence Medal	341. Vanuatu Independence Medal	341. Swaziland Independence Medal
341. St. Christopher Independence Medal	341. Ghana Independence Medal	341. Kenya Independence Medal
342. Malta GC Anniversary Commemorative Medal	346. Shanghai Volunteer Fire Brigade Long Service Medal	347. Shanghai Volunteer Corps Long Service Medal
349. Shanghai Municipal Police LS Medal	351. Shanghai Municipal Council Emergency Medal	352. Automobile Association Service Cross
353. Automobile Association Service Medal	354. Suffragette Medal	355. Florence Nightingale Medal

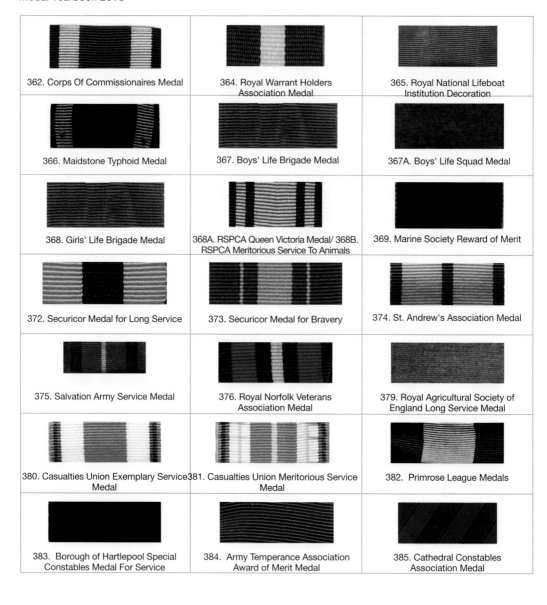

362. Corps Of Commissionaires Medal	364. Royal Warrant Holders Association Medal	365. Royal National Lifeboat Institution Decoration
366. Maidstone Typhoid Medal	367. Boys' Life Brigade Medal	367A. Boys' Life Squad Medal
368. Girls' Life Brigade Medal	368A. RSPCA Queen Victoria Medal/ 368B. RSPCA Meritorious Service To Animals	369. Marine Society Reward of Merit
372. Securicor Medal for Long Service	373. Securicor Medal for Bravery	374. St. Andrew's Association Medal
375. Salvation Army Service Medal	376. Royal Norfolk Veterans Association Medal	379. Royal Agricultural Society of England Long Service Medal
380. Casualties Union Exemplary Service Medal	381. Casualties Union Meritorious Service Medal	382. Primrose League Medals
383. Borough of Hartlepool Special Constables Medal For Service	384. Army Temperance Association Award of Merit Medal	385. Cathedral Constables Association Medal

LIFESAVING MEDAL RIBBONS

(Not all shown to scale, see reference number for actual sizes)

L1. Royal Humane Society (1921)

L1. Stanhope Gold Medal

L3. Hundred of Salford Humane Society Medals

L4. RNLI Medal

L4B. Port of Plymouth Swimming Assc. and Humane Society Medal

L5. Medals of the Society for the Protection of Life from Fire

L6. Lloyd's Medal for Saving Life at sea

L7. Liverpool S&H Society's Marine Medals

L8. SF&MRB Society Medal

L9. Tayleur Fund Medal

L10A. Jersey Humane Society Medal

L12. Lifesaving Medal of the Order of St John (Original)

L12. Lifesaving Medal of the Order of St John (1888 on)

L12. Lifesaving Medal of the Order of St John (1950–1953)

L12. Lifesaving Medal of the Order of St John (1954 on)

L13. Shropshire Society Life Saving Medal

L14. Liverpool Shipwreck and Humane Society's Fire Medal

L15. Liverpool Shipwreck and Humane Society's Swimming Medal

L15A. Ally Sloper's Medal

L16. Answers Medal for Heroism

L17. Lloyd's Medal for Meritorious Service

L18. Liverpool Shipwreck and Humane Society's General Medal

L19. Today Gallantry Fund Medal

L20. Imperial Merchant Service Guild Medal

L21. Pluck Medal for Heroism

L22. Tynemouth Medal

L23. Drummond Castle Medal

L24. New Foundland Silver Star for Bravery

L26. Humane Society of NZ medals first type

L26. Humane Society of NZ medals second type

L27. The Sheffield Society For The Recognition Of Bravery Medal

L28. Boys' Brigade Cross for Heroism

L30A Hamstead Colliery Medal 1908

L31. RSPCA Lifesaving Medal (Silver)

L31A. National Canine Defence League Medal

L32. Scout Association Gallantry Medal (bronze)

L32. Scout Association Gallantry Medal (silver)

L32. Scout Association Gallantry Medal (gilt)

L33. CQD Medal

L33A. Bolton & District Humane Society Medal

L34. Carpathia and Titanic Medal

L35. Lloyd's Medal for Services to Lloyds

L36. Order of Industrial Heroism

L37. Corporation of Glasgow Bravery Medal

L37A. Imperial Chemical Industries Bravery Award

L38. RSPCA Margaret Wheatley Cross

L38A. Dundee Corporation Medal For Gallantry

L39. Lloyd's Medal for Bravery at Sea

L40. London, Midland and Scottish Railway Medal

L41. Southern Railway Meritorious Service Medal

L42. Dale Medal

L43. London Passenger Transport Board Medal for Bravery

L44. London and North Eastern Railway Gallantry Medal

L44A. Dickin Medal

L46/L47. Sea Cadet Gallantry Cross/Medal

L47A. Gallantry Medallists' League Gold Medal for Courage

L49A. Royal Life Saving Proficiency Medals

L51. Tyne & Wear Fire and Civil Defence Authority Medal for Bravery

IRISH REPUBLIC (EIRE) MEDAL RIBBONS
(Not all shown to scale, see reference number for actual sizes)

E1. 1916 Medal

E2. Military Medal for Gallantry

E2. Military Medal for Gallantry

E2. Military Medal for Gallantry

E3. Distinguished Service Medal

E4. Civil Medal for Bravery

E5. General Service Medal 1917-21

E6. The Emergency Service Medal 1939–46

E7. Merchant Service Medal 1939–46

E8. Permanent Defence Forces Service Medal

E10. St John Ambulance Brigade of Ireland Service Medal.

E11. The United National Peacekeepers Medal

E12. 1916–66 "Survivors" Medal

E13. 1921–71 "Survivors" Medal

E14. Reserve Defence Forces Long Service Medal

E14. Reserve Defence Forces Long Service Medal

E15. Scott Medal for Valor

E16. Garda Siochana Forces Long Service Medal

E17. Garda Siochana Golden Jubilee Service Medal

E18. Garda Siochana Millennium Medal

E19. Garda United Nations Services Medal

E20. Civil Defence Long Service Medal

E21. Civil Defence Millennium Medal

Incorporating Military Chest and Medals International
MEDAL NEWS

INDEX TO MEDAL NEWS

Following a number of requests we are, once again, including the Cumulative Subject Index to the MEDAL YEARBOOK's parent magazine MEDAL NEWS, commencing with the March 1989 issue, when it split from COIN & MEDAL NEWS to become a separate publication and running until 2014—it is planed to update it in this YEARBOOK every year,

MEDAL NEWS was born in 1981 from the amalgamation of *Medals International* and *Coins & Medals*, into the popular title *Coin & Medal News*. However, the success of this magazine and the continuing growth of both the coin and the medal collecting hobbies prompted the separation of the two sections in March 1989. Since then both *Coin News* and MEDAL NEWS have grown from strength to strength and today are the hobby's leading publications, not only in the UK but MEDAL NEWS is the only independent magazine in the world devoted to the collecting and study of medals, battles and the history of heroes.

Many issues of MEDAL NEWS are still available for purchase at £5 per issue inclusive of postage—some of the earlier magazines may not be available to buy in their entirety but we may be able to provide photocopies of articles for readers. Please enquire whether we have the issue you are interested in before placing an order. Subscribers to MEDAL NEWS are able to access digital copies (from September 2007) of the magazine on-line for free, as long as their subscription is active. Simply log on to your account and find them all under "digital magazines" (earlier issues are pdf only, later ones give an option of downloadable pdf or reading them on-line as a "flip book"). We regret that at this stage we cannot sell individual digital magazines.

NOTES

References are indicated **year, month, page**, for example 0404.18 means April 2004 issue, page 18; 0606.24 means June/July 2006 issue, page 24; 1101.12-14 means December 2010/January 2011 issue, pages 12 through 14. As a rule the early pages (06-08) shown are "news" pages which will only carry a small piece on the relevant subject. Later pages e.g. 20-23/33-36 etc. will indicate an article where the subject indexed is mentioned a number of times or where it/they are the main subject of the article. Please note that it has not been possible to index every medal group or recipient highlighted in the "Market Scene" section, however, medal groups/recipients of importance (Victoria Crosses, George Crosses, medals for famous actions etc.) that appear in the news section will be indexed.

Each year runs from December/January to November. For example the year 2012 includes the December 2011/January 2012 issue which is indexed thus 1201/xx (n.b. there are 10 issues per annum). The June/July issue is normally indexed as 06 with August as 08 (number 07 is therefore omitted) however, there was initial confusion over this with the original third-party indexer (the task is now done in house) so once again please check before ordering an issue.

Names of ships are indicated in italics.

Names of people have been included where they appear to be the major subject of an article or where more than trivial information is included.

Abbreviations used:
(cr)	Indicates the inclusion of a full or partial casualty list.
(mr)	Indicates the inclusion of a medal roll.
(nr)	Indicates nominal roll.
(i)	Indicates that the reference gives information rather than the object itself. For example it tells you where to find a medal roll rather than reproducing the roll itself.
(p)	Indicates that the reference is to a picture of a person or object where little or no other information is given.
(mp)	Same as (p) except that the picture is of medals.
(br)	Indicates Book Review.
(obit)	Indicates an obituary or death notice with reasonable detail.

The index is not exhaustive but it has been compiled with a view to aid research; however, despite our best efforts there will be errors and omissions, and items indexed that readers feel were not worthy of such, and for those we apologise in advance.

To order back issues contact us (Token Publishing Ltd) at the address on page 1.

A

Royal Sussex Regt 9412.22-23
Royal Tank Regt 9204.24-25
Royal Warwickshire Regt 0703.34-36
Royal Welsh Fusiliers 0410.29-30
Royal Welch Fusiliers 9606.20-21
Royal West Kent Regiment 1305.41-43 & 1306.46-48
Royal Wiltshire Regiment 0011.31-32
Russian for the Nord-ost Rescuers 0502.33
St John Ambulance (Boer War) 9303.25
Scots Guards 1302.47-49
Scots Guards 9707.25-26
Scottish Rifles (Cameronians) 0211.29-30
Scottish Yeomanry Regts 9209.24-25, 9210.24-25
shako plates 9208.24-25
shoulder-belt plates 9011.20-21
volunteer forces 9109.26-27
Somerset Light Infantry 1406.49-51 & 1408.39-41
South Lancashire Regt 9609.20
South Wales Borderers 9606.20-21
South Wales Borderers 0209.24-26
Sphinx 9002.24-25
423 Squadron RCAF 9003.17, 9009.11
Staff Band Brigade of Gurkhas 9504.20-21
Suffolk Regiment 0104.26-27
Territorial Infantry 9108.25-26
The Militia 0405.26-27, 0406.35-36 and 0408.24-26
University Volunteer and Training Corps 0901.46-48 and 0902.38-40
Voluntary Medical Corps serving with army 9303.25
Volunteer Engineers 9311.22-23, 9312.24-25
Volunteer Force 1914 Part I 0606.23-24
Volunteer Force 1914 Part II 0608.37-39
Volunteer Force 1914 Part II 0608.37-39
Volunteer Force (1914-18) 8912.21-22
Welsh Brigade 9608.20-21, 9809.28
Welch Regiment 1104.37-39, 1105.39-41
Welsh Guards 9707.25-26
Welsh Regiment 9608.20-21
Welsh Yeomanry 9704.25-26
Wessex Brigade 9709.27
West Riding Regt 9602.20-21
West Riding Yeomanry 1002.38-40
West Suffolk Regt 9009.22-23
West Surreys – the Queen's Regiment 0206.37-38
West Yorkshire Regt 9512.22-23
Women's Services 9212.24-25
World War I lapel 0802.34-35
York and Lancaster Regiment 9603.20-21
Yorkshire Brigade 9603.20-21, 9709.27
Yorkshire Regt (Green Howards) 9602.20-21
Yorkshire Volunteers 9603.20-21
Yorkshire Yeomanry 9206.24-25
Other Yeomanry badges
Bedfordshire 9801.27
Berkshire 9801.27
Berkshire and Westminster Dragoons 9801.28
Royal Buckinghamshire Hussars 9801.28
Caernavon and Denbigh 9704.25-26
Cheshire (Earl of Chester's) 9801.28
Denbighshire Hussars 9704.25-26
Derbyshire 9802.26
Royal North Devon 9802.26
Royal West Kent Regiment 1305.41-43 & 1306.46-48
Queen's Own Dorset 9802.26
Queen's Own Dorset and West Somerset 9802.27
Essex 9802.27
Glamorgan 9704.25-26
Royal Gloucestershire 9802.26
Hampshire Carabiniers 9803.26-27
Herefordshire 9803.26-27
Hertfordshire and Bedfordshire 9803.26-27
Inns of Court and City 9803.26-27
Royal East Kent 9803.26-27
West Kent (Queen's Own) 9803.26-27
Kent and County 9803.26-27
King's Colonials 9803.26-27
King's Colonials 9803.26-27
King Edward's Horse 9804.26-27
Duke of Lancaster's Own 9804.26-27
Lancashire Hussars 9804.26-27
Leicestershire (Prince Albert's Own) 9804.26-27
Leicestershire and Derbyshire (Prince Albert's Own) 9804.26-27
Lincolnshire Regiment 9909.35-36
Lincolnshire Yeomanry9804.26-27
London 9804.26-27
City of London (Rough Riders) 9804.26-27 and 9805.27-28
2nd County of London (Westminster Dragoons) 9805.27-28
3rd County of London (Sharpshooters) 9805.27-28
4th County of London 9805.27-28
London and Territorials 9805.27-28
Royal Mercian and Lancastrian 9805.27-28
Middlesex (Duke of Cambridge's Hussars) 9805.27-28

Montgomeryshire 9704.25-26
Norfolk (King's Own Royal Regt.) 9807.25-26
Northamptonshire 9807.25-26
Northumberland Hussars 9807.25-26
Nottinghamshire (Sherwood Rangers) 9807.25-26
South Nottinghamshire Hussars 9807.25-26
Pembrokeshire 9704.25-26
Queen's Own Oxfordshire Hussars 9807.25-26
Queen's Own 9807.25-26
9th Queens Royal Lancers 0609.31-32
Royal 9807.25-26
Shropshire 9808.27-28
North Somerset 9808.27-28
North Somerset and Bristol 9808.27-28
West Somerset 9808.27-28
Staffordshire (Queen's Own Royal Regt.) 9808.27-28
Duke of York's Own Loyal Suffolk Hussars 9808.27-28
Suffolk and Norfolk 9808.27-28
Surrey (Queen Mary's) 9808.27-28
Sussex 9809.27-28
Warwickshire 9809.27-28
Queen's Own Warwickshire and Worcestershire 9809.27-28
Welsh Horse 9704.25-26
Wessex 9809.27-28
West Yorkshire Regt. 1506.42-44 & 1508.38-40
Westmoreland and Cumberland 9809.27-28
Royal Wiltshire 9809.27-28
Queen's Own Royal Worcestershire 9809.27-28
Yorkshire 9809.27-28
Yorkshire Dragoons 1001.45-47
Yorkshire Hussars 1001.45-47
Bagot Lt A. G. DSC, AM, RNVR and Lt Cmdr K R Hoare, DSO, DSC , AM RNVR heroes of the Albert Medal, 0311.27
Bagur and Palamos Medal 0811.17-18 and 0903.30 and 1102.16-17
Bailey, Captain Ian MM 1002.06
Bailey, Derrick Bourchier, RAF bomber pilot 0209.31-32
Bainbridge, James Scott, Yorkshire Regt (WWI) 9002.10
Bain, Sgt James Fortune CGM (flying) 0601.42-43
Baird, Corporal Cameron Stewart VC. Posthumous Award. 1403.06 & 1404.06
Bahamian Hurricane 1926 HMS Valerian (cr)1609.38-40
Bahrain, Air France Disasters, June 12 and 14 1950 0006.24-25
Baker, Armr. Sgt. Alf - family heirlooms of 0205.26
Baker, John GC (ob) 0103.07
Baker, Pte Garnet Baker Middlesex Regt WWI 1101.31-33
Baker, Samuel, Sir: Nile explorations 9312.21-22
Baker Troop, Cyprus 1955 0708.34-35
Baker Troop, Suez 1956 (mr) 0709.39-40
Baku, South Russia, Dunster Force, 1401.37-39
Balabac, sinking (mr) 9002.20-22
Balaclava, Troop-Sergeant William Bentley, Light Brigade 0101.27-28
Balaclava 8908.15-18, 0811.21
    Crimea Medal clasp 9002.28
    Light Brigade & Policemen 8909.05
Balaklava: Battlefield Tour 0506.39
Balaklava. Charge of the Heavy Brigade 0910.19-21
Baldrey, Lt-Col Andrew 5th Dragoon Guards 1108.32-34
Baldwin, Florence ISM 1310.36-37
Balcombe, Quartermaster James 57th Regiment; Crimea 0705.24-25
Baldock, Flt. Engr. Lewis George RAFVR lost over Norway 22 February 1945 0805.31-32
Baldwin, Sgt. F.W. DCM R.E. 0801.18-20
Baldwins First Medal Auction 0203.11
Balkans and the Black Sea 1918-20 (mr) 0302.18-20
Balkans and the Black Sea 1918-20 Part II MIDs (mr) 303.16-18
Balkans: clasp to Australia Service Medal (1975) 9403.11
Ball, Albert VC RFC statue 1610.33-35
Ball, B.M., Maj 39/Foot 9308.24-25
Ball, Frederick Markam, Flt Lt RAFVR: MC Java (1945) 9605.13
Ball, Stanley: Wanderer 9006.10-12
Ball, William: Wanderer 9006.10-12
Ballard: Guadalcanal 9209.20-21
Ballenden, Lt John, Korea 1301.43-45
Balloonist's medals 9005.21, 9008.28
Baltic Medal (1854-55): naming 9003.23
Baluch Horse: badge 9410.22
Baly, Lindsay 'Horsemen Pass By' (br) 0506.51
Bapaume, Battle of. (mr) 1105.22-23
Bambatha Rebellion, Natal 1906 0711.15-17
Bamber, Iain, 'From Pouch to Passport – A History of the King's and Queen's Messenger Insignia' (br) 1003.41
Bambrick, Rifleman Valentine VC – plaque unveiled 0211.08
Banfield, Arthur, London Fire Brigade and RN 0103.16-17
Banks, N.L.R. 'Over the Front' (br) 9303.23
Bannister, John, Pte: 'The Life and Death of . . .' service in India (background) 9803.23-25
Banting, Major Sir Frederick G. KBE MC Canadian Memorial Cross, record for 0308.08
'Baptism of Fire' (br) Marsay, Mark 9906.24
Barasat, Outrages at 0603.30-31
Barber, C., Sgt Maj R. Regt Fus (p) 8904.25
Barber, Henry James Frederick MBE 1106.39-41 Barber, W.H. Tpr 44

Kosovo clasp NATO medal 0002.06
KOYLI, Badges 0511.34-35
'K' reports in PRO 9410.15-17
Krikly, Ivan, Capt: Ord of Patriotic War (USSR) 9409.17-18
Kroomen in the Boer War 0306.26-27
Kroomen of the Nemesis 0408.14-16
Kroomen rating titles RN 9106.17
KRRC in Egypt and the Sudan 1882-86 (mr) 0104.31
KRRC, Pte Stephen Ernest Brown 0608.24-25
KSLI, Sgt George Eardley VC 0609.20-21
Krygger, A., Pte. Western Australians: Slingersfontein (1900) 8909.19-20
KSLI and the Hong Kong Plague 0308.33
Ku Lang Su police: badge 9303.26
Kulm Cross (Russia/Prussia) 9110.20
Kumar, Signalman T. Signal Corps 1311.35-38
Kursk Salient, Battle of 0609.27
Kut (1916): RFA, RGA, RHA (nr) 9406.15-19
Kutuzov, Order of(USSR) 9409.17-19
Kuwait: clasp to Australia Service Medal (1975) 9403.11
Kuwait Military Service Miniature Medals 1605.42
Kuwaiti Liberation Medal 9304.10, (p) 9305.06
Kwai Bridge: Buddhist temple 9210.20-21
Kyle, Sgt RA: MSM 9303.28, 9503.21

L

'L' Battery, Royal Horse Artillery, Nery 1914 0402.25-260409.4-26
L/Cpl Joshua Leakey VC. Para. Victoria Cross Citation 1504.06
'LRDG Rhodesia' Jonathon Pittaway and Craig Fourie (br) 0309.36
Lacey, Bill. Dunkirk (obit) 1108.08
Lady Brassey: Glatton (1918) 8909.15-17
"Lady Under Fire on the Western Front: The Great War Letters of Lady Dorothie Feilding MM' Andrew and Nicola Hallam (editors) (br) 1104.41Ladysmith and Tugela Heights, General Buller's advance (cr) 0002.18-21
Ladybird, HMS Incident 1101.34-37 Laffin, J. 'A Western Front Companion' (br) 9504.22
Laffin, J. 'British VCs of World War 2, A study in Heroism" (br): 9802.25
Lagden, Alan and Sly, John '2/73rd at Waterloo: Including a Roll of all Ranks Present, with Biographical notes' (br) 9808.25-26
Laird, Cpl. Royal Scots, Hong Kong 1941 0801.28-30
28th Lahore Mountain Battery: Somaliland (1903-04) 9006.15
Lake George (Australia) (1956): Boating disaster 9512.10-11
Lake Superior Scottish: badge 9106.27
Lale, Grp Capt Horace Percy DSO DFC* Medals for sale 1701.07
Lally, S., Pte Connaught Rangers 9305.20-21
Lama, Captain Ganju VC (obit) 0008.09
Lambourne 1st Class Sergeant Instructor Samuel 0303.30-31
Lamin, Bill 'Letters from the Trenches: A Soldier of the Great War' (br) 0909.41
Lame Deer, Chief 0711.27-29
Lanark & Renfrew Scottish: badge 9106.27
Lanarkshire Yeomanry: badge 9209.24
1/Lancashire Fusiliers. Boer War Pte Abner Settle, 1301.22-23
Lancashire Fusilier Officers in Multan 1911 (pic) 0911.29-31
Lancashire Fusiliers, Pte John Lynn VC, DCM 1111.24-25
Lancashire Fusiliers
    (2/8th) World War I 1202.35-38
    8th (Territorials) 1303.17-19
    11th (Service) Battalion, medals to (mr) 0003.28-31
    Applin, Col. Reginald DSO OBE 1311.19-21 1401.27-29 & 1402.25-27
    Boer War & World War I 1203.18-21
    Sgt W. Jones Ambush at Macroom 1010.30-32
    at Gallipoli (mr) 0101.16-17, 0102.16-17
    badges 0904.39-41 and 0905.37-39
    badges 9611.21-22
    cap 9202.24
    Musician 9403.24
    Haspres War Memorial (nr) 9512.13
    Salford Battalion badge WWI 9012.22
    Spion Kop (1900) (cr) 9408.14-17
Lancashire Landing, Gallipoli Gallantry (mr) 0101.16-17, 0102.16-17
Lancashire Regt: badges 9612.28
Lancashire Yeomanry, Badges 1102.39-41
Lancaster, Pte. Victor Leslie DCM AIF 0706.33
Lancastrian Brigade: badges 9612.28, 9708.25-26
Lancashire Hussars: badges 9804.26-27
Lancers
    12th Boer War 1510.24-26 at Waterloo 0401.33-35
    badges
        1st Duke of York's 9409.22-23
        2nd 9306.22-23, 9409.22-23
    4th 9409.22-23
    5th 9304.24-24
    6th Duke of Connaught's 9410.22-23
    7th Hariana 9409.22-23
    9th; Captain Douglas K Lucas-Tooth DSO WWI 0604.26-28
    9th Queen's Royal, badges of 0609.31-32
    9th/12th 9306.22-23

11th Prince of Wales' Own 9409.22-23
12th 9304.24-25
12th and 9th/12th, badges of 0610.40-42
13th Duke of Connaught's 9409.22-23
14th Murray's Jat 9409.22-23
15th 9410.22-23
16th/5th 9306.22-23
16th 9305.24-25
16th Sutlej Medal 0403.16-20
17th/21st 9306.22-23
17th 9305.24-25
17th/21st Lancers, badges 0110.27-28
18th Tiwana 9409.22-23
19th 9409.22-23
19th King George's Own 9410.22-23
20th 9410.22-23
21st 9305.24-25
Lancers, 21st at Omdurman and Bir Es Gundai (cr) 0908.15-19
Le Marchant, Major Thomas. Charge of the Heavy Brigade 0910.19-21
21st Lancers Omdurman and Bir Es Gundai (cr) 0908.15-19
24th 9306.22-23
27th 9306.22-23
29th 9410.22-23
30th 9410.22-23
31st Duke of Connaught's 9410.22-23
32nd 9410.22-23
37th 9410.22-23
arm 9004.24, 9008.28
harness 9408.22-23
tropical helmet 9405.22-23
Campaign Service medal (1962) 9006.18
Gemaizah (1885) 9308.17-18
Sutlej medal 0403.16-20
Wagon Hill (1900) (cr) 9306.14-18
Lane, Reg (obit) 0403.08
Langford, George 19/Foot: Hazara (1868) 9310.13-14
Langley, Marcus L., Flt Sgt RNZAF: CGM(F) WWII 9609.15
Langridge AB Basil, RFR 1304.26-27
Lanman, FO Allan John MBE AFC, RFC/RNAS 1309.25-26
Lapel Badge Miniature Medals 1306.50
Lapel Badges, World War I 0802.34-35
Lapwing: Persian Gulf (1909-14) (mr) 9309.13-17
Largs Bay, RFA. Firmin Sword of Peace 1202.06
Larpool: sinking (1941) 9403.14-15
Larut: sunk (1942) 9504.12-13
Lascelles, John F., 2nd Lt RFC (p) 9210.08
Lashly, William, Idg Stoker: Antarctic Expeditions 9402.17-19
Lassen, Anders VC 0109.29-30
Lassen, Anders, VC MC and two bars 0708.27-28
Lassen, Brigadier Peter DSO (obit) 0408.07
Latham, Captain Matthew 1/3rd (the East Kent) Regiment of Foot, 1408.37
Latvia, Russian soldiers reburied 1205.17
Lavery, B. 'Nelson's Navy' (br) 9010.20
Lawrence. 2/Lt Frank Helier 1/Gloucestershires 1108.37-38
Lawrence, Captain James War of 1812 1211.21-22
Lawrence, T.E.: as AC Shaw 9111.21
Lawrence, T.E., brother of 1108.37-38
Lawrenson, E., SPR RE 9208.13
Lawson, Lt Charles Indian Volunteers 1310.28-30
Lawson, Major General Richard, Congo 1962 0609.28
Lawson Pte Claude and the Anzac Artillery at Gallipoli, 0401.27-30
Lawson, Richard G., Royal Tank Regt: Congo DSO 9408.10-11
LCI see Landing Craft, Infantry
Leach, Edgar, 2nd lt 2/Manchester 9309.26
Leach, Gnr Robert RA 1203.31-33
Leach, Pte E. Derbyshire Yeomanry 1208.26-28
Leander: Albania (1946) 9008.16-17
Le Cateau; Saving the Guns 0401.24-25
le Chene, Evelyn 'Silent Heroes' Bravery & Devotion of Animals in War 9503.20
Lee, James "Scotty"; 61 Tunnelling Company South African Engineers 0711.34-36
Lee, Fireman George 1506.21-24
Lee Flt Lt H.A. Battle of Britain 0009.16-19
Lee, Joseph, Surgeon (mp) 9402.09
Lee, Harriet; Grenadier Guards 0605.18-19
Lee, Pte Thomas 20th Hussars 1406.29-31
Leech, Henry James AM, R101 Airship Disaster. Medals sold 1205.06
Lees, Jonnie GM (obit) 0304.07
Leeds Pals: badge WWI 9012.22
Leefe-Robinson, William Lt RFC, VC. 9801.16-17
Le Geyt, Alice Bell: RNLI Medal 8905.21
Legion of Frontiersmen, medals to 0004.24-25
Legion d'honneur. D-Day veterans 1509.40-41
Legion of Honour (France): Napoleon's Legacy 9702.24-25
    award to surviving British veterans of WWI 9901.06
Legion of Honour Star (France) (p) 9512.07
Legion of Merit (USA): Australian awards (Vietnam) 9602.13
Legion Wallonie (German Army WWII) 9502.16-17

Queen's Own Oxfordshire Hussars: badges 9807.25-26
Queen's Own Royal Glasgow Yeomanry: badge 9210.24-25
Queen's Own Royal West Kent Regt
   Kent County Battn badge WWI 9012.22
   Musician badge 9403.25
   Yeomanry badges 9803.26-27
Queen's Own Warwickshire and Worcestershire Yeomanry: badges 9809.27-28
Queen's Own Royal Worcesteshire Yeomanry: badges 9809.27-28
Queen's Own Yeomanry: badges 9807.25-26
Queen's Own Yorkshire Yeomanry Badges1002.38-40
Queen's Police Medal, Special Constable Peter Smith 1402.06
Queen's Regt: badge 9412.23
Queen's Royal Irish Hussars: badge 9306.23
   9th Queens Royal Lancers, badges of 0609.31-32
Queen's Royal Irish Hussars: (mri) 9406.26
Queen's Royal Rifles: badges 9604.20-21
Queen's Royal Surrey Regt. museum 9810.22-23
Queen's Silver Jubilee Medal (1977): ribbon 8909.26
Queen's South Africa Medal 8904.08-09
   clasps 9502.20
   ghost dates 9012.24, 9211.27, 9212.27
   Irish Hospital (mr QSA) 9405.16-17
   and KSA 8905.05
   naming 8904.09, 9002.18, 9004.18
   Pelorus (mr) 9111.15-18
   with raised dates (mp) 9612.10
   Rifle Brigade (mr) 8904.15-18
   Spion Kop (1900) 9408.14-17
   Volunteer Co (mr) 9104.15-17
Queen's Victoria Rifles: badges 9604.20-21
Queen's Volunteer Service medal: First Awarded 0002.07
Queen's Westminter & Civil Service Rifles: badges 9604.20-21
Queensland Museum VC Exhibition 1003.25-26
Quetta Earthquake (1883): Joynt, Christopher 9502.14
Quetta Earthquake (1935) (mr) 9305.11-13
Quick. C.F.H. 1509.27-29
Quigg, Sgt Robert VC. Statue unveiled 1608.08
Quinn, Betty – St John's Ambulance Brigade's first George Medal 0310.26
Quiver Medal for Heroic Conduct in the saving of life (mp) 9409.08

R

R101 airship 9005.08-09
R101 Airship Disaster, Captain Herbert Carmichael Irwin. Medals sold 1205.06
R101 Airship Disaster, Henry James Leech AM. Medals sold 1205.06
115/ Railway Company (RE): WWI 9606.14
RAAF, peacetime awards to 0111.19-20
RAC, 1914 Stars to (mr) 0408.31
Racoon HMS 1604.17-18
Radcliffe, Major Derwent George St John, Green Howards 1410.33-34
Radcliffe, Richard. Lancashire Fusiliers 1406.29-31
RAF (Bomber Command) Herbert Henry Sandford OBE, DFM 0501.47-48
RAF bomber pilot, Derrick Bourchier Bailey, 0209.31-32
RAF LS&GC Miniatures 1202.30
RAF Museum Hendon 0206.31-33
Raglan, Field Marshal Lord, Medals for sale 1408.08
Rahman, Seaman Motiur 0708.18-19
Railwaymen: served in WWI 9606.14-17, 9608.24
Railway Operating Division (RE) 9606.14
Railways, Cape Government. Boer War 0803.17-19
Raj, Agansing VC (obit) 0008.09
Raj, Major Harkasing 6/Gurkhas 0810.24-25
Raj, personalities of 1109.26-27, 1111.32-33 & 1201.29-31
Raj Singh, Merchant Navy: Ord of Red Star (USSR) 9409.16
Raj, soldiers of the. (NAM exhibit) 9710.25
Rajputana HMS 1003.31-32
Raleigh, HMS, Boer War (pic) 0903.20-23
Raleigh, HMS at Zeebrugge 0804.26-27
Ralph, Gunner George RA St Jean d'Acre Medal 1605.40
Ram, Capt Bhandari VC (obit) 0208.08
RAMC 89th Field Ambulance at Gallipoli 0106.30-31
RAMC and the Third China War (mr) 0103.32-33
RAMC at Siege of Kimberley 1502.28-30
Ramillies, HMS 1608.27-29
Ramsay, Bertram, Adm Sir: Diary (br) 9406.25
Ramsey, John, Sgt Maj RFC MC 9005.21
Ramsden, Lt. Edward. 5th Lancers (p) 1509.31-32
Ramilles, Madagascar 1942 0901.40-43
Ranchi HMS 1003.31-32
Randall, Peter RAVC: award of George Medal 9804.22-23
'Random Shots from a Rifleman' Kincade, John Capt: (br) 9807.29
Ranjuhosho (Japan) 9002.26
Ranpura HMS 1003.31-32
Ransted, Chris 'Bomb Disposal and the British Casualties of WWII' (br) 0601.49
Rapson, Victor, Ch/Sted Madura: MBE WWII 9504.19
Ratcliffe, Lt Leonard RNVR 1210.28-29

Rattey, Cpl Reginald Roy VC 0304.34-35
Rattray, David (obit) 0703.08
Ravenhill, Pte George 0608.28-31Rawnsey C.F. and Wright R. 'Night Fighter'(br) 9908.37
Ravenor, Pte Percy Villers-Cotterets September 1 1914 (cr) 0810.35-39
Rawalpindi HMS 1003.31-32
Rawson, Andrew 'The Peninsular War: A Battlefield Guide' (br) 1001.51
Rayner, Lt. Maurice Edward. 66th (Berkshire) Regt. at Maiwand 1880 (p) 1601.26-28
Raysbrook, Robert D, Sgt 1/7 US Marines: CGM Guadalcanal 9209.19-22, 28
Razeby, Captain E.I 1511.31-33
Read, LAC Samuel William, bomb disposal 0706.39-40
Read, Thomas, Master Mariner NGS 0701.35-37
Reckless, "Sergeant". Dickin Medal 1610.06
Reconnaissance Corps (mr) 9106.19-21, 9110.24
Reconnaissance Regiment, Sgt Charles Boyce DCM 0506.20-21
Recruiting in the 19th Century 9902.23-25
Redding, Tony 'War in the Wilderness: The Chindits in Burma 1943-1944' (br) 1602.44
Red Banner of Labour, Order of the (USSR) 9409.17
Red Banner of the RSFR, Order of 9409.15-19
Red Banner of the USSR, Order of the 9409.15-19
Red Cross, British: WWII 8909.07
Red Hot Shot Medal 1211.24 & 1305.27
Red Ribbon Merit Medal (Japan) 9002.26-27
Red River Campaign (1870) (mr) 9012.15-20
Red Star, order of (USSR) 9409.15-17
Reed, Capt (Major General) Hamilton Lyster 0608.28-31
Reed, Ensign (later Captain) John 68th Foot 1309.21-23
Reed, M.M. 2/Marine AA Bat RA: George Cross WWII 9402.04
Reedham (Norfolk): published history of the casualties remembered on the war Memorial 9901.06
Rees, D.P., Maj: GSM Malaya 9512.26
Rees, Gethryn J. 'Dartford and the Great War' (br) 9905.26
Reeve, Act. Bomb. J H Colenso 0608.28-31
Reeve, L.D., LSto Beryl: DSM WWII 9609.23
Reeves, Dennis, Hal Giblin and David Evans 'Bravest of Hearts—The Liverpool Scottish in the Great War' (br) 0104.35
Reference books for beginners 9004.19
Reformation of the British Honours system 0303.19-20
8th Regiment Spain 1836 1310.17-19
14th Regiment at Bhurtpoor 0809.23-26
31st Regiment, Afghanistan 0708.15-17
57th Regiment, Crimea 0705.24-25
66th Regiment Mascot 1701.19-21
68th Regiment of Foot (Durham Light Infantry) through the ages 0506.46-48
Regimental Changes - Light Infantry 0809.23-24
Regimental numbers on medals 9109.20-21
Regimental numbers since 1914 0002.33-34
'Regimental Records of the Royal Welch Fusiliers/23rd Foot. Volume VI 1945-69 and Volume VII 1969-2000', J P Riley (br) 0202.34
Regimental restructuring, British Army 1003.39-40
Regular Defence Force Service Medal (Ireland) 9204.21
Reid, Flt Lt William VC and Sergeant James Norris CGM (Flying)0304.15
Reid, Fl Lt William (obit) 0202.09
Reid, Lt W "Bill" VC Sold at auction 1001.06
Reid, Major Charles, 2nd Sirmoor Gurkhas. Indian Mutiny 1406.18-22
Reilly, James L., Staff Cadet: killed Lake George (Australia) (1956) 9512.10-11
Relative's Medal (Italy) 9011.23
Relief of Mafeking and Cape Colony Combination QSA (mr) 1208.21-24
REME: Badges 0906.45-47
'Remember Nelson' Thomas A Hardy (br) 0602.41
Renny, Major-General G. A. VC. Cross Sold 1102.06
Renown, HMS 1511.39-41
Renown, HMS 1939-45 1303.24-27
Rensburg (1900): Yorkshire Regt (cr) 9011.15-17
Repton, Helena, Matron (p) 9103.09
Replacement VC Samuel Mitchell 0606.37-39
Repulse, HMS 1603.25-27
Repulse, HMS 1939-45 1303.24-27 & 0710.34-36
Research:
   biographical 1308.21-23
   Births Marriages and Deaths 1308.21-23
   Boer War Medals, Medal Rolls and casualty lists 0502.15-16
   British Newspaper Library 9506.18-19
   Census research 1308.21-23
   civil registration indicies 9608.12-13, 9610.26
   Commonwealth War Graves Commission 9603.13
   India Office 8905.22 9807.27
   Local History 1105.28-29
   Military General Service Medal 1793-1814 0911.38-39
   Newspapers on-line 1406.29-31
   Notes 0708.21-22 and 0801.16-17
   Pension invalidity papers 0306.44-47
   Public Record Office 8905.22
   re-uniting broken groups through 0401.41-42
   reuniting medals 0508.40-41

Index Of Medals

IRELAND

NOTES